Analysis of
Linear Circuits

Passive and Active Components

Victor M. Rooney
University of Dayton

Charles E. Merrill Publishing Company
A Bell & Howell Company
Columbus, Ohio

Published by
Charles E. Merrill Publishing Co.
A Bell & Howell Company
Columbus, Ohio 43216

International Standard Book Number: 0-675-08886-0

Library of Congress Catalog Number: 73-93111

1 2 3 4 5 6—79 78 77 76 75

Printed in the United States of America

Preface

Analysis of Linear Circuits: Passive and Active Components approaches circuit analysis in a logical manner and stresses concepts rather than mechanical operations. Because of this approach the text not only presents new material but also strengthens prerequisite material. To be more explicit, topics such as passive component behavior, device theory, electrical sources, and nodal and mesh analysis are covered in a manner such that the essentials of the fundamental concepts presented are first and then more sophisticated concepts are developed from these rudimentary concepts. This material "ties in" with the total picture of circuit analysis, which allows the reader to understand conceptually the individual tasks he performs in finding his solution to a circuit problem.

In the course of studying the prerequisite material one discovers the need to solve differential equations. This provides a natural entrance for Laplace transforms. Laplace transforms are covered with the view that they are a means to an end and not an end in themselves. Hence, only those transforms considered representative are derived. Other helpful transforms are given, and appear with those derived in Table 4–2.

Many examples are worked in each chapter. In fact, most of the concepts are taught through examples; for that reason you should work all examples. When going through an example be certain that *you* actually work the example in parallel with the author. This is especially true in chapters 4, 5, and 6.

To add more dimensions to the analysis of circuits, frequency-plane analysis—via Bode plots—is covered in chapter 7. In addition, signal flow using some feedback techniques is discussed in chapter 8.

Problems for each chapter are found at the end of the text, beginning on page 549.

The text is written for electronic and electrical engineering and engineering technology schools. The prerequisites are considered to be elementary circuit analysis, such as dc and ac circuits, some device theory, and calculus. However, the text is written so that one could use it without the circuit and device prerequisites. It depends on the depth of understanding one wishes.

Contents

To my wife, Loretta,
son, Greg,
and
mother, Ada Rooney

1   Preliminary Topics

1–1   Introduction

This chapter will discuss material which is general and has frequent application in subsequent chapters. Specifically, we will discuss mathematical notation, linearity, and two-port network analysis.

The justification for discussing mathematical notation is to be certain that the reader knows the intent of the author's notation. The subject of linearity is discussed to allow us to better understand the approximations and limitations we will make in component modeling. Also, by investigating linearity we can better understand some concepts used in circuit analysis. Two-port network analysis is presented so that we may begin to think in terms of macroscropic representation of circuits. This will provide a natural flow for us to model active devices.

1–2   Notation

When writing an equation in terms of variables a mathematical expression is given which shows the interdependence of these variables. This relationship between variables is a functional one; that is, if one variable is expressed in terms of the other variables it is said that this variable is a *function* of the others. As an example, if we had the expression

$$2x + y - 3z + 2 = 0$$

it could be written that

1st case: $$x = \frac{3}{2}z - \frac{1}{2}y - 1$$

or

2nd case: $$y = 3z - 2x - 2$$

or

3rd case $$z = \frac{2}{3}x + \frac{1}{3}y + \frac{2}{3}$$

The first case states that by substituting numerical values for y and z a numerical value is determined for x. Then it could be said that the value of x depends on the values of y and z. Hence, x is termed as the dependent variable and y and z are known as the independent variables. A shorthand method to express that x is a function of y and z is to write the expression $x = x(y, z)$. This tells us x is a function of y and z; this type of expression is termed *functional notation*. It is important to realize that functional notation only implies that x varies as a function of y and z where the equation of x written for the first case tells us explicitly how x varies due to y and z. For these reasons functional notation is termed as being an implicit (implied) function, while the exact equation governing the behavior of x is termed an explicit function.

The equations given before in explicit form (cases 1, 2, 3) are written here in implicit notation:

1st case $x = x(y, z)$ (Read: x is a function of y and z.)
2nd case $y = y(x, z)$ (Read: y is a function of x and z.)
3rd case $z = z(x, y)$ (Read: z is a function of x and y.)

Let us consider one other equation:

$$y - 2x = 0$$

This equation may be written as

$$y = 2x$$

or

$$x = \frac{1}{2}y \quad \text{(in explicit form)}$$

or as

$$y = y(x)$$

or

$$x = x(y) \quad \text{(in functional notation)}$$

Convention has it that the dependent variable *usually* appears on the left side of the equation with no other terms present and the coefficient of the dependent variable being unity. As a result of this convention, and what we have already seen, we understand that the variables may interchange their roles simply by rearrangement of the equation. This makes the variable classification into dependent and independent variables appear rather arbitrary; however, we should remember that by the arrangement of the equation implication is being made that values for the independent variables are known. It is this criterion which will aid in determining which variables are independent and which are dependent. If it is not known which variable has known values to be substituted for it, then the manner in which the equation is written to indicate dependent and independent variable is arbitrary. Table 1-1 is offered as an aid in understanding the concepts discussed.

TABLE 1–1   Functional Notation Examples

Explicit Notation	Implicit Functional Notation	Independent Variable(s)	Dependent Variable
$y = 3x + 6$	$y = y(x)$ Read: y is a function of x.	x	y
$t = \frac{1}{2}v + av^2$ $a = $ constant	$t = t(v)$ Read: t is a function of v.	v	t
$h = \frac{1}{2}gt + v$ $g = $ constant	$h = h(t, v)$ Read: h is a function of t and v.	t and v	h
$z = 10 \cos \omega_1 t$ $\omega_1 = $ constant	$z = z(t)$ Read: z is a function of t.	t	z

We must also have mathematical notation which distinguishes between variables and constants. In general we will designate a variable by algebraically writing it in lowercase letters and designate a constant by algebraically expressing it in uppercase letters. That is, if we wished to algebraically express some time-variant voltage v implicitly we could write it as $v(t)$ volts, and to express some dc voltage algebraically we could designate it as being E volts. However, there will be a time later when we will also use uppercase letters for variables. This exception occurs when mathematically expressing transformed variables, but as we shall see they are written slightly different than constants and will be easily distinguished.

Sometimes it is desirable to imagine a waveform as being composed of some time-dependent, or time-variant, waveform superimposed upon a dc component. For this condition we will usually designate the resultant waveform with a prime. Then the prime will indicate that its associated variable is composed of two functions: one a variable and the other a constant. As an example, suppose we wish to mathematically express the resultant voltage of the time-variant voltage $v(t)$ that is E volts above the zero reference. We would write this as $v'(t) = v(t) + E$. Specifically, if $v = V \sin \omega_1 t$ then $v'(t) = V \sin \omega_1 t + E$.

We will also use prime notation to indicate that we are measuring the same variable, but from a different reference or to a different scale. That is, if we were algebraically representing time in an equation measured from a given reference point we could use the symbol t. And if we wish to represent time with the symbol t in the same equation, but measured from a different reference, we will modify the symbol t with a prime. This allows us to use the symbol t in both cases, but the prime designates that two different quantities are being represented. In short, using primes is just a means to get more mileage out of a symbol.

When we wish to mathematically indicate that a variable is being evaluated at some point, or under some condition, we will use a vertical bar to indicate this. As example, the equation

$$y \Big|_{x=5} = 2z + 4$$

is read as: y, with x evaluated at 5, is equal to $2z + 4$. And the equation

$$\frac{dx}{dt} \Big|_{t=2} = 15$$

states that the first derivative of x with respect to t is equal to 15 when t is evaluated at 2.

And lastly, the symbol $\equiv$ is used to indicate a definition. For example, the equation $d \equiv bc$ means d is defined as the product of b and c. And the symbol $\cong$ means "approximately equal to."

1–3 Linearity

We are concerned with linearity because of its mathematical and physical properties. Linearity allows us to determine the resultant response of various simultaneous excitations by determining the response of each excitation separately and then summing those responses. This of course is the principle of superposition. Linearity also has the property that if the excitation is multiplied by a constant scale factor the response is multiplied by the same scale factor.

Let us now put these two properties in mathematical formula and consider examples of each. For the principle of superposition we stated that for excitations $e_1(t), e_2(t), e_3(t), \ldots, e_n(t)$ the responses yielded were $r_1(t), r_2(t), r_3(t), \ldots, r_n(t)$ respectively. Then $e_1(t) \longrightarrow r_1(t), e_2(t) \longrightarrow r_2(t),$ $e_3(t) \longrightarrow r_3(t)$, etc., where the arrow indicates "yields." To determine the resultant response $r_R(t)$ we sum each separate response, or

$$r_R(t) = r_1(t) + r_2(t) + r_3(t) + \cdots + r_n(t) = \sum_{k=1}^{n} r_k(t) \qquad (1\text{--}1)$$

Notice Eq. (1–1) also implies that excitations $e_1(t), e_2(t), e_3(t), \ldots, e_n(t)$ make up the resultant excitation $e_R(t)$ or

$$e_R(t) = e_1(t) + e_2(t) + e_3(t) + \cdots + e_n(t) = \sum_{k=1}^{n} e_k(t) \qquad (1\text{--}2)$$

From Eqs. (1–1) and (1–2) we have the relationship between resultant excitation and resultant response as shown in Eq. (1–3):

$$\sum_{k=1}^{n} e_k(t) \longrightarrow \sum_{k=1}^{n} r_k(t) = r_R(t) \qquad (1\text{--}3)$$

Now let us define a new symbol so that we may rid ourselves of the arrow shown in Eq. (1–3). The new symbol is $\otimes$ and means "operate upon." Then the equation $d \otimes b = c$ would be read as: d operates upon b to equal c. If the operation is specifically addition, then we would write the equation as $d + b = c$. If the operation is multiplication, then the equation $d \cdot b = c$ would be in order. And if the operation is to be differentiation with respect to t, then d would represent d/dt and the equation would be written as $db/dt = c$. We may now state mathematically $r_1(t) = o(t) \otimes$ $e_1(t), r_2(t) = o(t) \otimes e_2(t)$ etc., which verbally says that some function $o(t)$ operates on excitation $e(t)$ to produce resultant $r(t)$. Then Eq. (1–3) can be written as:

$$r_R(t) = \sum_{k=1}^{n} r_k(t) = o(t) \otimes \sum_{k=1}^{n} e_k(t)$$
$$= o(t) \otimes e_1(t) + o(t) \otimes e_2(t) + \cdots + o(t)e_n(t) \qquad (1\text{--}4)$$

To reiterate, the explicit mathematical form of $o(t)$ depends on the system which is operating on the excitation. If the system differentiates, then $o(t)$ is d/dt and the operation is differentiation. If the system multiplies by some scale factor K, then $o(t)$ is K and the operation is multiplication.

It is important to understand that Eq. (1–4) states that if linearity is present we may either sum the excitations and then let $o(t)$ operate on that sum, as mathematically stated by $o(t) \otimes \sum_{k=1}^{n} e_k(t)$, or we may find the separate responses first and then sum those responses, as stated by $o(t) \otimes$ $e_1(t) + o(t) \otimes e_2(t) + \cdots + o(t)e_n(t)$ or $\sum_{k=1}^{n} r_k(t)$. Then for a linear equation of the form $y = mx + b$ the mathematical operation

$$o(t) \otimes \sum_{k=1}^{n} e_k(t)$$

of Eq. (1–4) would be equal to

$$o(t) \otimes \sum_{k=1}^{n} e_k(x) = m \sum_{k=1}^{n} x_k + nb$$
$$= m(X_1 + X_2 + X_3 + \cdots + X_n) + nb$$

where X_1, X_2, X_3, etc., are specific values for x. Notice we had to multiply the constant b by the number of summations n. And for

$$\sum_{k=1}^{n} r_k(t)$$

of Eq. (1–4) applied to $y = mx + b$ we would have

$$\sum_{k=1}^{n} y_k(x) = Y_1 + Y_2 + \cdots + Y_n = (mX_1 + b) + (mX_2 + b) + \cdots$$
$$+ (mX_n + b) \cdot$$

Now, we can rearrange $\sum_{k=1}^{n} y_k(x)$ to equal $m(X_1 + X_2 + X_3) + \cdots + X_n) + n, b$, which is equal to $o(x) \otimes \sum_{k=1}^{n} e_k(x)$.

We will now consider some examples to add concreteness to our discussion.

Example 1–1   Our first example will be a numerical evaluation of a linear equation, which will demonstrate Eq. (1–4). As we previously stated linear equations have the general form of $y = mx + b$, which is the equation of a straight line. For our example, we will evaluate the specific linear equation $y = 5x + 4$ at the points $X_1 = 3$ and $X_2 = 6$ and show that

$$Y_R = Y_1 + Y_2 = 5 \sum_{k=1}^{2} x_k + 2(4)$$

which is Eq. (1–4) for the case $o(t) \equiv 5$ and the operation being multiplication. Determining $Y_1 + Y_2$ first we have for $X_1 = 3$, $Y_1 = 5X_1 + 4 = 19$, and for $X_2 = 6$ we have $Y_2 = 5X_2 + 4 = 34$. So $Y_R = Y_1 + Y_2 = 19 + 34 = 53$. Now for a linear equation we must also be able to determine y_R by performing $5 \sum_{k=1}^{2} X_k + 8 = 5(X_1 + X_2) + 8$. Thus, $Y_R = 5(X_1 + X_2) + 2(4) = 5(9) + 8 = 53$. As shown, y_R has a value of 53, for $X_1 = 3$ and $X_2 = 6$ whether calculated as the sum of the resultants Y_1 and Y_2 or by first summing the excitations X_1 and X_2 and then substituting that resultant for x, which is what Eq. (1–4) mathematically states. To show this is not true for nonlinear equations let us numerically evaluate the nonlinear equation $y = 5x^2 + 4$ for the same values of X_1 and X_2. Calculating the resultant ys first we have $Y_1 = 5(3)^2 + 4 = 49$ and $Y_2 = 5(6)^2 + 4 = 184$; hence $Y_R = Y_1 + Y_2 = 49 + 184 = 233$. And calculating by first summing excitations, as we did in $Y_R = 5(X_1 + X_2) + 2b$, we would have $Y_R = 5(X_1 + X_2)^2 + 2(4) = 5(3 + 6)^2 + 8 = 413$. As seen, the superposition principle is not applicable to nonlinear equations.

Example 1–2   Another example of a nonlinear equation failing the superposition principle is to consider the power equation for a resistor, that is $p = i^2R$. Suppose that we have two loop currents, i_1 and i_2, flowing in the same direction through R and we wish to determine the net power due to these currents. If $p = i^2R$ were linear then $P_R = P_1 + P_2 = I_1^2R + I_2^2R = (I_1 + I_2)^2R$. But we know that $(I_1 + I_2)^2R \neq I_1^2R + I_2^2R$, therefore we cannot apply the principle of superposition.

Example 1–3   As another example consider the equation

$$v(t) = L\frac{di(t)}{dt} + \frac{1}{C}\int i(t)\,dt + Ri(t)$$

where L, C, and R are constants. Given excitations i_1 and i_2 we have for excitation i_1

$$v_1(t) = L\frac{di_1(t)}{dt} + \frac{1}{C}\int i_1(t)\,dt + Ri_1(t)$$

and for i_2

$$v_2(t) = L\frac{di_2(t)}{dt} + \frac{1}{C}\int i_2(t)\,dt + Ri_2(t)$$

Now, if the resultant response is $v_R(t)$, then for a linear system we may write $v_R(t) = v_1(t) + v_2(t)$. Therefore

$$v_R(t) = v_1(t) + v_2(t) = \left[L\frac{di(t)}{dt} + \frac{1}{C}\int i_1(t)\,dt + Ri_1(t)\right]$$
$$+ \left[L\frac{di_2(t)}{dt} + \frac{1}{C}\int i_2(t)\,dt + Ri_2(t)\right]$$

Since differentiation and integration are linear operators

we may write

$$v_R(t) = \left[L\frac{di_1(t)}{dt} + \frac{1}{C}\int i_1(t)\,dt + Ri_1(t) \right]$$

$$+ \left[L\frac{di_2(t)}{dt} + \frac{1}{C}\int i_2(t)\,dt + Ri_2(t) \right]$$

$$= L\frac{d}{dt}[i_1(t) + i_2(t)] + \frac{1}{C}\int [i_1(t) + i_2(t)]\,dt$$

$$+ R[i_1(t) + i_2(t)]$$

As we see, Eq. (1–4) is satisfied since

$$\left[L\frac{di_1(t)}{dt} + \frac{1}{C}\int i_1(t)\,dt + Ri_1(t) \right]$$

$$+ \left[L\frac{di_2(t)}{dt} + \frac{1}{C}\int i_2(t)\,dt + Ri_2(t) \right]$$

$$= v_1(t) + v_2(t)$$

and

$$L\frac{d}{dt}[i_1(t) + i_2(t)] + \frac{1}{C}\int [i_1(t) + i_2(t)]\,dt$$

$$+ R[i_1(t) + i_2(t)]$$

$$= o(t) \otimes \sum_{k=1}^{2} i_k(t),$$

where $o(t)$ is the operator

$$L\frac{d(\ )}{dt} + \frac{1}{C}\int (\ )\,dt + R$$

If we would have had the nonlinear equation

$$Li(t)\frac{di(t)}{dt} + \frac{i(t)}{C}\int i(t)\,dt + Ri^2(t) = i(t)v(t),$$

which is power, then $\sum_{k=1}^{2} v_k(t) \neq o(t) \otimes \sum_{k=1}^{2} i_k(t)$. To demonstrate this we first determine $\sum_{k=1}^{2} v_k(t)$ for i_1 and i_2. Thus,

$$\sum_{k=1}^{2} v_k(t) = v_1(t) + v_2(t)$$

$$= \left[Li_1(t)\frac{di_1(t)}{dt} + \frac{i_1(t)}{C}\int i_1(t)\,dt + Ri_1^2(t) \right]$$

$$+ \left[Li_2(t)\frac{di_2(t)}{dt} + \frac{i_2(t)}{C}\int i_2(t)\,dt + Ri_2^2(t) \right]$$

Next we determine $o(t) \otimes \sum_{k=1}^{2} i_k(t)$ for excitations i_1 and i_2, hence

$$o(t) \otimes \sum_{k=1}^{2} i_k(t) = \left\{ L[i_1(t) + i_2(t)] \frac{d[i_1(t) + i_2(t)]}{dt} \right.$$

$$+ \frac{[i_1(t) + i_2(t)]}{C} \int [i_1(t) + i_2(t)] \, dt$$

$$+ R[i_1(t) + i_2(t)]^2$$

As we see, it is true that $\sum_{k=1}^{2} v_k(t)$ does not equal $o(t) \otimes \sum_{k=1}^{2} i_k(t)$; hence this equation $i(t)v(t)$ is not linear.

Example 1–4   Show that

$$3t \frac{dy(t)}{dt} + 5y(t) = x^2(t)$$

is linear.

Solution   For excitations y_1 and y_2 we have the resultant

$$x_R^2(t) = \left[3t \frac{dy_1(t)}{dt} + 5y_1(t) \right] + \left[3t \frac{dy_2(t)}{dt} + 5y_2(t) \right]$$

$$= 3t \frac{d}{dt}[y_1(t) + y_2(t)] + 5[y_1(t) + y_2(t)]$$

where

$$x_1^2(t) + x_2^2(t) = x_R^2(t) = \left[3t \frac{dy_1(t)}{dt} + 5y_1(t) \right]$$

$$+ \left[3t \frac{dy_2(t)}{dt} + 5y_2(t) \right]$$

and

$$o(t) \otimes \sum_{k=1}^{2} y_k(t) = 3t \frac{d}{dt}[y_1(t) + y_2(t)] + 5[y_1(t) + y_2(t)]$$

Therefore

$$o(t) \otimes y_1(t) + o(t) \otimes y_2(t) = o(t) \otimes [y_1(t) + y_2(t)]$$

which agrees with Eq. (1–4).

In summary, algebraic equations of the form $y = mx + b$ are linear and the principle of superposition applies. Operational equations of the form

$$\left\{ \alpha \left[\frac{d^n y(t)}{dt} \right]^k + \beta \left[\underbrace{\int \int \cdots \int}_{h} y(t) \, dt \right]^m + \gamma y(t) \right\} y^p(t) = x^z(t)$$

are linear so long as $k = m = 1$, $p = 0$, and α and β are not functions of y; that is, $\alpha \neq \alpha(y)$ and $\beta \neq \beta(y)$. And under these conditions the principle of superposition applies.

The other property we wish to investigate is that for linear systems the excitation multiplied by a scale factor K multiplies the response also by K.

Then $Ke_1(t) = Kr_1(t)$; or

$$K \sum_{k=1}^{n} r_k(t) = Ko(t) \otimes \sum_{k=1}^{n} e_k(t) = Ko(t) \otimes e_1(t) + Ko(t) \otimes e_2(t)$$
$$+ \cdots + Ko(t) \otimes e_n(t) \qquad (1\text{-}5)$$

We will now consider an example of Eq. (1-5).

Example 1–5   Demonstrate that Eq. (1-5) is true for the linear equation $x = 2y + 5$.

Solution: Let us first determine a resultant value for x if y has the value 4 and 5. Thus for $Y_1 = 4$ and $Y_2 = 5$ we find $X_R = [2Y_1 + 5] + [2Y_2 + 5] = 2[(Y_1 + Y_2) + 5] = 28$. Now suppose we wish to amplify this value of X_R by a scale factor of 10. Then we wish to multiply X_R by K, where $K = 10$, or $KX_R = 280$. According to Eq. (1-5) we may also multiply the separate excitations by $K = 10$, thus $10[2Y_1 + 5] + 10[2Y_2 + 5] = 20[(Y_1 + Y_2) + 5] = 280$.

Thus far we have investigated mathematical relationships of linearity, but now we shall turn our attention to physical relationships. We will use graphical techniques to show that waveform fidelity is maintained between excitation (independent variable) and response (dependent variable) when the equation relating the response to the excitation is linear, where waveform fidelity is defined to mean the time-variant portions of the input and output differ only in a scale factor and/or phase. We shall also show that waveform fidelity is not maintained for nonlinear equations.

Consider the graph of Fig. 1–1(a), which graphically represents the relationship between the variables i and v. This graphical relationship can mathematically be described by the linear equation

$$i = \frac{I}{V}v = \frac{1}{R}v \qquad (1\text{-}6)$$

where the slope is $I/V = 1/R$ and the intersect is zero. Now graphically project on Fig. 1–1(a) at point V_Q (which is zero) some excitation of the independent variable v. We make this excitation time-variant and call it v_1. Specifically we will make v_1 sinusoidal. When applying excitation $v_1(t)$ we get a response $i_1(t)$ according to the equation $i_1(t) = (1/R)v_1(t)$, as derived from Eq. (1-6). As we see from Fig. 1–1(b) the response $i_1(t)$ is also sinusoidal, oscillating about point I_Q, which is zero. Then waveform fidelity was maintained.

To mathematically express what we just did graphically we substitute the explicit equation for excitation v_1 into Eq. (1-6). The equation expressing v_1 is $v_1 = V_1 \sin \omega_1 t$, where $\omega_1 = 2\pi/T$. Substituting this into Eq.

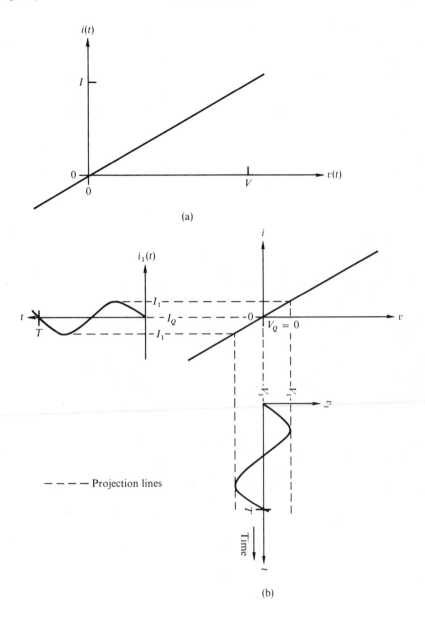

FIGURE 1–1

(1–6) we have $i_1 = (1/R)V_1 \sin \omega_1 t = I_1 \sin \omega_1 t$. We see that $1/R$ is a scaling factor since it scales the magnitude V_1 to I_1.

Let us now examine a nonlinear case. Consider the nonlinear equation

$i = mv^2$, which graphically appears in Fig. 1–2(a). Now, apply excitation $v_1'(t)$ of Fig. 1–1(b) and project it to determine response $i_1'(t)$, where the primes indicate both time-variant and dc components are present. That is, v_1' is composed of a dc voltage V_Q with a sine wave oscillating about it. Then mathematically $v_1'(t) = V_Q + v_1(t) = V_Q + V_1 \sin \omega_1 t$, where $v_1(t)$ implicitly represents the time-variant component. The graph of v_1' pro-

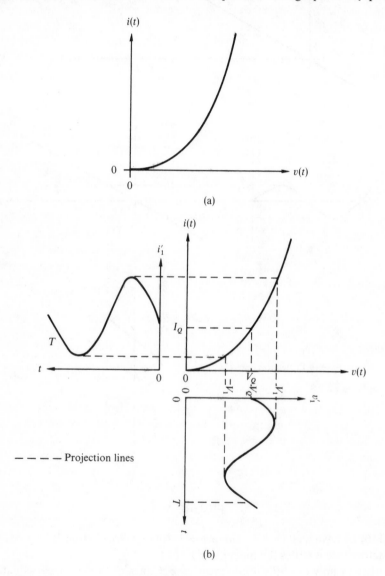

(a)

(b)

FIGURE 1–2

jected on $i = mv^2$ is shown in Fig. 1–2(b). Notice that i'_1 is also composed of a dc component I_Q and a time-variant component i_1, hence $i'_1 = I_Q + i_1(t)$.

We also see from Fig. 1–2(b) the waveform fidelity of the time-variant component is lost; or, stated another way, the dependent variable is distorted relative to the independent variable waveform v_1. Recall that when speaking of distortion we are interested only in the time-variant portion. A mathematical way to show this distortion is to actually substitute the equation for the excitation v'_1 into the equation $i = mv^2$. Writing v'_1 as $v'_1 = V_Q + V_1 \sin \omega_1 t$ then $i'_1 = m(V_Q + V_1 \sin \omega_1 t)^2$. Expanding the term $(V_Q + V_1 \sin \omega t)^2$ we have

$$i'_1 = m(V_Q^2 + 2V_Q V_1 \sin \omega_1 t + V_1^2 \sin^2 \omega_1 t)$$
$$= mV_Q^2 + m(2V_Q V_1 \sin \omega_1 t + V_1^2 \sin^2 \omega_1 t) = I_Q + i_1(t),$$

where

$$I_Q = mV_Q^2$$

and

$$i_1(t) = m(2V_Q V_1 \sin \omega_1 t + V_1^2 \sin^2 \omega_1 t)$$

As we see, the time-variant portion of i'_1, that is i_1, is distorted in waveform since it no longer has the form $K \sin \omega_1 t$, but now has the form $K_1 \sin \omega_1 t + K_2 \sin^2 \omega_1 t$. The term $K_2 \sin^2 \omega_1 t$ is what causes the distortion. That is, if the term $K_2 \sin^2 \omega_1 t$ was not present then i'_1 would be equal to $mV_Q(V_Q + 2V_1 \sin \omega t)$, or $mV_Q^2 + 2mV_Q V_1 \sin \omega_1 t = K_1 + K_3 \sin \omega_1 t$, which is a pure sinusoidal waveform $K_3 \sin \omega_1 t$ superimposed on a dc term K_1.

By this time one should have a feel for properties of linearity. We will require our passive and active components to be linear. In the case of active devices piecewise linear approximations will be made. As we progress to these topics these requirements will be pointed out.

1–4 Two-Port Network Analysis

Many times in circuit analysis we seek an equivalent circuit to represent a network, or active components. When these equivalent circuits are valid for only the time-variant portions of electrical signals they are termed as ac equivalent circuits, or as ac models in the case of active components. This need usually arises when one is interested in the response to time-variant signals and all one has available are the output and input terminals of a network and no specific knowledge as to actual components which form the circuitry. In the case of an active component no discrete components exist, hence, for active components we need an equivalent circuit made up of discrete components which represent the active component's behavior. In this section we will investigate a means to derive these equivalent circuits.

We will begin our analysis in a general manner by analyzing a "black box" network, however specific examples will be worked later. The black box of Fig. 1–3(a) shows four terminals with one pair of terminals forming the input and the other pair forming the output. On the input side we show

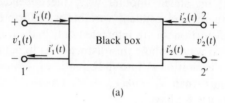

(a)

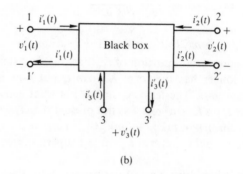

(b)

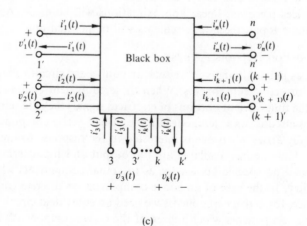

(c)

FIGURE 1–3   (a) Four-terminal or two-port network; (b) Six-terminal or three-port network; (c) 2-*n* terminal or *n*-port network.

current i'_1 and voltage v'_1 and the output shows i'_2 and v'_2. The primes on the quantities are to indicate they are composed of some time-variant function superimposed upon a constant. Terminal pairs are determined by matching like currents, flowing to or from the terminals—that is, terminals 1 and 1' are terminal pairs since current i'_1 flows in both terminals. Likewise, terminals 2 and 2' are terminal pairs since current i'_2 flows in both terminals.

We speak of each terminal pair as being a port, hence Fig. 1–3(a) is a two-port network. Under this definition we would classify Fig. 1–3(b) as a three-port network and Fig. 1–3(c) as an n-port network. Our analysis will be for two-port networks.

The current directions and voltage polarities shown in Fig. 1–3 are assumed. The reason these are assumptions is that this is an analysis of a general black box, hence, the actual directions and polarities are unknown to us. We will see later that for analyzing specific problems where the exact waveform of the electrical source(s) is known the mathematics and/or measurements will give us proper current directions and voltage polarities.

We now want mathematical expressions for the variables of Fig. 1–3(a). We know we can classify our variables into independent and dependent variables. Suppose for the input and output variables one of each type exists. Then if we choose the dependent variable for the input and output to be v'_1 and v'_2 respectively, the independent variables would be i'_1 and i'_2. Since all the variables are interrelated then we can implicitly write $v'_1 = v'_1(i'_1, i'_2)$ and $v'_2 = v'_2(i'_1, i'_2)$. If we had chosen the dependent variables to be v'_1 and i'_2 then we would have v'_2 and i'_1 as the independent variables. This choice would have been implicitly written as $v'_1 = v'_1(i'_1, v'_2)$ and $i'_2 = i'_2(i'_1, v'_2)$. Or if we would have chosen that both input variables be the independent variables then we would write $v'_2 = v'_2(i'_1, v'_1)$ and $i'_2 = i'_2(i'_1, v'_1)$. Of course, the physical network or component one wishes to derive an equivalent circuit for will dictate which variables are to be independent and which are to be dependent. As we shall see, these many possible ways to implicitly express the interrelationships of the network variables give rise to various equivalent circuits.

Before we attempt to derive some equivalent circuits for our black box of Fig. 1–3(a) we should first discuss the formula for differentiation of a multivariable function. Consider some function f, which is a function of two variables, x and y. The interrelationship of f, x, and y may be expressed as $f = f(x, y)$. If the independent variables x and y are time-variant functions then we may write

$$f = f[x(t), y(t)] \qquad (1\text{–}7)$$

To differentiate f with respect to t one applies the equation

$$\frac{df}{dt} = \frac{\partial f}{\partial x}\frac{dx}{dt} + \frac{\partial f}{\partial y}\frac{dy}{dt}$$

We can eliminate dt from this equation and simply write

$$df = \frac{\partial f}{\partial x} dx + \frac{\partial f}{\partial y} dy \qquad (1\text{-}8)$$

We will use Eq. (1–8) upon those equations which represent our black box in order to derive equivalent circuits.

For our first equivalent circuit let us choose the independent variables to be the currents i'_1 and i'_2; hence, we have the equations $v'_1 = v'_1(i'_1, i'_2)$ and $v'_2 = v'_2(i'_1, i'_2)$. Since the currents i'_1 and i'_2 are time-variant we may write

$$v'_1 = v'_1[i'_1(t), i'_2(t)] \qquad (1\text{-}9a)$$

$$v'_2 = v'_2[i'_1(t), i'_2(t)] \qquad (1\text{-}9b)$$

Using Eq. (1–8) to operate upon Eqs. (1–9) we have

$$dv'_1 = \frac{\partial v'_1}{\partial i'_1} di'_1 + \frac{\partial v'_1}{\partial i'_2} di'_2 \qquad (1\text{-}10a)$$

and

$$dv'_2 = \frac{\partial v'_2}{\partial i'_1} di'_1 + \frac{\partial v'_2}{\partial i'_2} di'_2 \qquad (1\text{-}10b)$$

Now, we know that the prime quantities are composed of time-variant and dc terms. Also we know that dv'_1 means change, or difference, in v'_1 and that di'_1 means change in i'_1 and likewise for dv'_2 and di'_2. This change we speak of must be the time-variant portion of the prime quantities since its other component is dc, or constant. Then generally speaking for some $x'(t) = X + x(t)$ we may write

$$dx' = \text{changing portion of } [X + x(t)] = x(t)$$

where $x(t)$ is the ac portion and X is the dc portion. Thus, we may write Eqs. (1–10) as

$$v_1(t) = \frac{\partial v_1}{\partial i_1} i_1(t) + \frac{\partial v_1}{\partial i_2} i_2(t) \qquad (1\text{-}11a)$$

$$v_2(t) = \frac{\partial v_2}{\partial i_1} i_1(t) + \frac{\partial v_2}{\partial i_2} i_2(t) \qquad (1\text{-}11b)$$

where $di'_1 = i_1(t)$, $di'_2 = i_2(t)$, $dv'_1 = v_1(t)$ and $dv'_2 = v_2(t)$. Also notice we can write $\partial v'/\partial i'$ as $\partial v/\partial i$ since again only the time-variant portions of the prime quantities are variables. This concept of dx' representing the variable term of a prime quantity x' will be graphically presented in chap. two when active components are modeled.

In order to model an equivalent circuit from Eqs. (1–11) we must derive components from the coefficients of i_1 and i_2. For i_1 we have the coefficient of $\partial v_1/\partial i_1$, which has the units of volts/amperes, or ohms. We see that all the coefficients are in units of ohms. Let us define $z_{kn} = \partial v_k/\partial i_n$, where our nomenclature was derived from z representing impedance and the left-hand subscript of z_{kn} being the same as the numerator and the right-hand subscript matching the denominator. Then Eqs. (1–11) become

$$v_1(t) = z_{11}i_1(t) + z_{12}i_2(t) \qquad \textbf{(1–12a)}$$

$$v_2(t) = z_{21}i_1(t) + z_{22}i_2(t) \qquad \textbf{(1–12b)}$$

Since all coefficients are impedances any model, or equivalent circuit, derived from Eqs. (1–12) is called a z-parameter model.

We can derive two models from Eqs. (1–12). To derive our first model we begin by realizing that since each equation in Eqs. (1–12) is a summation of voltages we are applying Kirchhoff's voltage law. Then the circuit for Eq. (1–12a) is as shown in Fig. 1–4(a) and the circuit for Eq. (1–12b) is that shown in Fig. 1–4(b). From these two figures we see that we are dealing with two circuits which have no common components. To show that both circuits are related we will combine the two circuits by putting them to the same reference as shown in Fig. 1–4(c). Hence, an ac model for the z-parameters of Fig. 1–3(a) is the dotted-in portion of Fig. 1–4(c).

Our second z-parameter ac model of Fig. 1–3(a) can be derived from Eqs. (1–12) by adding and subtracting $z_{12}i_1$ in Eq. (1–12a) and adding and subtracting $z_{12}i_2$ and $z_{12}i_1$ in Eq. (1–12b). This yields

$$v_1(t) = z_{11}i_1(t) + z_{12}i_2(t) + z_{12}i_1(t) - z_{12}i_1(t) \qquad \textbf{(1–13a)}$$

and

$$v_2(t) = z_{21}i_1(t) + z_{22}i_2(t) + z_{12}i_2(t)$$
$$- z_{12}i_2(t) + z_{12}i_1(t) - z_{12}i_1(t) \qquad \textbf{(1–13b)}$$

We now want to arrange Eqs. (1–13) so that a common term exists between each equation. The common term we seek is z_{12}, hence let us write Eqs. (1–13) as

$$v_1(t) = [(z_{11} - z_{12}) + z_{12}]i_1(t) + z_{12}i_2(t) \qquad \textbf{(1–14a)}$$

and

$$v_2(t) = [(z_{21} - z_{12}) + z_{12}]i_1(t)$$
$$+ [(z_{22} - z_{12}) + z_{12}]i_2(t) \qquad \textbf{(1–14b)}$$

For Eq. (1–14a) we have the circuit of Fig. 1–5(a). The circuit for Eq. (1–14b) is shown in Fig. 1–5(b). We are able to join Figs. 1–5(a) and (b) because of the mutual component z_{12}, hence we have Fig. 1–5(c). Notice from Fig. 1–5(c) if $z_{12} = z_{21}$ we have the circuit of Fig. 1–5(d). The case of $z_{12} = z_{21}$ covers circuits composed of passive components.

Next let us see how to determine the values of the various impedances. From Eq. (1–12a), if we wish to determine z_{11} we see that for $i_2 = 0$, which is accomplished by an open circuit where i_2 flows, we would have

$$z_{11} = \frac{v_1(t)}{i_1(t)}\bigg|_{i_2=0} \qquad \textbf{(1–15a)}$$

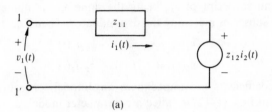

(a)

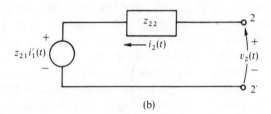

(b)

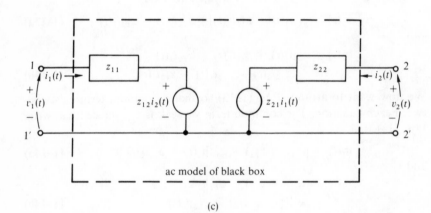

ac model of black box

(c)

FIGURE 1–4

And to determine z_{12} from Eq. (1–12a) we would force i_1 to zero so that

$$z_{12} = \frac{v_1(t)}{i_2(t)}\Bigg|_{i_1=0} \tag{1–15b}$$

Likewise, from Eq. (1–12b) we find

$$z_{21} = \frac{v_2(t)}{i_1(t)}\Bigg|_{i_2=0} \tag{1–15c}$$

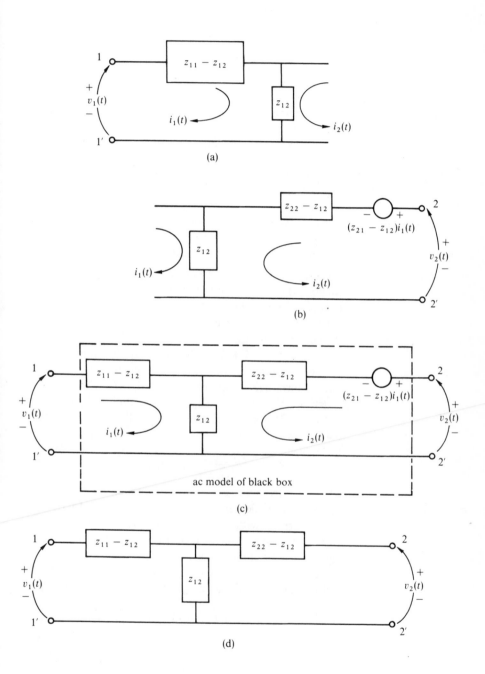

FIGURE 1–5

and

$$z_{22} = \left. \frac{v_2(t)}{i_2(t)} \right|_{i_1=0} \tag{1-15d}$$

These parameters are also known as open-circuit parameters since in each case $i_k = 0$. One thing we must keep in mind is that our variables $v_1, v_2, i_1,$ and i_2 are time-variant, or ac, terms only.

The impedance z_{11} is the input impedance, sometimes referred to as the input driving-point impedance. The impedance z_{22} is the output impedance and z_{12} and z_{21} are transfer impedances. We will now consider an example using two-port network analysis.

Example 1–6   Suppose we were given a black box of the type shown in Fig. 1–3(a), which we know contains only passive components, and are asked to derive an ac model of it.

Solution   Since we know the black box contains only passive components then we also know that $z_{12} = z_{21}$ and the model of Fig. 1–5(d) applies. We will determine the z-parameters of Fig. 1–5(d) by evaluating Eqs. (1–15) according to the current dictates of i_1 and i_2.

Equation (1–15a) states for us to apply a time-variant voltage v_1 and measure the input current i_1 with the output terminals open-circuited so that $i_2 = 0$, as illustrated in Fig. 1–6(a). Suppose we apply a sinusoidal voltage of 10V at 100 Hz for v_1 and measure a current of 0.43 A for i_1. Then

$$Z_{11} = \left. \frac{V_1(j\omega)}{I_1(j\omega)} \right|_{I_2=0} = \frac{10}{0.43} = 23.3 \ \Omega$$

where we wrote all variables in uppercase since it is convention from elementary ac circuit analysis to do so when working with sinusoidal waveforms. Notice this is an exception we spoke of in section 1–2 concerning writing all variables in lowercase letters.

Next we will determine Z_{21} according to Eq. (1–15c) and the measurement arrangement shown in Fig. 1–6(b). Equation (1–15c) states while v_1 is applied we must measure voltage v_2 and current i_1 with the output terminals open-circuited so that $i_2 = 0$. We already have the measurement of i_1 as being 0.43 A for a voltage of 10 V for v_1. Then all we need to do is measure v_2, which we find to be 1.42 V. Hence,

$$Z_{21} = \left. \frac{V_2(j\omega)}{I_1(j\omega)} \right|_{I_2=0} = \frac{1.42}{0.43} = 3.3 \ \Omega$$

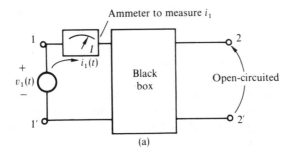

(a)

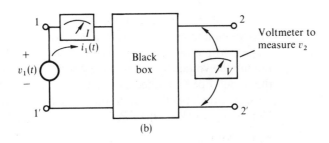

(b)

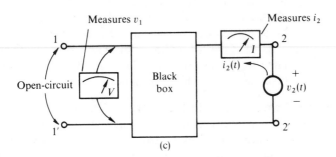

(c)

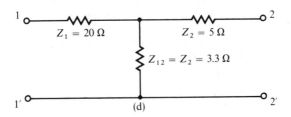

(d)

FIGURE 1–6   (a) To determine z_{11}; (b) To determine z_{21}; (c) To determine z_{22} and z_{12}; (d) ac model of Black Box.

We will now determine those parameters requiring $i_1 = 0$, of which the measurement arrangement is shown in Fig. 1–6(c). From Eq. (1–15d) we see that we must apply a voltage across the output terminals and measure current i_2 with the input terminals open-circuited so that $i_1 = 0$. Let us take our same signal generator we used for v_1 and apply it for v_2. Under this condition suppose we measured i_2 to have a value of 1.2 A. Thus

$$Z_{22} = \left. \frac{V_2(j\omega)}{I_2(j\omega)} \right|_{I_1=0} = \frac{10}{1.2} = 8.3 \ \Omega$$

We have already determined Z_{12} since $Z_{12} = Z_{21}$ for passive components, but as a check we now determine Z_{12} according to Eq. (1–15b). We determine Z_{12} by maintaining the voltage v_2 at the output terminals and having the input open-circuited so that $i_1 = 0$, and then we measure v_1. Under this condition we measure v_1 to be 4 V. Hence, $Z_{12} = \left. [V_1(j\omega)/I_2(j\omega)] \right|_{I_1=0} = 4/1.2 = 3.33 \ \Omega$, which agrees with Z_{21}.

The equivalent circuit of Fig. 1–5(d) shows that we wish quantities $Z_{11} - Z_{12}$ and $Z_{22} - Z_{12}$. Let us define $Z_1 \equiv Z_{11} - Z_{12}$, $Z_2 \equiv Z_{22} - Z_{12}$ and $Z_3 \equiv Z_{12} = Z_{21}$ as a matter of convenience. Hence, $Z_1 = 23.3 - 3.3 = 20 \ \Omega$, $Z_2 = 8.4 - 3.3 = 5.1 \ \Omega$ and $Z_3 = 3.3 \ \Omega$ calculated to the nearest tenth. The equivalent circuit of our black box is shown in Fig. 1–6(d).

The equivalent circuit shown in Fig. 1–6(d) is known as a T-network. In some analysis it is convenient to put circuits into their equivalent T form through the application of Eqs. (1–15) rather than measurement. We will see how to do this in an up-and-coming example. The example circuit we will undertake next is the actual circuit which formed the black box of Ex. 1–6. This example is to serve two purposes: (1) it should demonstrate how one can mathematically convert a circuit to its equivalent T-network; (2) it should verify that the measurement technique of Ex. 1–6 is valid.

Example 1–7   Using Eqs. (1–14) convert the circuit given in Fig. 1–7 to its equivalent T-network. Compare the results to Fig. 1–6(d).

Solution   The equations of Eqs. (1–14) appear as

$$v_1(t) = [(z_{11} - z_{12}) + z_{12}]i_1(t) + z_{12}i_2(t) \quad \textbf{(1–16a)}$$

$$v_2(t) = z_{12}i_1(t) + [(z_{22} - z_{12}) + z_{12}]i_2(t) \quad \textbf{(1–16b)}$$

since $z_{12} = z_{21}$.

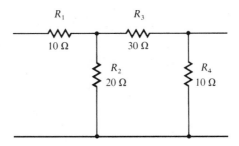

FIGURE 1–7

We will write equations for the circuit given and make them appear in the same form as Eqs. (1–16).

Drawing the circuit showing the loop currents and terminal voltages we have the circuit of Fig. 1–8, from

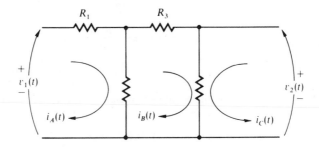

FIGURE 1–8

which we write the loop equations:

$$v_1(t) = (R_1 + R_2)i_A(t) - R_2 i_B(t)$$
$$0 = -R_2 i_A(t) + (R_2 + R_3 + R_4)i_B(t) + R_4 i_C(t)$$
$$v_2(t) = R_4 i_B(t) + R_4 i_C(t)$$

From Figs. 1–3(a) and 1–8 we see that $i_A = i_1$, and $i_C = i_2$. Substituting $i_A = i_1$ and $i_C = i_2$ into our loop equations we have

$$v_1(t) = (R_1 + R_2)i_1(t) - R_2 i_B(t) \qquad \text{(1–17a)}$$
$$0 = -R_2 i_1(t) + (R_2 + R_3 + R_4)i_B(t) + R_4 i_2(t)$$
$$\text{(1–17b)}$$
$$v_2(t) = R_4 i_B(t) + R_4 i_2(t) \qquad \text{(1–17c)}$$

Our next task is to rid ourselves of current i_B. Hence, solving for i_B from Eq. (1–17b) we find

$$i_B(t) = -\frac{R_4}{R_2 + R_3 + R_4}i_2(t) + \frac{R_2}{R_2 + R_3 + R_4}i_1(t)$$

We may now substitute this expression into Eqs. (1–17a) and (1–17c), hence,

$$v_1(t) = (R_1 + R_2)i_1(t) + \frac{R_2 R_4}{R_2 + R_3 + R_4}i_2(t)$$

$$- \frac{R_2^2}{R_2 + R_3 + R_4}i_1(t)$$

$$v_2(t) = -\frac{R_4^2}{R_2 + R_3 + R_4}i_2(t) + \frac{R_4 R_2}{R_2 + R_3 + R_4}i_1(t)$$

$$+ R_4 i_2(t)$$

which when terms are collected yields

$$v_1(t) = \left[(R_1 + R_2) - \frac{R_2^2}{R_2 + R_3 + R_4}\right]i_1(t)$$

$$+ \frac{R_2 R_4}{R_2 + R_3 + R_4}i_2(t) \qquad \textbf{(1–18a)}$$

$$v_2(t) = \frac{R_2 R_4}{R_2 + R_3 + R_4}i_1(t)$$

$$+ \left[R_4 - \frac{R_4^2}{R_2 + R_3 + R_4}\right]i_2(t) \qquad \textbf{(1–18b)}$$

Comparing coefficients of Eqs. (1–16a) and (1–18a) we see that

$$(Z_{11} - Z_{12}) + Z_{12} = Z_1 + Z_3 = (R_1 + R_2)$$

$$- \frac{R_2^2}{R_2 + R_3 + R_4} \quad \text{and} \quad Z_{12} = Z_3 = \frac{R_2 R_4}{R_2 + R_3 + R_4}$$

where $Z_1 = Z_{11} - Z_{12}$ and $Z_3 = Z_{12}$. On comparing Eqs. (1–16b) and (1–18b) we see that $Z_{12} = Z_3 = (R_2 R_4/R_2 + R_3 + R_4)$, which equals Z_{21} as it should, and

$$(Z_{22} - Z_{12}) + Z_{12} = Z_2 + Z_3 = R_4 - \frac{R_4^2}{R_2 + R_3 + R_4}$$

Then algebraically:

$$Z_1 = \left[(R_1 + R_3) - \frac{R_2^2}{R_2 + R_3 + R_4}\right] - Z_3$$

$$= \left[(R_1 + R_3) - \frac{R_2^2}{R_2 + R_3 + R_4}\right] - \frac{R_2 R_4}{R_2 + R_3 + R_4}$$

$$Z_2 = \left(R_4 - \frac{R_4^2}{R_2 + R_3 + R_4}\right) - Z_3$$

$$= \left(R_4 - \frac{R_4^2}{R_2 + R_3 + R_4}\right) - \frac{R_2 R_4}{R_2 + R_3 + R_4}$$

and

$$Z_3 = \frac{R_2 R_4}{R_2 + R_3 + R_4}$$

The T-network showing these quantities appears in Fig. 1–9.

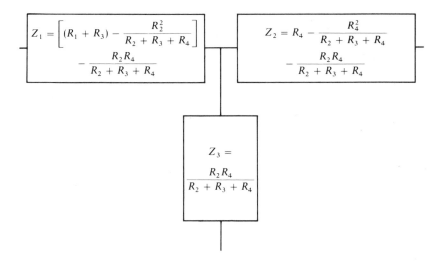

FIGURE 1–9

Numerically evaluating these equations for Z_1, Z_2, and Z_3 to slide-rule accuracy we have

$$Z_1 + Z_3 = 30 - \frac{400}{60} = 23.3 \; \Omega$$

$$Z_3 = \frac{200}{60} = 3.33 \; \Omega$$

and

$$Z_2 + Z_3 = 10 - \frac{100}{60} = 8.33 \; \Omega$$

From these values we find that $Z_1 = 23.33 - Z_3 = 23.33 - 3.33 = 20 \; \Omega$ and $Z_2 = 8.33 - Z_3 = 8.33 - 3.33 = 5.00 \; \Omega$, which agrees with the model of Fig. 1–6(d).

From elementary ac circuits we realize that if the black box of Ex. 1–6 would have contained capacitors and/or inductors we would need a phase measurement for Eqs. (1–15). Then for sinusoidal analysis of passive components Eqs. (1–15) would appear as

$$Z_{11} = |Z_{11}| \angle \Theta_{11} = \frac{V_1(j\omega)}{I_1(j\omega)}\bigg|_{I_2=0} \tag{1-19a}$$

$$Z_{12} = |Z_{12}| \angle \Theta_{12} = |Z_{21}| \angle \Theta_{21} = \frac{V_1(j\omega)}{I_2(j\omega)}\bigg|_{I_1=0} = \frac{V_2(j\omega)}{I_1(j\omega)}\bigg|_{I_2=0} \tag{1-19b}$$

$$Z_{22} = |Z_{22}| \angle \Theta_{22} = \frac{V_2(j\omega)}{I_2(j\omega)}\bigg|_{I_1=0} \tag{1-19c}$$

where $|Z|$ is the magnitude and $\angle \Theta$ is the phase angle. We will now work an example using Eqs. (1-19).

Example 1–8   Suppose we were given a black box and told to determine the equivalent T-network for it using sinusoidal voltage sources.

Solution: Let us begin by arbitrarily labeling one pair of terminals as X and X' and the remaining pair as Y and Y'. This will give us a reference for measurement purposes.

With our new labeling system we may write for Eqs. (1-19)

$$Z_{XX} = \frac{V_X(j\omega)}{I_X(j\omega)}\bigg|_{I_Y=0}$$

$$Z_{XY} = Z_{YX} = \frac{V_X(j\omega)}{I_Y(j\omega)}\bigg|_{I_X=0} = \frac{V_Y(j\omega)}{I_X(j\omega)}\bigg|_{I_Y=0}$$

and

$$Z_{YY} = \frac{V_Y(j\omega)}{I_Y(j\omega)}\bigg|_{I_X=0}$$

where we arbitrarily assigned X to replace 1 and Y to replace 2 in the subscripts of Eq. (1-19).

Suppose that with the Y-terminals open-circuited and a sinusoidal voltage of 10 volts at a frequency of 10^3 Hz applied to the X-terminals we measured a current of 29.4 mA at a phase shift relative to the 10 volts applied of 28°. Then $V_X = 10 \angle 0°$ volts, $I_X = 29.4 \times 10^{-3} \angle 28°$ and

$$Z_{XX} = \frac{10 \angle 0°}{29.4 \times 10^{-3} \angle 28°}\bigg|_{I_Y=0} = 340 \angle -28° \ \Omega$$

Now, with V_X still applied and the Y-terminals still open-circuited we measure voltage V_Y, which measures to be $0.59 \angle 28°$ volts. Then $Z_{XY} = Z_{YX} = (0.59 \angle 28°/29.4 \times 10^{-3} \angle 28°) = 200 \angle 0° \ \Omega$. Lastly we apply a voltage to terminals Y-Y' and measure I_Y with terminals X-X' open-circuited so that we may determine Z_{YY}. For variety let us apply 20 volts at the *same frequency* to terminals Y-Y'. Under these conditions we measure current I_Y to be $77 \times 10^{-3} \angle -14°$. Thus, $Z_{YY} = (20\angle 0°/77 \times 10^{-3} \angle -14°) = 260\angle 14°$.

From Fig. 1–5(d) we see that $Z_1 \equiv Z_{XX} - Z_{XY}$, $Z_2 \equiv Z_{YY} - Z_{XY}$, and $Z_3 = Z_{XY} = Z_{YX}$. Thus,

$$Z_1 = 340\angle -28° - 200 = (300 - j159) - 200$$
$$= 100 - j159 = 188\angle -57.8° \ \Omega$$
$$Z_2 = 260\angle 14° - 200 = (252 + j63) - 200$$
$$= 52 + j63$$

and

$$Z_3 = 200 \ \Omega$$

The equivalent T-network for these values is shown in Fig. 1–10(a).

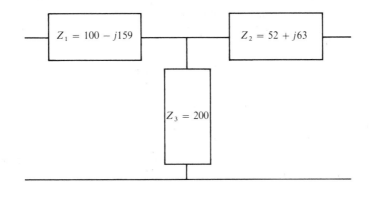

(a)

(b)

FIGURE 1–10

However, suppose that we wished to have our equivalent T-network appear in component form rather than impedance. Since we know the frequency we may determine the equivalent components. For Z_1 we know it is composed of a pure resistance of 100 ohms and a capacitor which offers 159 ohms' impedance for a frequency of 10^3 Hz. Then, since $X_C = 1/\omega C$ we know that $C = 1/\omega X_C = 1/2\pi f X_C = 1/6.28(10^3)(159) = 10^{-6}$ farad $= 1$ μF. We know that Z_2 is composed of a 52-ohm resistor and an inductor whose value is $L = X_L/\omega = (63/6.28 \times 10^3) \cong 10 \times 10^{-3}$ henry. And lastly we see that Z_3 is composed of a pure resistor of 200 ohms. The equivalent circuit showing the components is shown in Fig. 1–10(b).

Returning to Fig. 1–3(a) let us now derive the model for currents i_1' and i_2' (the dependent variables) and voltages v_1' and v_2' (the independent variables). Thus $i_1' = i_1'(v_1', v_2')$ and $i_2' = i_2'(v_1', v_2')$, and applying Eq. (1–8) we have

$$di_1' = \frac{\partial i_1'}{\partial v_1'} dv_1' + \frac{\partial i_1'}{\partial v_2'} dv_2'$$

$$di_2' = \frac{\partial i_2'}{\partial v_1'} dv_1' + \frac{\partial i_2'}{\partial v_2'} dv_2'$$

Since $di_1' = i_1(t)$, $dv_1' = v_1(t)$, etc., then

$$i_1(t) = \frac{\partial i_1}{\partial v_1} v_1(t) + \frac{\partial i_1}{\partial v_2} v_2(t) \qquad (1\text{–}20a)$$

and

$$i_2(t) = \frac{\partial i_2}{\partial v_1} v_1(t) + \frac{\partial i_2}{\partial v_2} v_2(t) \qquad (1\text{–}20b)$$

We see the coefficients of Eqs. (1–20) have the units of siemens (termed mhos in some texts) since

$$\frac{\partial i}{\partial v} = \frac{A}{V} = \mho$$

which is admittance y. We will evaluate these coefficients much as we did the coefficients of Eqs. (1–12). That is,

$$y_{11} \equiv \frac{\partial i_1}{\partial v_1}\bigg|_{v_2=0} = \frac{i_1(t)}{v_1(t)}\bigg|_{v_2=0} \equiv \text{Input admittance} \qquad (1\text{–}21a)$$

$$y_{12} \equiv \frac{\partial i_1}{\partial v_2}\bigg|_{v_1=0} = \frac{i_1(t)}{v_2(t)}\bigg|_{v_1=0} \equiv \text{Transfer admittance from terminal 1 to 2}$$

$$(1\text{–}21b)$$

$$y_{21} \equiv \frac{\partial i_2}{\partial v_1}\bigg|_{v_2=0} = \frac{i_2(t)}{v_1(t)}\bigg|_{v_2=0} \equiv \text{Transfer admittance from terminal 2 to 1}$$

$$\text{(1-21c)}$$

$$y_{22} \equiv \frac{\partial i_2}{\partial v_2}\bigg|_{v_1=0} = \frac{i_2(t)}{v_2(t)}\bigg|_{v_1=0} \equiv \text{Output admittance} \qquad \text{(1-21d)}$$

These parameters for obvious reasons are termed y-parameters. Notice in Eqs. (1–21) we evaluate the y-parameters by short-circuiting some voltage v_k, where $k = 1$ or 2; hence, these are also termed short-circuit parameters. Substituting the coefficients of Eqs. (1–21) into Eqs. (1–20) we have

$$i_1(t) = y_{11}v_1(t) + y_{12}v_2(t) \qquad \text{(1-22a)}$$

$$i_2(t) = y_{21}v_1(t) + y_{22}v_2(t) \qquad \text{(1-22b)}$$

In some cases, such as active devices, we must short circuit v_1 or v_2 to determine the y-parameters without short circuiting the dc component. To do this we can use capacitors since they appear as an open circuit to dc but can be designed to appear as an approximate short circuit for the ac component.

To model an equivalent circuit from Eqs. (1–22) we begin by realizing that since the form of Eqs. (1–22) is the summing of currents each equation represents a node. Then Eq. (1–22a) says that the current i_1 is the sum of currents $y_{11}v_1(t)$ and $y_{12}v_2(t)$, and Eq. (1–22b) says current i_2 is made up of currents $y_{21}v_1(t)$ and $y_{22}v_2(t)$. Figure 1–11(a) was derived from Eq. (1–22a) and Fig. 1–11(b) from Eq. (1–22b). Figure 1–11(c) is the combination of Fig. 1–11(a) and Fig. 1–11(b).

For passive networks $y_{12} = y_{21}$ and we can write as

$$i_1(t) = y_{11}v_1(t) + y_{12}v_2(t) - y_{12}v_1(t) + y_{12}v_1(t)$$

$$i_2(t) = y_{12}v_1(t) + y_{12}v_2(t) - y_{12}v_2(t) + y_{22}v_2(t)$$

by adding $\pm y_{12}v_1(t)$ to Eq. (1–22a) and $\pm y_{12}v_2(t)$ to Eq. (1–22b). Factoring these equations we have

$$i_1(t) = (y_{11} + y_{12})v_1(t) + y_{12}[v_2(t) - v_1(t)] \qquad \text{(1-23a)}$$

and

$$i_2(t) = (y_{22} + y_{12})v_2(t) + y_{12}[v_1(t) - v_2(t)] \qquad \text{(1-23b)}$$

The only way for us to have a physically realizable circuit from Eqs. (1–23) is to define the current $y_{12}[v_2(t) - v_1(t)]$ as a negative value (negative means flowing in opposite direction). Hence, let us define y_{12} as $-y_C$. Let us also define $y_A \equiv y_{11} + y_{12} = y_{11} - y_C$ since $y_{12} = -y_C$, and $y_B \equiv y_{22} + y_{12} = y_{22} - y_C$. Equations (1–23) become

$$i_1(t) = y_A v_1(t) - y_C[v_2(t) - v_1(t)] = y_A v_1(t) + y_C[v_1(t) - v_2(t)] \quad \text{(1-24a)}$$

$$i_2(t) = y_B v_2(t) - y_C[v_1(t) - v_2(t)] = y_B v_2(t) + y_C[v_2(t) - v_1(t)] \quad \text{(1-24b)}$$

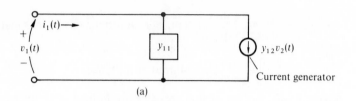

(a)

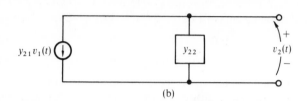

(b)

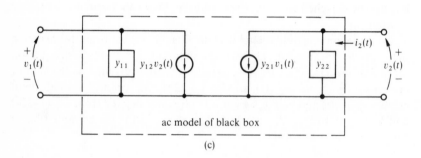

ac model of black box

(c)

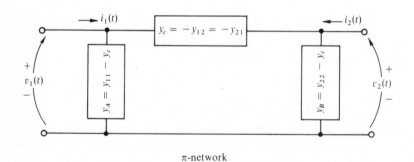

π-network

(d)

FIGURE 1–11

The equivalent circuit for Eqs. (1–24) is shown in Fig. 1–11(d), which is termed a π-network.

To reiterate, we must keep in mind that the models we have derived are valid only for the ac portion of the input waveform(s). The examples we have considered thus far have had no dc component, hence we have not had to separate the dc and ac components of the input waveform(s). This concept of dc and ac components will be made clearer when we model active components in chap. 2.

We will conclude our examples with an example which will offer concreteness to the use of Eqs. (1–21).

Example 1–9   For a given black box make an equivalent π-network using measurement techniques.

Solution   For reference purposes we label one pair of terminals as 1-1′ and the other 2-2′. We first determine Y_{11} according to Eq. (1–21a) by applying some sinusoidal voltage for v_1, say 10 volts, and then measuring i_1 with terminals 2-2′ short-circuited so that $v_2 = 0$. Under these conditions i_1 measured 0.456 A, hence

$$Y_{11} = \frac{I_1(j\omega)}{V_1(j\omega)}\bigg|_{V_2=0} = \frac{0.456}{10} = 0.0456 \; \mho$$

We next determine Y_{21} according to Eq. (1–21c) by keeping v_1 applied with terminals 2-2′ still short-circuited and measuring i_2. In doing this we notice that the current flows in the opposite direction than that indicated in Fig. 1–11(d), hence we assign a negative sign to the value. The magnitude of i_2 was 0.182 A, therefore $I_2 = -0.182 \, \text{A}$. Hence,

$$Y_{21} = \frac{I_2(j\omega)}{V_1(j\omega)}\bigg|_{V_2=0} = \frac{-0.182}{10} = -0.0182 \; \mho$$

We will next determine those y-parameters requiring terminals 1-1′ to be short-circuited so that $v_1 = 0$. For these y-parameters, Y_{12} and Y_{22}, we will apply a 10-volt sinusoidal waveform for v_2 and measure i_1 and i_2. Under these conditions it was found that i_1 measured -0.181 A, where the negative sign indicates the measured i_1 flows opposite to that shown in Fig. 1–11(d) and i_2 measures 1.280 A. Thus from Eqs. (1–21b and d) we find

$$Y_{22} = \frac{I_2(j\omega)}{V_2(j\omega)}\bigg|_{v_1=0} = \frac{1.280}{10} = 0.1280 \; \mho$$

and

$$Y_{12} = \frac{I_1(j\omega)}{V_2(j\omega)}\bigg|_{v_1=0} = \frac{-0.181}{10} = -0.0181 \text{ ℧}$$

As we see $Y_{12} = Y_{21}$, which verifies the black box can be treated as containing passive components.

We are in a position now to determine the π-network admittances Y_A, Y_B, and Y_C. Thus

$$Y_A = Y_{11} + Y_{12} = 0.0456 - 0.0181 = 0.0275 \text{ ℧}$$

$$Y_B = Y_{22} + Y_{12} = 0.1280 - 0.0181 = 0.1099 \text{ ℧}$$

and

$$Y_C = -Y_{12} = -Y_{21} = -(-0.0181) = 0.0181 \text{ ℧}$$

The π-network for this example is illustrated in Fig. 1–12.

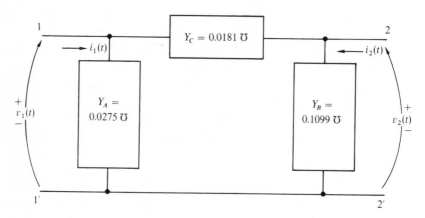

FIGURE 1–12[1]

There are other models we could derive for the black box of Fig. 1–3(a); however, we shall not derive any more until chap. 2. In chap. 2 we will model active devices.

Notice the principle of superposition may be applied to Eqs. (1–11) and those equations [Eqs. (1–12) and Eqs. (1–22)] which were derived from it, so long as the coefficients of each independent variable are not a function of that independent variable. That is, if $z_{11} = z_{11}(i_1)$, $z_{12} = z_{12}(i_2)$, $z_{21} = z_{21}(i_1)$, and $z_{22} = z_{22}(i_2)$, then the principle of superposition cannot be applied. In our problems these coefficients, or parameters, are either constants or can be approximated to be so.

---

[1]Note: This black box is the same black box of Ex. 1–6.

In summary, when modeling a black box or circuit using two-port network analysis we must first determine the independent and dependent variables. Once this determination has been made we are able to write two implicit equations expressing the variables' relationship. Equations of this type are written in Eqs. (1–9). After writing the implicit relationships we may apply Eq. (1–8), which yields equations like that of Eqs. (1–10). Considering only the ac portion of the variables results in equations such as Eqs. (1–11). From these equations we define and derive the various parameters. The units of the parameters dictate the type parameters used in the model. After substituting the parameters back into the equation from which they were derived we have an equation from which we can model, see Eqs. (1–12) and Fig. 1–4(c). Usually these equations need some modification in order to be able to make a unified model of the type shown in Fig. 1–5(d). The modification is done by adding and subtracting terms which will result in a mutual term such as z_{12} in Eqs. (1–15).

2 Circuit Components

2–1 Introduction

This chapter concerns itself with mathematically describing the effect of a component on an electrical excitation. We will need these equations in order to mathematically express the electronic behavior of a circuit. We have written many such equations in elementary circuit analysis, but here we wish to write the equations using derivatives and integrals. We will also want to view each component with respect to its linearity.

The section on inductance has a very basic beginning and proceeds to mutually coupled components. The reason for this basic approach is so the reader can build his understanding without having to recall earlier material from other courses. It is hoped also that because the total picture is presented the reader will be able to understand the more complex concepts of mutually coupled components with greater ease and to a greater depth.

The material in the section on active components is presented in such a way that it follows very naturally from earlier work in this text. As in the case of inductance, we begin considering active components from a relatively basic concept. This allows us to point out some critical rudimentary concepts which are necessary to understanding the modeling of active components.

We must remember in our study of each component that our goal is to be able to mathematically express the effects a component has on an electrical excitation. It is from these mathematical expressions of the components that we can determine the overall effects of a circuit on an electrical excitation. The writing of the overall circuit equations will be undertaken in chap. 3 for there we will view writing loop and nodal equations. Since the most meaningful examples which utilized the concepts developed in this chapter require the material of chap. 3 few examples are presented in this chapter. It is rationalized that sufficient material is presented in this chapter to understand the writing of equations describing component behavior and more than enough examples utilizing these equations in circuit analysis are given in chap. 3.

2–2 Resistance

Before the circuit as a whole can be analyzed we must understand the parts that make up that circuit. For that reason we shall investigate the mathematical equations describing the current and voltage relationship of the various components. We will also determine the requirements for linearity of these components.

Our first component to consider is the resistor, whether it represents the resistance of a wire, the internal resistance of a signal generator, or a resistor purposely added to the circuit. From Ohms' law we know that the current i_R flowing through a resistor R of constant value is governed by the relationship

$$i_R = \frac{1}{R} v_R, \quad \text{or} \quad i_R(t) = \frac{1}{R} v_R(t) \tag{2-1}$$

for a time-variant voltage v_R existing across R. Thus, resistance is expressed by the equation

$$R = \frac{v_R}{i_R} \tag{2-2}$$

It is measured in units of ohms, which are symbolized by Ω. We see that Eq. (2–1) is the equation of a straight line, which is a linear equation. Therefore the principle of superposition can be applied. This is true so long as R is not a function of the voltage v_R or the current i_R.

As we know, the resistance of components varies with temperature, and temperature is a function of the power loss of that component. Then resistance of R in practice is a function of the power p_R, which is a function of the current i_R and voltage v_R. Let us express this relationship as

$$r \propto p_R = i_R v_R \tag{2-3}$$

where $\propto$ means proportional and resistance is now a variable and is represented by r. Under this condition the current i_R is

$$i_R \propto r \frac{1}{v_R} \tag{2-4}$$

or, in words, the current i_R is directly proportional to the resistance r but inversely proportional to the voltage v_R. This equation makes physical sense since as the voltage v_R is increased the power loss due to heating goes up; this increases r and decreases i_R. A graph of Eq. (2-4) would appear similar to that shown in Fig. 2–1(b). From Fig. 2–1(b) and also from Eq. (2-4) we see that Eq. (2-4) is a nonlinear equation; hence, the principle of superposition cannot be applied.

Even though all physical resistors change value due to heat, in our design we never purposely exceed their power rating. In fact we allow a margin of safety. From Fig. 2–1(b) we see that if we operate within this safety margin we can approximate the curve with a straight line as shown in Fig. 2–1(c). The straight-line approximation behaves according to Eq. (2-2), which is linear.

In summary, the resistance must be a constant, or approximated to be so, in order for the principle of superposition to be applicable. The approximation of the actual curve as shown in Fig. 2–1(c) is very realistic. In practice we are probably approximating a difference of less than 1% while the tolerance of the resistor is from 5% to 10%. Also, the lag time it takes to "heat up" a resistor due to the power applied plays an important role in helping a resistor remain linear over large ranges of power.

2–3   Capacitance

Capacitance is defined to be the ratio of accumulated charge between two points, x_1 and x_2, and the potential existing between these two points, where the potential is due to the charge accumulation. Hence,

$$C \equiv \frac{q_C}{v_C} \tag{2-5}$$

or $q_C(t) = Cv_C(t)$ for a time-variant potential v_C. From Eq. (2-5) it is seen that capacitance is a measure of the *charge-per-volt* existing between points x_1 and x_2, as illustrated in Fig. 2–2. Capacitance is measured in units of farads, which are symbolized by F.

From Eq. (2–5) it is seen that if the ratio of charge accumulated, q_C, to voltage, v_C, is constant then the equation $q_C = Cv_C$ is a linear equation. As was the case for the resistor we may reasonably approximate the capacitance C to be constant. Under this approximation the principle of superposition applies.

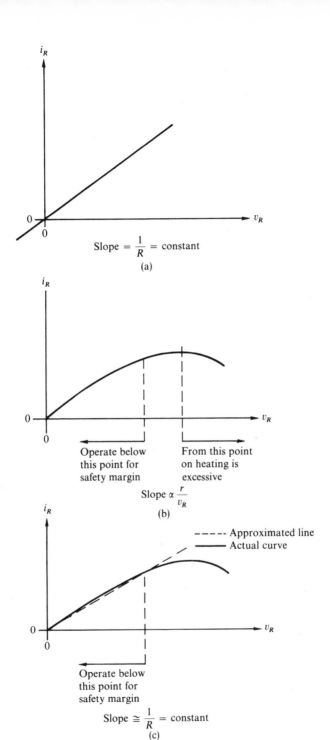

Slope $= \dfrac{1}{R} =$ constant

(a)

Operate below
this point for
safety margin

From this point
on heating is
excessive

Slope $\alpha \dfrac{r}{v_R}$

(b)

- - - - - Approximated line
——— Actual curve

Operate below
this point for
safety margin

Slope $\cong \dfrac{1}{R} =$ constant

(c)

FIGURE 2–1

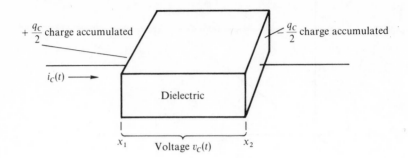

Charge of Dielectric = Difference of Charge
Between Points x_1 and x_2

Charge of Dielectric $C = \dfrac{q_C}{v_C} = q_C = \dfrac{q_C}{2} - \left(\dfrac{-q_C}{2}\right)$

FIGURE 2–2

To determine the current i_C which *passes*[1] through capacitor C we must determine the change of charge with respect to time, that is, $dq_C(t)/dt$. From Eq. (2–5) we find that for a time-variant voltage v_C we have

$$i_C(t) = C\frac{dv_C(t)}{dt} \qquad (2\text{–}6)$$

The voltage v_C is determined by first solving Eq. (2–6) for dv_C and then integrating. Hence,

$$v_C(t) = \frac{1}{C} \int i_C(t)\, dt \qquad (2\text{–}7)$$

or $(1/C) \int_0^t i_C(t)dt$ for definite integrals.

Example 2–1   Given that the voltage across capacitor C is $v_C = 5(1 - e^{-10^3 t})$ volts for the time interval 0 to t seconds.
(a) Determine the current i_C.
(b) Use your answer of part (a) to derive v_C.

---

[1]An ideal capacitor, one with no leakage, does not actually transfer charge through its dielectric but rather displaces charges as the potential across the capacitor is varied. As the charges are displaced, that is, moved back and forth, current is created, but no transfer of charge takes place from x_1 and x_2. This is why only a varying potential produces current "through" a capacitor.

Solution   (a) From Eq. (2–6)

$$i_C = C\frac{d}{dt}[5(1 - e^{-10^2t}] = 5 \times 10^3 Ce^{-10^3t} \text{ A}$$

(b) From Eq. (2–7)

$$v_C = \frac{1}{C}\int_0^t 5 \times 10^3 Ce^{-10^3t} \, dt = -\frac{5 \times 10^3}{10^3}e^{-10^3t}\Big|_0^t$$

$$= 5(1 - e^{-10^3t}) \text{ V}$$

or

$$v_C = \frac{1}{C}\int 5 \times 10^3 Ce^{-10^3t} \, dt = -5e^{-10^3t} + K$$

where K is constant of integration. Now, at $t = 0$ we know that $v_C = 0$. Therefore

$$v_C(0) = -5 + K = 0, \quad \text{so} \quad K = 5$$

Then

$$v_C = -5e^{10^3t} + K = -5e^{-10^3t} + 5$$
$$= 5(1 - e^{-10^3t}) \text{ V}$$

2–4 Inductance

In this section we will investigate inductors and transformers. We will begin with the very basics of inductance and proceed to transformers. Our discussion of transformers will include the dot notation, which is a means to determine voltage polarities and current directions.

Whenever a current is passed through a wire a force field is set up about the wire. This force field is imagined to exist as dynamic force lines encompassing the wire and to be continuous axially. These lines are given the name magnetic flux and are designated as ϕ. An illustration of this concept is given in Fig. 2–3. By dividing magnetic flux by an area in which it exists we have magnetic flux density, which is designated by the symbol B and equals ϕ/area. Notice from Fig. 2–3 the flux density increases as one approaches the wire.

Now, suppose wire A has current i_A flowing through it and wire B is passed through the flux ϕ_A such that it cuts ϕ_A. This will induce a voltage which is termed v_B, as is illustrated in Fig. 2–4.

Whenever a voltage is induced in wiring and/or components, through the interaction of flux ϕ and the circuit, the phenomenon is termed magnetic coupling. Magnetic coupling occurs because of movement of the circuit relative to the flux field, where the flux's field is the space in which the flux is present. Then not only will a voltage be induced in a circuit if that circuit is passed through a static magnetic flux field, as illustrated in

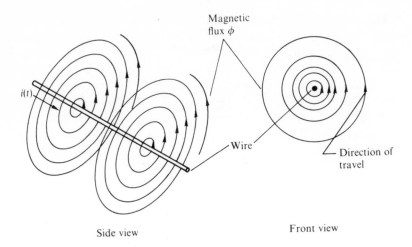

FIGURE 2-3

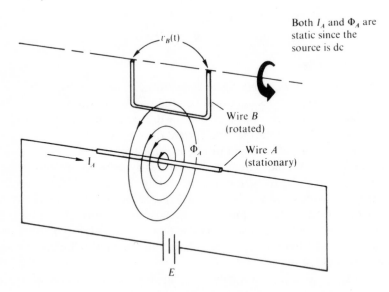

FIGURE 2-4

Fig. 2–4, but also a voltage will be induced in the circuit if it is stationary in a flux field and the flux field varies with respect to time, that is, $[d\phi(t)/dt]$. Of course both circuit and flux could vary to produce an induced voltage so long as relative motion exists between the two and the circuit cuts the flux. Since in most circuit analysis the circuit remains stationary our analysis will be for a varying magnetic flux field.

The component we shall first investigate which utilizes magnetic coupling is the inductor. An inductor is usually constructed from a series of N turns arranged such that the magnetic flux field from each turn encompasses some or all of the remaining turns. As a result each individual turn has a voltage induced across it (if the flux is time-variant) which is a function of the flux from the other turns. It is the sum of the voltages of each individual turn that determines the voltage across the inductor. This is demonstrated in Fig. 2–5.

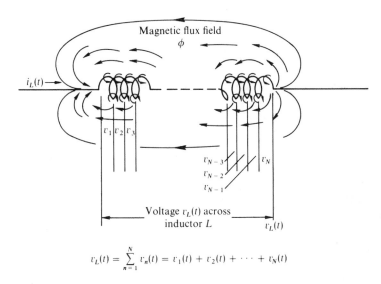

$$v_L(t) = \sum_{n=1}^{N} v_n(t) = v_1(t) + v_2(t) + \cdots + v_N(t)$$

FIGURE 2–5   Induced Voltage v_L Across an Inductor with N Turns

To mathematically arrive at an equation to determine the voltage v_L across the inductor we begin with the concept that the voltage v_L is proportional to the rate of change of the flux ϕ which cuts each turn with respect to time and the number of turns which make up the inductor. This is expressed as

$$v_L = (\text{no. of turns}) \times (\text{rate of change of } \phi \text{ with respect to time})$$

$$= N\frac{d\phi(t)}{dt} \tag{2–8}$$

Now, the flux ϕ is caused from the current i_L passing through the turns of the inductor, where i_L is a function of time [recall $i = (dq/dt)$], therefore, we may write $d\phi/dt$ as

$$\frac{d\phi}{dt} = \frac{d\phi(i_L)}{di_L}\frac{di_L(t)}{dt}$$

Substituting this in Eq. (2–8) we have

$$v_L = N \frac{d\phi(i_L)}{di_L} \frac{di_L(t)}{dt}$$

The quantity $N[d\phi(i_L)/di_L]$ is defined as inductance and designated as L. It is measured in units of henries, which are symbolized by H. For linear analysis L must be constant.

Physically this means the material making up the core of the inductor must not be saturated. What do we mean by ". . . the core of the inductor must not be saturated"? We begin by referring to Fig. 2–5. We see that flux is concentrated in the center of the coil. Now from the definition of inductance $[N(d\phi/di)]$ we see that for a given change in current the more of the flux change that can be concentrated the higher the inductance value. Since we want as high a value of inductance as possible for N turns we want the material which forms the core of the inductor to offer little resistance, or reluctance as it is termed, to ϕ so that we will have a high concentration of ϕ. Therefore, inductors are usually made from turns of wire wound on a magnetic material.

Many different types of magnetic materials exist and all have a limit as to the flux density they will accept and still be linearly proportional to the current and turns of wire responsible for the flux density. A graph which shows the acceptance of flux density is termed a B-H curve [see Fig. 2–6(a)]. It derives its name from its coordinates of B, the flux density, and the magnetizing force, H, which is termed the magnetic field intensity. The magnetic field intensity magnitude is determined by the product of the number of turns of the inductor and the current flowing in those turns, termed amp-turns, which are creating B in the core divided by the length l of the material through which ϕ travels, hence

$$H = \frac{NI}{l} \tag{2–9}$$

To mathematically express the relationship between B and H we have the equation

$$B = \mu H$$

where μ is permeability and varies in value for various materials. If we require that the core not be saturated so that we are operating in the linear region of the core material, then H must be less than H_S, as shown in Fig. 2–6(a). For the region $H < H_S$ we may approximate the B-H curve with a straight line whereby μ becomes a constant since $\mu = (B/H)$. This linear approximation is shown in Fig. 2–6(b).

By requiring μ to be a constant we have also required L to be a constant, which means that the principle of superposition can be applied to the equations $L[di_L(t)/dt]$ and $(1/L) \int v_L(t)dt$ that are to be derived shortly.

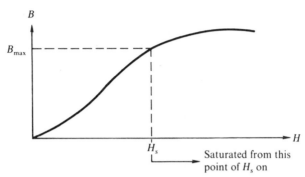

B_{max} is maximum flux density allowed in order to
approximate linearity

(a)

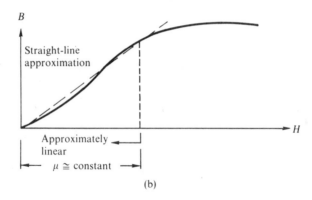

(b)

FIGURE 2–6

To show that L is constant if μ is constant we begin with the equation

$$\mu = \text{constant} = \frac{B}{H} \quad \text{for } H < H_S$$

Since

$$B = \frac{\phi}{A}$$

and

$$H = \frac{Ni}{l}$$

then

$$\mu = \text{constant} = \frac{\phi/A}{Ni/l} = \frac{\phi}{i}\frac{l}{NA}$$

Now l, N, and A are constants so ϕ/i must be a constant also. Since ϕ/i is a constant and is the slope of ϕ versus i, then $d\phi/di$ is also a constant for that same graph. In fact, $(d\phi/di) = (\phi/i)$, so $\mu = $ constant $= (d\phi/di)(l/NA)$. Let us now multiply both sides of this equation by N^2, therefore μN^2 $= $ constant $= N(d\phi/dt)(l/A)$, or $N(d\phi/di) = (\mu N^2 A)/l = $ constant. By definition $L = N(d\phi/di)$ so

$$L = N\frac{d\phi}{di} = \frac{\mu N^2 A}{l} = \text{constant} \tag{2-10}$$

for μ being constant.

For our problems we shall require that the core material not be saturated. Therefore Eq. (2–10) is true and we may apply the principle of superposition to our inductive components. As in the case of our straight-line approximations for other components it is also realistic to make that assumption for inductors. Now, substituting L for $N(d\phi/di)$ we may write v_L as

$$v_L(t) = L\frac{di_L(t)}{dt} \tag{2-11}$$

From Eq. (2–11) we can determine the current through an inductor. This is accomplished by solving for di_L from Eq. (2–11) and then integrating. Hence,

$$di_L = \frac{1}{L}v_L(t)\,dt$$

so

$$i_L(t) = \frac{1}{L}\int v_L(t)\,dt \tag{2-12}$$

The type of inductance just discussed is termed *self-inductance*. The reason for this terminology is because the induced voltage is the resultant voltage of each individual turn making up the inductor L where these individual turn voltages are caused by the flux from the other turns making up the inductor. That is, the turn induces the voltage across itself, or the voltage is *self-induced* (see Fig. 2–5).

There is another type of inductance termed *mutual inductance*. Mutual inductance is conceptually the same as self-inductance, but differs in that the magnetic flux field inducing the voltage is not self-induced, but rather, the flux is from some other source. Let us examine Fig. 2–7 for this concept of mutual inductance. In Fig. 2–7(a) it is seen that ϕ_2 will cause a voltage to be induced in L, where ϕ_2 is a function of some current i_2. The voltage v_L can be determined from Eq. (2–8), that is,

$$v_L = N\frac{d\phi_2(t)}{dt} = N\frac{d\phi_2(i_2)}{di_2}\frac{di_2(t)}{dt} \tag{2-13}$$

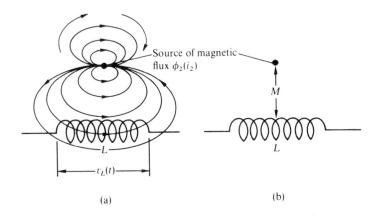

FIGURE 2-7 Mutual Inductance

since
$$\phi_2 = \phi_2(i_2)$$
and
$$i_2 = i_2(t)$$

As before, the quantity $N[d\phi_2(i_2)/di_2]$ is termed inductance and is measured in henries. However, there is a difference and that difference is the induced voltage is not self-induced but rather is induced by some other source which is mutually sharing its flux. Because the induced voltage v_L is caused by this mutual arrangement it is said that a mutual inductance $[N(d\phi_2/di_2)]$ exists between them. In order to distinguish between self-inductance and mutual inductance, mutual inductance is designated as M and its physical presence is represented as shown in Fig. 2–7(b). To continue with the analysis, then, Eq. (2–13) is written as

$$v_L = M\frac{di_2(t)}{dt}, \quad \text{where} \quad M = N\frac{d\phi(i_2)}{di_2} \qquad \textbf{(2–14)}$$

Now let us imagine the inductor L of Fig. 2–7(a) has a current i_1 flowing through it with the flux ϕ_2 still present. Under these conditions we can expect the voltage across the inductor L, that is v_L, to be a resultant voltage of the self-induced and the mutually induced voltage. This condition is illustrated in Fig. 2–8 where

$$\text{mutually induced voltage} = v_{L_{i_2}}(t) = M\frac{di_2(t)}{dt}$$

(caused by i_2 flowing in source)

$$\text{self-induced voltage} = v_{L_{i_1}}(t) = L\frac{di_1(t)}{dt}$$

(caused by i_1 flowing in L)

Then the true voltage across L, v_L, is found by summing the superimposed voltages across L, which is

$$v_L = v_{L_{i_1}}(i_1) \pm v_{L_{i_2}}(i_2) = L\frac{di_1(t)}{dt} \pm M\frac{di_2(t)}{dt}$$

The polarity signs at this point are not of main concern since their derivation will be given shortly, but what is of importance is the concept of how self- and mutual inductance affect the voltage across the inductor L.

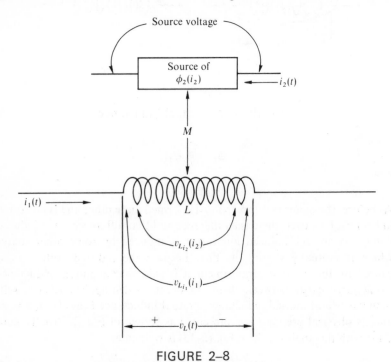

FIGURE 2–8

Note in Fig. 2–8 that the term *source voltage* is used to describe the voltage drop caused by the current i_2, where i_2 is the source of the flux ϕ_2. The term source voltage will be used in this sense, that is, it will be the voltage resulting from the current causing the flux under discussion.

To elaborate on the concept of having the superposition of two voltages, where one is caused from self-inductance and the other from mutual inductance, consider the transformer shown in Fig. 2–9. The resultant voltage across the primary, v_{L_1}, and the secondary, v_{L_2}, is the result of the resultant flux ϕ_1' and ϕ_2' cutting through the coils composing L_1 and L_2 respectively. To derive expressions for, ϕ_1' and ϕ_2' we suppose only a portion of the flux ϕ_2 cuts L_1 and only some portion of ϕ_1 cuts L_2. Let us represent the proportionality constants which indicate the portions of

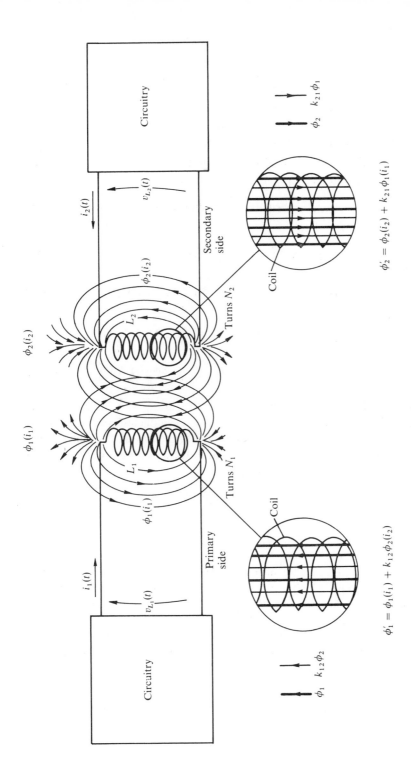

FIGURE 2-9

47

flux ϕ_1 and ϕ_2 cutting (called coupling flux) L_2 and L_1 respectively as k_{21} and k_{12} where these terms are known as coupling coefficients. Then $\phi_1' = \phi_1(i_1) \pm k_{12}\phi_2(i_2)$ and $\phi_2' = \phi_2(i_2) \pm k_{21}\phi_1(i_1)$, where flux direction determines the sign of $k_{mn}\phi_n$. Now, since the flux ϕ_1 and the coupling flux $k_{12}\phi_2$ are in the same direction in the coil center we may write

$$\phi_1' = \phi_1(i_1) + k_{12}\phi_2(i_2) = \text{resultant flux cutting } L_1 \qquad \textbf{(2–15a)}$$

Also the same can be said of ϕ_2 and $k_{21}\phi_1$, hence

$$\phi_2' = \phi_2(i_2) + k_{21}\phi_1(i_1) = \text{resultant flux cutting } L_2 \qquad \textbf{(2–15b)}$$

From Eq. (2–8) we know

$$v_{L_1}(t) = N_1 \frac{d\phi_1'}{dt} = N_1 \frac{d}{dt}[\phi_1(i_1) + k_{12}\phi_2(i_2)] \qquad \textbf{(2–16a)}$$

$$v_{L_2}(t) = N_2 \frac{d\phi_2'}{dt} = N_2 \frac{d}{dt}[\phi_2(i_2) + k_{21}\phi_1(i_1)] \qquad \textbf{(2–16b)}$$

which can be written as

$$v_{L_1}(t) = N_1 \frac{d\phi(i_1)}{di_1}\frac{di_1(t)}{dt} + k_{12}N_1 \frac{d\phi_2(i_2)}{di_2}\frac{di_2(t)}{dt} \qquad \textbf{(2–17a)}$$

$$v_{L_2}(t) = N_2 \frac{d\phi_2(i_2)}{di_2}\frac{di_2(t)}{dt} + k_{21}N_2 \frac{d\phi_1(i_1)}{di_1}\frac{di_1(t)}{dt} \qquad \textbf{(2–17b)}$$

Using our definition of inductance we see that in Eqs. (2–17) the quantities $N_1[d\phi_1(i_1)/di_1]$ and $N_2[d\phi_2(i_2)/di_2]$ are the self-inductance of the primary and secondary respectively. Since we have defined L_1 as the primary self-inductance and L_2 as the secondary self-inductance, then we may mathematically write that

$$L_1 = N_1 \frac{d\phi_1(i_1)}{di_1} \qquad \textbf{(2–18a)}$$

and

$$L_2 = N_2 \frac{d\phi_2(i_2)}{di_2} \qquad \textbf{(2–18b)}$$

Also in Eqs. (2–17) we have the quantities $k_{12}N_1[d\phi_2(i_2)/di_2]$ and $k_{21}N_2[d\phi_1(i_1)/di_1]$, which also have the units of inductance since coupling coefficients are unitless. The quantity $k_{12}N_1[d\phi_2(i_2)/di_2]$ was derived from the coupling flux $k_{12}\phi_2$ cutting the turns of L_1; hence, $k_{12}N_1[d\phi_2(i_2)/di_2]$ describes the mutual inductance which exists between L_1 and L_2. We shall designate this mutual inductance as M_{12}, and the mutual inductance $k_{21}N_2[d\phi_1(i_1)/di_1]$ as M_{21}. Therefore,

$$M_{12} = k_{12}N_1 \frac{d\phi_2(i_2)}{di_2} \qquad \textbf{(2–19a)}$$

and

$$M_{21} = k_{21}N_2 \frac{d\phi_1(i_1)}{di_1} \qquad \textbf{(2–19b)}$$

We shall show later that for our problems $M_{12} = M_{21}$ and we shall designate any mutual inductance as M.

Substituting Eqs. (2–18) and (2–19) into Eq. (2–17) we have

$$v_{L_1}(t) = L_1 \frac{di_1(t)}{dt} + M_{12} \frac{di_2(t)}{dt} = L_1 \frac{di_1(t)}{dt} + M \frac{di_2(t)}{dt} \qquad \textbf{(2–20a)}$$

$$v_{L_2}(t) = L_2 \frac{di_2(t)}{dt} + M_{21} \frac{di_1(t)}{dt} = L_2 \frac{di_2(t)}{dt} + M \frac{di_1(t)}{dt} \qquad \textbf{(2–20b)}$$

where $M_{12} = M_{21} = M$. Equations (2–20) result in v_{L_1} and v_{L_2} as being expressed as the superposition of two voltages. It is important to understand that in reality the resultant flux ϕ'_1 and ϕ'_2 determine the voltage magnitudes of v_{L_1} and v_{L_2}. However, from an analysis viewpoint we shall imagine that two voltages, the self-induced and the mutually induced, are superimposed—as Eqs. (2–20) mathematically state.

Transformers are usually wound on a core of magnetic material similar to the core material of inductors. As was the case for inductors this will increase the inductance value. It will also increase the coupling coefficients. In order to apply the principle of superposition to transformers we must be certain we are operating within the linear region of the transformer's core. To determine the linear region of a transformer's core we view its *B-H* curve. The *B-H* curve of Fig. 2–10 was purposely made different from that of Fig. 2–6 by showing hysteresis in such a way that it would not present a problem in concept, whether we wanted to discuss inductor or transformer cores.

Hysteresis produces distortion and for that reason for our application is an undesirable effect to be present in cores. If the magnetic core material provides a continuous path the effective hysteresis loop can be reduced by adding an air gap to the path. This is usually suitable for an inductor and hysteresis becomes negligible, especially if its core is a section of straight cylindrical material. Then the air gap is from one end of the inductor to the other. However, transformer cores usually require the air gap to be small or nonexistent; therefore some hysteresis is always present. Fortunately, cores are available which have hysteresis loops small enough that distortion is within most tolerances.

The *B-H* curve of Fig. 2–10(a) is exaggerated for labeling purposes, while Fig. 2–10(b) might be more realistic. Notice in Fig. 2–10 that while in the linear portions of the *B-H* curves the inductance has a constant value. This is true since according to Eq. (2–10) the inductance is directly proportional to the slope of the *B-H* curve; that is, $L = (N^2 A/l)\mu = (N^2 A/l) \cdot (\text{slope of } B\text{-}H \text{ curve})$, and for Fig. 2–10 all lines in the linear regions are parallel straight lines. We will have more to say concerning the linearity of cores at the end of this section, but for now we move on analyzing the transformer as a linear component.

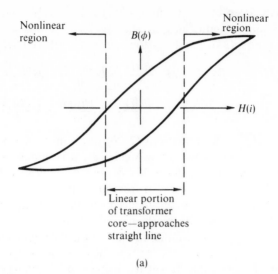

(a)

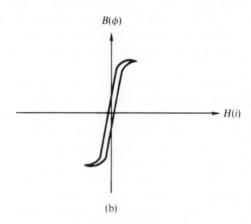

(b)

FIGURE 2–10

Returning to Fig. 2–9, if one of the currents had been reversed, or if one of the coil winding directions had been reversed, then the coupling fluxes $k_{12}\phi_2$ and $k_{21}\phi_1$ would have opposed ϕ_1 and ϕ_2 in L_1 and L_2, which would mean some reduction of the resultant flux ϕ_1' and ϕ_2'. Then $\phi_1' = \phi_1 - k_{12}\phi_2$ and $\phi_2' = \phi_2 - k_{21}\phi_1$. Under these conditions Eqs. (2–20a) and (2–20b) would be

$$v_{L_1}(t) = L_1 \frac{di_1(t)}{dt} - M\frac{di_2(t)}{dt}$$

and

$$v_{L_2}(t) = L_2 \frac{di_2(t)}{dt} - M\frac{di_1(t)}{dt}$$

As seen, the mutual voltages are reversed in polarity.

In order to determine the polarity of the mutually induced voltages the following information is needed: (1) the current direction creating the flux which is causing mutual coupling (knowing the current direction allows the flux direction to be determined using the right-hand rule); and (2) the coil-winding direction of the coil being coupled via the flux. (Knowing the coil winding's direction and the coupling flux direction allows the polarity of the mutually induced voltage to be determined.) Obviously, having to know the direction of the coil winding is a handicap in circuit analysis since most persons are not artistic enough to draw a schematic of an inductor, or a transformer, which clearly shows coil-winding direction (this would require a pictorial). A convention has been established to determine the polarities of the mutually induced voltage. The convention is termed *dot notation*. This terminology describes the technique used. Dot notation prescribes that a dot be placed on the primary (L_1) and secondary (L_2) of the transformer such that the self-induced voltage *polarity* is the same as the mutually induced voltage *polarity at the dots*. This concept can be better understood by examining Fig. 2–11.

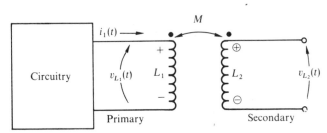

$$v_{L_1}(t) = L_1 \frac{di_1(t)}{dt}$$

$$v_{L_2}(t) = M \frac{di_1(t)}{dt}$$

FIGURE 2–11

The convention used in Fig. 2–11 and for the remainder of this text is that a self-induced voltage polarity will not be circled while a mutually induced voltage polarity will be circled. In Fig. (2–11) a self-induced voltage v_{L_1} is developed due to the current $i_1(t)$. The positive side of v_{L_1} is at the dot of L_1. Mutually induced into the secondary side L_2 is the voltage v_{L_2} with its polarity at the dot of L_2 the same as the polarity of v_{L_1} at the dot of L_1.

It is important to notice in Fig. 2–11 that the secondary is open-circuited, hence no current flows in the secondary. If the secondary were not open-circuited and current were allowed to flow a mutually induced voltage would also be created in the primary. Let us examine this case where current is flowing in both primary and secondary, as illustrated in Fig. 2–12.

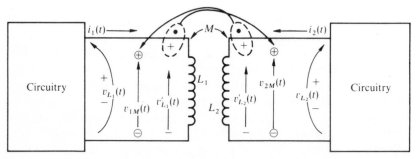

$v_{L_1}(t)$ and $v_{L_2}(t)$ = Self-induced voltage + mutually-induced voltage

$$v_{L_1}(t) = v'_{L_1}(t) + v_{1M}(t) \text{ and } v_{L_2}(t) = v'_{L_2}(t) + v_{2M}(t)$$

$$v_{L_1}(t) = L_1 \frac{di_1(t)}{dt} + M \frac{di_2(t)}{dt} \text{ and } v_{L_2}(t) = L_2 \frac{di_2(t)}{dt} + M \frac{di_1(t)}{dt}$$

(a)

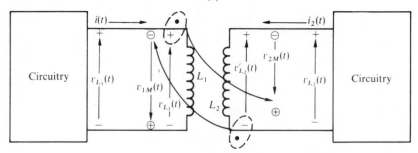

$$v_{L_1}(t) = v'_{L_1}(t) - v_{1M}(t) \text{ and } v_{L_2}(t) = v'_{L_2}(t) - v_{2M}(t)$$

$$v_{L_1}(t) = L_1 \frac{di_1(t)}{dt} - M \frac{di_2(t)}{dt} \qquad v_{L_2}(t) = L_2 \frac{di_2(t)}{dt} - M \frac{di_1(t)}{dt}$$

(b)

FIGURE 2–12

Notice polarities of self-induced voltages and mutually induced voltages are same at the dots.

We can see that on both the primary and secondary side of the transformer in Fig. 2–12 three voltages are identified. The voltages v_{L_1} and v_{L_2} are the resultant voltages (made up of the self- and mutually induced voltages) across the primary and secondary respectively. The polarities shown for v_{L_1} and v_{L_2} are assumed and therefore are arbitrary in sign. The self-induced voltage in the primary is v_{L_1} and is viewed as the result of i_1 flowing in L_1. The mutually induced voltage in the primary is v_{1M} and is due to the current i_2 flowing through L_2. To recall the mechanism by which the mutually induced voltage occurs realize that the current flowing in L_2 creates a magnetic flux ϕ_2 which is coupled to inductor L_1 and hence induces voltage v_{1M}. Examining the secondary we can see that the self-induced voltage is v'_{L_2} and the mutually induced voltage is v_{2M} where v_{2M} is the result of coupling between the flux of L_1 and the inductance of L_2.

The polarities of the self-induced voltages v'_{L_1} and v'_{L_2} are of course determined by the direction of the currents causing them, which in this case is i_1, and i_2 respectively. In this text conventional current flow is used, therefore the polarity is positive where the current enters the passive component. The polarity of the mutually induced voltage is determined from both the dot placement and the polarity of the source voltage. In Fig. 2–12(a) it is shown that the *polarity* of v'_{L_2}, which serves as the source voltage for v_{1M}, is "transferred" to the primary, thereby determining the *polarity* of v_{1M}. The transfer of polarities is accomplished by assigning the same polarity sign appearing at the dot of the source voltage to the dot of the induced voltage. This concept is demonstrated in Fig. 2–12(a) and (b) by using dotted lines to show which polarities are determined from which source voltages.

Equations to determine the magnitudes of the self- and mutually induced voltages have already been derived and appear in Fig. 2–12. For clarity those equations for Fig. 2–12(b) will be derived here. Summing the voltages in the primary and secondary circuit in order to determine an equation for the resultant voltage across the primary and secondary, that is, v_{L_1} and v_{L_2} respectively, we have

$$v_{L_1}(t) + v_{1M}(t) - v'_{L_1}(t) = 0$$

for the primary and

$$v_{L_2}(t) + v_{2M}(t) - v'_{L_2}(t) = 0$$

for the secondary. Hence,

$$v_{L_1}(t) = v'_{L_1}(t) - v_{1M}(t) \tag{2–21a}$$

and

$$v_{L_2}(t) = v'_{L_2}(t) - v_{2M}(t) \tag{2–21b}$$

Now, the magnitudes are

$$v'_{L_1}(t) = L_1 \frac{di_1(t)}{dt}, \quad v_{1M}(t) = M \frac{di_2(t)}{dt},$$

$$v'_{L_2}(t) = L_2 \frac{di_2(t)}{dt} \quad \text{and} \quad v_{2M}(t) = M \frac{di_1(t)}{dt}$$

Then Eq. (2–21) can be written as

$$v_{L_1}(t) = L_1 \frac{di_1(t)}{dt} - M \frac{di_2(t)}{dt} \qquad \text{(2–22a)}$$

$$v_{L_2}(t) = L_2 \frac{di_2(t)}{dt} - M \frac{di_1(t)}{dt} \qquad \text{(2–22b)}$$

We shall now consider an example.

Example 2–2   (a) If for the circuit of Fig. 2–12(a) the currents i_1 and i_2 have values of $i_1 = 2 \sin 2.12 \times 10^4 t$ mA and $i_2 = 5 \sin 2.12 \times 10^4 t$ mA, determine v_{L_1} and v_{L_2}.

Solution

$$v_{L_1} = v'_{L_1}(t) + v_{1M}(t) = L_1 \frac{di_1(t)}{dt} + M \frac{di_2(t)}{dt}$$

$$= L_1 \frac{d}{dt} (2 \times 10^{-3} \sin 2.12 \times 10^4 t)$$

$$+ M \frac{d}{dt} (5 \times 10^{-3} \sin 2.12 \times 10^4 t)$$

$$= 2 \times 10^{-3} (2.12 \times 10^4) L_1 \cos 2.12 \times 10^4 t$$

$$+ 5 \times 10^{-3} (2.12 \times 10^4) M \cos 2.12 \times 10^4 t$$

$$= 42.4 L_1 \cos 2.12 \times 10^4 t + 106 M \cos 2.12 \times 10^4 t \text{ V}$$

and

$$v_{L_2} = v'_{L_2}(t) + v_{2M}(t) = L_2 \frac{di_2(t)}{dt} + M \frac{di_1(t)}{dt}$$

$$= L_2 \frac{d}{dt} (5 \times 10^{-3} \sin 2.12 \times 10^4 t)$$

$$+ M \frac{d}{dt} (2 \times 10^{-3} \sin 2.12 \times 10^4 t)$$

$$= 5(2.12) \times 10 L_2 \cos 2.12 \times 10^4 t$$

$$+ 2(2.12) \times 10 M \cos 2.12 \times 10^4 t$$

$$= 106 L_2 \cos 2.12 \times 10^4 t + 42.4 M \cos 2.12 \times 10^4 t \text{ V}$$

(b) Determine voltages v_{L_1} and v_{L_2} if: $i_1 = 3 \cos 10^3 t$ mA and $i_2 = 2 \sin (10^3 t + \Theta)$ mA.

Solution   From part (a):

$$v_{L_1} = L_1 \frac{d}{dt} (3 \times 10^{-3} \cos 10^3 t)$$

$$+ M \frac{d}{dt} [2 \times 10^{-3} \sin (10^3 t + \Theta)]$$

$$= -3 L_1 \sin 10^3 t + 2 M \cos (10^3 t + \Theta) \text{ V}$$

and

$$v_{L_2} = L_2 \frac{d}{dt}[2 \times 10^{-3} \sin(10^3 t + \Theta)]$$

$$+ M \frac{d}{dt}(3 \times 10^{-3} \cos 10^3 t)$$

$$= 2L_2 \cos(10^3 t + \Theta) - 3M \sin 10^3 t \text{ V}$$

Lastly, let us consider multicoupled circuit components. The same concepts apply in this case as in the two-component case, that is, the resultant voltage across a component will be the superimposition of the self-induced voltage and the mutually induced voltages. To illustrate, suppose we have the condition of Fig. 2–13. The resultant voltage across

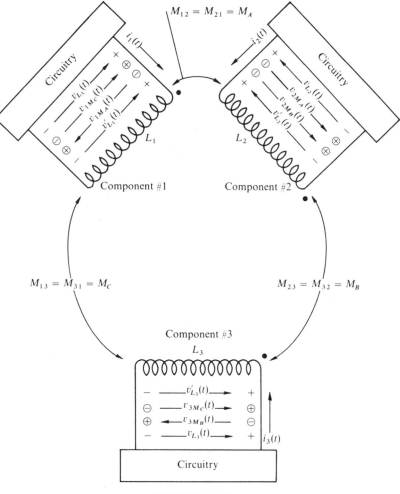

FIGURE 2–13

components $\#1$, $\#2$, and $\#3$ is v_{L_1}, v_{L_2}, and v_{L_3} respectively. The self-induced voltage for each component is v'_{L_1}, v'_{L_2}, and v'_{L_3}. As Fig. 2–13 illustrates there are two mutually induced voltages per component. These mutually induced voltages are due to the mutual inductance existing between the components. The voltage v_{1M_A} of component $\#1$ is the mutually induced voltage resulting from the mutual inductance M_A, which exists between L_1 and L_2. The polarity of v_{1M_A} is determined from the polarity of the source voltage v'_{L_2} and the dot arrangements of components $\#1$ and $\#2$. As shown, the negative sign of the self-induced voltage of component $\#2$, v'_{L_2}, appears at the dot of component $\#2$ and this polarity is the polarity of v_{1M_A} at the dot of component $\#1$. The mutually induced voltage v_{1M_C} of component $\#1$ is the effect of the mutual inductance M_C. The polarity of v_{1M_C} is the same at the dots placed on components $\#1$ and $\#3$. The other components are determined as component $\#1$ was.

To determine the resultant voltage across L_1, L_2, and L_3 we sum the voltages of each component. Hence:

Component $\#1$ $\quad v_{L_1}(t) - v_{1M_C}(t) + v_{1M_A}(t) - v'_{L_1}(t) = 0$

$\#2$ $\quad v_{L_2}(t) + v_{2M_A}(t) + v_{2M_B}(t) - v'_{L_2}(t) = 0$

$\#3$ $\quad v_{L_3}(t) + v_{3M_B}(t) - v_{3M_C}(t) - v'_{L_3}(t) = 0$

Then

$$v_{L_1}(t) = v'_{L_1}(t) - v_{1M_A}(t) + v_{1M_C}(t) \tag{2–23a}$$

$$v_{L_2}(t) = v'_{L_2}(t) - v_{2M_A}(t) - v_{2M_B}(t) \tag{2–23b}$$

$$v_{L_3}(t) = v'_{L_3}(t) - v_{3M_B}(t) + v_{3M_C}(t) \tag{2–23c}$$

The Self-Induced Voltages. The magnitudes for self-induced voltage are:

$$v'_{L_1}(t) = L_1 \frac{di_1(t)}{dt}$$

$$v'_{L_2}(t) = L_2 \frac{di_2(t)}{dt}$$

$$v'_{L_3}(t) = L_3 \frac{di_3(t)}{dt}$$

The Mutually Induced Voltages. The magnitudes for mutually induced voltages are:

Component $\#1$	Component $\#2$
$v_{1M_A}(t) = M_A \dfrac{di_2(t)}{dt}$	$v_{2M_A}(t) = M_A \dfrac{di_1(t)}{dt}$
$v_{1M_C}(t) = M_C \dfrac{di_3(t)}{dt}$	$v_{2M_B}(t) = M_B \dfrac{di_3(t)}{dt}$

<u>Component #3</u>

$$v_{3M_C}(t) = M_C \frac{di_1(t)}{dt}$$

$$v_{3M_B}(t) = M_B \frac{di_2(t)}{dt}$$

Then Eqs. (2–23) can be written as

$$v_{L_1}(t) = L_1 \frac{di_1(t)}{dt} - M_A \frac{di_2(t)}{dt} + M_C \frac{di_3(t)}{dt} \qquad (2\text{-}24a)$$

$$v_{L_2}(t) = L_2 \frac{di_2(t)}{dt} - M_A \frac{di_1(t)}{dt} - M_B \frac{di_3(t)}{dt} \qquad (2\text{-}24b)$$

$$v_{L_3}(t) = L_3 \frac{di_3(t)}{dt} - M_B \frac{di_2(t)}{dt} + M_C \frac{di_1(t)}{dt} \qquad (2\text{-}24c)$$

From Eqs. (2–24) and realizing

$$M_A = M_{12} = M_{21}, \; M_B = M_{23} = M_{32}, \text{ and } M_C = M_{13} = M_{31}$$

we may develop a very general equation describing the voltage across a component with mutual coupling. This equation will not usually be used but is of interest because of its mathematical form. That is

$$v_{L_n}(t) = L_n \frac{di_n(t)}{dt} \pm \sum M_{nm} \frac{di_m(t)}{dt} \qquad (2\text{-}25)$$

where $n \neq m$
$n = 1, 2, 3, \ldots$
$m = 1, 2, 3, \ldots$

where it is assumed v_{L_n} is assigned the same polarity as v'_{L_n}.

Example 2–3   For the circuit given in Fig. 2-14 determine v_{L_1}, v_{L_2}, and v_{L_3} if $i_1 = -5 \sin 10^4 t$ mA, $i_2 = 2 \cos 10^4 t$ mA, and $i_3 = 6 \sin (10^4 t + \Theta)$ mA where $M_{12} = 0.1$ mH, $M_{13} = 0.05$ mH, and $M_{23} = 0.01$ mH.

Solution   We first determine the self-induced voltage polarities v'_{L_1}, v'_{L_2}, and v'_{L_3} which are determined by the current directions of i_1, i_2, and i_3 respectively. Once we have the polarities for v'_{L_1}, v'_{L_2}, and v'_{L_3} we can determine the voltage polarities for the mutually induced voltages $v_{1M_{12}}$ and $v_{1M_{13}}$ for L_1, $v_{2M_{12}}$, and $v_{2M_{23}}$ for L_2, and $v_{3M_{23}}$ and $v_{3M_{13}}$ for L_3. These are shown in Figure 2-15.

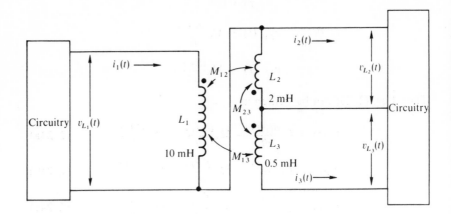

FIGURE 2–14

We now write the voltage equations by summing those across L_1, L_2, and L_3. Hence

$$v_{L_1}(t) = v'_{L_1}(t) + v_{1M_{12}}(t) + v_{1M_{13}}(t)$$

$$= L_1 \frac{di_1(t)}{dt} + M_{12} \frac{di_2(t)}{dt} + M_{13} \frac{di_3(t)}{dt}$$

$$v_{L_2}(t) = -[v'_{L_2}(t) + v_{2M_{12}}(t) + v_{2M_{23}}(t)]$$

$$= -L_2 \frac{di_2(t)}{dt} - M_{12} \frac{di_1(t)}{dt} - M_{23} \frac{di_3(t)}{dt}$$

[Notice the negative sign for v'_{L_2} resulted since we assumed a polarity for v_{L_2} opposite to that of v'_{L_2}. Also Eq. (2–25) does not apply since for M_{21} we used M_{12} and for M_{32} we used M_{23}.]

$$v_{L_3}(t) = v'_{L_3}(t) + v_{3M_{13}}(t) + v_{3M_{23}}(t)$$

$$= L_3 \frac{di_3(t)}{dt} + M_{13} \frac{di_1(t)}{dt} + M_{23} \frac{di_2(t)}{dt}$$

Then

$$v_{L_1} = L_1 \frac{d}{dt}(-5 \times 10^3 \sin 10^4 t) + M_{12} \frac{d}{dt}(2 \times 10^{-3} \cos 10^4 t)$$

$$+ M_{13} \frac{d}{dt}[6 \times 10^3 \sin (10^4 t + \Theta)] \text{ V}$$

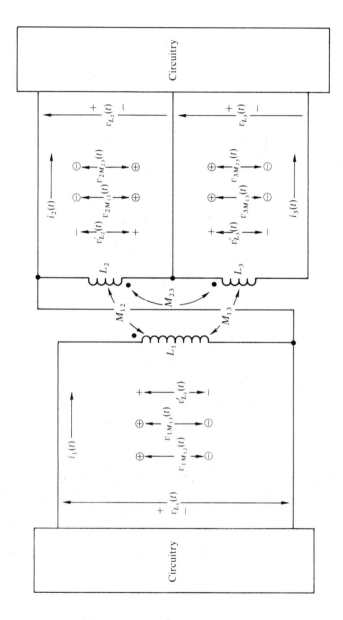

FIGURE 2-15

Note: The polarities of v_{L_1}, v_{L_2}, and v_{L_3} are assumed.

$$v_{L_2} = -L_2 \frac{d}{dt}(2 \times 10^{-3} \cos 10^4 t)$$

$$- M_{12}\frac{d}{dt}(-5 \times 10^{-3} \sin 10^4 t)$$

$$- M_{23}\frac{d}{dt}[6 \times 10^{-3} \sin (10^4 t + \Theta)] \text{ V}$$

$$v_{L_3} = L_3 \frac{d}{dt}[6 \times 10^{-3} \sin (10^4 t + \Theta)]$$

$$+ M_{13}\frac{d}{dt}(-5 \times 10^{-3} \sin 10^4 t)$$

$$+ M_{23}\frac{d}{dt}(2 \times 10^{-3} \cos 10^4 t) \text{ V}$$

$$v_{L_1} = -50 L_1 \cos 10^4 t - 20 M_{12} \sin 10^4 t$$
$$+ 60 M_{13} \cos (10^4 t + \Theta) \text{ V}$$

$$v_{L_2} = 20 L_2 \sin 10^4 t + 50 M_{12} \cos 10^4 t$$
$$- 60 M_{23} \cos (10^4 t + \Theta) \text{ V}$$

$$v_{L_3} = 60 L_3 \cos (10^4 t + \Theta) - 50 M_{13} \cos 10^4 t$$
$$- 20 M_{23} \sin 10^4 t$$

Therefore

$$v_{L_1} = -500 \cos 10^4 t - 2 \sin 10^4 t$$
$$+ 3 \cos (10^4 t + \Theta) \text{ mV}$$

$$v_{L_2} = 40 \sin 10^4 t + 5 \cos 10^4 t$$
$$- 0.6 \cos (10^4 t + \Theta) \text{ mV}$$

$$v_{L_3} = 30 \cos (10^4 t + \Theta) - 2.5 \cos 10^4 t$$
$$- 0.20 \sin 10^4 t \text{ mV}$$

Thus far we have not discussed the currents resulting from mutually induced voltages. We shall now undertake that task. Considering the transformer in Fig. 2–12(a) (redrawn in Fig. 2–16) we have the voltages

$$v_{L_1}(t) = L_1 \frac{di_1(t)}{dt} + M \frac{di_2(t)}{dt} \qquad (2\text{–}26a)$$

$$v_{L_2}(t) = L_2 \frac{di_2(t)}{dt} + M \frac{di_1(t)}{dt} \qquad (2\text{–}26b)$$

From Eqs. (2–26) we get

$$v_{L_1}(t)dt = L_1 \, di_1 + M \, di_2$$
$$v_{L_2}(t)dt = L_2 \, di_2 + M \, di_1 \text{ (by manipulating } dt\text{)}$$

By integrating over the time period that currents i_1 and i_2 flow, we have

$$\int_0^t v_{L_1}(t) \, dt = L_1 \int_{i_1(0)}^{i_1(t)} di_1 + M \int_{i_2(0)}^{i_2(t)} di_2$$

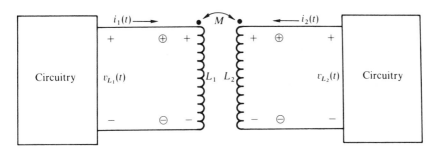

FIGURE 2–16

and

$$\int_0^t v_{L_2}(t)\,dt = L_2 \int_{i_2(0)}^{i_2(t)} di_2 + M \int_{i_1(0)}^{i_1(t)} di_1$$

where $i_k(t) =$ the final current for some upper limit t.
$i_k(0) =$ the initial current at $t = 0$.

Thus

$$\int_0^t v_{L_1}(t)\,dt = L_1[i_1(t) - i_1(0)] + M[i_2(t) - i_2(0)]$$

and

$$\int_0^t v_{L2}(t)\,dt = L_2[i_2(t) - i_2(0)] + M[i_1(t) - i_1(0)]$$

Rearranging the terms we have

$$\int_0^t v_{L_1}(t)\,dt = L_1 i_1(t) + M i_2(t) - \underbrace{[L_1 i_1(0) + M i_2(0)]}_{\text{Initial Conditions}} \qquad \textbf{(2–27a)}$$

$$\int_0^t v_{L_2}(t)\,dt = M i_1(t) + L_2 i_2(t) - \overbrace{[M i_1(0) + L_2 i_2(0)]} \qquad \textbf{(2–27b)}$$

To solve for the currents i_1 and i_2 Eqs. (2–27a) and (2–27b) shall be used. To solve for i_2 multiply Eq. (2–27a) by $(-M)$ and Eq. (2–27b) by L_1, and then add. Hence,

$$L_1 \int_0^t v_{L_2}(t)\,dt - M \int_0^t v_{L_1}(t)\,dt = L_1 L_2 i_2(t) - M^2 i_2(t) + (M^2 - L_1 L_2) i_2(0)$$

or

$$L_1 \int_0^t v_{L_2}(t)\,dt - M \int_0^t v_{L_1}(t)\,dt = (L_1 L_2 - M^2)[i_2(t) - i_2(0)]$$

therefore,

$$i_2(t) = \frac{L_1}{L_1 L_2 - M^2} \int_0^t v_{L_2}(t)\,dt - \frac{M}{L_1 L_2 - M^2} \int_0^t v_{L_1}(t)\,dt + i_2(0) \qquad \textbf{(2–28a)}$$

By multiplying Eq. (2–27a) by L_2 and Eq. (2–27b) by $(-M)$ the current

i_1 could be found to be

$$i_1(t) = \frac{L_2}{L_1 L_2 - M^2} \int_0^t v_{L_1}(t)\, dt - \frac{M}{L_1 L_2 - M^2} \int_0^t v_{L_2}(t)\, dt + i_1(0)$$

(2–28b)

To simplify writing equations (1–28) let us define

$$\Gamma_1 \equiv \frac{L_2}{L_1 L_2 - M^2} = \frac{1}{H}$$

(2–29a)

$$\Gamma_2 \equiv \frac{L_1}{L_1 L_2 - M^2}$$

(2–29b)

and

$$\Gamma_M \equiv \frac{M}{L_1 L_2 - M^2}$$

(2–29c)

Then Eqs. (2–28) become

$$i_1(t) = \Gamma_1 \int_0^t v_{L_1}(t)\, dt - \Gamma_M \int_0^t v_{L_2}(t)\, dt + i_1(0)$$

(2–30a)

$$i_2(t) = \Gamma_2 \int_0^t v_{L_2}(t)\, dt - \Gamma_M \int_0^t v_{L_1}(t)\, dt + i_2(0)$$

(2–30b)

Let us investigate Eqs. (2–30) in view of Fig. 2–16 and attempt to generalize. Begin by viewing Fig. 2–17, which is Fig. 2–16 redrawn, but

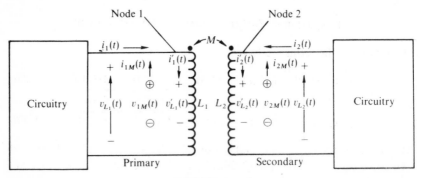

FIGURE 2–17

now the current flow is emphasized. We see three currents present in the primary and secondary sides. The currents i_1 and i_2 are the resultant currents of the superimposition of i'_1, i_{1M}, and i'_2, i_{2M} respectively, where the self-induced and mutually induced currents are thought of as existing *within* the transformer's primary and secondary L_1 and L_2. Currents i'_1 and i'_2 are also thought of as currents caused by the resultant voltage across L_1 and L_2 respectively, that is, v_{L_1} and v_{L_2} respectively. These two currents (i'_1 and i'_2) are the current analogies of the self-induced voltages v'_{L_1} and v'_{L_2} and for that reason they will be termed the "self-induced currents."

We shall now determine the flow directions for the various currents of Fig. 2–17. The flow direction of self-induced currents determines the polarity of the self-induced voltages; hence, the side at which the current enters the component is positive and that side which it leaves is negative. To be explicit, the self-induced current i_1' flows into the positive side of v_{L_1}' and i_2' flows into the positive side of v_{L_2}'. The currents i_{1M} and i_{2M} are the currents resulting from the mutually induced voltages and hence will be termed "mutually induced currents." Since the mutually induced voltages are sources, that is, they are like voltage generators *induced* in the circuit, the mutual currents flow out of their positive signs. Again, to be explicit, i_{1M} flows out of the positive sign of the voltage v_{1M}, and likewise i_{2M} flows out of v_{2M}.

Summing the currents at nodes 1 and 2 in Fig. 2–17 we have

Node 1 $\qquad\qquad\qquad i_1(t) = i_1'(t) - i_{1M}(t)$ $\qquad\qquad$ (2–31a)

Node 2 $\qquad\qquad\qquad i_2(t) = i_2'(t) - i_{2M}(t)$ $\qquad\qquad$ (2–31b)

In view of Eqs. (2–30a), (2–30b), (2–31a), and (2–31b) we see that

$i_1'(t) = \Gamma_1 \int_0^t v_{L_1}(t)\, dt$ = Self-induced current of primary side (This current is caused by the source-voltage v_{L_1}.)

$i_2'(t) = \Gamma_2 \int_0^t v_{L_2}(t)\, dt$ = Self-induced currents of secondary side (This current is caused by the source-voltage v_{L_2}.)

$i_{1M} = \Gamma_M \int_0^t v_{L_2}(t)\, dt$ = Mutually induced current of primary side (This current is in the primary but caused by the secondary side voltage v_{L_2}.)

$i_{2M} = \Gamma_M \int_0^t v_{L_1}(t)\, dt$ = Mutually induced current of secondary side (This current is in the secondary but caused by the primary side voltage v_{L_1}.)

Another example of the current considerations is in Fig. 2–18. The currents of Fig. 2–18 are:

Node 1 $\qquad\qquad\qquad i_1(t) - i_1'(t) - i_{1M}(t) = 0$

and at

Node 2 $\qquad\qquad\qquad i_2(t) - i_2'(t) - i_{2M}(t) = 0$

where i_1', i_2', i_{1M}, and i_{2M} are not shown. The magnitudes are:

$$i_1'(t) = \Gamma_1 \int_0^t v_{L_1}(t)\, dt \qquad i_{1M}(t) = \Gamma_M \int_0^t v_{L_2}(t)\, dt$$

$$i_2'(t) = \Gamma_2 \int_0^t v_{L_2}(t)\, dt \qquad i_{2M}(t) = \Gamma_M \int_0^t v_{L_1}(t)\, dt$$

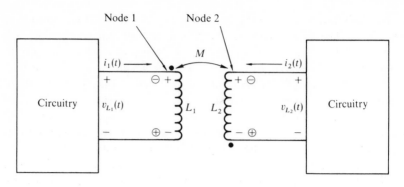

FIGURE 2–18

Then the currents i_1 and i_2 can be written as

$$i_1(t) = \Gamma_1 \int_0^t v_{L_1}(t)\, dt + \Gamma_M \int_0^t v_{L_2}(t)\, dt \qquad \textbf{(2–32a)}$$

$$i_2(t) = \Gamma_2 \int_0^t v_{L_2}(t)\, dt + \Gamma_M \int_0^t v_{L_1}(t)\, dt \qquad \textbf{(2–32b)}$$

Example 2–4   If for the circuit shown in Fig. 2–19 $v_{L_1} = E(1 - e^{-10^3 t})$ V and $v_{L_2} = 2e^{-10^3 t}$ V determine i_1 and i_2.

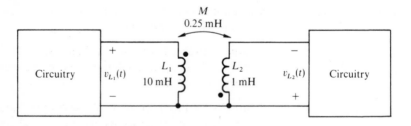

FIGURE 2–19

Solution   For variety we will work this problem two different ways. The first will make the currents behave according to the polarities shown, while the second will assume current directions and then require the polarities to be assigned accordingly.

Method 1. From the polarities shown for v_{L_1} and v_{L_2} we can determine the mutually induced voltage polarities, which will allow us to determine the current directions of the mutually induced currents i_{1M} and i_{2M} (current will flow out of positive side of mutually induced voltages). And by knowing the polarities of v_{L_1} and v_{L_2} we can determine the directions of the self-induced currents i_1'

and i_2' since these currents flow into the positive side of
their respective self-induced voltages v_{L_1}' and v_{L_2}', which
have the same polarity as v_{L_1} and v_{L_2} respectively. These
voltages and current directions are illustrated in Fig.
2–20.

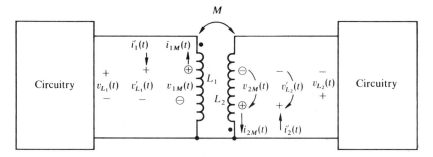

FIGURE 2–20

We now assign current directions to the resultant currents
i_1 and i_2. We will assign these current directions to be the
same through L_1 and L_2 as i_1' and i_2', as we have done in
the past. Our circuit now appears as shown in Fig. 2–21.

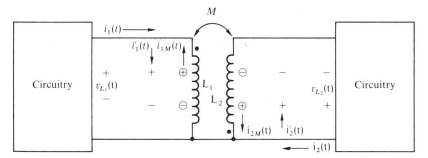

FIGURE 2–21

We now sum the currents at the dots letting those
entering the dot be positive and those leaving be negative.
Hence

$$i_1(t) - i_1'(t) + i_{1M}(t) = 0$$

and

$$i_2(t) - i_2'(t) + i_{2M}(t) = 0$$

Therefore

$$i_1(t) = i_1'(t) - i_{1M}(t)$$

and

$$i_2(t) = i_2'(t) - i_{2M}(t)$$

Since the magnitudes are

$$i_1'(t) = \Gamma_1 \int v_{L_1}(t)\, dt, \quad i_{1M}(t) = \Gamma_M \int v_{L_2}(t)\, dt$$

$$i_2'(t) = \Gamma_2 \int v_{L_2}(t)\, dt$$

and

$$i_{2M}(t) = \Gamma_M \int v_{L_1}(t)\, dt$$

then

$$i_1(t) = \Gamma_1 \int v_{L_1}(t)\, dt - \Gamma_M \int v_{L_2}(t)\, dt$$

and

$$i_2(t) = \Gamma_2 \int v_{L_2}(t)\, dt - \Gamma_M \int v_{L_1}(t)\, dt$$

Notice we have a two-part problem: one of determining current directions (polarities if we were working with voltages) and then determining magnitudes.

Substituting in v_{L_1} and v_{L_2} we have

$$i_1 = \Gamma_1 \int E(1 - e^{-10^3 t})\, dt - \Gamma_M \int 2e^{-10^3 t}\, dt$$

$$= \Gamma_1 \left(Et + \frac{1}{10^3} e^{-10^3 t} \right) + \frac{2\Gamma_M}{10^3} e^{-10^3 t} + I_1 \text{ A}$$

where I_1 is the constant of integration.

$$i_2 = \Gamma_2 \int 2e^{-10^3 t}\, dt - \Gamma_M \int E(1 - e^{-10^3 t})\, dt$$

$$= -\frac{2\Gamma_2}{10^3} e^{-10^3 t} - \Gamma_M \left(Et + \frac{e^{-10^3 t}}{10^3} \right) + I_2 \text{ A}$$

where I_2 is the constant of integration.

Since

$$\Gamma_1 = \frac{L_2}{L_1 L_2 - M^2} = \frac{10^{-3}}{(10 - 0.0625) \times 10^{-6}}$$

$$\cong 0.1 \times 10^3 \frac{1}{H}$$

$$\Gamma_2 = \frac{L_1}{L_1 L_2 - M^2} \cong \frac{10 \times 10^{-3}}{10 \times 10^{-6}} = 1 \times 10^3 \frac{1}{H}$$

and

$$\Gamma_M \cong \frac{0.25}{10 \times 10^{-3}} = 0.025 \times 10^3 \frac{1}{H}$$

Therefore

$$i_1 = 100 \left(Et + \frac{e^{-10^3 t}}{10^3} \right) + \frac{50 e^{-10^3 t}}{10^3} + I_1 \text{ A}$$

and

$$i_2 = -2e^{-10^3 t} - 25 \left(Et + \frac{e^{-10^3 t}}{10^3} \right) + I_2 \text{ A}$$

Notice we knew to use designations for currents for the integration constants I_1 and I_2 because of the units of the equations for i_1 and i_2.

Method 2. For this method we will again have a two-part problem, that of determining direction and magnitude of the currents. To determine directions this time we will assume the current directions for the resultant currents i_1 and i_2, which will dictate the direction for i'_1 and i'_2 if we require they be the same as i_1 and i_2 respectively. This results in the circuit shown in Fig. 2–22.

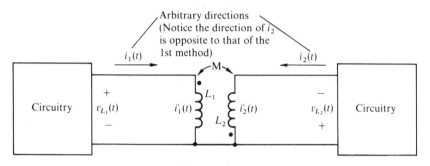

FIGURE 2–22

Now that we have i'_1 and i'_2 we can determine v'_{L_1} and v'_{L_2}, which will allow us to determine the polarities of

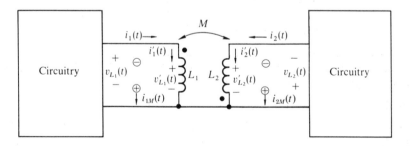

FIGURE 2–23

v_{1M} and v_{2M}. This is shown in Fig. 2–23. Now, summing the currents at the dots we have

$$i_1(t) - i'_1(t) - i_{1M}(t) = 0$$

and

$$i_2(t) - i'_2(t) - i_{2M}(t) = 0$$

Then

$$i_1(t) = i'_1(t) + i_{1M}(t)$$

and

$$i_2(t) = i_2'(t) + i_{2M}(t)$$

Now

$$i_1'(t) = \Gamma_1 \int v_{L_1}(t)\, dt$$

and

$$i_{1M}(t) = \Gamma_M \int [-v_{L_2}(t)]\, dt = -\Gamma_M \int v_{L_2}(t)\, dt$$

The reason $-v_{L_2}$ is used for i_{1M} is that the polarity of v_{L_2}' is the negative of v_{L_2} and v_{L_2}' was used to determine the direction for i_{1M}; hence, we use the negative sign to show that v_{L_2}' is the negative of v_{L_2}. So

$$i_1(t) = \Gamma_1 \int v_{L_1}(t)\, dt - \Gamma_M \int v_{L_2}(t)\, dt$$

which agrees with the first method. For i_2' we have

$$i_2'(t) = \Gamma_2 \int [-v_{L_2}(t)]\, dt$$

and for i_{2M} we have

$$i_{2M} = \Gamma_M \int v_{L_1}(t)\, dt$$

Hence

$$i_2(t) = -\Gamma_2 \int v_{L_2}(t)\, dt + \Gamma_M \int v_{L_1}(t)\, dt$$

$$= -\left[\Gamma_2 \int v_{L_2}(t)\, dt - \Gamma_M \int v_{L_1}(t)\, dt \right]$$

which is the negative of the first method, as it should be, since we choose i_2 for the second method to be the opposite of the first method. The first method is probably the better of the two.

To complete the analysis let us consider our problem of three components with mutual coupling, as illustrated in Fig. 2–24. Summing the currents at the nodes or dots we have

Node 1 $i_1(t) - i_1'(t) + i_{1M_A}(t) - i_{1M_C}(t) = 0$ (2–33a)

Node 2 $i_2(t) - i_2'(t) + i_{2M_A}(t) - i_{2M_B}(t) = 0$ (2–33b)

Node 3 $i_3(t) - i_3'(t) - i_{3M_B}(t) + i_{3M_C}(t) = 0$ (2–33c)

The magnitudes are

$$i_1'(t) = \Gamma_1 \int v_{L_1}(t)\, dt, \qquad\qquad i_2'(t) = \Gamma_2 \int v_{L_2}(t)\, dt$$

$$i_{1M_A}(t) = \Gamma_{1M_A} \int v_{L_2}(t), \qquad\qquad i_{1M_C}(t) = \Gamma_{1M_C} \int v_{L_3}(t)\, dt$$

$$i_{2M_A}(t) = \Gamma_{2M_A} \int v_{L_1}(t)\, dt, \qquad\qquad i_{2M_B}(t) = \Gamma_{2M_B} \int v_{L_3}(t)\, dt$$

$$i_{3M_C}(t) = \Gamma_{3M_C} \int v_{L_1}(t)\, dt \quad \text{and} \quad i_{3M_B}(t) = \Gamma_{3M_B} \int v_{L_2}(t)\, dt$$

where all the Γs are yet to be determined. Then

$$i_1(t) = \Gamma_1 \int v_{L_1}(i)\,dt - \Gamma_{1M_A} \int v_{L_2}(t)\,dt + \Gamma_{1M_C} \int v_{L_3}(t)\,dt \qquad \text{(2–34a)}$$

$$i_2(t) = \Gamma_2 \int v_{L_2}(t)\,dt - \Gamma_{2M_A} \int v_{L_1}(t)\,dt + \Gamma_{2M_B} \int v_{L_3}(i)\,dt \qquad \text{(2–34b)}$$

$$i_3(t) = \Gamma_3 \int v_{L_3}(t)\,dt + \Gamma_{3M_B} \int v_{L_2}(t)\,dt + \Gamma_{3M_C} \int v_{L_1}(t)\,dt \qquad \text{(2–34c)}$$

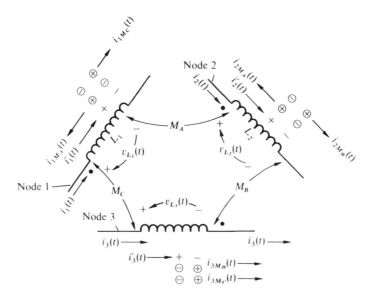

FIGURE 2–24

To determine the Γs we proceed as before by beginning with the loop voltage equation and solve for currents i_1, i_2, and i_3. Once these quantities are found and compared with the equations in Eqs. (2–34) the Γs are determined. Then from Fig. 2–24 the voltage equations are

$$v_{L_1}(t) = L_1 \frac{di_1(t)}{dt} + M_A \frac{di_2(t)}{dt} - M_C \frac{di_3(t)}{dt} \qquad \text{(2–35a)}$$

$$v_{L_2}(t) = M_A \frac{di_1(t)}{dt} + L_2 \frac{di_2(t)}{dt} - M_B \frac{di_3(t)}{dt} \qquad \text{(2–35b)}$$

$$v_{L_3}(t) = -M_C \frac{di_1(t)}{dt} - M_B \frac{di_2(t)}{dt} + L_3 \frac{di_3(t)}{dt} \qquad \text{(2–35c)}$$

From Eqs. (2–35) we get by integration

$$\int v_{L_1}(t)\,dt = L_1 i_1(t) + M_A i_2(t) - M_C i_3(t) \qquad \text{(2–36a)}$$

$$\int v_{L_2}(t)\,dt = M_A i_1(t) + L_2 i_2(t) - M_B i_3(t) \qquad \text{(2–36b)}$$

$$\int v_{L_3}(t)\,dt = -M_C i_1(t) - M_B i_2(t) + L_3 i_3(t) \qquad \text{(2–36c)}$$

where it is assumed the initial currents are zero $[i_n(0) = 0]$ in order to simplify the analysis. Realize from Eqs. (2–30) this does not affect the Γs. Then solving Eqs. (2–36) for i_1, i_2, and i_3:

$$\Delta = \begin{vmatrix} L_1 & M_A & -M_C \\ M_A & L_2 & -M_B \\ -M_C & -M_B & L_3 \end{vmatrix} = L_1 L_2 L_3 - L_1 M_B^2 - L_2 M_C^2 - L_3 M_A^2$$

(2–37)

and

$$\Delta i_1(t) = \begin{vmatrix} \int v_{L_1}(t)\, dt & M_A & -M_C \\ \int v_{L_2}(t)\, dt & L_2 & -M_B \\ \int v_{L_3}(t)\, dt & -M_B & L_3 \end{vmatrix}$$

So

$$i_1(t) = \frac{L_2 L_3 - M_B^2}{\Delta} \int v_{L_1}(t)\, dt - \frac{L_3 M_A - M_B M_C}{\Delta} \int v_{L_2}(t)\, dt$$
$$- \frac{L_2 M_C - M_A M_B}{\Delta} \int v_{L_3}(t)\, dt$$

(2–38)

Solving for i_2,

$$\Delta i_2(t) = \begin{vmatrix} L_1 & \int v_{L_1}(t)\, dt & -M_C \\ M_A & \int v_{L_2}(t)\, dt & -M_B \\ -M_C & \int v_{L_3}(t)\, dt & L_3 \end{vmatrix}$$

then

$$i_2(t) = -\frac{L_3 M_A - M_B M_C}{\Delta} \int v_{L_1}(t)\, dt + \frac{L_1 L_3 - M_C^2}{\Delta} \int v_{L_2}(t)\, dt$$
$$+ \frac{L_1 M_B - M_A M_C}{\Delta} \int v_{L_3}(t)\, dt$$

(2–39)

Lastly,

$$\Delta i_3(t) = \begin{vmatrix} L_1 & M_A & \int v_{L_1}(t)\, dt \\ M_A & L_2 & \int v_{L_2}(t)\, dt \\ -M_C & -M_B & \int v_{L_3}(t)\, dt \end{vmatrix}$$

$$i_3(t) = \frac{L_1 L_2 - M_A^2}{\Delta} \int v_{L_3}(t)\, dt + \frac{L_1 M_B - M_A M_C}{\Delta} \int v_{L_2}(t)\, dt$$
$$+ \frac{L_2 M_C - M_A M_B}{\Delta} \int v_{L3}(t)\, dt$$

(2–40)

Comparing Eqs. (2–38), (2–39), and (2–40) with equations in Eqs. (2–34) we see that

$$\Gamma_1 \equiv \frac{L_2 L_3 - M_B^2}{\Delta}, \quad \Gamma_2 \equiv \frac{L_1 L_3 - M_C^2}{\Delta}$$

and

$$\Gamma_3 \equiv \frac{L_1 L_2 - M_A^2}{\Delta} \tag{2–41}$$

Also,

$$\Gamma_{1 M_A} \equiv \frac{L_3 M_A - M_B M_C}{\Delta}, \quad \Gamma_{2 M_A} \equiv \frac{L_3 M_A - M_B M_C}{\Delta}$$

$$\Gamma_{1 M_C} \equiv \frac{L_2 M_C - M_A M_B}{\Delta}, \quad \Gamma_{3 M_C} \equiv \frac{L_2 M_C - M_A M_B}{\Delta} \tag{2–42}$$

$$\Gamma_{2 M_B} \equiv \frac{L_1 M_B - M_A M_C}{\Delta}, \quad \Gamma_{3 M_B} \equiv \frac{L_1 M_B - M_A M_C}{\Delta}$$

Investigating the quantities in Eqs. (2–42) we shall redefine some terms, hence

$$\Gamma_{M_A} \equiv \Gamma_{1 M_A} = \Gamma_{2 M_A} = \frac{L_3 M_A - M_B M_C}{\Delta} \tag{2–43a}$$

$$\Gamma_{M_B} \equiv \Gamma_{2 M_B} = \Gamma_{3 M_B} = \frac{L_1 M_B - M_A M_C}{\Delta} \tag{2–43b}$$

$$\Gamma_{M_C} \equiv \Gamma_{1 M_C} = \Gamma_{3 M_C} = \frac{L_2 M_C - M_A M_B}{\Delta} \tag{2–43c}$$

The equations of Eqs. (2–34) can be simplified to

$$i_1(t) = \Gamma_1 \int v_{L_1}(t)\, dt - \Gamma_{M_A} \int v_{L_2}(t)\, dt + \Gamma_{M_C} \int v_{L_3}(t)\, dt \tag{2–44a}$$

$$i_2(t) = \Gamma_2 \int v_{L_2}(t)\, dt - \Gamma_{M_A} \int v_{L_1}(t)\, dt + \Gamma_{M_B} \int v_{L_3}(t)\, dt \tag{2–44b}$$

$$i_3(t) = \Gamma_3 \int v_{L_3}(t)\, dt + \Gamma_{M_B} \int v_{L_2}(t)\, dt + \Gamma_{M_C} \int v_{L_1}(t)\, dt \tag{2–44c}$$

Before leaving this analysis return to Eqs. (2–44) and notice the polarities of the mutuals. The mutuals with the same subscripts have the same sign.

Example 2–5   For the circuit given in Fig. 2–25 the voltages v_{L_1}, v_{L_2}, and v_{L_3} were measured to be $v_{L_1} = 5e^{-10^4 t}$ V, $v_{L_2} = -2e^{-10^3 t}$ V, and $v_{L_3} = 3(1 - e^{-10^2 t})$ V for a time interval from some reference time defined as $t = 0$ to some general time t. Determine the resultant currents i_1, i_2, and i_3 during this same period of time.

Solution   We will begin by determining the polarities of the mutually induced voltages, which determine the current

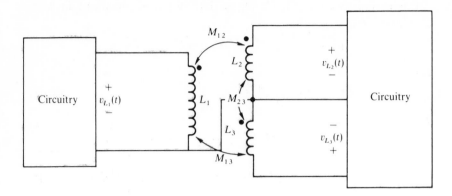

FIGURE 2–25

directions for the mutually induced currents $i_{1M_{12}}$, $i_{1M_{13}}$, $i_{2M_{12}}$, $i_{2M_{23}}$, $i_{3M_{23}}$, and $i_{3M_{13}}$. Then we shall assign current directions for the resultant currents i_1, i_2, and i_3 such that they flow into the positive side of their respective self-induced voltages v'_{L_1}, v'_{L_2}, and v'_{L_3}, where the self-induced voltages are to have the same polarities as their respective resultant voltages v_{L_1}, v_{L_2}, and v_{L_3}. This is shown in Fig. 2–26.

Notice v_{L_n} and v'_{L_n} have the same polarities and that i_n and i'_n have the same flow direction *through* L_n.

Summing the currents at the dots we have

$$i_1(t) - i'_1(t) + i_{1M_{12}}(t) - i_{1M_{13}}(t) = 0$$

$$i_2(t) - i'_2(t) + i_{2M_{12}}(t) - i_{2M_{23}}(t) = 0$$

$$-i_3(t) + i'_3(t) + i_{3M_{13}}(t) + i_{3M_{23}}(t) = 0$$

or

$$i_1(t) = i'_1(t) - i_{1M_{12}}(t) + i_{1M_{13}}(t)$$

$$= \Gamma_1 \int_0^t v_{L_1}(t)\,dt - \Gamma_{M_{12}} \int_0^t v_{L_2}(t)\,dt + \Gamma_{M_{13}} \int_0^t v_{L_3}(t)\,dt$$

$$i_2(t) = i'_2(t) - i_{2M_{12}}(t) + i_{2M_{23}}(t)$$

$$= \Gamma_2 \int_0^t v_{L_2}(t)\,dt - \Gamma_{M_{12}} \int_0^t v_{L_1}(t)\,dt + \Gamma_{M_{23}} \int_0^t v_{L_3}(t)\,dt$$

$$i_3(t) = i'_3(t) + i_{3M_{13}}(t) + i_{3M_{23}}(t)$$

$$= \Gamma_3 \int_0^t v_{L_3}(t)\,dt + \Gamma_{M_{13}} \int_0^t v_{L_1}(t)\,dt + \Gamma_{M_{23}} \int_0^t v_{L_2}(t)\,dt$$

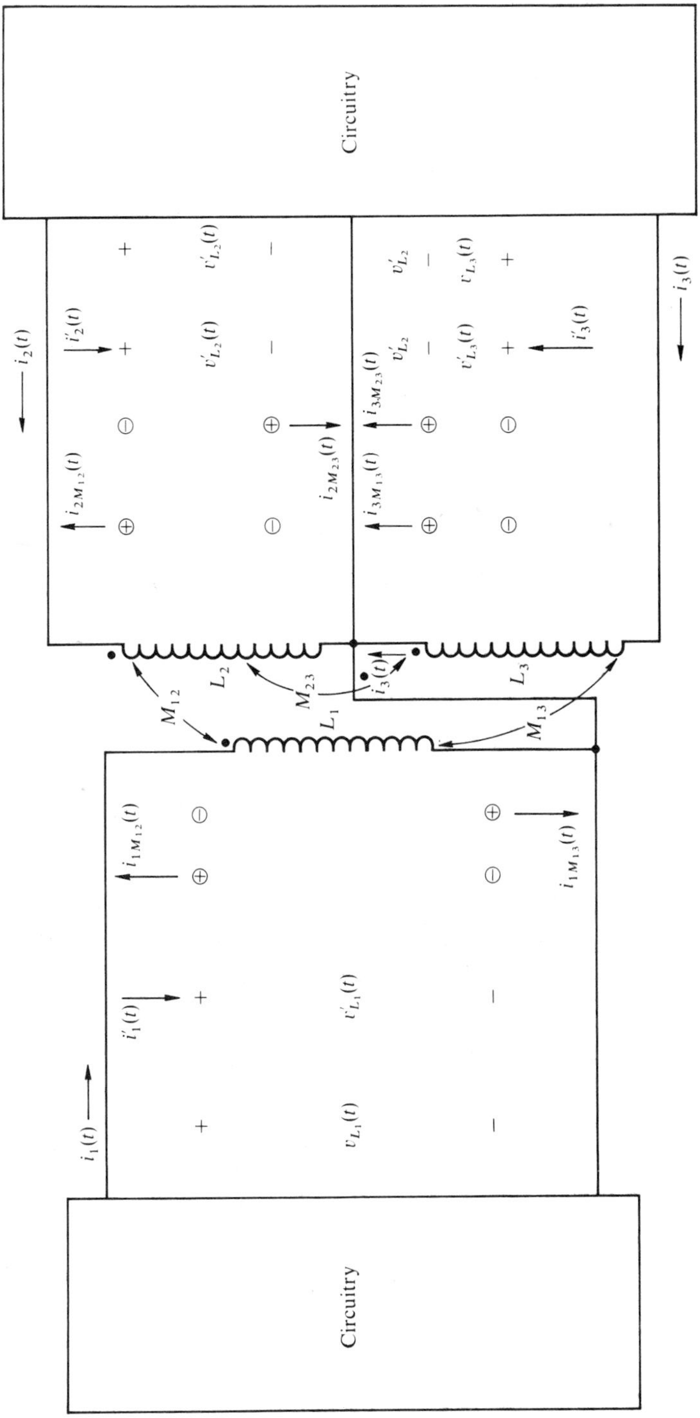

FIGURE 2-26

73

Thus

$$i_1(t) = \Gamma_1 \int_0^t 5e^{-10^4 t}\, dt + \Gamma_{M_{12}} \int_0^t 2e^{-10^3 t}\, dt$$

$$+ \Gamma_{M_{13}} \int_0^t 3(1 - e^{-10^2 t})\, dt$$

$$\frac{5\Gamma_1}{-10^4} e^{-10^4 t} \Big|_0^t + \frac{2\Gamma_{M_{12}}}{-10^3} e^{-10^3 t} \Big|_0^t + 3\Gamma_{M_{13}}\left(t - \frac{e^{-10^2 t}}{-10^2}\right) \Big|_0^t$$

Therefore i_1 is equal to

$$i_1 = 5 \times 10^{-4}\Gamma_1(1 - e^{-10^4 t}) + 2 \times 10^{-3}\Gamma_{M_{12}}(1 - e^{-10^3 t})$$
$$+ 3\Gamma_{M_{13}}(t + 10^{-2} \times e^{-10^2 t} - 10^{-2})\ \text{A}$$

And

$$i_2 = -\Gamma_2 \int_0^t 2e^{-10^3 t}\, dt - \Gamma_{M_{12}} \int_0^t 5e^{-10^4 t}$$

$$+ \Gamma_{M_{23}} \int_0^t 3(1 - e^{-10^2 t})\, dt$$

$$= 2\Gamma_2(1 - e^{-10^3 t}) + 5\Gamma_{M_{12}}(1 - e^{-10^4 t})$$
$$+ 3\Gamma_{M_{23}}[t + (1 - e^{-10^2 t}) \times 10^{-2}]\ \text{A}$$

$$i_3 = \Gamma_3 \int_0^t 3(1 - e^{-10^2 t})\, dt + \Gamma_{M_{13}} \int_0^t 5e^{-10^4 t}\, dt$$

$$- \Gamma_{M_{23}} \int_0^t 2e^{-10^3 t}\, dt$$

$$= 3\Gamma_3[t + (1 - e^{-10^2 t})] - 5\Gamma_{M_{13}}(1 - e^{-10^4 t})$$
$$+ 2\Gamma_{M_{23}}(1 - e^{-10^3 t})$$

Note: The author realizes it is better, and correct, to change the variables under the integral to some dummy variable different than t. However, it is more convenient to leave them as shown. Using the dummy variable x we would have for i_1'

$$i_1' = \Gamma_1 \int_0^t v_{L_1}(t)\, dt = \Gamma_1 \int_{x=0}^{x=t} 5e^{-10^4 x}\, dx = 5\Gamma_1 e^{-10^4}\Big|_{x=0}^{x=t}$$

$$= -5\Gamma_1(1 - e^{-10^4 t})$$

where $\quad \Gamma_1 = \dfrac{L_2 L_3 - M_{23}^2}{\Delta}, \quad \Gamma_2 = \dfrac{L_1 L_3 - M_{13}^2}{\Delta},$

$$\Gamma_3 = \frac{L_1 L_2 - M_{12}^2}{\Delta}, \quad \Gamma_{M_{12}} = \frac{L_3 M_{12} - M_{13}M_{23}}{\Delta},$$

$$\Gamma_{M_{23}} = \frac{L_1 M_{23} - M_{12}M_{13}}{\Delta}, \quad \Gamma_{M_{13}} = \frac{L_2 M_{13} - M_{12}M_{23}}{\Delta}$$

and $\quad \Delta = L_1 L_2 L_3 - L_1 M_{23}^2 - L_2 M_{13}^2 - L_3 M_{12}^2 \quad$ as derived from Eqs. (2–37), (2–41), and (2–43) for $M_A \equiv M_{12}$, $M_B \equiv M_{23}$, and $M_C = M_{13}$.

Earlier it was stated that $M_{12} = M_{21}$. We shall now demonstrate that this is true. The transformer of Fig. 2–27(a) shows a voltage generator e_1 on the primary and the secondary is open-circuited.

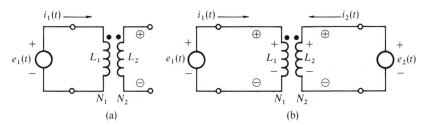

FIGURE 2–27

The voltage equation for the primary is

$$e_1 = L_1 \frac{di_1(t)}{dt} \tag{2-45}$$

Power is the time rate of doing work or expending energy, since electric power is the product of voltage and current, so the instantaneous power delivered to the transformer is

$$p_1(t) = e_1(t)i_1(t) \tag{2-46}$$

Power has the units of work-per-time, which is expressed as

$$p = \frac{dw}{dt}$$

where w is work, in differential form. Thus

$$dw = p\, dt$$

and upon integrating

$$w = \int_0^t p\, dt \tag{2-47}$$

Equation (2–47) represents the electrical energy expended over the time period of t seconds. Using Eqs. (2–46) and (2–47) we may find the energy in the field of the transformer at any given time, that is,

$$w_1 = \int_0^t e_1(t)i_1(t)\, dt$$

Substituting Eq. (2–45) into this equation we find

$$w_1 = \int_0^t \left[L_1 \frac{di_1(t)}{dt} \right] i_1(t)\, dt = L_1 \int_0^{i_1(t)} i_1\, di_1 = \frac{L_1}{2} i_1^2(t) \tag{2-48}$$

which states that from time 0 to some general time t we let the current i_1 increase from 0 to some general current i_1. The energy stored in the magnetic field under these conditions is expressed in Eq. (2–48). We now add a voltage generator e_2 to the secondary while maintaining e_1 in the primary as shown in Fig. 2–27(b). We will increase the current i_2 from 0 to some general value expressed as $i_2(t)$, but maintaining i_1 at the value expressed in Eq. (2–48). The secondary voltage e_2 is

$$e_2(t) = L_2 \frac{di_2(t)}{dt} + M_{21} \frac{di_1(t)}{dt}$$

The energy contributed to the field from the presence of i_2 is

$$w_2 = \int_0^t e_2(t) i_2(t)\, dt = L_2 \int_0^{i_2(t)} i_2\, di_2 + M_{21} \int_0^{i_1(t)} i_2\, di_1$$

$$w_2 = \frac{L_2}{2} i_2^2(t) + M_{21} i_1(t) i_2(t) \tag{2–49}$$

since

$$\int_0^{i_1(t)} i_2\, di_1 = i_2 \int_0^{i_1(t)} di_1$$

From Eqs. (2–48) and (2–49) we may determine the total energy of the field by summing Eqs. (2–48) and (2–49). Summing w_1 and w_2 we get

$$w_{\text{total}} = w_1 + w_2 = \frac{L_1}{2} i_1^2(t) + \frac{L_2}{2} i_2^2(t) + M_{21} i_1(t) i_2(t) \tag{2–50}$$

Let us now reverse the process by opening the primary and increasing i_2 from 0 to some general current $i_2(t)$, which will be the same value as before. From this we will determine the energy stored in the field of the transformer due to i_2 as we did for i_1 in Eq. (2–48). Then we will add e_1 and increase i_1 from 0 to $i_1(t)$, where i_1 will be of the same value as expressed in Eqs. (2–48) and (2–49). This will add an additional amount of energy to the field. Again, we may find the total energy stored in the field by summing the energy contributions from these two conditions. Let us follow the same procedure as before, but add a prime to differentiate between each case. If we apply e_2 and open-circuit the primary we get

$$e_2 = L_2 \frac{di_2(t)}{dt}$$

Then

$$w_2' = \int_0^t e_2(t) i_2(t)\, dt = L_2 \int_0^{i_2(t)} i_2\, di_2 = \frac{L_2}{2} i_2^2(t) \tag{2–51}$$

Applying e_1 and increasing i_1 from 0 to $i_1(t)$

$$e = L_1 \frac{di_1(t)}{dt} + M_{12} \frac{di_2(t)}{dt}$$

from which

$$w_1' = \int_0^t e_1(t) i_1(t)\, dt = \frac{L_1}{2} i_1^2(t) + M_{12} i_1(t) i_2(t) \tag{2–52}$$

Summing Eqs. (2–51) and (2–52) we have

$$w'_{total} = w'_1(t) + w'_2(t) = \frac{L_1}{2}i_1^2(t) + \frac{L_2}{2}i_2^2(t) + M_{12}i_1(t)i_2(t) \qquad (2\text{–}53)$$

Since for each operation we maintained the same current values then w_{total} and w'_{total} should be equal. Thus from Eqs. (2–50) and (2–53)

$$w_{total} = w'_{total} = \frac{L_1}{2}i_1^2(t) + \frac{L_2}{2}i_2^2(t) + M_{21}i_1(t)i_2(t)$$

$$= \frac{L_1}{2}i_1^2(t) + \frac{L_2}{2}i_2^2(t) + M_{12}i_1(t)i_2(t)$$

or

$$M_{12} = M_{21} = M \qquad (2\text{–}54)$$

which verifies our statement.

If one wishes to determine what is meant by "energy stored in the field" consider the equation for energy, which from Eqs. (2–48), (2–49), (2–51), and (2–52) we see can be expressed in general terms as

$$w(t) = \frac{L}{2}i^2(t)$$

From the definition of L this equation may be written as

$$w(t) = \frac{L}{2}\left[\frac{N\phi(t)}{L}\right]^2 = \frac{N^2\phi^2(t)}{2L} \qquad (2\text{–}55)$$

for a linear field. Thus from Eq. (2–55) we see the energy is stored via the flux ϕ.

Another investigation worthy of the effort is the derivation of the term coupling coefficient. Return again to our definitions of M_{12} and M_{21}:

$$M_{12} = k_{12}N_1\frac{d\phi_2(i_2)}{di_2}$$

and

$$M_{21} = k_{21}N_2\frac{d\phi_1(i_1)}{di_1}$$

Now since

$$L_1 = N_1\frac{d\phi_1(i_1)}{di_1}$$

then M_{21} may be written as

$$M_{21} = k_{21}N_2\frac{L_1}{N_1} \qquad (2\text{–}56a)$$

and M_{12} may be written

$$M_{12} = k_{12}N_1\frac{L_2}{N_2} \qquad (2\text{–}56b)$$

since

$$L_2 = N_2 \frac{d\phi_2(i_2)}{di_2}$$

From Eqs. (2–56) solve for N_2/N_1, hence

$$\frac{N_2}{N_1} = \frac{M_{21}}{k_{21}L_1} = \frac{k_{12}L_2}{M_{12}}$$

from which we find

$$k_{12}k_{21} = \frac{M_{12}M_{21}}{L_1L_2}$$

Utilizing Eq. (2–54) we have

$$k_{12}k_{21} = \frac{M^2}{L_1L_2}$$

Defining $k_{12}k_{21}$ as k^2, which is termed the coupling coefficient, we have

$$k^2 = \frac{M^2}{L_1L_2}, \quad \text{or} \quad k = \frac{M}{\sqrt{L_1L_2}} \equiv \text{coupling coefficient} \qquad (2\text{–}57)$$

For coupling coefficients of more than two inductors it is necessary to subscript the coupling coefficients. Hence for coupling between three inductors, L_1, L_2, and L_3, we have

$$k_{12} = \frac{M_{12}}{\sqrt{L_1L_2}} = \frac{M_{21}}{\sqrt{L_1L_2}} = k_{21}$$

$$k_{13} = \frac{M_{13}}{\sqrt{L_1L_3}} = \frac{M_{31}}{\sqrt{L_1L_2}} = k_{31}$$

and

$$k_{23} = \frac{M_{23}}{\sqrt{L_2L_3}} = \frac{M_{32}}{\sqrt{L_2L_3}} = k_{32}$$

The coupling coefficient is a measure of merit describing the relative amount of coupling between inductors L_n and L_m. For perfect coupling (the ideal case) the value of k is unity. For the worst case, no coupling, k is zero. Then the possible values for k may be expressed as

$$0 \leq k \leq 1 \qquad (2\text{–}58)$$

Before we leave transformers let's consider the primary and secondary voltages, currents, and inductance interdependence under ideal conditions—that is, when $k = 1$. Again, returning to our original definitions of M_{12} and M_{21}

$$M_{21} = k_{21}N_2 \frac{d\phi_1(i_1)}{di_1}$$

and

$$M_{12} = k_{12}N_1 \frac{d\phi_2(i_2)}{di_2}$$

From Eq. (2–49) and the definition of k_{12} and k_{21} [see Eq. (2–57)] we may write these equations as

$$M = kN_2\frac{d\phi_1(i_1)}{di_1} = N_2\frac{d\phi_1(i_1)}{di_1}$$

$$M = kN_1\frac{d\phi_2(i_2)}{di_2} = N_1\frac{d\phi_2(i_2)}{di_2}$$

for $k = 1$. Then solving for $d\phi$ and integrating we have

$$\phi_1(t) = \frac{M}{N_2}i_1(t) \qquad\qquad (2\text{–}59a)$$

and

$$\phi_2(t) = \frac{M}{N_1}i_2(t) \qquad\qquad (2\text{–}59b)$$

Now let us see what we mean physically when we say $k = 1$. The illustration of Fig. 2–28 compared to Fig. 2–9 simply says that there is a

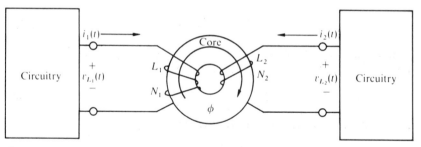

FIGURE 2–28   Ideal Coupling $k = 1$

resultant flux ϕ going through L_1 and L_2 and not two ϕ_1' and ϕ_2'. Recall from Fig. 2–9 the resultant flux being $\phi_1 + k_{12}\phi_2$ through L_2 and $\phi_2 + k_{21}\phi_1$ through L_2, where $k_{12}\phi_2$ is that portion of ϕ_2 reaching L_1 and $k_{21}\phi_1$ is that portion of ϕ_1 reaching L_2. Now $k^2 = k_{12}k_{21}$, so for this case $k_{12} = k_{21} = 1$. Hence,

$$\phi_1 + k_{12}\phi_2 = \phi_1 + \phi_2 \qquad\qquad (2\text{–}60a)$$

and

$$\phi_2 + k_{21}\phi_1 = \phi_2 + \phi_1 \qquad\qquad (2\text{–}60b)$$

which mathematically shows that both L_1 and L_2 have the same flux ϕ in their coils. Then as we have previously done let us apply the superposition principle to determine v_{L_1} and v_{L_2}

$$v_{L_1}(t) = N_1 \frac{d}{dt}[\phi_1(t) + k_{12}\phi_2(t)] = N_1 \frac{d}{dt}[\phi_1(t) + \phi_2(t)] \qquad \text{(2–61a)}$$

$$v_{L_2}(t) = N_2 \frac{d}{dt}[\phi_2(t) + k_{21}\phi_1(t)] = N_2 \frac{d}{dt}[\phi_2(t) + \phi_1(t)] \qquad \text{(2–61b)}$$

since $k_{12} = k_{21} = k = 1$. Since both L_1 and L_2 have the same flux, as Eqs. (2–60) and Fig. 2–28 demonstrate, let us define the resultant flux as ϕ. Hence $\phi(t) = \phi_1(t) + \phi_2(t)$. Notice we are assuming linear conditions. Then Eqs. (2–61) become

$$v_{L_1}(t) = N_1 \frac{d\phi(t)}{dt}$$

and

$$v_{L_2}(t) = N_2 \frac{d\phi(t)}{dt}$$

Solving for $d\phi(t)/dt$ and equating we have

$$\frac{d\phi}{dt} = \frac{v_{L_1}(t)}{N_1} = \frac{v_{L_2}(t)}{N_2}$$

or

$$\frac{v_{L_2}(t)}{v_{L_1}(t)} = \frac{N_2}{N_1} \equiv n \qquad \text{(2–62)}$$

Since we have defined $\phi = \phi_1 + \phi_2 = 2\phi_1 = 2\phi_2$, where $\phi_1 = \phi_2$, Eqs. (2–59a) and (2–59b) may be written as

$$\frac{\phi}{2} = \frac{M}{N_2}i_1(t) = \frac{M}{N_1}i_2(t) \qquad \text{(2–63)}$$

Hence, the currents i_1 and i_2 have the relationship

$$\frac{i_1(t)}{i_2(t)} = \frac{N_2}{N_1}$$

and from Eq. (2–62)

$$\frac{v_{L_2}(t)}{v_{L_1}(t)} = \frac{i_1(t)}{i_2(t)} = \frac{N_2}{N_1} = n \qquad \text{(2–64)}$$

for $k = 1$.

For $k = 1$ and $M_{12} = M_{21} = M$, it can be written from Eqs. (2–56) that

$$\frac{N_2}{N_1} = \frac{M}{L_1} = \frac{L_2}{M} \qquad \text{(2–65)}$$

Now, from Eq. (2–57) $M = \sqrt{L_1 L_2}$, therefore Eq. (2–65) becomes

$$\frac{N_2}{N_1} = \frac{\sqrt{L_1 L_2}}{L_1} = \frac{L_2}{\sqrt{L_1 L_2}} = \sqrt{\frac{L_2}{L_1}}$$

Applying this to Eq. (2–64) we may write

$$\frac{v_{L_2}(t)}{v_{L_1}(t)} = \frac{i_1(t)}{i_2(t)} = \sqrt{\frac{L_2}{L_1}} = \frac{N_2}{N_1} \equiv n \qquad \text{(2–66)}$$

In order that we may determine the input and output impedance for this ideal case let's use Eq. (2–66) to determine the equation

$$\frac{v_{L_2}(t)}{i_1(t)} = \frac{v_{L_1}(t)}{i_2(t)} \tag{2–67}$$

Also from Eq. (2–66) we find

$$i_1(t) = ni_2(t) \tag{2–68}$$

or

$$i_2(t) = \frac{i_1(t)}{n}$$

Substituting Eq. (2–68) into (2–67) we have

$$\frac{v_{L_2}(t)}{ni_2(t)} = \frac{v_{L_1}(t)n}{i_1(t)}$$

Then

$$\frac{v_{L_2}(t)}{i_2(t)} = \frac{v_{L_1}(t)}{i_1(t)}n^2$$

We know that the ratio $v_{L_2}(t)/i_2(t)$ is the output impedance and $v_{L_1}(t)/i_1(t)$ is input impedance, hence

$$z_2(t) = z_1(t)n^2$$

or

$$\frac{z_2(t)}{z_1(t)} = n^2 \tag{2–69}$$

Putting Eq. (2–69) into Eq. (2–66) we find

$$\frac{v_{L_2}(t)}{v_{L_1}(t)} = \frac{i_1(t)}{i_2(t)} = \sqrt{\frac{L_2}{L_1}} = \sqrt{\frac{z_2(t)}{z_1(t)}} = \frac{N_2}{N_1} \equiv n \tag{2–70}$$

for an ideal transformer.

To reiterate, the analysis we have performed for transformers was under the assumption of linearity as shown in Fig. 2–10(a). We will now determine the conditions for this assumption to be valid in terms of the applied voltage source v' where the prime indicates dc is present as shown in Fig. 2–29. Beginning with $B = (\phi/A)$ we take the derivative with respect to

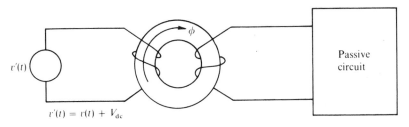

$$v'(t) = v(t) + V_{dc}$$

FIGURE 2–29

time, hence

$$\frac{dB}{dt} = \frac{1}{A}\frac{d\phi(t)}{dt}$$

Multiplying this equation by N_1, where N_1 is the number of turns on the excitation side of the transformer, we have

$$N_1\frac{dB}{dt} = \frac{N_1}{A}\frac{d\phi(t)}{dt}$$

Now $N_1[d\phi(t)/dt]$ describes the voltage time-variant portion of v', that is, $v(t)$, hence

$$N_1\frac{dB}{dt} = \frac{1}{A}v(t)$$

Solving for dB we have

$$dB = \frac{1}{N_1 A}v(t)\,dt$$

or

$$B = \frac{1}{N_1 A}\int_{t_1}^{t_2} v(t)\,dt \qquad (2\text{--}71)$$

If there is no dc component to v', that is $V_{dc} = 0$, and using B_{max} to represent the maximum allowable flux density for the core to be linear, as shown in Fig. 2–6(a), we will require that $(1/N_1 A)\int_{t_1}^{t_2} v(t)\,dt$ be less than this value. Thus

$$B_{max} > \frac{1}{N_1 A}\int_{t_1}^{t_2} v(t)\,dt \qquad (2\text{--}72)$$

which mathematically describes our conditions for linearity. B_{max} is to be gathered from the manufacturer's specification sheet. If there is a dc component this must also be calculated in determining if B of the core is less than B_{max}. We realize that Eq. (2–71) was derived from $[d\phi(t)/dt]$, which is zero for any dc considerations. To determine the dc contribution to the total flux density B_T consider the equation $B = \mu H$. Substituting the quantity $H_{dc} = (NI_{dc}/l)$ we have,

$$B_{dc} = \frac{\mu NI_{dc}}{l} \qquad (2\text{--}73)$$

Then for B_T we sum Eqs. (2–71) and (2–73), which is

$$B_T = B(t) + B_{dc} = \frac{1}{N_1 A}\int_{t_1}^{t_2} v(t)\,dt + \frac{\mu N_1 I_{dc}}{l} \qquad (2\text{--}74)$$

Hence, to operate in the linear portions of the core we require,

$$B_{max} > B(t) + B_{dc} = \frac{1}{N_1 A}\int_{t_1}^{t_2} v(t)\,dt + \frac{\mu NI_{dc}}{l} \qquad (2\text{--}75)$$

Let us now determine the requirements of Eq. (2–75) if v is sinusoidal.

The integral $\int_{t_1}^{t_2} v(t)\, dt$ of Eq. (2–75) can be expressed in terms of the average voltage V_{avg} since

$$V_{avg} = \frac{1}{t_2 - t_1} \int_{t_1}^{t_2} v(t)\, dt, \quad \text{then} \quad \frac{1}{N_1 A} \int_{t_1}^{t_2} v(t)\, dt = \frac{V_{avg}(t_2 - t_1)}{N_1 A}$$

Knowing that $v = N(d\phi/dt)$, then we know that for a sine wave when ϕ is a maximum, v is a minimum; and vice versa. Therefore, for a half period the flux density B has made a full swing. That is, from Fig. 2–30(a) we see

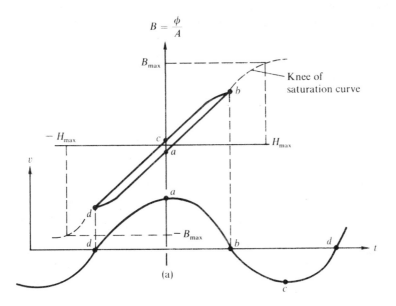

(a)

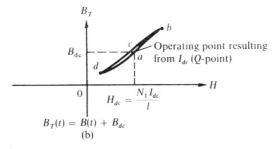

$$B_T(t) = B(t) + B_{dc}$$
(b)

FIGURE 2–30

that for the positive half cycle of v the B-H curve goes from point d to a and then to b, and for the negative portion of v we go from point b to c and then to d. Now we want only the swing of B from point a to b, or c to d, that is we want one-half of $[V_{avg}(t_2 - t_1)/N_1 A]$ for $t_2 - t_1 = (T/2)$. Thus

$$B = \frac{1}{2}\frac{V_{avg}(t_2 - t_1)}{N_1 A} = \frac{V_{avg}\frac{T}{2}}{2N_1 A} = \frac{V_{avg}T}{4N_1 A} \qquad (2\text{–}76a)$$

Now we prefer to work with rms rather than average values. The form factor for rms and average values is ($V_{rms}/V_{avg} = 1.11$), hence

$$B = \frac{V_{rms}T}{4.44 N_1 A} = \frac{V_{rms}}{4.44 f N_1 A} \qquad (2\text{–}76b)$$

where frequency f equals $1/T$. Thus Eq. (2–75) becomes

$$B_{max} > \frac{V_{rms}}{4.44 f N_1 A} + \frac{\mu N_1 I_{dc}}{l} \qquad (2\text{–}77)$$

Figure 2–30(b) shows the flux density B of Eq. (2–76) oscillating about the flux density caused by the dc current I_{dc} as expressed by Eq. (2–73).

Example 2–6   It can be shown (see problem 2–11) that the product $i(t)L$ has units of $\phi \cdot$turns. If the transformer core of Fig. 2–29 has an inductance of 10 mH on the primary side and the primary current i_1' has a value of $i_1' = 5 \sin 10^3 t + 10$ mA determine if this core is linear for this case. Transformer specifications: $B_{max} = 45$ milliweber/square meter $A = 3.14 \times 10^{-4}$ square meter $N_1 = 50$ turns.

Solution   Since

$$i_1'(t)L_1 = \phi \cdot \text{turns}$$

then

$$(5 \sin 10^3 t + 10) \times 10^{-3} \times 10^{-2}$$
$$= (5 \sin 10^3 t + 10) \times 10^{-5} \text{ Wb-turn}$$

where weber (Wb) is the unit of ϕ using the RMKS system.

Thus

$$\phi(t)N_1 = i_1'(t)L_1 = (5 \sin 10^3 t + 10) \times 10^{-5} \text{ Wb-turn}$$

so

$$\phi(t) = \frac{(5 \sin 10^3 t + 10) \times 10^{-5}}{N_1}$$
$$= 0.1 \times 10^{-5}(\sin 10^3 t + 10) \text{ Wb}$$

Notice that the secondary of the transformer has nothing to do with the problem since all the flux-producing energies are from the primary side. That is not to say that a current in the secondary does not exist; but the current in the secondary represents the effects of ϕ cutting the coils which make up the secondary L_2, whereas ϕ is created due to i'_1 flowing in L_1.

To determine B we divide by A, hence

$$B_T = B(t) + B_{dc} = \frac{(0.1 \times 10^{-5} \sin 10^3 t + 10^{-5})}{3.14 \times 10^{-4}}$$

$$= 3.18 \sin 10^3 t + 31.80 \text{ mWb/sq m}$$

Thus

$$B(t) = 3.18 \sin 10^3 t \text{ mWb/sq m}$$

and

$$B_{dc} = 31.80 \text{ mWb/sq m}$$

Now, from the specifications $B_{max} = 45$ mWb/sq m and for the maximum we have

$$B(t)\Big|_{t=\pi n/2 \times 10^{-3}} + B_{dc}$$

where $n = 1, 5, 9, 13 \ldots$ since $B(t)$ is at a maximum when $\sin 10^3 t$ has a value of $+1$. Then B_T at a maximum we have

$$B_{Tmax} = 3.18 + 31.80 = 34.98 \text{ mWb/sq m}$$

Therefore

$$B_{Tmax} < B_{max}$$

and the core is linear. Realize that

$$B_{dc} = 31.80 \text{ mWb/sq m}$$

is that point shown in Fig. 2–30(b) and $B(t)$ forms the curve abcd.

2—5 Electrical Sources

There are two types of electrical sources we shall encounter: voltage sources and current sources. We shall define the two from a practical point of view; that is, we shall make our definitions such that they comply within the working limits of the sources.

We shall consider a voltage source as being capable of maintaining a relative *constant* voltage over some range of current. Of course the range of values over which the current may vary is a practical consideration which must be determined from the particular source's characteristics. Also, what we mean by constant voltage is a matter of practical consideration where the determination would be relative to an *allowable variance*; that is, if for a given current variation the voltage varies 5% and the system will tolerate 10% then the voltage is constant. Similarly we shall consider a current source that source which provides a relatively constant current (at least within tolerance of the working system) over some range of voltage.

To give a concrete example of these concepts let us consider a vacuum tube's and transistor's characteristics. First, let us consider a triode vacuum tube's plate characteristics as shown in Fig. 2–31.

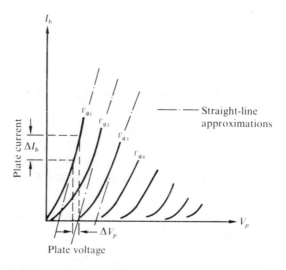

FIGURE 2–31   Plate Characteristics of Triode

Notice in Fig. 2–31 that the plate voltage is relatively constant (ΔV_p is small) for a relatively large ΔI_b; that is, for a small change in plate voltage a large change (relatively) in plate current occurs. Of course, what is relatively constant is based on engineering judgment, and as previously stated this judgment depends upon the specific problem. Obviously if there could be no variance of the voltage the graph would have to have appeared as that in Fig. 2–32, but no such ideal voltage source exists. Then, in summary, one must make a judgment of what approximates a voltage source close enough to be considered as such for *his* analysis.

Much of what was said of voltage sources can be said of current sources, that is, current sources shall be considered as capable of supplying a con-

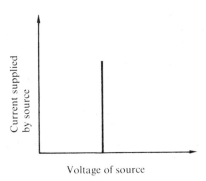

FIGURE 2–32   Ideal Voltage Source

stant current over some reasonable range of voltage. Again, it is for you to determine if the variation in the current is within tolerance of the specifications. A transistor or pentode might be considered as current sources. The common-emitter characteristics of a bipolar transistor are shown in Fig. 2–33(a).

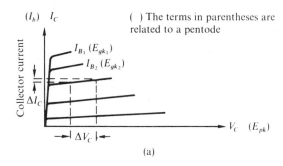

(a)

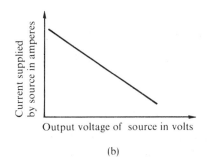

(b)

FIGURE 2–33 (a) Collector Characteristics of Transistor; (b) Dependent Source

It should have been noticed that what was essentially said was that our constant electrical sources, voltage and current, must be deemed independent of current or voltage respectively. For that reason these constant sources are termed *independent sources*.

Now, if the voltage supplied by the source is dependent on how much current is being required from the source and vice versa the source is said to be a *dependent source*. The characteristic curve of such a source might appear as shown in Fig. 2–33(b). Then an analysis containing a dependent source must be such that for each circuit parameter change the source will require a new value. For instance, consider Ex. 2–7 (see Fig. 2–34).

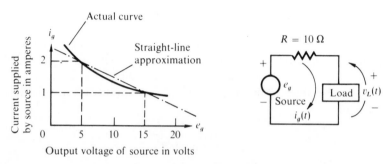

FIGURE 2-34   Dependent Source Characteristics

Example 2–7   We must write the current i_g as a function of the voltage since they are dependent.

(a) Using the equation of a straight line

$$i_g = -\frac{1}{10}e_g + 2.5$$

(b) Writing a loop equation

$$e_g = Ri_g + v_L$$

Then substituting i_g from (a) into e_g of (b)

$$e_g = (-0.1e_g + 2.5)R + v_L$$

or

$$e_g(1 + 0.1R) = v_L + 2.5R$$

$$\therefore \quad e_g = \frac{v_L + 2.5R}{1 + 0.1R}$$

Now if the load required 10 volts the source could be represented as a voltage source of

$$e_g = \frac{10 + 2.5(10)}{1 + 0.1(10)} = 17.5 \text{ V}$$

and from the graph we see it would deliver approximately 0.9 A of current. It is important to realize the schematic of Fig. 2–35 is valid so long as the load and current requirements remain the same. If these requirements change so does the terminal voltage value of e_g. We could make a similar analysis for the current.

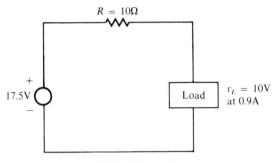

FIGURE 2-35

The symbolic representation of voltage sources and current sources will be that of Fig. 2–36 for both independent and dependent sources.

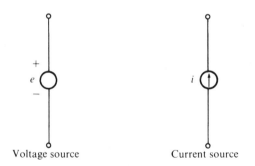

FIGURE 2-36

2-6   Active Components—Transistors and Vacuum Tubes

The analysis about to be made will be adaptable to any active device, however we will make specific references to transistors and vacuum tubes. Our general approach of analysis will be to separate the analysis into dc and ac components. Then we will use the "black box" scheme to develop an ac circuit which is equivalent in behavior to the device. This ac model of the device can be substituted for the device when an ac analysis of the circuit containing that device is wanted. As we will see there will be limitations imposed on our model and as a result we must understand when the model is applicable.

Figure 2–37(a) represents some general device and Fig. 2–37(b) is a graphical representation of its output characteristics. For the device of Fig. 2–37(a) two input and output parameters exist, which are i'_1, v'_1 and i'_2, v'_2 respectively. In general, these parameters are plotted such that the output parameters appear as the independent and dependent variables with one of the input parameters held constant. This parameter is termed the parametric parameter. The other input parameter is not controlled and usually not plotted. The input parameter which is not controlled is that parameter which has little control of the device. To be specific, if we were plotting common-emitter transistors we would choose the base current as the parametric variable which is i'_1 in Fig. 2–37(a), and not its base voltage v'_1. For a vacuum tube operating as an amplifier the parametric variable would be the grid-to-cathode voltage and the noncontrolled variable would be the grid current, which is approximately zero.

Now that we have discussed how to determine which input variable is the parametric variable let's make some decision on choosing the correct dependent and independent variable for the output variables. Convention has it that the dependent variable, plotted on the vertical axis, is the output current i'_2 and the independent variable is the output voltage v'_2.

To reiterate, Fig. 2–37(b) shows the output characteristics of the device shown in Fig. 2–37(a). From the output characteristics we see that the parametric variable is the input current i'_1. We also see that the output current is relatively constant for a given parametric variable, which means the device behaves as a current generator. This device is a bipolar transistor or at least behaves as one.

Let us begin to investigate the device mathematically by writing an equation which describes the device's operational behavior. From this mathematical description we will define the term "load line." We will see that there are two types of load lines: dc and ac. To express the output characteristics implicitly we have

$$i'_2 = i'_2(v'_2) \qquad\qquad (2\text{–}78)$$

In order to find an explicit equation which satisfies Eq. (2–78) we must write an equation such that i'_2 and v'_2 appear in the same equation. Let us write a loop equation in the output circuit of the device of Fig. 2–37(a). Hence,

$$v'_2 + R_L i'_2 - V_{\text{supply}} = 0$$

Solving for i_2' as indicated by Eq. (2–78) we have

$$i_2'' = -\frac{1}{R_L}v_2'(t) + \frac{V_{\text{supply}}}{R_L} \qquad (2\text{--}79)$$

Comparing Eq. (2–79) with the general equation describing a straight line, $y = mx + b$, we see that the slope m is $m = -(1/R_L)$, $y = i_2'$, and the y-intercept b is $b = (V_{\text{supply}}/R_L)$. Then Eq. (2–79) is a straight line equation. The general term for a straight line equation whose dependent and independent variables correspond to that of the device's graphed characteristics is the *load line equation* for that graph. That is, Eq. (2–79) is the *load line* for the characteristics of Fig. 2–37(b). Notice from this general definition a load line could be written for input characteristics by writing an explicit straight equation which satisfies $i_1' = i_1'(v_1')$ if the plot of i_1' vs v_1' is considered as the device's input characteristics.

Now let us plot Eq. (2–79) on the output characteristics of Fig. 2–37(b). To plot a straight line we need two points, hence let us choose two convenient points, when $v_2' = 0$ and then when $i_2' = 0$. So,

$$i_2'\Big|_{v_2'=0} = I_{\text{SC}} = -\frac{1}{R_L}(0) + \frac{V_{\text{supply}}}{R}$$

and

$$v_2'\Big|_{i_2'=0} = V_{\text{OC}} = V_{\text{supply}}$$

where

$$I_{\text{SC}} = I \text{ short circuit}$$

$$V_{\text{OC}} = V \text{ open circuit}$$

from Eq. (2–79). The equation is shown plotted in Fig. 2–37(c). Notice also from Fig. 2–37(c) that the load line has given us a graphical means to determine the resulting value of one of the output variables when the values of the other output variable and parametric variable are known. That is, if the value of v_2' is V_{2A} and the parametric variable has a value of I_{1A} then a value of I_{2A} results for i_2' as determined from the intersection of $v_2' = V_{2A}$, $i_1' = I_{1A}$, the load line, and the projection to the resulting i_2', which is I_{2A}.

If we wish to determine the necessary value of the parametric variable to obtain a certain output current and voltage we simply locate the intersection of the output variables at the desired values, say $i_2' = I_{2B}$ and $v_2' = V_{2B}$, with the load line. The value of i_1' at that point is the value required, which in this case is I_{1B}, as shown in Fig. 2–37(e). Then the load line is just a collection of operating points, and we may change that load line by changing the value of the slope, which in the specific case of Eq. (2–79) means changing the value of R_L. This is shown in Fig. 2–37(d).

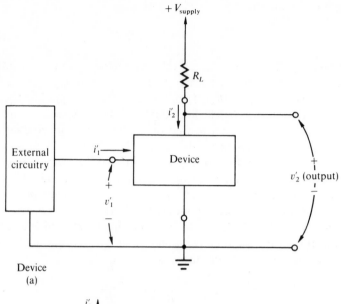

External circuitry

Device

$+V_{\text{supply}}$

R_L

i'_2

$i'_1 \longrightarrow$

$+$

v'_1

$-$

v'_2 (output)

$+$

$-$

Device
(a)

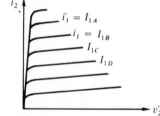

i'_2

$i'_1 = I_{1A}$

$i_1 = I_{1B}$

I_{1C}

I_{1D}

v'_2

The device's
output characteristics
(b)

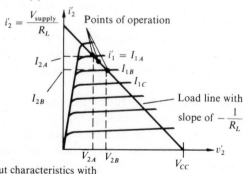

$i'_2 = \dfrac{V_{\text{supply}}}{R_L}$

i'_2

Points of operation

I_{2A}

I_{2B}

$i'_1 = I_{1A}$

I_{1B}

I_{1C}

Load line with
slope of $-\dfrac{1}{R_L}$

V_{2A} V_{2B}

V_{CC}

v'_2

Output characteristics with
load line superimposed
(c)

FIGURE 2–37

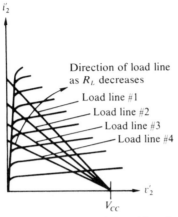

Output characteristics with various load lines superimposed for different values of R_L.

(d)

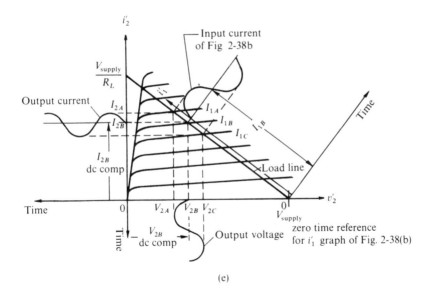

(e)

FIGURE 2–37 (cont)

Before continuing with our analysis of the device let us again review mathematical ways to express a time-variant waveform which is above or below the reference voltage. Figure 2–38(a) illustrates some voltage v'_{in}

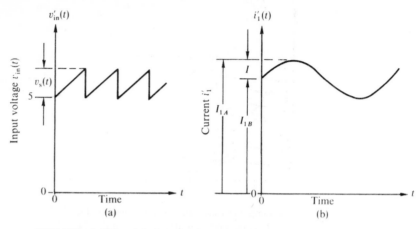

FIGURE 2–38   (a) Sawtooth waveform above ground; (b) Sinusoidal waveform I_{1B} amperes above zero

that is composed of a sawtooth which is five volts above zero. Since at this point we have not covered how to write an explicit equation for the sawtooth let us indicate it implicitly by the term v_s. Then to express v'_{in} we may write

$$v'_{in}(t) = \text{time-variant voltage} + \text{constant voltage, or}$$

$$v'_{in}(t) = v_s(t) + 5 \qquad\qquad (2\text{--}80)$$

Next consider the sinusoidal current waveform which varies about the constant current value I. Figure 2–38(b) illustrates this current. This current may be mathematically expressed as

$$i'_1 = \text{time-variant current} + \text{constant current, or}$$

$$i'_1 = I \sin \omega t + I_B$$

where $I =$ peak amplitude.

From Fig. 2–38(b) we see that

$$A = I_{1A} - I_{1B}$$

therefore

$$i'_1 = (I_{1A} - I_{1B}) \sin \omega t + I_{1B} \qquad\qquad (2\text{--}81)$$

From Eqs. (2–80) and (2–81) we see that each of these waveforms could be said to be composed of dc and ac components, where by ac we mean the time-variant component.

Returning to the analysis of the device let the current of Fig. 2–38(b) be the input current to the device of Fig. 2–37(a), or simply the parametric variable i_1'. Do not be alarmed that we are no longer holding i_1' constant, this was done only while we were collecting the data to plot Fig. 2–37(b). If we wish to see graphically how this input current i_1' will affect our other device parameters we may superimpose Fig. 2–38(b) on Fig. 2–37(c), which is Fig. 2–37(e). Since all variations in operation must occur along the load line we aligned the vertical axis of Fig. 2–38(b) with the load line of Fig. 2–37(c) as we see in Fig. 2–37(e). From Fig. 2–37(e) and our previously developed notations we see that at $i_1' = I_{1B}$ we have $v_2' = V_{2B}$ and $i_2' = I_{2B}$. Then as i_1' increases to a peak of $i_1' = I_{1A}$ we have $v_2' = V_{2A}$ (a decrease in output voltage) and $i_2' = I_{2A}$. Likewise if i_1' decreases to a value of I_{1C} we have $v_2' = V_{2C}$ (an increase in output voltage). As a result of i_1''s variation the output voltage and current varied as shown in Fig. 2–37(e). Notice each of these output variables is composed of a dc and an ac component just as the input current.

Let us write expressions for these quantities. Hence

$$v_2' = \text{time-variant term} + \text{constant term}$$

$$v_2' = v_2(t) + V_2 = (V_{2C} - V_{2B}) \sin \omega t + V_{2B} \qquad (2\text{–}82)$$

where $v_2(t)$ expresses the time-variant waveform of v_2' and V_2 expresses the constant value of v_2' (for this case $V_2 = V_{2B}$). Notice this terminology is in keeping with our earlier definitions of using lowercase letters for varying quantities and capital letters for constants. Also notice v_2' could have been expressed as

$$v_2' = -(V_{2A} - V_{2B}) \sin \omega t + V_{2B} = (V_{2B} - V_{2A}) \sin \omega t + V_{2B}$$

The output current i_2' can be written as

$$i_2' = i_2(t) + I_2 = (I_{2A} - I_{2B}) \sin \omega t + I_{2B} \qquad (2\text{–}83)$$

where $I_2 = I_{2B}$ for this particular case.

In view of expressing a waveform as being composed of a dc and ac component, as expressed in Eqs. (2–82) and (2–83), let us return to the general load line equation of Eq. (2–79) and develop the concept of having a dc and ac load line. Substituting $v_2'(t) = v_2(t) + V_2$ and $i_2'(t) = i_2(t) + I_2$ in Eq. (2–79) we have

$$i_2(t) + I_2 = -\frac{1}{R_L}[v_2(t) + V_2] + \frac{V_{\text{supply}}}{R_L}$$

where $v_2(t)$ and $i_2(t)$ are general time-variant variables. Now let us separate these equation into dc and ac terms, that is,

$$i_2(t) + I_2 = \left[-\frac{1}{R_L}V_2 + \frac{V_{\text{supply}}}{R_L}\right] - \frac{1}{R_L}v_2(t) \qquad (2\text{–}84)$$

To determine the dc load line we shall require that the ac terms be forced to zero, or simply we will not put in a time-variant signal, hence $v_2(t) = 0$ and $i_2(t) = 0$. Then from Eq. (2–84) we have

$$I_2 = -\frac{1}{R_L}V_2 + \frac{V_{\text{supply}}}{R_L} \qquad (2\text{–}85)$$

which is the dc load line. For specific values return to Eqs. (2–82) and (2–83) and Fig. 2–37(c) and (e). Since to derive Eq. (2–85) we required $\vartheta_2(t) = 0$ and $i_2(t) = 0$, then Eqs. (2–82) and (2–83) become

$$v_2'(t)\Big|_{v_2(t)=0} = V_2 \qquad (2\text{–}86a)$$

and

$$i_2'(t)\Big|_{i_2(t)=0} = I_2 \qquad (2\text{–}86b)$$

Thus the dc load line can be determined as it was for Eq. (2–79). In fact, it is the same as shown in Fig. 2–37(c). That is, to find our needed two points in order to plot Eq. (2–85) we choose

$$I_2\Big|_{V_2=0} = \frac{V_{\text{supply}}}{R_L}$$

and

$$V_2\Big|_{I_2=0} = V_{\text{supply}}$$

Now let us determine the ac load line. We shall require all dc components to be forced to zero *by redefining our coordinate system.* We will have to accomplish forcing the dc components to zero this way since the presence of V_{supply} is required in order for the device to operate properly. Then from Eq. (2–85) we have

$$0' = -\frac{1}{R_L}V_2 + \frac{V_{\text{supply}}}{R_L} - I_2 \qquad (2\text{–}87)$$

where $0'$ is the new origin. To be specific suppose $V_2 = V_{2B}$ and $I_2 = I_{2B}$, then

$$0' = -\frac{1}{R_L}V_{2B} + \frac{V_{\text{supply}}}{R} - I_{2B} \qquad (2\text{–}88)$$

and the new origin is at these values, shown in Fig. 2–39(a).

From Eqs. (2–84) and (2–87) we have

$$i_2(t) = -\frac{1}{R_L}v_2(t) \qquad (2\text{–}89)$$

which is the ac load line. Remember that the ac load line has a different

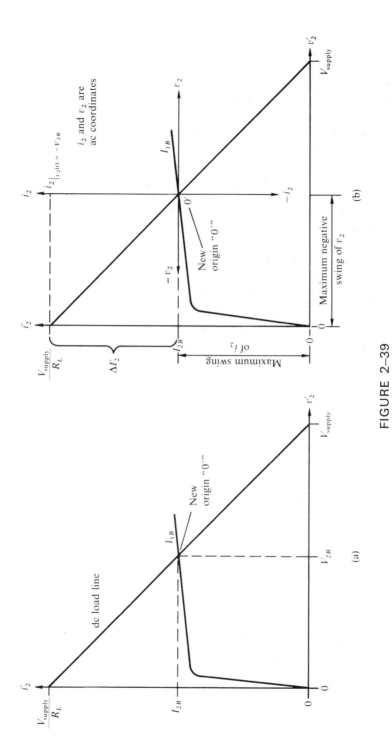

FIGURE 2-39

coordinate system than the dc load line and if we want to view one set of coordinates in terms of the other we will have to translate from one coordinate system to the other.

Let us graphically apply the coordinates i_2 and v_2 on Fig. 2–39(a) at the origin $0'$. This is shown in Fig. 2–39(b). Next we will determine two points for the ac load line so that we may draw that load line. Looking at Fig. 2–39(b) we see the maximum that v_2 can vary in the negative direction is $-V_{2B}$ volts, for beyond this no value of v_2 can exist. Also, when v_2 equals $-V_{2B}$ this corresponds to v_2' equal to zero in the i_1', v_2' coordinate system. Hence, at this point we can find what point this corresponds to in the coordinate i_2', v_2' system and then have a correlation between i_2 and i_2' at $v_2 = -V_{2B}$. Then let $v_2 = -V_{2B}$ and we shall determine the corresponding i_2. From Eq. (2–89) we find for $v_2 = -V_{2B}$ that

$$i_2(t)\bigg|_{v_2=-V_{2B}} = -\frac{1}{R_L}v_2(t)\bigg|_{v_2(t)=-V_{2B}} = \frac{1}{R_L}V_{2B} \qquad (2\text{–}90)$$

Now let us translate back to the coordinate system of i_2' and v_2' by substituting Eq. (2–90) into Eq. (2–88), once we have solved Eq. (2–90) for V_{2B}. Hence

$$0' = -i_2(t)\bigg|_{v_2=-V_{2B}} + \frac{V_{\text{supply}}}{R_L} - I_{2B}$$

or

$$i_2(t)\bigg|_{v_2=-V_{2B}} = \frac{V_{\text{supply}}}{R_L} - I_{2B} \qquad (2\text{–}91)$$

which is equal to $\Delta I_2'$ of Fig. 2–39(b). Notice this is the same point as $I_2\big|_{V_2=0} = (V_{\text{supply}}/R_L)$ for the dc load line. We may also view this in terms of i_2' by manipulation of Eq. (2–91). From Eq. (2–91) we have

$$\left[i_2(t)\bigg|_{v_2=-V_{2B}} + I_{2B}\right] = \frac{V_{\text{supply}}}{R_L}$$

or

$$\left[i_2(t)\bigg|_{v_2=-V_{2B}} + I_2\bigg|_{I_2=I_{2B}}\right] = \frac{V_{\text{supply}}}{R_L}$$

(we have an ac term present, therefore we can no longer state $I_2 = i_2$). We may write this equation as

$$[i_2(t) + I_2]\bigg|_{\substack{v_2=-V_{2B} \\ I_2=I_{2B}}} = \frac{V_{\text{supply}}}{R_L}, \quad \text{but} \quad i_2(t) + I_2 = i_2'(t)$$

hence,

$$i_2'(t)\Big|_{\substack{v_2=-V_{2B}\\I_2=I_{2B}}} = \frac{V_{\text{supply}}}{R_L}$$

which corresponds to the dc load line point when

$$I_2\Big|_{V_2=0} = \frac{V_{\text{supply}}}{R_L}$$

as previously derived.

To pick the second point let i_2 vary to its maximum, which is $i_2 = -I_{2B}$, as can be seen from Fig. 2–39(b). From Eq. (2–89) we have

$$i_2(t)\Big|_{i_2=-I_{2B}} = -I_{2B} = -\frac{1}{R_L}v_2(t)\Big|_{i_2=-I_{2B}}$$

Translating back to the terms of i_2' and v_2' we again use Eq. (2–88). Thus,

$$0' = -\frac{1}{R_L}V_{2B} + \frac{V_{\text{supply}}}{R_L} - I_{2B} = -\frac{1}{R_L}V_{2B} + \frac{V_{\text{supply}}}{R_L} - \frac{1}{R_L}v_2(t)\Big|_{i_2=-I_{2B}}$$

or

$$-\frac{1}{R_L}[V_2 + v_2(t)]\Big|_{\substack{i_2=-I_{2B}\\V_2=V_{2B}}} + \frac{V_{\text{supply}}}{R_L} = 0'$$

But

$$V_2 + v_2(t) = v_2'(t)$$

therefore

$$v_2(t)\Big|_{\substack{i_2=-I_{2B}\\V_2=V_{2B}}} = V_{\text{supply}}$$

which is the same point for the dc case of

$$V_2\Big|_{I_2=0} = V_{\text{supply}}$$

In conclusion it can be said for this case the dc and ac load lines coincided due to their having the same slopes. However, there are many circuits where the dc and ac load lines differ.

For an example when the dc and ac load lines do not coincide consider the circuit of Fig. 2–40(a), where the transformer windings are approximately dc short circuits. Writing a load line equation from the equivalent output circuit of Fig. 2–40(b), where the primary side of the transformer is replaced with its reflected impedance n^2R_L, yields $R_E i_2' + v_2' + n^2R_L i_2' - V_{CC}$. Solving this equation for the dependent variable i_2' of the characteristic curves of Fig. 2–40(c) we get

$$i_2'(t) = -\frac{1}{R_E + n^2R_L}v_2'(t) + \frac{V_{CC}}{R_E + n^2R_L}$$

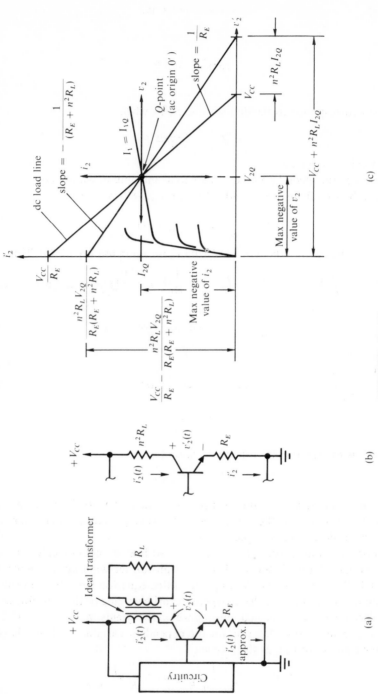

FIGURE 2-40

Again using the notation of dc and ac components, or

$$i_2(t) + I_2 = -\frac{1}{R_E + n^2 R_L}[v_2(t) + V_2] + \frac{V_{CC}}{R_E + n^2 R_L}$$

where $i_2'(t) = i_2(t) + I_2$ and $v_2'(t) = v_2(t) + V_2$. Collecting this expression into dc and ac terms we have

$$\underbrace{i_2(t)}_{\text{ac term}} + \underbrace{I_2}_{\text{dc term}} = \underbrace{\left[-\frac{1}{R_E + n^2 R_L}V_2 + \frac{V_{CC}}{R_E + n^2 R_L}\right]}_{\text{dc term}} - \underbrace{\frac{1}{R_E + n^2 R_L}v_2(t)}_{\text{ac term}} \quad (2\text{-}92)$$

But Eq. (2–92) is not quite correct, that is $n^2 R_L = 0$ (a short circuit) for the dc component, hence

$$i_2(t) + I_2 = \underbrace{\left[-\frac{1}{R_E}V_2 + \frac{V_{CC}}{R_E}\right]}_{\text{dc term}} - \underbrace{\frac{1}{R_E + n^2 R_L}v_2(t)}_{\text{ac term}} \quad (2\text{-}93)$$

As before we will solve for the dc load line by forcing the ac input signal to zero, then from Eq. (2–93) for the ac terms equal to zero we have

$$I_2 = -\frac{1}{R_E}V_2 + \frac{V_{CC}}{R_E} \quad (2\text{-}94)$$

When we design for a dc bias we will design for specific values of I_2 and V_2, and as before this point will become the origin for the ac coordinates i_2, v_2. This point is called the quiescent point and is designated as the Q-point. It is about the Q-point that the ac excursions occur. For our analysis of Fig. 2–37(e) the Q-point was (I_{2B}, V_{2B}). From this time on, the origin of the ac coordinates shall be designated with a subscript Q, that is, I_{2Q}, V_{2Q} as the Q-point is shown in Fig. 2–40(c). Then forcing the dc components to zero, which locates the Q-point of Fig. 2–40(c), requires Eq. (2–94) to become

$$0' = -I_{2Q} - \frac{1}{R_E}V_{2Q} + \frac{V_{CC}}{R_E} \quad (2\text{-}95)$$

With the requirements of Eq. (2–95) fulfilled we can determine the ac load line from Eq. (2–93), which is

$$i_2(t) = -\frac{1}{R_E + n^2 R_L}v_2(t) \quad (2\text{-}96)$$

We can see that the load lines do not coincide from the inspection of Eqs. (2–94) and (2–96), that is, the dc load line slope is $-(1/R_E)$ while the ac load line slope is $-(1/R_E + n^2 R_L)$. To be more explicit we shall locate points necessary to draw the load lines on the characteristic curves, just as was done previously. From Eq. (2–94) we will locate points for the dc load line. As before

$$I_2\Big|_{V_2=0} = \frac{V_{CC}}{R_E}$$

and

$$V_2\bigg|_{I_2=0} = V_{CC}$$

These points are located on Fig. 2–40(c).

For determining two points necessary for drawing the ac load line we shall proceed as before by going to the origin of the ac coordinates (Q-point) and letting the ac coordinates (i_2, v_2) take on their maximum negative values one at a time, since these points intersect with the i_2', v_2' coordinates, and then solve for the value of the i_2', v_2' coordinates at these maximum values. To reiterate, these are the steps followed in the previous analysis of dc and ac load lines.

From Fig. 2–40(c) we see that the maximum negative value of i_2 is $i_2 = -I_{2Q}$. For this value substituted in Eq. (2–96) we have

$$-I_{2Q} = -\frac{1}{R_E + n^2 R_L} v_2(t)\bigg|_{i_2=-I_{2Q}} \tag{2–97}$$

Then solving for v_2 we have

$$v_2(t)\bigg|_{i_2=-I_{2Q}} = (R_E + n^2 R_L)I_{2Q} = R_E I_{2Q} + n^2 R_L I_{2Q} \tag{2–98}$$

Equation (2–98) does not give us a familiar reference with which to locate the point $v_2(t)\big|_{i_2=-I_{2Q}}$. So let us return to Eq. (2–94) and evaluate it at the same current value of I_{2Q}. This will allow us to manipulate into the familiar coordinates i_2', v_2'.

From Eq. (2–94) we have for $I_2 = I_{2Q}$ the equation

$$I_{2Q} = -\frac{1}{R_E}V_{2Q} + \frac{V_{CC}}{R_E}$$

or

$$R_E I_{2Q} = V_{CC} - V_{2Q} \tag{2–99}$$

Solving for $R_E I_{2Q}$ of Eq. (2–98) and substituting into Eq. (2–99) yields

$$v_2(t)\bigg|_{i_2=-I_{2Q}} - n^2 R_L I_{2Q} = V_{CC} - V_{2Q}$$

Then

$$[v_2(t) + V_2]\bigg|_{\substack{V_2=V_{2Q} \\ i_2=-I_{2Q}}} = V_{CC} + n^2 R_L I_{2Q}$$

but $v_2(t) + V_2 = v_2'(t)$, therefore

$$v_2'(t)\bigg|_{\substack{V_2=V_{2Q} \\ i_2=-I_{2Q}}} = V_{CC} + n^2 R_L I_{2Q} \tag{2–100}$$

Equation (2–100) states that the ac load line intersects v_2' coordinate at the quantity $V_{CC} + n^2 R_L I_{2Q}$, which is $n^2 R_L I_{2Q}$ more than the intersection of the dc load line. This is shown in Fig. 2–40(c).

For the second point let $v_2 = -V_{2Q}$, as determined from Fig. 2–40(c).

From Eq. (2–96) for this value we have

$$i_2\bigg|_{v_2=-V_{2Q}} = -\frac{1}{R_E+n^2R_L}(-V_{2Q}) = \frac{V_{2Q}}{R_E+n^2R_L} \qquad (2\text{-}101)$$

Evaluating Eq. (2–94) at V_{2Q} volts we have

$$I_{2Q} = -\frac{1}{R_E}V_{2Q} + \frac{V_{CC}}{R_E} \qquad (2\text{-}102)$$

Solving for V_{2Q} from Eq. (2–101) and substituting this into Eq. (2–102) yields

$$I_{2Q} = -\frac{1}{R_E}(R_E+n^2R_L)i_2\bigg|_{v_2=-V_{2Q}} + \frac{V_{CC}}{R_E}$$

or

$$I_{2Q} = -\left(1+\frac{n^2R_L}{R_E}\right)i_2\bigg|_{v_2=-V_{2Q}} + \frac{V_{CC}}{R_E}$$

Then

$$i_2\bigg|_{v_2=-V_{2Q}} + I_{2Q} = \frac{V_{CC}}{R_E} - \frac{n^2R_L}{R_E}i_2\bigg|_{v_2=-V_{2Q}}$$

$$i_2'(t)\bigg|_{\substack{I_2=I_{2Q}\\v_2=-V_{2Q}}} = [i_2(t)+I_2]\bigg|_{\substack{I_2=I_{2Q}\\v_2=-V_{2Q}}} = \frac{V_{CC}}{R_E} - \frac{n^2R_L}{R_E}i_2\bigg|_{v_2=-V_{2Q}}$$

Since

$$i_2\bigg|_{v_2=-V_{2Q}} = \frac{V_{2Q}}{R_E+n^2R_L}$$

from Eq. (2–101) then

$$i_2'(t)\bigg|_{\substack{I_2=I_{2Q}\\v_2=-V_{2Q}}} = \frac{V_{CC}}{R_E} - \frac{n^2R_LV_{2Q}}{R_E(R_E+n^2R_L)} \qquad (2\text{-}103)$$

Equation (2–103) states that the intersection of i_2' coordinate and the ac load line occurs at the value of $i_2'\big|_{\substack{I_2=I_{2Q}\\v_2=-V_{2Q}}}$, which equals V_{CC}/R_E $-[n^2R_LV_{2Q}/R_E(R_E+n^2R_L)]$. Notice that this value differs from the dc load line intersection by a value of $-[n^2R_LV_{2Q}/R_E(R_E+n^2R_L)]$, therefore the ac load line is less than the dc load line intercept, as shown in Fig. 2–40(c).

In summary of load line analysis, it is most important for one to understand that when speaking of an ac analysis of a device he means that the analysis requires the Q-point to be the origin of the ac coordinates. For that reason we may speak of a negative ac signal on the base-to-emitter of an NPN-type transistor, or a positive ac signal on the grid of a vacuum tube. Of course what we really mean, in the case of the transistor, is a negative-going ac signal. But it has an absolute positive signal. The same concept applies to the vacuum tube's grid and the output of each device. This will be emphasized in the ac modeling of a device.

2–7   AC Linear Model of Active Components

We shall now approach both vacuum tubes and transistors from a modeling standpoint. That is, we will attempt to devise an equivalent circuit, or as near equivalent as we can reasonably get, which will represent the physical behavior of the active device. We will use two-port network analysis techniques as discussed in section 1–4.

Each model is derived from the basic block diagram of Fig. 2–41, which is a two-port device. For this two-port device we have four variables

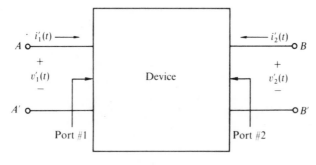

FIGURE 2–41

(i'_1, v'_1, i'_2, and v'_2), whereas in section 1–4 the primes mean dc and ac terms may be present. We may choose any two of these variables to be independent variables; hence, the remaining two are dependent variables (so long as they exist). Suppose we choose i'_1 and v'_2 to be the independent variables, then

$$i'_2 = i'_2(i'_1, v'_2) \tag{2-104}$$

and

$$v'_1 = v'_1(i'_1, v'_2) \tag{2-105}$$

Recalling the equation for differentiating multivariable functions, which is Eq. (1–8),

$$df = \frac{\partial f}{\partial x} dx + \frac{\partial f}{\partial y} dy \tag{1-8}$$

and applying it to Eqs. (2–104) and (2–105) we have

$$di'_2 = \frac{\partial i'_2}{\partial i'_1} di'_1 + \frac{\partial i'_2}{\partial v'_2} dv'_2 \tag{2-106}$$

and

$$dv_1' = \frac{\partial v_1'}{\partial i_1''}\, di_1'' + \frac{\partial v_1'}{\partial v_2'}\, dv_2' \qquad (2\text{-}107)$$

We previously stated in section 1–4 that dx' was simply the variable of x', which is x. However, let us now view this graphically.

If Eq. (2–106) is descriptive of the graphs shown in Fig. 2–42 and if we write the differentials as deltas (differences) we have

$$\Delta i_2' = \frac{\partial i_2'}{\partial i_1'}\, \Delta i_1' + \frac{\partial i_2'}{\partial v_2'}\, \Delta v_2' \qquad (2\text{-}108)$$

We are able to do this since the graphs are linear. Let us next investigate the partial derivatives in view of the graphs being straight lines. Now $\partial x'/\partial y' = \partial x/\partial y$ since only x and y are variables for x' and y' respectively.

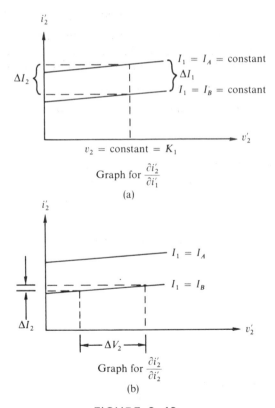

FIGURE 2–42

And for straight lines the partial derivatives are:

$$\frac{\partial i_2}{\partial i_1} = \frac{di_2}{di_1}\bigg|_{\substack{v_2=K_2 \\ v_2=K_2=\text{constant}}} = \frac{\Delta I_2}{\Delta I_1}\bigg|_{v_2=K_2} = m_1 = \text{slope [see Fig. 2–42(a)]} \qquad (2\text{–}109)$$

and

$$\frac{\partial i_2}{\partial v_2} = \frac{di_2}{dv_2}\bigg|_{\substack{i_1=I_A \\ i_1=I_A \text{ (or } I_B)=\text{constant}}} = \frac{\Delta I_2}{\Delta V_2}\bigg|_{i_1=I_A} = m_2 = \text{slope} \qquad (2\text{–}110)$$

since for a straight line $dy/dx = \lim_{\Delta x \to 0} \Delta y/\Delta x = \Delta y/\Delta x$. Hence, Eq. (2–108) may be written as

$$\Delta i_2' = m_1 \Delta i_1' + m_2 \Delta v_2' \qquad (2\text{–}111)$$

Now $\Delta i_2'$ of Eq. (2–111) is the varying portion of i_2', which from Fig. 2–42(a) and (b) we see is ΔI_2.

Also $\Delta i_1'$ is ΔI_1 and $\Delta v_2'$ is ΔV_2, hence we may write Eq. (2–111) as

$$\Delta I_2 = m_1 \Delta I_1 + m_2 \Delta V_2 \qquad (2\text{–}112)$$

Since the delta terms represent variables for our analysis they must be the swing about a fixed reference. To be specific, consider ΔV_2 as a sinusoidal wave, then ΔV_2 could be mathematically expressed as

$$\Delta V_2 = E \sin \omega t \qquad (2\text{–}113)$$

Graphically projecting this on the graph of Fig. 2–43 we see that we have a ΔI_2, which is

$$\Delta I_2 = -I \sin \omega t \qquad (2\text{–}114)$$

As we previously agreed we shall represent the time-variant quantities of Eqs. (2–113) and (2–114) as $v_2(t)$ and $i_2(t)$ respectively. Then Eq. (2–112) becomes

$$i_2(t) = m_1 i_1(t) + m_2 v_2(t) \qquad (2\text{–}115)$$

By a similar analysis we may write Eq. (2–107) as

$$v_1(t) = m_3 i_1(t) + m_4 v_2(t) \qquad (2\text{–}116)$$

where

$$m_3 = \frac{\Delta V_1}{\Delta I_1}\bigg|_{v_2=\text{constant}}$$

and

$$m_4 = \frac{\Delta V_1}{\Delta V_2}\bigg|_{i_1=\text{constant}}$$

We should have recognized the coordinates of Fig. 2–43 as being the same as those of Fig. 2–40(c) where only the ac load line is shown. That is, in Fig. 2–43 we have shown the absolute coordinates i_2' and v_2' with the relative coordinates i_2 and v_2 superimposed.

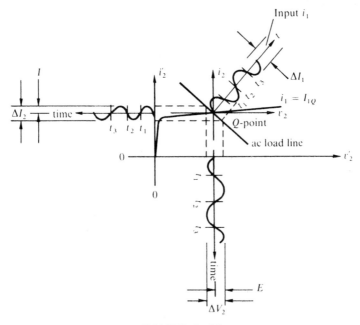

FIGURE 2–43

Hence, we see that we have also made an analysis of the output characteristic curves of a transistor (a pentode vacuum tube has similar characteristics). It is important to realize that our analysis is only for the linear (straight-line approximation) portions of the graphs.

Next we shall determine the units of m_1 and m_2. From Eqs. (2–109) and (2–110) we saw

$$m_1 = \frac{\Delta I_2}{\Delta I_1}\bigg|_{v_2=K_2} \quad \text{and} \quad m_2 = \frac{\Delta I_2}{\Delta V_2}\bigg|_{\substack{i=\text{some constant value of} \\ \text{current } (I_A \text{ or } I_B, \text{ etc.})}}$$

We define these parameters by checking their units: m_1 is the ratio of input current to output current, which is current gain, and m_2 is the reciprocal of output resistance. Since m_1 and m_2 are a hybrid of units we will define them as h-parameters. Hence,

$$m_1 = \frac{\Delta I_2}{\Delta I_1}\bigg|_{v_2=\text{constant}} = \text{current gain} = h_f \text{ (unitless)} \qquad (2\text{–}117)$$

$$m_2 = \frac{\Delta I_2}{\Delta V_2}\bigg|_{i_1=\text{constant}} = \text{output conductance} = h_o \text{ (units of mhos)} \qquad (2\text{–}118)$$

To determine m_3 and m_4 of Eq. (2–116) let us realize the input curves of a transistor are similar to a forward-biased diode, and as a result are nonlinear. Also, the relationship of input voltage to output voltage is nonlinear. Such nonlinear curves could appear as shown in Fig. 2–44.

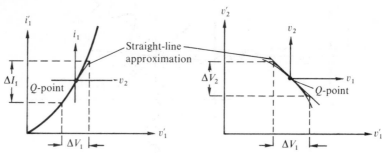

(a) Input characteristic curve of i_1', v_1'.   (b) Output voltage v_2' vs input voltage v_1'.

FIGURE 2–44   (a) Input characteristic curve of i_1', v_1' ; (b) Output voltage v_2' vs input voltage v_1'.

However, from our definition of m_3 and m_4 of Eq. (2–116) we have required that the graphs of Fig. 2–44 be linear. Then we must approximate these curves to be linear. From Fig. 2–44 we see that straight-line approximations can be made.

To determine m_3 and m_4 we will analyze the problem as was done for finding m_1 and m_2. That is,

$$dv_1 = \frac{\partial v_1}{\partial i_1}\, di_1 + \frac{\partial v_1}{\partial v_2}\, dv_2 = \frac{dv_1}{di_1}\bigg|_{v_2 = K_2 = \text{constant}} di_1 + \frac{dv_1}{dv_2}\bigg|_{i_1 = I = \text{constant}} dv_2$$

$$= \frac{\Delta V_i}{\Delta I_1}\bigg|_{v_2 = K_2} di_1 + \frac{\Delta V_1}{\Delta V_2}\bigg|_{i_1 = I} dv_2$$

Our only difference between analysis is that we have made straight-line approximations for the nonlinear curves of Fig. 2–44. Notice that the smaller ΔV_1 and ΔI_1 are, the closer our approximations are to being a straight line. Hence, this shall be a limitation on our analysis: *that our input signals be small.*

Then performing a similar analysis for Eq. (2–116) to determine m_3 and m_4, as was done to find m_1 and m_2, would yield

$$m_3 = \frac{\Delta V_1}{\Delta I_1}\bigg|_{v_2 = \text{constant}} = \text{Input resistance} \equiv h_i \text{ (units of ohms)} \quad \textbf{(2–119)}$$

and

$$m_4 = \frac{\Delta V_1}{\Delta V_2}\bigg|_{i_1 = \text{constant}} = \text{Reverse voltage transfer} \equiv h_r \text{ (unitless)} \quad \textbf{(2–120)}$$

Substituting Eqs. (2–119) and (2–120) into their proper places in Eqs.

(2–115) and (2–116) we have,

$$i_2(t) = h_f i_1(t) + h_o v_2(t) \qquad \qquad \textbf{(2–121)}$$

$$v_1(t) = h_i i_1(t) + h_r v_2(t) \qquad \qquad \textbf{(2–122)}$$

These equations can now be interpreted into a representative circuit which will serve as our ac model of a transistor. Of course, we must remember the restrictions of linearity and small signals we required for the derivation of this model; that is, it is only valid when operating in the straight-line portions of the output characteristic curves and from small signals being applied to the input circuit. Fortunately this covers a majority of the operations in nonlogic circuit applications.

Let us return to the derivation of the circuits to be derived from Eqs. (2–121) and (2–122). We see that Eq. (2–121) must be a nodal equation (see section 2–4) since currents are being summed (check units), and Eq. (2–122) is a loop equation since voltages are being summed. Let us derive the circuits on that basis. From Eq. (2–121) we see the current i_2 is the sum of the current source $h_f i_1$ and the current flowing through h_o caused by v_2. The circuit derived from Eq. (2–121) complying with Fig. 2–41 is shown in Fig. 2–45(a). From Eq. (2–122) and Fig. 2–41 the circuit of Fig. 2–45(b) is shown.

Figure 2–45(c) and (d) shows how a transistor would fit in the "device box" of Fig. 2–41. It is shown in each case that terminals A' and B' are common. This is also true for a common-collector circuit. Then to reference the circuits of Fig. 2–45(a) and (b) to the same point we make terminals A' and B' common and come up with the circuit of Fig. 2–45(e). Since this circuit of Fig. 2–45(e) is basic to all transistor configurations one merely adds the letter subscript to the h-parameter which indicates the common lead. If the model is to represent a transistor used in common-base configuration, then b (to represent base) is added as a subscript to all the h-parameters and i_1, i_2, v_1, and v_2 are identified as i_e, i_c, v_{eb}, and v_{cb} respectively. The model for common-base configuration is shown in Fig. 2–45(f). Likewise, the common-emitter configuration model is shown in Fig. 2–45(g). The common-collector model has not been discussed since it follows the same concept as the others.

One last important point remains to be discussed concerning the models developed. The polarities of v_1 and v_2 are subject to being the opposite of that shown, and the directions of i_1 and i_2 may be the reverse shown. We must remember that these models are ac models only; hence, any dc component of voltage or current does not appear, as we demonstrated earlier. To again illustrate this point, consider Fig. 2–46 (keeping in mind our ac coordinate system), which shows a base voltage v'_{be} that is composed of a pure ac signal and a dc component. The voltage v'_{be} may be

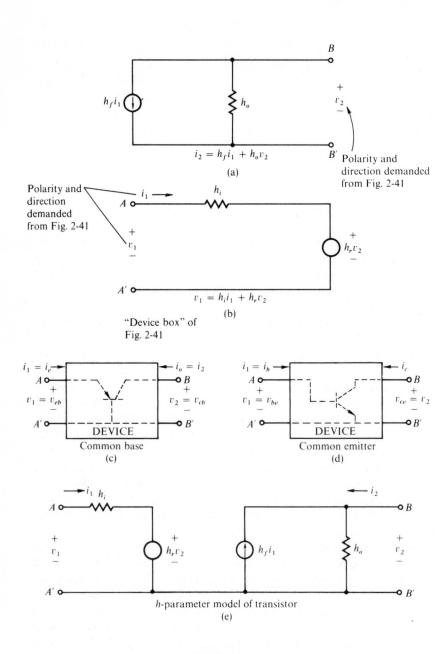

$i_2 = h_f i_1 + h_o v_2$

(a)

Polarity and direction demanded from Fig. 2-41

Polarity and direction demanded from Fig. 2-41

$v_1 = h_i i_1 + h_r v_2$

(b)

"Device box" of Fig. 2-41

Common base
(c)

Common emitter
(d)

h-parameter model of transistor
(e)

FIGURE 2–45

110

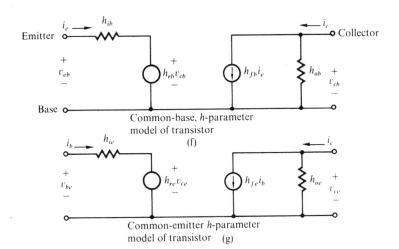

Common-base, *h*-parameter
model of transistor
(f)

Common-emitter *h*-parameter
model of transistor   (g)

FIGURE 2–45 (cont)

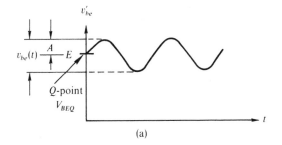

(a)

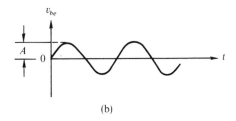

(b)

FIGURE 2–46 (a) Voltage V_{be} with dc component E;
(b) Voltage with no dc component

expressed as

$$v'_{be}(t) = v_{be}(t) + E = A \sin \omega t + E \quad \text{if} \quad v_{be} = A \sin \omega t$$

We know from device theory that the dc component of Fig. 2–45 is really the Q-point, $v'_{be} = V_{BEQ} = E$ and that v_{be} is the ac voltage which swings around the Q-point voltage E. Then picking the Q-point voltage as a reference voltage, or zero volts in the ac coordinates, we have Fig. 2–46(b). We see that v_{be} has positive and negative values *relative* to this new reference. This concept is also verified in Figs. 2–37(e), 2–38, and 2–43. Hence, from an absolute standpoint the total voltage (ac and dc components) from base to emitter for an NPN must be positive at the base with respect to the emitter to be forward-biased; but the ac models do not show the dc component and as a result may be either or both positive and negative relative to the Q-point of the device. Of course if v_{be} changes polarity from that of Fig. 2–45(f) so must i_e, i_c, and v_{cb}. The same may be said of the output voltage and current; that is, the absolute polarity and direction are fixed, but the relative polarities derived from the ac coordinates may be alternating in polarity and direction. To reiterate, the ac model is based on the ac coordinates i_1, i_2, v_1 and v_2.

If we were analyzing a pentode instead of a transistor we could define the independent variables as v_1 and v_2 while defining i_2 as a dependent variable. We should understand that $i_1 = 0$ since i_1 is the grid current for common cathode configurations. Applying Eq. (1–8) to the time-variant variables

$$i_2 = i_2 (v_1, v_2)$$

we have

$$di_2 = \frac{\partial i_2}{\partial v_1} dv_1 + \frac{\partial i_2}{\partial v_2} dv_2 \qquad (2\text{–}123)$$

As shown in Fig. 2–47(a) $i_2 = i_p$, $v_1 = v_{gk}$, and $v_2 = v_{pk}$. From the output characteristics we see that the analysis will be basically the same as for the transistor since both have similar output curves (see Fig. 2–33). Thus Eq. (2–123) is written as

$$i_2 = m_1 v_{gk}(t) + m_2 v_{pk}(t) \qquad (2\text{–}124)$$

where $\quad m_1 = \dfrac{\partial i_2}{\partial v_{gk}}\bigg|_{v_{pk}=\text{constant}} = \dfrac{1}{\Omega} \equiv g_m = \begin{array}{l}\text{the transconductance} \\ \text{of the device}\end{array}$

$$m_2 = \frac{\partial i_p}{\partial v_{pk}}\bigg|_{v_{pk}=\text{constant}} = \frac{1}{\Omega} \equiv \frac{1}{r_d} = \frac{1}{\text{the plate resistance } r_d}$$

Hence,

$$i_p(t) = g_m v_{gk}(t) + \frac{1}{r_d} v_{pk}(t) \qquad (2\text{–}125)$$

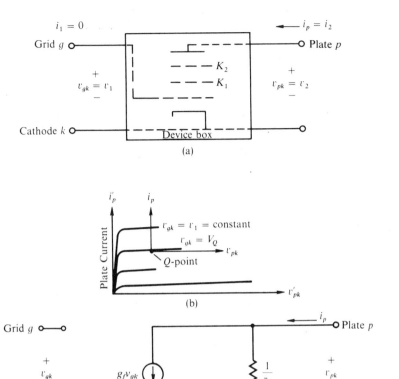

FIGURE 2–47   (a) AC coordinates only; (b) Plate-to-cathode voltage; (c) Equivalent AC model for a pentode

where the limitations of linearity apply. We should realize that we have no input circuit for the device since $i_1 = 0$. The ac model for the pentode is shown in Fig. 2–47. Everything stated for the transistor's equivalent circuit concerning ac current direction and voltage polarity applies to the pentode model as well.

Since devices are never isolated by themselves but contain external circuitry let us make an observation concerning dc sources. Consider the circuit of Fig. 2–48(a), where primed lowercase letters mean both ac and dc components are present while the unprimed lowercase letters are defined as pure ac signals. The resistors R_1, R_2, and R_3 could be con-

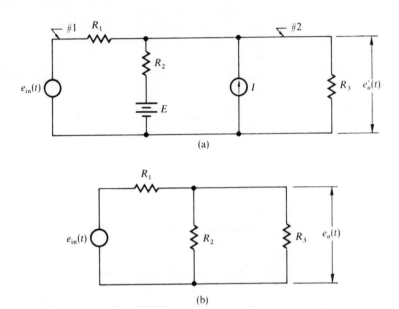

FIGURE 2–48

sidered as internal resistors to e_{in}, E, and I respectively. Summing the currents at node #2 we have

$$0 = \frac{e_{in}(t) - e_o'(t)}{R_1} + \frac{E - e_o'(t)}{R_2} + I - \frac{e_o'(t)}{R_3}$$

or

$$\frac{e_{in}(t)}{R_1} + \frac{E}{R_2} + I = \left(\frac{1}{R_g} + \frac{1}{R_2} + \frac{1}{R_3}\right)e_o'(t) = \frac{1}{R_{eq}}e_o'(t)$$

Defining e_o as ac and E_o as the dc component of e_o', then $e_o'(t) = e_o(t) + E_o$. Substituting $e_o'(t) = e_o(t) + E_o$ into the equation we have

$$\frac{e_{in}(t)}{R_1} + \frac{E}{R_2} + I = \frac{1}{R_{eq}}[e_o(t) + E_o]$$

As was done for the ac load line for active devices let us reference the circuit to the ac coordinate origin. Therefore, the dc components will be set equal to 0'. Thus

$$\frac{E}{R_2} + I - \frac{E_o}{R_{eq}} = 0' \text{ (the "Q-point")}$$

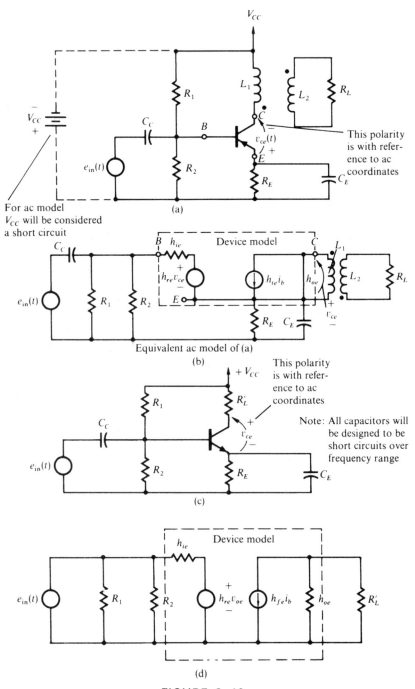

For ac model
V_{CC} will be considered
a short circuit

(a)

Device model

Equivalent ac model of (a)

(b)

This polarity
is with refer-
ence to ac
coordinates

Note: All capacitors will
be designed to be
short circuits over
frequency range

(c)

Device model

(d)

FIGURE 2–49

115

Hence, the remainder of the equation is

$$\frac{e_{in}(t)}{R_1} = \frac{1}{R_{eq}}e_o(t) = \left(\frac{1}{R_1} + \frac{1}{R_2} + \frac{1}{R_3}\right)e_o(t)$$

or

$$\frac{e_{in}(t) - e_o(t)}{R_1} = \left(\frac{1}{R_2} + \frac{1}{R_3}\right)e_o(t) = \frac{e_o(t)}{R_2} + \frac{e_o(t)}{R_3} \qquad (2\text{-}126)$$

Equation (2–126) is a nodal equation since it is the summation of current (check units) in terms of voltages. Then three branches exist: one containing R_1 with a voltage of $e_{in}(t) - e_o(t)$ across it, and two others containing R_2 and R_3 with e_o across them. This yields the circuit of Fig. 2–48(b). We must remind ourselves that Fig. 2–48(b) is an ac equivalent of Fig. 2–48(a) and our analysis of Fig. 2–48(b) is only good for an ac analysis. Notice we could have arrived at Fig. 2–48(b) from Fig. 2–48(a) merely by short circuiting the dc voltage source E and open circuiting the dc current source I. From this analysis we shall derive a general rule: when making an ac analysis of any circuit, with or without an active device, to obtain the ac equivalent circuit short-circuit all dc voltage sources and open-circuit all dc current sources.

To give examples of determining the ac models of circuits containing active devices consider the circuits of Fig. 2–49(a) and (c) and the equivalent circuits shown in Fig. 2–49(b) and (d). Notice Fig. 2–49(a) and (b) could be representing the same circuit if we consider the transformer as an ideal one and replace the primary with its reflected impedance, that is, $R'_L = n^2 R_L$ for Fig. 2–49(c), and if C_E and C_C were designed to be near short circuits over the frequency range of operation. Also notice the device ac model is the same for NPN and PNP type transistors. This is true since it is an ac model and our reference is from the Q-point.

3 Mathematical Description of Circuits

3–1 Introduction

The contents of this chapter are largely material covered in more elementary courses. However, here we shall look at the contents from a slightly different mathematical viewpoint; that is, we will concern ourselves with writing differential equations which describe the electrical behavior of circuits. In chap. 4 we will develop a means to solve for solutions for these differential equations.

The approach taken in this chapter is that an understanding of the analysis concepts is desired and rigorous mechanical procedures should not be established. For this reason the concepts of describing a circuit mathematically are emphasized rather than a formal set of rules which will allow one to write the necessary equations upon inspection. In some cases we do discuss such a set of rules, but only to provide us with a check of our analysis. Those topics which are mostly review we shall present only briefly.

3–2 Loop Analysis

The first method of analysis we shall consider is the mesh-current, or loop-current, method. This method is an application of: (1) Kirchhoff's voltage law, which simply stated is: *The algebraic sum of all voltage drops and rises in a closed path is zero*; and (2) the mathematical solution to simultaneous equations, which require *n* equations for *n* unknowns. To apply this law let us investigate what is meant by "... voltage drops and rises ..." and "... a closed path ...." The term voltage drop, and therefore a negative voltage, means to go from the + sign to − sign as one travels through a voltage in following a given path of a circuit. Similarly, a voltage rise, which is a positive voltage, is going from − to + in traveling through a voltage. A closed path is any path which begins and ends at the same point in a circuit and the path is never retraced. Notice a path may or may not be electrically closed; that is, a path may contain some open circuits. These concepts are illustrated in Fig. 3–1 and accompanying Eq. (3–1). Summing

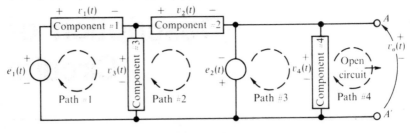

FIGURE 3–1

the voltage of the various paths we have:

$$\text{Path } \#1 \quad e_1(t) - v_1(t) - v_3(t) = 0 \tag{3-1a}$$

$$\text{Path } \#2 \quad v_3(t) - v_2(t) + e_2(t) = 0 \tag{3-1b}$$

$$\text{Path } \#3 \quad -e_2(t) - v_4(t) = 0 \tag{3-1c}$$

$$\text{Path } \#4 \quad v_4(t) - v_o(t) = 0 \tag{3-1d}$$

Whenever a path is closed electrically a current may flow in that path. The electrically closed path is termed a loop and the current is known as a loop current. Loop currents are *assumed currents* and for that reason one need not be concerned with their true direction; in fact, since the loop is rather arbitrary so is the loop current. However, once a loop current is chosen all voltages caused (voltages across passive components) by that current must be voltage drops, if one travels the loop *in the same direction as the loop current*, that is, where the current enters is + and leaves is − for passive components. Notice in Fig. 3–1 paths #1, #2, and #3 are loops (since they are electrically closed) but not path #4; it has an open circuit from A to A'.

Let us take another look at Fig. 3–1 but redrawn in Fig. 3–2 such that

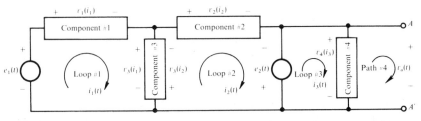

$i_n(t)$ = loop current in n^{th} loop where $n = 1, 2, 3$

FIGURE 3–2

paths #1, #2, and #3 are identified as loops by showing the flow of loop currents. Also we shall omit the polarity signs of Fig. 3–1 and determine new ones based on the loop currents' directions. The polarities are such that for each passive component (#1, #2, #3, #4) where the loop current enters is + and leaves is —. The polarity of the active components (energy sources) is not affected by the loop currents.

From Fig. 3–2 it can be generalized that the superposition principle is applied to those components that are common to more than one loop. In the case of Fig. 3–2 component #3 is the only mutual component. The voltage generator e_2 is not a function of current and therefore is not affected by the loop currents. The voltages $v_3(i_1)$ and $v_3(i_2)$ are the voltages developed across component #3 due to loop currents i_1 and i_2 respectively, which is why they are written as $v_3(i_1)$ and $v_3(i_2)$. Then the *true* voltage across component #3 is the algebraic sum of $v_3(i_1)$ and $v_3(i_2)$ and the *true* current is the algebraic sum of the loop currents flowing through it. To see how $v_3(i_1)$ and $v_3(i_2)$ are functions of i_1 and i_2 respectively suppose component #3 is resistor R_3. Then

$$v_3(i_1) = R_3 i_1(t)$$

and

$$v_3(i_2) = R_3 i_2(t)$$

Next we shall write the voltage equations for the various paths and loops of which for n paths, or loops, we need n equations. Hence performing

$$\sum_{m=1}^{M} v_m = 0$$

where $\sum v_m$ is meant to represent all voltages in the nth loop, or path. We have for the various loops:

Loop #1 $e_1(t) - v_1(i_1) - \underbrace{v_3(i_1) + v_3(i_2)}_{\substack{\text{Both voltages are} \\ \text{common to loop #1}}} = 0$

Loop #2 $\underbrace{v_3(i_1) - v_3(i_2)}_{\substack{\text{Both voltages are} \\ \text{common to loop } \#2}} - v_2(i_2) + e_2(t) = 0$

Loop #3 $-e_2(t) - v_4(i_3) = 0$

If one wishes to sum the voltages in path #4 we have,

Path #4 $v_4(i_3) - v_0(t) = 0$ (Notice no loop current flows in path #4.)

Since the loop currents are assumed, their path of flow (that is, the loops) could have been chosen differently. However, it is usually a good practice to look at the circuit as made up of "widows" and each widow is a loop, as is illustrated in Fig. 3–3. This technique will also satisfy another rule when using loop analysis, and that rule is: *Every component must have*

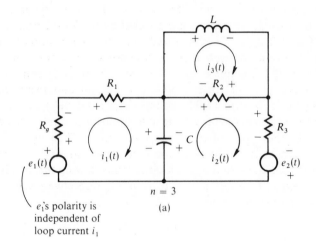

e_1's polarity is
independent of
loop current i_1

(a)

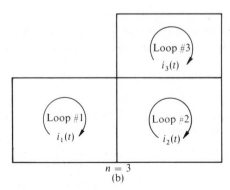

FIGURE 3–3

at least one loop current flowing through it if it constitutes some portion of a loop.

It might have been noticed that while the direction of the loop currents is arbitrary a definite pattern was followed: the loop currents were chosen to flow in a clockwise direction. This pattern is purely for mechanical reasons and can aid in "quick" circuit analysis. This will be pointed out now by writing the loop equations for Fig. 3–3. Hence,

Loop #1

$$e_1(t) - R_g i_1(t) - R_1 i_1(t) - \frac{1}{C} \int i_1(t)\, dt + \frac{1}{C} \int i_2(t)\, dt = 0$$

Loop #2

$$-\frac{1}{C} \int i_2(t)\, dt + \frac{1}{C} \int i_1(t)\, dt - R_2 i_2(t) + R_2 i_3(t) - R_3 i_2(t) + e_2(t) = 0$$

Loop #3

$$-R_2 i_3(t) + R_2 i_2 t - L\frac{di_3(t)}{dt} = 0$$

Then

Loop #1

$$e_1(t) = \left[R_g i_1(t) + R_1 i_1(t) + \frac{1}{C} \int i_1(t)\, dt \right] - \frac{1}{C} \int i_2(t)\, dt \qquad (3\text{–}2a)$$

Loop #2

$$e_2(t) = -\frac{1}{C} \int i_1(t)\, dt + \left[\frac{1}{C} \int i_2(t)\, dt + R_2 i_2(t) + R_3 i_2(t) \right]$$

$$-R_2 i_3(t) \qquad (3\text{–}2b)$$

Loop #3

$$0 = -R_2 i_2(t) + \left[R_2 i_3(t) + L\frac{di_3(t)}{dt} \right] \qquad (3\text{–}2c)$$

Notice that all voltages resulting from the loop current of the loop where we are summing the voltages are positive while the others are negative. This is a direct result of having all loop currents flow in the same direction. Mathematically this could be stated as

[Algebraic sum of all voltage generators in loop n] $= -\Sigma v_k(i_j) + \Sigma v_k(i_n)$

$$(3\text{–}3)$$

where $$j \neq n$$

While Eq. (3–3) is a quick way to write the loop equations for a given circuit we shall use it more as a check.

In order to see the superposition principle being applied let us take another look at the equations in Eqs. (3–2). First, to see the superposition of the loop currents rearrange those equations so that like coefficients (component values) are factored. Then, for

Loop #1

$$e_1(t) = R_g i_1(t) + R_1 i_1(t) + \frac{1}{C}\left[\int i_1(t)\,dt - \int i_2(t)\,dt\right]$$

$$= (R_g + R_1)i_1(t) + \frac{1}{C}\int [i_1(t) - i_2(t)]\,dt$$

where $[i_1(t) - i_2(t)]$ is the resultant true current flowing through capacitor C.

Loop #2

$$e_2(t) = -\frac{1}{C}\int [i_1(t) - i_2(t)]\,dt + R_2[i_2(t) - i_3(t)] + R_3 i_2(t)$$

where $[i_2(t) - i_3(t)]$ is the resultant true current flowing through resistor R_2.

Loop #3 $0 = -R_2[i_2(t) - i_3(t)] + L\dfrac{di_3(t)}{dt}$

We shall consider two more examples before going to another topic.

Example 3–1 For this example consider Fig. 3–4.

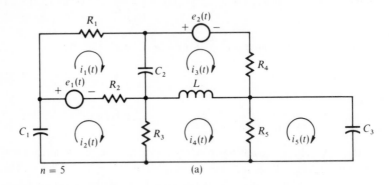

(a)

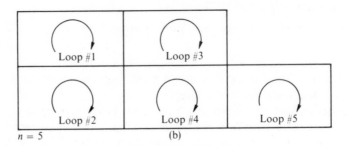

(b)

FIGURE 3–4

Writing the loop equations we have

Loop #1

$$e_1(t) - R_1 i_1(t) - \frac{1}{C_2} \int i_1(t)\,dt + \frac{1}{C_2} \int i_3(t)\,dt$$
$$- R_2 i_1(t) + R_2 i_2(t) = 0$$

Loop #2

$$-e_1(t) - R_2 i_2(t) + R_2 i_1(t) - R_3 i_2(t) + R_3 i_4(t)$$
$$- \frac{1}{C_1} \int i_2(t)\,dt = 0$$

Loop #3

$$-e_2(t) - R_4 i_3(t) - L\frac{di_3(t)}{dt} + L\frac{di_4(t)}{dt} - \frac{1}{C_2} \int i_3(t)\,dt$$
$$+ \frac{1}{C_2} \int i_1(t)\,dt = 0$$

Loop #4

$$-R_3 i_4(t) + R_3 i_2(t) - L\frac{di_4(t)}{dt} + L\frac{di_3(t)}{dt}$$
$$+ R_5 i_5(t) - R_5 i_4(t) = 0$$

Loop #5

$$-R_5 i_5(t) + R_5 i_4(t) - \frac{1}{C_3} \int i_5(t)\,dt = 0$$

Rearranging the equations to take the form of Eqs. (3–2) and (3–3) we have,

Loop #1

$$e_1(t) = \left[R_1 i_1(t) + \frac{1}{C_2} \int i_1(t)\,dt + R_2 i_1(t) \right]$$
$$- R_2 i_2(t) - \frac{1}{C_2} \int i_3(t)\,dt$$

Loop #2

$$-e_1(t) = -R_2 i_1(t)$$
$$+ \left[R_2 i_2(t) + R_3 i_2(t) + \frac{1}{C_1} \int i_2(t)\,dt \right]$$
$$- R_3 i_4(t)$$

Loop #3

$$-e_2(t) = -\frac{1}{C_2} \int i_1(t)\,dt$$
$$+ \left[R_4 i_3(t) + L\frac{di_3(t)}{dt} + \frac{1}{C_2} \int i_3(t)\,dt \right]$$
$$- L\frac{di_4(t)}{dt}$$

Loop #4

$$0 = -R_3 i_2(t) - L\frac{di_3(t)}{dt}$$
$$+ \left[R_3 i_4(t) + L\frac{di_4(t)}{dt} + R_5 i_4(t) \right]$$
$$- R_5 i_5(t)$$

Loop #5

$$0 = -R_5 i_4(t) + \left[R_5 i_5(t) + \frac{1}{C_3} \int i_5(t)\, dt \right]$$

Example 3–2　　For this example consider Fig. 3–5. Writing the required loop equations we have

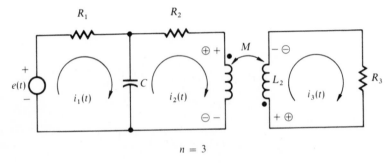

$$n = 3$$

FIGURE 3–5

Loop #1

$$e(t) - R_1 i_1(t) - \frac{1}{C} \int i_1(t)\, dt + \frac{1}{C} \int i_2(t)\, dt = 0$$

Loop #2

$$-\frac{1}{C} \int i_2(t)\, dt + \frac{1}{C} \int i_1(t)\, dt - R_2 i_2(t) - L_1 \frac{di_2(t)}{dt}$$
$$- M\frac{di_3(t)}{dt} = 0$$

Loop #3

$$-L_2 \frac{di_3(t)}{dt} - M\frac{di_2(t)}{dt} - R_3 i_3(t) = 0$$

These equations tell us we will have to modify Eq. (3–3) to include induced voltages, hence,

$$\sum_{m=1}^{M} [e_m(t) \text{ of loop } n]$$
$$= -\sum v_k(i_j) + \sum v_k(i_n) \pm \sum v_{MT}(i_q) \qquad \textbf{(3–4)}$$

where $v_{MT}(i_q)$ is the mutually induced voltage due to current i_q.

Since the loop equations contain loop currents it can be generally stated that loop equations are written if one is solving for currents. Later we will use this criterion as an aid to help us decide whether to use loop analysis or some other method when analyzing a circuit.

3–3 Nodal Analysis

Nodal analysis employs: (1) Kirchhoff's current law, which states: *the algebraic sum of all currents into a node is zero*; and (2) simultaneous equations, *which require n unknown quantities to have n equations*. A node is the junction of two or more components. In nodal analysis the currents are summed at these nodes except for those nodes which have a known voltage generator source that is common to the reference node, such as the input voltage e_{in} of Fig. 3–6 and the node which is chosen as a reference

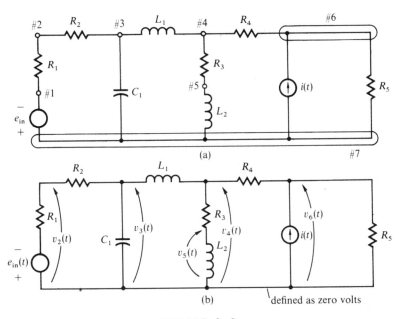

FIGURE 3–6

node. The reference node is arbitrary in choice, but as we shall see some choices are more convenient than others. Also, the currents are written in terms of the voltages causing them, therefore, if one wished to solve for an unknown voltage appearing at a node then nodal analysis should generally be used.

To demonstrate some of the concepts mentioned here consider Fig. 3–6(a) which shows the nodes of a circuit. Figure 3–6(b) shows the unknown nodal voltage associated with each node. Node #7 was chosen as the reference node, that is node #7 is the node from which all the other nodal voltages are referenced. Then the voltage at node #7 is defined to be zero. The reason for selecting node #7 as the reference node is because it had the most components common to it. Notice node #1 has the nodal voltage $-e_{in}$ and this nodal voltage, unlike the others, is a known, hence, we can eliminate having to write an equation for this node. A very important point is the polarities of the unknown nodal voltages $v_2, v_3, v_4, v_5,$ and v_6. They are arbitrarily chosen just as were the loop current directions in loop analysis.

Now let us sum the currents at each node. We will arbitrarily state that those currents entering a node are positive and those leaving are negative for this textbook. Then at

Node #2:   (current through R_1) + (current through R_2) = 0

If the current flowing through R_1 is assumed to be into node #2 it is positive and has a magnitude of

$$(\text{current through } R_1) = i_{R_1}(t) = \frac{\text{Voltage across } R_1}{R_1} = \frac{v_{R_1}(t)}{R_1}$$

Now, the voltage across R_1 must be such that the greatest potential is on the side of the component which the current enters and the least potential on the side which the current leaves, for this potential difference forces the current in that direction assumed. Hence, what we are doing is *assuming a current direction through the component and once that direction is assumed we are writing the potential difference across the component such as to make that assumption true.* Therefore, v_{R_1} = voltage across R_1 = highest potential − lowest potential = $[-e_{in}(t) - v_2(t)]$, where the algebraic sign of each voltage is carried. Then the current i_{R_1} is

$$i_{R_1}(t) = \frac{-e_{in}(t) - v_2(t)}{R_1} \tag{3-5}$$

Notice the highest potential has a negative sign, which must be considered. What if we would have chosen i_{R_1} to be leaving the junction? Then

$$i_{R_1}(t) = \frac{v_2(t) - [-e_{in}(t)]}{R_1} \tag{3-6}$$

Likewise, for the current through R_2 we have: if i_{R_2} is leaving the node

$$i_{R_2}(t) = \frac{v_2(t) - v_3(t)}{R_2} \tag{3-7}$$

and if i_{R_2} is entering the node

$$i_{R_2}(t) = \frac{v_3(t) - v_2(t)}{R_2} \tag{3-8}$$

Then let us sum the currents at node #2 *assuming* all currents enter the node. From Eqs. (3–5) and (3–8)

$$i_{R_1}(t) + i_{R_2}(t) = 0 = \frac{-e_{in}(t) - v_2(t)}{R_1} + \frac{v_3(t) - v_2(t)}{R_2} \qquad (3\text{–}9)$$

If we would have chosen to say i_{R_2} was leaving we would have from Eqs. (3–5) and (3–7)

$$i_{R_1}(t) - i_{R_2}(t) = 0 = \frac{-e_{in}(t) - v_2(t)}{R_1} - \frac{v_2(t) - v_3(t)}{R_2} \qquad (3\text{–}10)$$

Clearing the negative sign of Eq. (3–10) we have

$$i_{R_1}(t) - i_{R_2}(t) = \frac{-e_{in}(t) - v_2(t)}{R_1} + \frac{v_3(t) - v_2(t)}{R_2} \qquad (3\text{–}11)$$

which yields the same equations as (3–9). Therefore, to reiterate, we can state it makes *no difference* as to the assumed current directions through a component so long as *once the direction is chosen the voltages are written accordingly*. For a check assume i_{R_1} leaving the node and use Eq. (3–6) and see if the results change. Then for the nodes we have:

Node #2 $0 = \dfrac{-e_{in}(t) - v_2(t)}{R_1} + \dfrac{v_3(t) - v_2(t)}{R_2}$

Node #3   (abitrarily assume all currents into node)

$$0 = \frac{\left[\begin{array}{l}\text{voltage across } R_2 \text{ written} \\ \text{such as to require its current} \\ \text{to flow into node } \#3\end{array}\right]}{R_2} + C_1 \frac{d}{dt}\left[\begin{array}{l}\text{voltage across } C_1 \text{ written} \\ \text{such as to require its current} \\ \text{to flow into node } \#3\end{array}\right]$$

$$+ \frac{1}{L}\int \left[\begin{array}{l}\text{voltage across } L_1 \text{ written} \\ \text{such as to require its current} \\ \text{to flow into node } \#3\end{array}\right] dt, \text{ hence}$$

$$0 = \frac{v_2(t) - v_3(t)}{R_2} + C_1 \frac{d}{dt}[\underset{\underset{\text{voltage at node } \#7}{\uparrow}}{0} - v_3(t)] + \frac{1}{L_1}\int [v_4(t) - v_3(t)]\, dt$$

which can be written

$$0 = \frac{v_2(t) - v_3(t)}{R_2} \underset{\underset{\text{states: current is leaving node } \#3}{\uparrow}}{\mp} C_1 \frac{dv_3(t)}{dt} + \frac{1}{L_1}\int [v_4(t) - v_3(t)]\, dt$$

Node #4   (arbitrarily assume all currents into the node)

$$0 = \frac{1}{L_1}\int [v_3(t) - v_4(t)]\, dt + \frac{v_5(t) - v_4(t)}{R_3} + \frac{v_6(t) - v_4(t)}{R_4}$$

or by factoring a minus sign

$$0 = \underset{\underset{\text{states: current is leaving node } \#4}{\uparrow}}{\mp \frac{1}{L_1}\int [v_4(t) - v_3(t)]\, dt} + \frac{v_5(t) - v_4(t)}{R_3} \mp \frac{v_4(t) - v_6(t)}{R_4} = 0$$

Node #5   (arbitrarily assume all currents leaving the node)

$$-\frac{v_5(t) - v_4(t)}{R_3} - \frac{1}{L_2} \int [v_4(t) - \underset{\uparrow}{0}] \, dt = 0$$

voltage at node #7

Multiply through by negative one

$$\underset{\uparrow}{+} \frac{v_4(t) - v_5(t)}{R_3} + \frac{1}{L_2} \int [0 - v_4(t)] \, dt = 0$$

states current is entering node #5

Node #6   (arbitrarily assume all currents leave the node: note $i(t)$'s direction is mandatory)

voltage at node #7

$$-\frac{v_6(t) - v_4(t)}{R_4} + i(t) - \frac{v_6(t) - 0}{R_5} = 0$$

Multiply through by negative one

$$+\frac{v_4(t) - v_6(t)}{R_4} + i(t) + \frac{0 - v_6(t)}{R_5} = 0$$

states: currents are entering node #6

In order to fix our concepts more firmly let us consider another example where the nodal equations will be written under different current direction assumptions. Then we shall see again that our assumptions can be purely arbitrary.

Example 3–3   Consider the circuits of Fig. 3–7. Writing the nodal equations for Fig. 3–7 we have:

First Case: Assume all component currents to enter the nodes.

Node A:

$$-i_1(t) + \frac{0 - v_A(t)}{R_1} + C\frac{d}{dt}[v_B(t) - v_A(t)]$$

$$+ \frac{[v_B(t) - v_A(t)]}{R_2} - i_2(t) = 0$$

Node B:

$$C\frac{d}{dt}[v_A(t) - v_B(t)] + \frac{v_A(t) - v_B(t)}{R_2} + i_2(t)$$

$$+ \frac{e_1(t) - v_B(t)}{R_3} + \frac{1}{L_1} \int [v_C(t) - v_B(t)] \, dt = 0$$

Node C:

$$\frac{1}{L} \int [v_B(t) - v_C(t)] \, dt + \frac{-e_2(t) - v_C(t)}{R_4} = 0$$

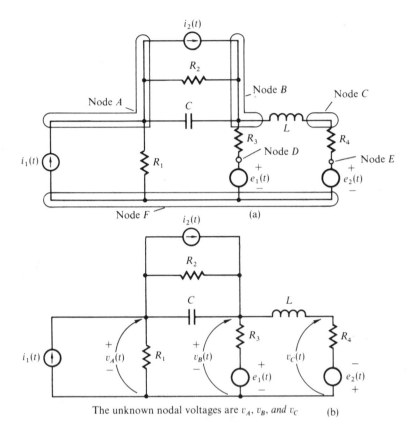

FIGURE 3–7

Second Case: Assume all component currents to leave the nodes.

Node A:

$$-i_1(t) - \frac{v_A(t) - 0}{R_1} - C\frac{d}{dt}[v_A(t) - v_B(t)]$$

$$- \frac{v_A(t) - v_B(t)}{R_2} - i_2(t) = 0$$

Node B:

$$-C\frac{d}{dt}[v_B(t) - v_A(t)] - \frac{v_B(t) - v_A(t)}{R_2} + i_2(t)$$

$$- \frac{v_B(t) - e_1(t)}{R_3} - \frac{1}{L}\int [v_B(t) - v_C(t)]\,dt = 0$$

Node C:

$$-\frac{1}{L} \int [v_\mathrm{C}(t) - v_\mathrm{B}(t)]\, dt - \frac{v_\mathrm{C}(t) - [-e_2(t)]}{R_4} = 0$$

Now, to show that we have the exact same equations for the first and second case let us compare each node equation after we have dropped the zero term in node A equation and factored a sign here and there. Thus for the first case:

Node A:

$$-i_1(t) - \frac{v_\mathrm{A}(t)}{R_1} + C\frac{d}{dt}[v_\mathrm{B}(t) - v_\mathrm{A}(t)]$$

$$+ \frac{v_\mathrm{B}(t) - v_\mathrm{A}(t)}{R_2} - i_2(t) = 0$$

Node B:

$$C\frac{d}{dt}[v_\mathrm{A}(t) - v_\mathrm{B}(t)] + \frac{[v_\mathrm{A}(t) - v_\mathrm{B}(t)]}{R_2} + i_2(t)$$

$$+ \frac{e_1(t) - v_\mathrm{B}(t)}{R_3} + \frac{1}{L}\int [v_\mathrm{C}(t) - v_\mathrm{B}(t)]\, dt = 0$$

and

Node C:

$$\frac{1}{L}\int [v_\mathrm{B}(t) - v_\mathrm{C}(t)]\, dt - \frac{v_\mathrm{C}(t) + e_2(t)}{R_4} = 0$$

which is the same set of equations as the second case.

3–4 Thevenin's Theorem

It may have been noticed that current sources were avoided in loop analysis. This is because of some minor difficulties which could arise; however, these problems can be completely overcome by converting the current source to an *equivalent* voltage source. To convert a current source into an equivalent voltage source we shall apply Thevenin's theorem. Be certain to understand that this conversion is not absolutely necessary, but rather, it just simplifies the analysis in some ways. Examples of converting and not converting the current source will be given and then each can make his own mind up as to which is the more suitable for his application.

Thevenin's theorem generally states: any network containing linear (passive and active) components can be converted into an equivalent two-terminal network consisting of a voltage source e_oc and series resistor R_T. The voltage source's magnitude and polarity e_oc are determined by finding the open-circuited voltage of the circuit, which is the voltage existing across the terminals when the network to be converted is removed from the rest of the network [see Fig. 3–8(b)]. The resistor R_T is the resistance (or

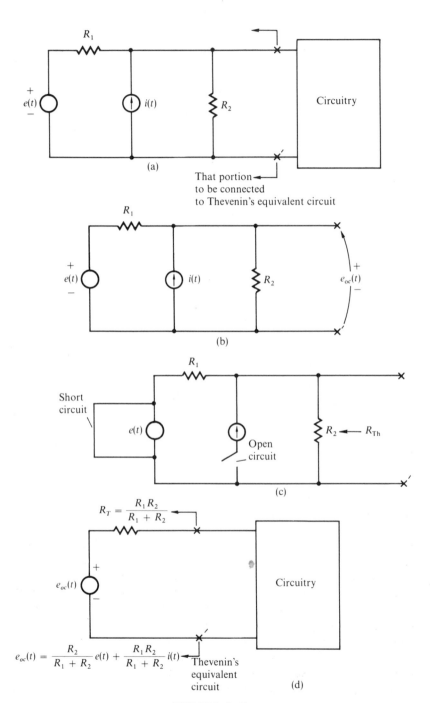

FIGURE 3–8

131

impedance) looking back into the circuit from the open-circuited terminals with all electrical sources replaced by their internal resistance. These electrical sources are open-circuited if they are current sources and short-circuited if they are voltage sources [see Fig. 3–8(c)].

To calculate e_{oc} and R_T we shall use Fig. 3–8(b) and (c) respectively. Hence, writing a nodal equation for Fig. 3–8(b) and solving for e_{oc} we have

$$\frac{e(t) - e_{oc}(t)}{R_1} + i(t) - \frac{e_{oc}(t)}{R_2} = 0$$

from which we get

$$\frac{e(t)}{R_1} + i(t) = \left(\frac{1}{R_1} + \frac{1}{R_2}\right) e_{oc}(t) = \frac{R_1 + R_2}{R_1 R_2} e_{oc}(t)$$

or

$$e_{oc}(t) = \frac{R_2}{R_1 + R_2} e(t) + \frac{R_1 R_2}{R_1 + R_2} i(t) \qquad (3\text{--}12)$$

where $e(t)$ and $i(t)$ are knowns.

To determine R_T we use Fig. 3–8(c); hence

$$R_T = \frac{R_1 R_2}{R_1 + R_2} \qquad (3\text{--}13)$$

Then our equivalent circuit is shown in Fig. 3–8(d) where the values of $e_{oc}(t)$ and R_T are given in Eqs. (3–12) and (3–13) respectively.

Let us next convert a current source to an equivalent voltage source. Consider the current source shown in Fig. 3–9(a) where the equivalent current source is shown in Fig. 3–9(d).

To generalize from Fig. 3–9(a) and (d): For one to convert a current source to a voltage source simply find the open-circuit voltage e_{oc}, which can be found by multiplying the current i and shunt resistance R_s. Then put the shunt resistor R_s in series with the voltage source e_{oc}.

Let us now use loop analysis to analyze a circuit containing a current source. We will first analyze the circuit without converting the current source to a voltage source. The loop currents of Fig. 3–10(a), i_1 and i_2, represent the true currents through R_1 and R_2 respectively, and the true current through C is $i_1(t) - i_2(t)$. The current through R_3 is $i_2(t) - i_3(t)$; however, i_3 is i so the true current through R_3 is $i_2(t) - i(t)$. Since i is the current supplied by a current source and is a known variable it need not be solved for, therefore, if one did not wish to convert the current source to a voltage source the circuit would appear as Fig. 3–10(b). Notice we *must* say i_3 equals i rather than i equals i_3. This is true since i is a known current source and *demands* that the current it supplies have a magnitude of $|i|$ and

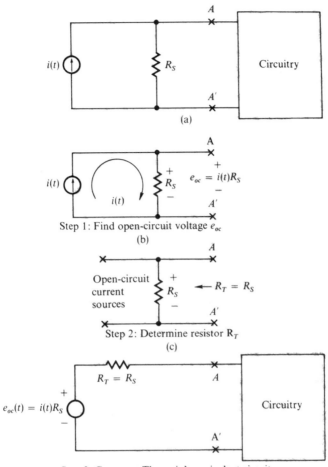

(a)

Step 1: Find open-circuit voltage e_{oc}
(b)

Step 2: Determine resistor R_T
(c)

Step 3: Construct Thevenin's equivalent circuit
(d)

FIGURE 3–9

a direction as indicated. Since i is known this would eliminate one required equation from our n simultaneous equations, or we now need $(n - 1)$ equations. Writing the loop equations of Fig. 3–10(b) we have

Case 1

Loop #1 $e(t) - R_1 i_1(t) - \dfrac{1}{C} \displaystyle\int i_1(t)\, dt + \dfrac{1}{C} \displaystyle\int i_2(t)\, dt = 0$

Loop #2 $\dfrac{1}{C} \displaystyle\int i_1(t)\, dt - R_2 i_2(t) - R_3 i_2(t) + R_3 i(t) = 0$

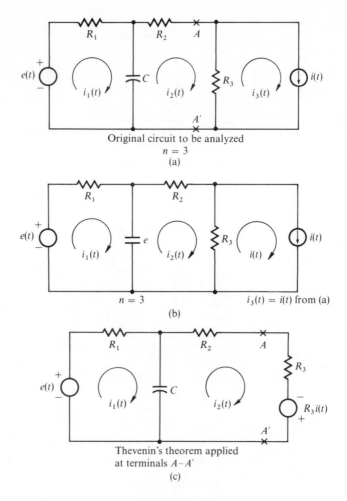

Original circuit to be analyzed
n = 3
(a)

n = 3 $i_3(t) = i(t)$ from (a)
(b)

Thevenin's theorem applied
at terminals $A-A'$
(c)

FIGURE 3–10

Notice a loop equation was not written for the loop containing i. Again, this is because i is a known, therefore we need not write an equation to solve for it, or more simply from mathematics we have two unknowns, i_1 and i_2, and as a result we need two equations to solve for them.

If we chose to convert the current source we would open the circuit at A-A′ and find the equivalent voltage source as shown in Fig. 3–10(c). Writing the loop equations we have

Case 2

Loop #1 $\quad e(t) - R_1 i_1(t) - \dfrac{1}{C} \displaystyle\int i_1(t)\, dt + \dfrac{1}{C} \displaystyle\int i_2(t)\, dt = 0$

Loop #2 $\quad \dfrac{1}{C} \displaystyle\int i_1(t)\, dt - R_2 i_2(t) - R_3 i_2(t) + R_3 i(t) = 0$

which is the same as before. Notice the difference in the current through R_3 in Fig. 3–10(b) and (c). The current $i_2(t) - i_3(t)$ in Fig. 3–10(b) is the true value, while i_2 of Fig. 3–10(c) is not the actual current flowing in R_3. Remember, anything after points A–A' (to the right) is equivalent circuitry and therefore does not necessarily represent actual physical components; that is, R_3 of Fig. 3–10(c) is R_T, which has a magnitude equal to R_3. The current i_2 in R_2 is the true current in both Fig. 3–10(b) and (c). It is seen that cases 1 and 2 yield the same resultant equations.

3–5 Norton's Theorem

As in the loop analysis when a current source is present we sometimes choose to convert that current source to an equivalent voltage source; similarly, in nodal analysis we may wish to convert a voltage source to an equivalent current source. The only time this is usually an advantage is if the voltage source is not referenced to the reference node of the circuit. To convert a voltage source to a current source Norton's theorem is used.

To state Norton's theorem in a general way we may say: any network containing passive and active components can be converted into an equivalent two-terminal network consisting of an equivalent current source i_{sc} and a shunt resistor R_N. The current source's magnitude and direction are determined by finding the short-circuit current, i_{sc}, which is the current that flows when the network to be converted is short circuited at the terminals that are formed by removing it from the rest of the network. The direction must be consistent with the *direction of the supply network* [see Fig. 3–11(b)]. The resistor R_N is the resistance (or impedance) looking back into the circuit from the terminals formed by separating the network to be converted from the remainder of the network. As in Thevenin's theorem, when finding R_N, all electrical sources are to be replaced by their internal resistance and these electrical sources open-circuited if they are current sources and short-circuited if they are voltage sources [see Fig. 3–11(c)]. The equivalent circuit is formed by putting the short-circuit current source i_{sc} and R_N in parallel. This equivalent circuit is connected to the remaining circuitry, as shown in Fig. 3–11(d).

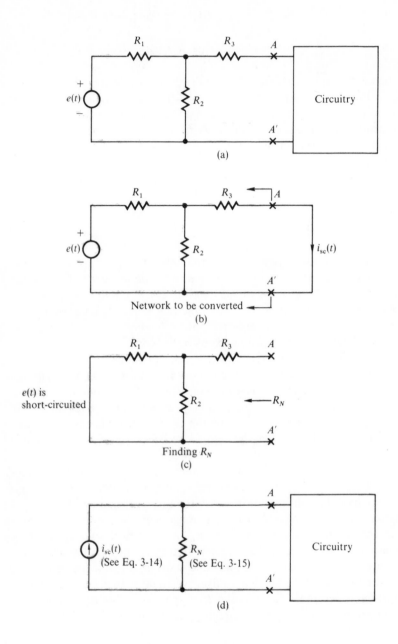

FIGURE 3–11

To determine i_{sc} consider Fig. 3–11(b). Thus

$$i_{sc}(t) = \frac{R_2}{R_2 + R_3} \cdot \frac{e(t)(R_2 + R_3)}{R_1 R_2 + R_1 R_3 + R_2 R_3} = \frac{R_2 e(t)}{R_1 R_2 + R_1 R_3 + R_2 R_3}$$

(3–14)

The resistance R_N is

$$R_N = R_3 + \frac{R_1 R_2}{R_1 + R_2} = \frac{R_1 R_2 + R_1 R_3 + R_2 R_3}{R_1 + R_2}$$

(3–15)

Let us now convert a voltage source, with its internal series resistance R_g, to an equivalent current source. Consider Fig. 3–12(a), which is the

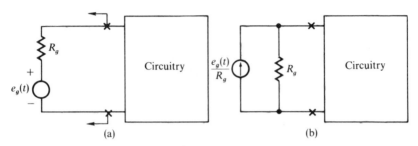

(a)   (b)

FIGURE 3–12

voltage source to be converted, and then Fig. 3–12(b), which is the equivalent current source. From Fig. 3–12(a) it is seen that

$$i_{sc}(t) = \frac{e_g(t)}{R_g} \quad \text{and} \quad R_N = R_g$$

We shall now see where we may want to apply Norton's theorem in nodal analysis. We will write the nodal equations for Fig. 3–13(a). Thus

Node A: $\dfrac{e_1(t) - v_A(t)}{R_1} - i(t) - \dfrac{v_A(t)}{R_2} + \left[\begin{matrix}\text{The current flowing} \\ \text{through } R_3\end{matrix}\right] = 0$

We see we have a problem in writing the current flowing through R_3 since the voltage source is not referenced to the common node. If we convert that voltage source and the series resistor R_3 into an equivalent current source we would have the circuit of Fig. 3–13(b).

Writing the nodal equations from Fig. 3–8(b) we get:

Node A: $\dfrac{e_1(t) - v_A(t)}{R_1} - i(t) = \dfrac{v_A(t)}{R_2} + \dfrac{e_2(t)}{R_3} + \dfrac{v_B(t) - v_A(t)}{R_3} = 0$

Node B: $-\dfrac{e_2(t)}{R_3} + \dfrac{v_A(t) - v_B(t)}{R_3} - \dfrac{v_B(t)}{R_4} = 0$

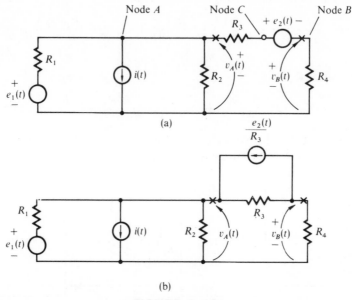

FIGURE 3–13

As demonstrated the nodal equations are easier to write now. If we would have wanted to we could have converted all voltage sources to current sources.

Next, let's see how we could write the nodal equations *without* converting the voltage source. To do this we will assume a current i_3 to flow in R_3 in the direction toward node A of Fig. 3–13(a). Then we will write a loop equation, being careful to include only nodal voltages, v_A, v_B, the voltage source e_2, and the product of $R_3 i_3(t)$ in the loop. We do this so as to be able to write the current equation as a function of known voltages, unknown nodal voltages, and the components of that portion of the circuit. Hence, writing the loop equation we get,

$$v_A(t) + R_3 i_3(t) - e_2(t) - v_B(t) = 0$$

Solving for i_3 we find

$$i_3(t) = \frac{e_2(t) + v_B(t) - v_A(t)}{R_3} \tag{3–16}$$

Of course if we had chosen to say the current was traveling toward node B we would have found

$$i_3(t) = -\frac{[e_2(t) + v_B(t)] - v_A(t)}{R_3} = \frac{v_A(t) - [e_2(t) + v_B(t)]}{R_3} \tag{3–17}$$

Look at Eqs. (3–16) and (3–17) closely. They state that e_2 and v_B have an additive effect, and since they are in series this appears to verify the physical case. Then we could have considered a nodal voltage to appear at node C, which would be

$$v_C(t) = e_2(t) + v_B(t) \qquad (3\text{–}18)$$

Writing the nodal equations from Fig. 3–13(a) and using v_A, v_B, and v_C nodal voltages we have

Node A: $\dfrac{e_1(t) - v_A(t)}{R_1} - i(t) - \dfrac{v_A(t)}{R_2} + \dfrac{v_C(t) - v_A(t)}{R_3} = 0$

Substituting Eq. (3–18) for v_C we have

Node A: $\dfrac{e_1(t) - v_A(t)}{R_1} - i(t) - \dfrac{v_A(t)}{R_2} + \dfrac{[e_2(t) + v_B(t)] - v_A(t)}{R_3} = 0$

and

Node B: $\dfrac{v_A(t) - v_C(t)}{R_3} - \dfrac{v_B(t)}{R_4} = 0$

Again substituting Eq. (3–18) for v_C we have

Node B: $\dfrac{v_A(t) - [e_2(t) + v_B(t)]}{R_3} - \dfrac{v_B(t)}{R_4} = 0$

These equations agree with those previously written for nodes A and B.

To gain some practice let us consider two examples. For these examples we shall write the nodal equations both ways: (1) by converting the voltage sources in question, those not referenced to the reference node, to equivalent current sources; and (2) by writing those same equations without converting them.

Example 3–4   The circuit to be analyzed is shown in Fig. 3–14(a). Let us begin by writing the nodal equations of Fig. 3–14(b). Hence,

Node A:

$$i_1(t) - \frac{v_A(t)}{R_1} + \frac{1}{L} \int [v_B(t) - v_A(t)]\, dt$$
$$+ \frac{v_C(t) - v_A(t)}{R_2} = 0$$

Node B:

$$\frac{1}{L} \int [v_A(t) - v_B(t)]\, dt + \underbrace{\frac{v_A(t) - v_C(t)}{R_2}}$$

The current through R_2 is the same current as the one through e_1.

$$+ \frac{[-e_2(t)] - v_B(t)}{R_3} - C\frac{d}{dt} v_B(t) + \frac{e_3(t) - v_B(t)}{R_4} = 0$$

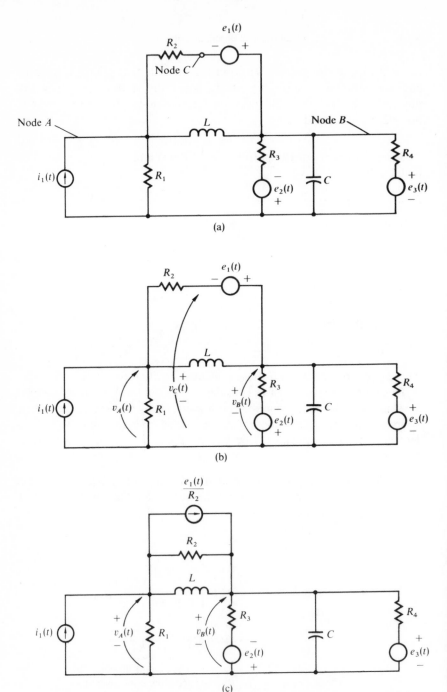

FIGURE 3–14 (a) Circuit to be analyzed; (b) The circuit of (a) with unknown node voltages labeled; (c) The circuit of (a) with voltage source e_1 converted to equivalent current source

Node C: We experience some difficulty here because of the voltage source e_1.

To find a suitable solution for node C let us recall that for n unknowns we need n equations. Now, we have three unknowns, v_A, v_B, and v_C, and to this point only two equations. However, we can gain our third by writing one of the node voltages v_C in terms of another node voltage v_B. Then

$$v_C(t) + e_1(t) - v_B(t) = 0$$

or

$$v_C(t) = v_B(t) - e_1(t) \tag{3-19}$$

Substituting this equation in those written at nodes A and B we will then have two unknowns and two equations. Thus,

Node A:

$$i_1(t) - \frac{v_A(t)}{R_1} + \frac{1}{L} \int [v_B(t) - v_A(t)]\, dt$$

$$+ \frac{[v_B(t) - e_1(t)] - v_A(t)}{R_2} = 0 \tag{3-20a}$$

Node B:

$$\frac{1}{L} \int [v_A(t) - v_B(t)]\, dt + \frac{v_A(t) - [v_B(t) - e_1(t)]}{R_2}$$

$$+ \frac{[-e_2(t)] - v_B(t)}{R_3} - C\frac{v_B(t)}{dt} + \frac{e_3(t) - v_B(t)}{R_4} = 0$$

$$\tag{3-20b}$$

These are the necessary simultaneous equations for this circuit. Return to our previous analysis of Fig. 3–13(a), where no conversions were performed, and see that the same technique was used in each case.

To analyze Fig. 3–14(a) again, but now converting the voltage source e_1 to a current source, we consider Fig. 3–14(c). It should be realized that the current direction of the equivalent current source is as shown since the current supplied from e_1 must be in that direction. Also, realize we could have converted all voltage sources to equivalent current sources and analyzed the circuit, but this is just some extra steps to take; however, just for the "fun" of it the reader might perform this sort of analysis to verify that he gets the same results. Analyzing Fig. 3–14(c) we get,

Node A:

$$i_1(t) - \frac{v_A(t)}{R_1} + \frac{1}{L} \int [v_B(t) - v_A(t)] \, dt$$

$$+ \underbrace{\frac{v_B(t) - v_A(t)}{R_2} - \frac{e_1(t)}{R_2}}_{\substack{\text{Put under common} \\ \text{denominator}}} = 0$$

Node B:

$$\overbrace{\frac{e_1(t)}{R_2}}^{\substack{\text{Put under common} \\ \text{denominator}}} + \frac{v_A(t) - v_B(t)}{R_2} + \frac{[-e_2(t)] - v_B(t)}{R_3}$$

$$- C\frac{dv_B(t)}{dt} + \frac{e_3(t) - v_B(t)}{R_4} = 0$$

Put those terms labeled "under common denominator" and compare with Eqs. (3–20) and it is seen they are the same equations.

Example 3–5   For this example consider Fig. 3–15.
        Analyzing Fig. 3–15(a) first, and realizing

$$v_C(t) = e_2(t) + v_D(t) \qquad (3–21)$$

which was obtained by writing the proper loop equation. Then

Node A:

$$\frac{e_1(t) - v_A(t)}{R_1} - C\frac{dv_A(t)}{dt} + \frac{1}{L} \int [v_B(t) - v_A(t)] \, dt = 0$$

Node B:

$$\frac{1}{L} \int [v_A(t) - v_B(t)] \, dt + \frac{[e_2(t) + v_D(t)] - v_B(t)}{R_2} = 0$$

Node D:

$$\frac{v_B(t) - [e_2(t) + v_D(t)]}{R_2} - \frac{v_D(t)}{R_3} + i(t) = 0$$

where Eq. (3–21) was used in place of v_C. Writing the nodal equation from Fig. 3–15(b) we get:

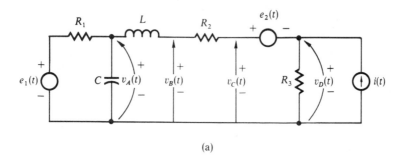

(a)

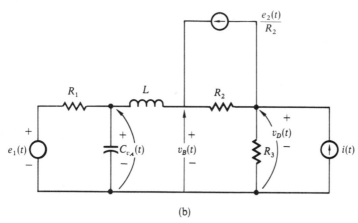

(b)

FIGURE 3–15   (a) Circuit with the unknown nodal voltages v_A, v_B, v_C, v_D labeled; (b) Circuit of figure (a) with equivalent current source

Node A:

$$\frac{e_1(t) - v_A(t)}{R_1} - C\frac{dv_A(t)}{dt} + \frac{1}{L}\int [v_B(t) - v_A(t)]\, dt = 0$$

Node B:

$$\frac{1}{L}\int [v_A(t) - v_B(t)]\, dt + \underbrace{\frac{e_2(t)}{R_2} + \frac{v_D(t) - v_B(t)}{R_2}}_{\substack{\text{Put under common} \\ \text{denominator}}} = 0$$

Node D: $$-\frac{e_2(t)}{R_2} + \frac{v_B(t) - v_D(t)}{R_2} - \frac{v_D(t)}{R_3} + i(t) = 0$$

Compare these equations with those preceding to verify they are the same.

3–6　Summary

To summarize, we have two basic methods of analysis: (1) loop and (2) nodal. The loop method is performed by summing voltages within a closed path or loop. The voltages are written in terms of the voltage sources and the passive component voltages (v_R, v_C, and v_L), where the component voltages are written in terms of the loop current causing them. As a result of the manner in which the component voltages are written the loop current method is *usually* used if one is solving for an unknown current. The nodal method is accomplished by summing currents at a node, where the currents are written in terms of current sources and the nodal potentials producing the currents. Since the currents are written in terms of nodal voltages the nodal method of anaysis is *usually* used if one wishes to solve for a voltage.

The procedure of each method is offered in outline form here.

LOOP METHOD

1. Assume loop currents in each widow.
   - (a) If the wrong direction was chosen the final numerical answer will be negative. This is to be demonstrated later.
   - (b) If only one loop current flows through a component it is the true current, otherwise the true current is the superposition of all the loop currents flowing through the component.
2. To determine the number (l) of loop equations required count the loops (L), subtract the number of current sources (b). Hence,
   $$\text{Loop equations required} = L - b \equiv l$$
3. Sum the voltages in the loop traveling in the same direction as the loop current.
   - (a) An algebraic $+$ is assigned to those voltages which one goes from $-$ to $+$ when traveling through them. An algebraic $-$ is given to those voltages when one goes from $+$ to $-$.
   - (b) If a troublesome current source is present it may be replaced by an equivalent voltage source using Thevinin's theorem. However, most of the time this is not necessary.
4. Solve for the desired unknown loop current, or currents.

NODAL METHOD

1. Assign nodal voltages at each node that is *unknown*.
   - (a) The nodal voltages are referenced with respect to a reference node and this node is assigned as zero volts potential.
   - (b) The polarity of the nodal voltages is assumed and if chosen wrong the final numerical answer will be negative. This is a point to be shown later.

2. To determine the nodal equations required (n) count the nodes (N) then subtract the number of known voltage sources (C). Then subtract one for the reference node. Hence,

$$n = N - C - 1 = N - (C + 1)$$

3. Sum the currents at the nodes where unknown nodal voltages exist.

   (a) It is purely arbitrary as to whether we decide if a current is leaving or entering a node, unless the current is from a current source. If a current is entering the node it is said to be positive and gets a $+$. For currents leaving a node a $-$ is given.

   (b) Troublesome voltage sources may be converted to equivalent current sources using Norton's theorem.

4. Solve for the desired unknown nodal-voltage or voltages.

4 Laplace Transforms

4-1 Introduction

We are now capable of writing the necessary differential equations to mathematically describe the dynamic behavior of a circuit. Our next undertaking will be to develop a means to solve those equations. To solve a differential equation the classical approach of solving the differential equations could be taken, or the operational mathematics (derivatives and integrals) can be transformed into algebraic mathematics. As an example of what was just said suppose we had the following differential equation

$$2\frac{d}{dx}y(x) + 4y(x) = 10$$

Now suppose that we developed a *mathematical transform* which would transform the operation d/dx into some algebraic term, say s. Then the equation would be transformed to

$$2sy + 4y = 10$$

We may now solve for y

$$y = \frac{10}{2s + 4} \qquad (4\text{-}1)$$

This method of transformation is the approach we shall take. The specific transformation we will develop is Laplace transforms.

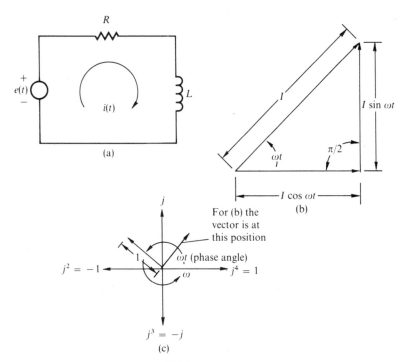

FIGURE 4-1

Using transforms is not a new subject to us. We have used them in ac circuit analysis. To demonstrate, consider Fig. 4–1(a). From Fig. 4–1(a) let us solve for the current i by writing a loop equation. Hence,

$$e(t) - Ri(t) - L\frac{di(t)}{dt} = 0$$

or

$$e(t) = Ri(t) + L\frac{di(t)}{dt} \tag{4-2}$$

If e (the excitation) is sinusoidal, then i (the response) is also sinusoidal. Now, let us suppose that $i(t) = I \sin \omega t$ where I is the amplitude. Then from Eq. (4–2)

$$e(t) = R[I \sin \omega t] + L\frac{d}{dt}[I \sin \omega t]$$

$$e(t) = R(I \sin \omega t) + \omega L(I \cos \omega t) \tag{4-3}$$

Figure 4–1(b) illustrates the physical position of ($I \cos \omega t$) and ($I \sin \omega t$) with respect to each other. Let us use another method to differentiate between the horizontal and vertical axes rather than ($I \cos \omega t$) and ($I \sin \omega t$). This method is illustrated in Fig. 4–1(c). We see in Fig. 4–1(c) that we have a unit vector, known as a phasor, rotating at a velocity of ω and at any time t the phase angle is ωt. Thus, the $\sin \omega t$ axis can be represented as j and $\cos \omega t$ as j^2. Equation (4–3) becomes $|E(j\omega)| \angle \theta' = jR\,I(j\omega) + \omega L j^2 I(j\omega)$, where $|E(j\omega)|$ and $I(j\omega)$ show that the quantities e and i are functions of $j\omega$ and θ' is the resultant angle of voltage $E(j\omega)$. Thus

$$|E(j\omega)| \angle \theta' = (R + j\omega)jI(j\omega) = (R + j\omega)I(j\omega)\angle \pi/2$$

since $j = 1 \angle \pi/2$. Thus

$$|E(j\omega)| \angle \theta = (R + j\omega L)I(j\omega) = RI(j\omega) + j\omega L I(j\omega) \qquad \textbf{(4-4)}$$

where $\theta = \theta' - \pi/2$. Comparing Eq. (4–2) with Eq. (4–4) we see we have transformed from the time plane (t-plane) to the frequency plane (ω-plane). In doing so we transformed d/dt into $j\omega$. Notice we went from operational mathematics to algebraic, and to demonstrate the dependence of the voltage e and current i on ω we write $E(j\omega)$ and $I(j\omega)$. We write the voltage and current in upper case as another means to show we have transformed e and i out of the t-plane and into the ω-plane.

From Eq. (4–4) we may solve for I as was done for y in Eq. (4–1). Thus

$$I(j\omega) = \frac{E(j\omega)\angle \theta}{R + j\omega L} = \frac{E}{R + j\omega L} \qquad \textbf{(4-5)}$$

from Eqs. 4–3 and 4–4, where $E(j\omega)\angle \theta \equiv E$, i.e., $\theta \equiv 0°$. If we had a means to take Eq. (4–5) and transform back to the t-plane we would have a means to solve a differential equation, but in a sinusoidal circuit analysis Eq. (4–5) is sufficient. However, in Laplace transforms we will be able to transform back to the t-plane.

As a last example of a transform consider the mathematical operation of multiplication

$$c = a \cdot b$$

This operation may be transformed to a simpler operation of addition by taking the logarithm of both sides of the equation, thus

$$\log c = \log a + \log b$$

To find the value of c the value of log a and log b are simply looked up in a table. Their sums form log c and then c is determined by looking up the antilogarithm of log c.

Laplace transforms may also be paralleled to the logarithm example just given. It takes the operational mathematics and transforms it into algebraic mathematics, which is simpler to solve, and then the anti-Laplace transform is "looked up" in a set of transform tables for the solution.

4-2   Definition of Laplace Transform

Let the variable h be a function of the variable t (t may or may not be time, in this case it represents any independent variable), which is written as

$$h = h(t) \tag{4-6}$$

By definition, the Laplace transform, written $\mathcal{L}$, of $h(t)$ is

$$\mathcal{L}[h(t)] \equiv \int_0^\infty h(t)e^{-st}\, dt \tag{4-7}$$

where s = complex variable = $\sigma + j\omega$
  σ = variable on real axis
  ω = variable on the imaginary axis = $2\pi f$
  f = frequency

Notice from the limits of the integral we are integrating over positive values of the independent variable t. Upon integrating Eq. (4-7) and substituting in the limit values (0 and ∞) for t the variable s is the only variable remaining. Then the transformed function becomes a function of s, which is written as

$$\mathcal{L}[h(t)] = H(s) = \int_0^\infty h(t)e^{-st}\, dt \tag{4-8}$$

The lower-case letter h was changed to upper-case H to indicate that the function had been transformed. The functional notation $H(s)$ states that the transformed function H is now a function of s. Another way to view this notation is that we have transformed from dependence on t to s, or we have transformed h such that its independent variable is no longer t but now s. The convention in this text will be such that to indicate the Laplace transform has been performed lower-case letters will be changed to upper-case. Examples of this convention appear in Table 4–1.

To reiterate from Table 4–1 it is seen that regardless of the original

TABLE 4–1   *Laplace Transform Functional Notation*

Function	Laplace Transform Operation Indicated		Functional Notation		Defining Integral to Perform Transform
$f(x)$	$\mathcal{L}[f(x)]$	$=$	$F(s)$	$=$	$\int_0^\infty f(x)e^{-sx}\, dx$
$y(t)$	$\mathcal{L}[y(t)]$	$=$	$Y(s)$	$=$	$\int_0^\infty y(t)e^{-st}\, dt$
$g(f)$	$\mathcal{L}[g(f)]$	$=$	$G(s)$	$=$	$\int_0^\infty g(f)e^{-sf}\, df$
$h(y)$	$\mathcal{L}[h(y)]$	$=$	$H(s)$	$=$	$\int_0^\infty h(y)e^{-sy}\, dy$

independent variable the transformed dependent variable is a function of the independent variable s. This was pointed out in Eq. (4–8). This concept of transformation will be better shown by considering some actual transformations.

4–3   Laplace of Unit Step Function

The first specific function which we will transform is very basic and important. It appears so often that the symbol u is reserved to designate it. This function u, termed the Unit Step[1] function, is mathematically described as

$$u(t) = \begin{cases} 0 \text{ for } t < 0 \\ 1 \text{ for } t > 0 \end{cases} \tag{4-9}$$

where the Unit Step is unitless. Notice $t = 0$ is not defined; that is, $u(t)$ is discontinuous at $t = 0$. This "jump" allows us to describe a very real physical phenomena. Often we will have to analyze waveforms which are at one value and then jump to another value over some small amount of time, such as a pulse. Now, since nature does not change instantaneously there are always continuous values between when the change started and when it reached its final value; that is, the waveform is continuous. However, we may not know what this continuous waveform looks like if the change occurred too fast to measure. Also we may not care what values lie in this interval. Since the interval of change may be too small to give any practical consideration, we can many times ignore it by saying the interval *approached* zero (meaning it is too small to measure and/or be concerned about) and leave that interval undefined as shown in Fig. 4–2(a). If we

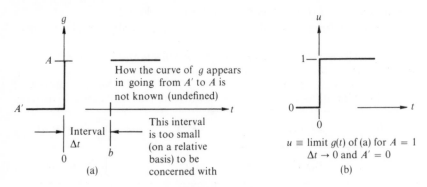

FIGURE 4–2

---

[1] Some texts define $u(t)$ as $u(t) = \begin{cases} 0 \text{ for } t < 0 \\ 1 \text{ for } t \geq 0 \end{cases}$. It is a matter of choice as to what one wishes to do with the function. For our purpose Eq. (4–9) is the better definition.

specially said that the interval of Fig. 4–2(a) was to approach zero duration ($\Delta t \longrightarrow 0$) and this was to be done by having b approach the origin, then we would have a "neighborhood" about $t = 0$ where we were not sure of the value of g. Since we are not sure of the value of g at $t = 0$ as we perform $\text{limit}_{\Delta t \to 0}\, g(t)$, of Fig. 4–2(a), then we will leave $t = 0$ as undefined, which means we will avoid that point. Notice as we perform $\text{limit}_{\Delta t \to 0}\, g(t)$ with $t = 0$ undefined we have defined $u(t)$ as written in Eq. (4–9). The Unit Step function is illustrated in Fig. 4–2(b) and is expressed as $\text{limit}_{\Delta t \to 0}\, g(t) = u(t)$.

The Laplace transform of the Unit Step function may be determined by applying Eq. (4–7), where $h(t) = u(t)$. Hence,

$$U(s) = \mathcal{L}[u(t)] = \int_0^\infty u(t) e^{-st}\, dt$$

Noticing that we are to integrate from $t = 0$, we might become concerned since $u(t)$ is not defined at that point. Recall from the definition of an integral that the lower limit is only approached as the limiting process is performed on the defining summation. That is,

$$\int_0^\infty h(t) e^{-st}\, dt = \int_0^\infty y(t)\, dt \equiv \lim_{\Delta t \to 0} \sum_{k=1}^\infty y(t_k)\, \Delta t$$

where $y(t) = h(t) e^{-st}$ for Laplace transforms. Now since Δt only approaches 0, as it does for the defining $u(t)$, then the lower limit of the integral is only approached. That is, the lower limit of $t = 0$ of the integral is only approached as is illustrated in Fig. 4–3. Then the point of $t = 0$ is conceptually not included in the integration. This also means that when we perform the Laplace transform we are really integrating from 0^+,

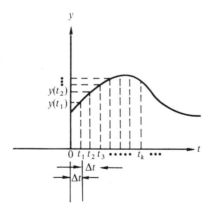

FIGURE 4–3

where 0^+ means just positive of zero. However we shall elect to use zero as the lower limit and understand what we mean, as has always been done in calculus. Then there is no conflict between the Unit Step function and the defining integral of Laplace transform. Let us continue with finding $U(s)$. Thus from before

$$U(s) = \int_0^\infty u(t)e^{-st}\, dt = \int_0^\infty 1 \cdot e^{-st}\, dt$$

since $u(t) = 1$ for $t > 0$. So

$$U(s) = -\frac{1}{s}e^{-st}\Big|_0^\infty = -\frac{1}{s}(e^{-s\cdot\infty} - e^{-s\cdot 0}) = -\frac{1}{s}(e^{-\infty} - e^0) = \frac{1}{s}$$

since $e^{-\infty} = 1/e^\infty = 0$. So

$$U(s) = \mathcal{L}[u(t)] = \frac{1}{s} \tag{4-10}$$

4–4 Laplace of a Constant

Suppose we wish to find the Laplace transform of the constant shown in Fig. 4–4(a). In order that the constant K comply with the limits of our

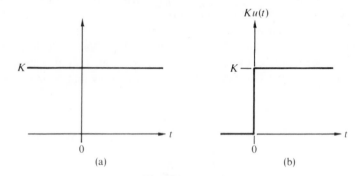

FIGURE 4–4

defining integral, expressed in Eq. (4–7), we will form the product $Ku(t)$, which is illustrated in Fig. 4–4(b). To understand this product return to Eq. (4–9), hence

$$Ku(t) = \begin{cases} 0 \text{ for } t < 0 \\ K \text{ for } t > 0 \end{cases} \tag{4-11}$$

Finding the Laplace transform of $Ku(t)$ is

$$\mathcal{L}[Ku(t)] = \int_0^\infty Ku(t)e^{-st}\, dt = K \int_0^\infty u(t)e^{-st}\, dt = KU(s) = \frac{K}{s} \quad \textbf{(4-12)}$$

Suppose we would have performed the Laplace transform of K rather than $u(t)$. Then we would have performed

$$\mathcal{L}[K] = \int_0^\infty Ke^{-st}\, dt = K \int_0^\infty e^{-st}\, dt = \frac{K}{s}$$

which yields the same results as Eq. (4–12). This occurs since the integral's lower limit essentially served the same function as the Unit Step function, insofar as the mathematics is concerned. Then one might say there is no difference between $\mathcal{L}[K]$ and $\mathcal{L}[Ku(t)]$, which is true mathematically; however there is a difference physically as we can see from Fig. 4–4. Then just to remind us of this difference and how we are effectively altering functions which exist for negative values of the independent variable we shall form the product of the function and $u(t)$. We will have to understand that even though our waveform may physically appear as Fig. 4–4(a) we are effectively transforming the waveform of Fig. 4–4(b). Many texts ignore $u(t)$ and write Eq. (4–12) as

$$\mathcal{L}[K] = \frac{K}{s}$$

We will demonstrate the use of Eq. (4–12) by working some examples.

Example 4–1   (a) Given $f(t) = 10u(t)$ find $F(s)$. Now $F(s) = \mathcal{L}[10u(t)]$ $= \mathcal{L}[Ku(t)]$, therefore $10u(t) = Ku(t)$, $K = 10$. So $F(s) = \mathcal{L}[10u(t)] = 10/s$. (b) $\mathcal{L}[-6u(t)] = -6\mathcal{L}[u(t)] = -6/s$.

4–5   Laplace of $e^{-\alpha t}$

A function which appears often is $e^{-\alpha t}$ where α is a constant, which is illustrated in Fig. 4–5(a) for both $\alpha > 0$ and $\alpha < 0$. Once again we will form the product of $e^{-\alpha t}u(t)$ in order to comply with the lower limit of Eq. (4–7). That is, $e^{-\alpha t}u(t) = 0$ for $t < 0$, which is illustrated in Fig. 4–5(b). Hence,

$$\mathcal{L}[e^{-\alpha t}u(t)] = \int_0^\infty e^{-\alpha t}u(t)e^{-st}\, dt = \int_0^\infty e^{-\alpha t}e^{-st}\, dt = \int_0^\infty e^{-(s+\alpha)t}\, dt$$

$$= -\frac{1}{s+\alpha}e^{-(s+\alpha)t}\Big|_0^\infty = \frac{1}{s+\alpha}$$

where $u(t)$ was omitted from beneath the integral since the limits of the integral served the same purpose.

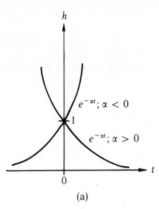

(a)

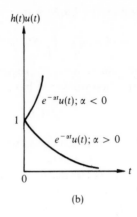

(b)

FIGURE 4–5

$$\mathcal{L}[e^{-\alpha t}u(t)] = \frac{1}{s + \alpha} \qquad \text{(4-13)}$$

Again, many times the $u(t)$ is omitted, but remember, in fact it is there. We will now consider some examples using Eq. (4–13).

Example 4–2   (a) $\mathcal{L}[e^{2t}u(t)] = $?
From Eq. (4–13) — $\alpha = 2$, therefore

$$\mathcal{L}[e^{2t}u(t)] = \frac{1}{s - 2}$$

(b) $\mathcal{L}[e^{(-5+j10)t}u(t)] = \dfrac{1}{s - (-5 + j10)} = \dfrac{1}{s + 5 - j10}$

(c) $\mathcal{L}[e^{(3-j\omega_1)t}u(t)] = \dfrac{1}{s - (3 - j\omega_1)} = \dfrac{1}{s - 3 + j\omega_1}$

where ω_1 is a constant.

(d) $\mathcal{L}[10e^{-5x}u(x)] = 10\mathcal{L}[e^{-5x}u(x)] = 10\left[\dfrac{1}{s + 5}\right]$

$$= \frac{10}{s + 5}$$

where x is the independent variable.

(e) $\mathcal{L}[5e^{-6y}u(y)] = 5\left[\dfrac{1}{s + 6}\right] = \dfrac{5}{s + 6}$

4–6   Laplace Transform of Sums of Functions

The Laplace transform is a linear operator; therefore, the Laplace transform of a function composed of sums of individual functions is equal to the sum of the Laplace transform of the individual functions. Hence, if

$$f(t)u(t) = g(t)u(t) + h(t)u(t)$$

then

$$\mathcal{L}[f(t)u(t)] = \mathcal{L}[g(t)u(t) + h(t)u(t)] = \int_0^\infty [g(t) + h(t)]e^{-st}\, dt$$

$$= \int_0^\infty g(t)e^{-st}\, dt + \int_0^\infty h(t)e^{-st}\, dt$$

$$\mathcal{L}[f(t)u(t)] = \mathcal{L}[g(t)u(t) + h(t)u(t)] = G(s) + H(s) \qquad \textbf{(4-14)}$$

An example demonstrating the use of Eq. (4–14) will be given later in the derivation of the Laplace transform of a sinusoidal function.

4–7 Laplace Transform of Sinusoidal Functions

To derive the Laplace transform of a sinusoidal function, as shown in Fig. 4–6(b), we shall utilize Eqs. (4–13) and (4–14). If we wish to find $\mathcal{L}[g(t)u(t)]$ of Fig. 4–6(b) we perform

$$\mathcal{L}[g(t)u(t)] = G(s) = \mathcal{L}[\sin \omega t u(t)] = \int_0^\infty \sin \omega t e^{-st}\, dt$$

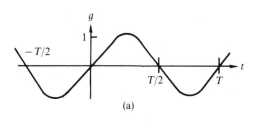
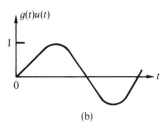

(a) (b)

FIGURE 4–6

Now,

$$\sin \omega t = \frac{e^{j\omega t} - e^{-j\omega t}}{2j}$$

therefore

$$\mathcal{L}[\sin \omega t u(t)] = \int_0^\infty \frac{e^{j\omega t} - e^{-j\omega t}}{2j} e^{-st}\, dt$$

$$= \frac{1}{2j}\left[\int_0^\infty e^{j\omega t}e^{-st}\, dt - \int_0^\infty e^{-j\omega t}e^{-st}\, dt\right]$$

$$= \frac{1}{2j}\{\mathcal{L}[e^{j\omega t}u(t)] - \mathcal{L}[e^{-j\omega t}u(t)]\}$$

As seen from Eq. (4–13) then

$$\mathscr{L}[(\sin \omega t)u(t)] = \frac{1}{2j}\left[\frac{1}{s - j\omega} - \frac{1}{s + j\omega}\right] = \frac{1}{2j}\left[\frac{(s + j\omega) - (s - j\omega)}{(s - j\omega)(s + j\omega)}\right]$$

$$\mathscr{L}[(\sin \omega t)u(t)] = \frac{\omega}{s^2 + \omega^2} \tag{4-15}$$

Using Eqs. (4–13), (4–14), and $\cos \omega t = e^{j\omega t} + e^{-j\omega t}/2$ it can be shown that

$$\mathscr{L}[(\cos \omega t)u(t)] = \frac{s}{s^2 + \omega^2} \tag{4-16}$$

Examples demonstrating the use of Eqs. (4–15) and (4–16) will now be given.

Example 4–3 (a) $\mathscr{L}[\sin 10tu(t)] = \dfrac{10}{s^2 + 10^2} = \dfrac{10}{s^2 + 100}$, where $\omega = 10$.

(b) $\mathscr{L}[\sin 5xu(x)] = \dfrac{5}{s^2 + 5^2} = \dfrac{5}{s^2 + 25}$, where $\omega = 5$.

(c) $\mathscr{L}[7 \sin 10xu(x)] = \dfrac{7\mathscr{L}[\sin 10x\,u(x)]}{7\mathscr{L}[\sin 10x\,u(x)]} = \dfrac{70}{s^2 + 100}$

(d) $\mathscr{L}[\cos 10yu(y)] = \dfrac{s}{s^2 + 10^2} = \dfrac{s}{s^2 + 100}$

(e) $\mathscr{L}[6 \cos(\omega_1 + \omega_2)tu(t)] = 6\left[\dfrac{s}{s^2 + (\omega_1 + \omega_2)^2}\right]$
$= 6\mathscr{L}[\cos \omega tu(t)]$, where $\omega = \omega_1 + \omega_2$.

(f) $\mathscr{L}[\sin(\omega t + \theta)] = ?$, where $\theta = $ constant.
From $\sin (x + y) = \sin x \cos y + \cos x \sin y$, we have $\sin (\omega t + \theta) = \sin \omega t \cos \theta + \cos \omega t \sin \theta$ for $x = \omega t$ and $y = \theta$. Then

$$\mathscr{L}[\sin(\omega t + \theta)] = \cos \theta \, \mathscr{L}[\sin \omega t] + \sin \theta \, \mathscr{L}[\cos \omega t]$$

since $\cos \theta$ and $\sin \theta$ are constants. So

$$\mathscr{L}[\sin(\omega t + \theta)] = \cos \theta\left[\frac{\omega}{s^2 + \omega^2}\right] + \sin \theta\left[\frac{s}{s^2 + \omega^2}\right]$$

Therefore,

$$\mathscr{L}[\sin(\omega t + \theta)] = \frac{\omega}{s^2 + \omega^2}\cos \theta + \frac{s}{s^2 + \omega^2}\sin \theta$$
$$= \frac{\omega \cos \theta + s \sin \theta}{s^2 + \omega^2}$$

4–8 Laplace of $mtu(t)$ (A Straight Line)

From Fig. 4–7(a) we may write the equation for the straight line as $f = mt$, where $m = \Delta f/\Delta t = $ constant. To comply with the lower limits of

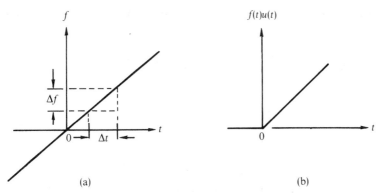

FIGURE 4–7   Equation of a Straight Line with Zero f-Intercept.

the defining integral we have $f(t)u(t) = mtu(t)$, which is illustrated in Fig. 4–7(b). Then

$$\mathcal{L}[f(t)u(t)] = F(s) = m \int_0^\infty te^{-st}\, dt \qquad (4\text{–}17)$$

Integrating by parts we have

$$\int_{y_1}^{y_2} x\, dy = xy \bigg|_{y_1}^{y_2} - \int_{y_1}^{y_2} y\, dx$$

for a definite integral. Let $x = t$ and $dy = e^{-st}\, dt$, then $dx = dt$ and $y = -(1/s)e^{-st}$. Therefore,

$$\int_0^\infty te^{-st}\, dt = -\frac{te^{-st}}{s}\bigg|_0^\infty + \int_0^\infty \frac{e^{-st}}{s}\, dt$$

The term $-(te^{-st}/s)\big|_0^\infty = -(1/s)[\infty \cdot e^{-\infty} - 0 \cdot e^{-0}] = 0$ since $e^{-st}\big|_{t\to\infty}$ approaches zero faster than t (of te^{-st}/s term) approaches infinity. Hence,

$$\int_0^\infty te^{-st}\, dt = \frac{1}{s}\int_0^\infty e^{-st}\, dt = -\frac{1}{s^2}e^{-st}\bigg|_0^\infty = \frac{1}{s^2}$$

Therefore Eq. (4–17) is

$$\mathcal{L}[mtu(t)] = m\left(\frac{1}{s^2}\right) = \frac{m}{s^2} \qquad (4\text{–}18)$$

where $m = $ constant.

Using the same technique it can be shown that

$$\mathcal{L}[mt^n u(t)] = \frac{mn!}{s^{n+1}} \qquad (4\text{–}19)$$

where $n! = 1 \cdot 2 \cdot 3 \cdot 4 \cdots n$.

Examples demonstrating the use of Eqs. (4–18) and (4–19) will now be given.

Example 4–4   (a) $\mathcal{L}[5tu(t)] = \mathcal{L}[mtu(t)] = \dfrac{5}{s^2}$

where $m = 5$ of Eq. (4–18).

(b) $\mathcal{L}[(6x + 5)u(t)] = \mathcal{L}[6xu(x)] + \mathcal{L}[5u(x)] = \dfrac{6}{s^2} + \dfrac{5}{s}$

(c) $\mathcal{L}[x^2u(x)] = \mathcal{L}[mx^nu(x)] = \dfrac{2!}{s^2 + 1} = \dfrac{2}{s^3}$

where $m = 1$ and $n = 2$ of Eq. (4–19).

(d) $\mathcal{L}[5y^2u(y)] = 5\left(\dfrac{2!}{s^3}\right) = \dfrac{10}{s^3}$

(e) $\mathcal{L}[5y^3u(y)] = 5\left(\dfrac{3!}{s^4}\right) = \dfrac{30}{s^4}$

4–9   Laplace Transform of a Derivative

Finding the Laplace transform of a derivative of a function results in transforming the derivative operation into an algebraic variable. Suppose

$$g(t) = \frac{df(t)}{dt} u(t)$$

then

$$\mathcal{L}[g(t)] = G(s) = \int_0^\infty \frac{df(t)}{dt} e^{-st}\, dt = \int_0^\infty e^{-st}\, df$$

Integrating by parts, where $\int_{y_1}^{y_2} x\, dy = xy \Big|_{y_1}^{y_2} - \int_{y_1}^{y_2} y\, dx$, and letting $x = e^{-st}$ and $dy = df$, then $dx = -se^{-st}\, dt$ and $y = f$. Thus

$$\int_0^\infty e^{-st}\, df = f(t)e^{-st} \Big|_0^\infty + s \int_0^\infty f(t)e^{-st}\, dt$$

$$= f(\infty)e^{-\infty} - f(0)e^0 + s \int_0^\infty f(t)e^{-st}\, dt$$

Now, $f(\infty)e^{-\infty} = 0$, $f(0)e^0 = f(0)$ and $\int_0^\infty f(t)e^{-st}\, dt = F(s)$, so we have $\int_0^\infty e^{-st}\, df = sF(s) - f(0)$. Therefore

$$\mathcal{L}\left[\frac{df(t)}{dt} u(t)\right] = sF(s) - f(0) \qquad\qquad \textbf{(4–20a)}$$

where $f(0)$ is the initial condition of f. When applying this equation it is always assumed that $f(0)$ is evaluated at a value approaching zero from the positive direction of the independent variable (t in this case), since the function $g(t)$ is not defined at $t = 0$ and does not exist for $t < 0$. For that reason we usually write Eq. (4–20a) as

$$\mathcal{L}\left[\frac{df(t)}{dt}u(t)\right] = sF(s) - f(0^+) \qquad \textbf{(4-20b)}$$

where 0^+ indicates we are approaching from positive values of t.

A more general form for the Laplace transform of derivative is

$$\mathcal{L}\left[\frac{d^n f(t)}{dt^n}u(t)\right] = s^n F(s) - \sum_{k=1}^{n} s^{n-k}f(0^+)^{(k-1)} \qquad \textbf{(4-21)}$$

where the quantity $(k-1)$ indicates
the derivatives of f evaluated at $t = 0^+$.

To reiterate, Eqs. (4–20b) and (4–21) demonstrate that the operation of taking a derivative was transformed to an algebraic quantity, where n indicates the order of the derivative. Examples of Eqs. (4–20b) and (4–21) are now given.

Example 4–5   (a) $\mathcal{L}\left[\dfrac{di(t)}{dt}u(t)\right] = sI(s) - i(0^+)$ from Eq. (4–20b).

(b) $\mathcal{L}\left[\dfrac{d^2 i(t)}{dt^2}u(t)\right] = s^2 I(s) - \sum_{k=1}^{2} s^{2+k}i(0^+)^{(k-1)}$ from Eq. (4–21). Then

$$\mathcal{L}\left[\frac{d^2 i(t)}{dt^2}u(t)\right] = s^2 I(s) - [si(0^+)^{(0)} + s^0 i(0^+)^{(1)}]$$

where $i(0^+)^{(1)} = di(t)/dt\,|_{t=0^+}$.

(c) $\mathcal{L}\left[\dfrac{d^3 y(x)}{dx}u(x)\right] = s^3 Y(s) - \sum_{k=1}^{3} s^{3-k}y_{(0^+)}^{(k-1)}$

$$= s^3 Y(s) - [s^2 y(0^+)^{(0)} + s^1 y(0^+)^{(1)} + s^0 y(0^+)^{(2)}]$$

$$= s^3 Y(s) - s^2 y(0^+) + sy(0^+)^{(1)} + y(0^+)^{(2)}$$

where $y(0^+)^{(1)} = \dfrac{dy(x)}{dx}\bigg|_{x=0^+}$ and $y(0^+)^{(2)} = \dfrac{d^2 y(x)}{dx^2}\bigg|_{x=0^+}$

(d) $\mathcal{L}\left\{\left[\dfrac{d^2 f(t)}{dt^2} + 5\dfrac{df(t)}{dt} + 10\right]u(t)\right\}$ where $f(0^+) = 2$, $f(0^+)^{(1)} = -1$

$$= s^2 F(s) - \sum_{k=1}^{2} s^{2-k}f(0^+)^{(k-1)} + 5[sF(s)$$

$$- \sum_{k=1}^{1} s^{1-k}f(0^+)] + \frac{10}{s}$$

$$= s^2 F(s) + 5sF(s) + \frac{10}{s} - sf(0^+) - f(0^+)^{(1)} - 5f(0^+)$$

$$= s^2 F(s) + 5sF(s) + \frac{10}{s} - 2s + 1 - 10$$

$$= s^2 F(s) + [5F(s) - 2]s + \frac{10}{s} - 9$$

(f) Given $e(t) = Ri(t) + L[di(t)/dt]$ solve for $I(s)$.

$$\mathcal{L}[e(t)] = E(s) = RI(s) + L\mathcal{L}\left[\frac{di(t)}{dt}\right], \quad \text{where } u(t) \text{ is}$$

understood.

$$= RI(s) + L[sI(s) - i(0^+)], \text{ therefore}$$

$E(s) + Li(0^+) = (R + Ls)I(s)$, or solving for $I(s)$

$$I(s) = \frac{E(s) + Li(0^+)}{R + Ls}. \quad \text{Notice our problem became}$$

an algebraic problem.

4–10 Laplace Transform of an Integral

Another mathematical operation which becomes algebraic when transformed is the integral. Considering the definite integral, suppose $h(t) = \int_0^t g(t)\,dt$, where the limits of the integral do away with the need for $u(t)$.[2] Then

$$\mathcal{L}[h(t)] = H(s) = \mathcal{L}\left[\int_0^t g(t)\,dt\right] = \int_0^\infty \left[\int_0^t g(t)\,dt\right]e^{-st}\,dt$$

Integrating by parts, that is, $\int_{y_1}^{y_2} x\,dy = xy\Big|_{y_1}^{y_2} - \int_{y_1}^{y_2} y\,dx$ by letting: $x = \int_0^t g(t)\,dt$ and $dy = e^{-st}\,dt$. Then $dx = g(t)\,dt$ and $y = -(1/s)e^{-st}$. Thus

$$H(s) = -\frac{e^{-st}}{s}\int_0^\infty g(t)\,dt\,\Big|_0^\infty + \frac{1}{s}\int_0^\infty e^{-st}g(t)\,dt \qquad (4\text{--}22)$$

Evaluating the first term of Eq. (4–22) we have

$$\frac{e^{-st}}{s}\int_0^\infty g(t)\,dt\,\Big|_0^\infty = \frac{e^{-\infty}}{s}\int_0^\infty g(t)\,dt - \frac{e^{-0}}{s}\int_0^0 g(t)\,dt = -\frac{1}{s}\int_0^0 g(t)\,dt$$

since $e^{-\infty} \to 0$. Now, the integral $\int_0^0 g(t)\,dt$ is interpreted as the area under the curve $g(t)$ starting at $t = 0$ and ending at $t = 0$. The area of course is zero, hence

$$-\frac{1}{s}\int_0^0 g(t)\,dt = 0$$

---

[2]Note: It is realized that the integral $\int_0^t g(t)\,dt$ is not properly written since we are saying that our independent variable with which we are integrating with respect to is t and likewise our upper limit is t. Then the integral is $\int_{t=0}^{t=t} g(t)\,dt$ and as we see the upper makes little sense. From calculus we know that the variable under the integral is a dummy variable, that is, even though we are integrating over the independent variable t we may use any other variable under the integral. If we use the dummy variable x then the integral $\int_{t=0}^{t=t} g(t)\,dt$ would be written $\int_{x=0}^{x=t} g(x)\,dx$. However, as long as we understand our nomenclature no trouble should arise; therefore we shall work with the integrals as they appear in Eq. (4–22).

The second term of Eq. (4–22) is the Laplace transform of $g(t)$. Equation (4–22) is

$$H(s) = \frac{1}{s} \int_0^\infty e^{-st}g(t)\,dt = \frac{1}{s}G(s)$$

or

$$\mathscr{L}\left[\int_0^t g(t)\,dt\right] = \frac{1}{s}G(s) \qquad (4\text{–}23)$$

The Laplace transform of an indefinite integral is evaluated much the same as a definite integral. Supposing

$$y(t) = \int x(t)\,dt$$

Then

$$\mathscr{L}[y(t)u(t)] = Y(s) = \int_0^\infty \left[\int x(t)\,dt\right]e^{-st}\,dt$$

Integrating by parts, where $\int v\,dy = vy - \int y\,dv$, by letting $v = \int x(t)\,dt$ and $dy = e^{-st}\,dt$. Then $dv = x(t)\,dt$ and $y = -(1/s)e^{-st}$. So

$$Y(s) = -\frac{e^{-st}}{s}\int x(t)\,dt\,\Big|_0^\infty + \frac{1}{s}\int_0^\infty e^{-st}x(t)\,dt$$

$$= \frac{1}{s}X(s) + \frac{1}{s}\int x(t)\,dt\,\Big|_{t=0}$$

Now, the integral $\int x(t)\,dt\,|_{t=0}$ is interpreted as stating we are to integrate $x(t)$, and then evaluate it at $t = 0$. The integral is written as $x^{(-1)}(t)$, hence $\int x(t)\,dt\,\big|_{t=0} = x^{(-1)}(0)$. Then $x^{(-1)}(0)$ is the initial condition of the integral of $x(t)$. It is also the integrating constant of the indefinite integral.

$$\mathscr{L}\left[\int x(t)\,dt\right] = \frac{1}{s}X(s) + \frac{x^{(-1)}(0^+)}{s} \qquad (4\text{–}24)$$

where again 0^+ is to indicate the independent variable is evaluated at zero, but from the positive side.

In general terms

$$\mathscr{L}[h^{(-n)}(t)u(t)] = \frac{1}{s^n}H(s) + \sum_{k=0}^{n-1} \frac{h^{(-k-1)}(0^+)}{s^{n-k}} \qquad (4\text{–}25)$$

for an indefinite integral. For the definite integral

$$\mathscr{L}\left[\underbrace{\int_0^t \int_0^t \cdots \int_0^t h(t)\,dt}_{n\ \text{Integrals}}\right] = \frac{1}{s^n}H(s) \qquad (4\text{–}26)$$

Example 4–6   (a) $\mathscr{L}\left[\displaystyle\int_0^y x(y)\,dy\right] = \dfrac{1}{s}X(s)$ from Eq. (4–26).

(b) $\mathscr{L}\left[\displaystyle\int_0^y \int_0^y x(y)\,dy\right] = \dfrac{1}{s^2}X(s)$

(c) $\mathcal{L}\left[\int x(y)\,dy\right] = ?$ where $x^{(-1)}(0^+) = 5$

$$\mathcal{L}\left[\int x(y)\,dy\right] = \frac{1}{s}X(s) + \frac{5}{s}$$

(d) If $h = 3t^3$ find $\mathcal{L}[h^{(-3)}(t)u(t)]$ by actual integration and then by

$$\mathcal{L}[h^{(-3)}(t)u(t)] = \frac{1}{s^3}H(s) + \sum_{k=0}^{2}\frac{1}{s^{3-k}}h^{(-k-1)}(0^+)$$

from Eq. (4–25). Now $h^{(-1)}(t) = \int 3t^3\,dt = \frac{3}{4}t^4 + C_1$, then letting $t = 0$ we find $h^{(-1)}(0^+) = C_1$. Also

$$h^{(-2)}(t) = \int\int 3t^3\,dt = \int\left(\frac{3}{4}t^4 + C_1\right)dt$$

$$= \frac{3t^5}{20} + C_1 t + C_2$$

so for $t = 0^+$

$$h^{(-2)}(0^+) = C_2$$

Likewise

$$h^{(-3)}(0^+) = C_3 \quad \text{and} \quad h^{(-4)}(0^+) = C_4$$

Then

$$\mathcal{L}[h^{(-3)}(t)u(t)] = \frac{1}{s^3}H(s) + \frac{C_1}{s^3} + \frac{C_2}{s^2} + \frac{C_1}{s} + C_4$$

Since we know $h(t)$ in explicit form we may find $H(s)$ in explicit form rather than implicit form as it now appears. That is,

$$\mathcal{L}[h(t)u(t)] = H(s) = \mathcal{L}[3t^3] = 3\left[\frac{3!}{s^4}\right] = \frac{18}{s^4}$$

hence

$$\mathcal{L}[h^{(-3)}(t)u(t)] = \frac{18}{s^7} + \frac{C_1}{s^3} + \frac{C_2}{s^2} + \frac{C_1}{s} + C_4$$

Confirm this transform using Eq. (4–25) [see example (g)].

(e) $\mathcal{L}\left[10\int_0^t t\,dt\right] = 10\mathcal{L}\left[\int_0^t t\,dt\right] = ?$

From Eq. (4–26) $h(t) = t$, therefore

$$\mathcal{L}[h(t)] = H(s) = \mathcal{L}[t] = \frac{1}{s^2}$$

Hence

$$\mathcal{L}\left[10\int_0^t t\,dt\right] = 10\frac{1}{s}\left[\frac{1}{s^2}\right] = \frac{10}{s^3}$$

This can be shown to be true since

$$10 \int_0^t t\, dt = 10\frac{t^2}{2}\Big|_0^t = 5t^2$$

and from Eq. (4-19)

$$\mathcal{L}[5t^2] = 5\left[\frac{2!}{s^3}\right] = \frac{10}{s^3}$$

(f) $\mathcal{L}\left[\displaystyle\int_{10}^t 6t\, dt\right] = ?$

The lower limit is no longer zero, therefore Eq. (4-26) no longer applies, but we could write the preceding

$$\int_{10}^t 6t\, dt = 6\int_0^t t\, dt - 6\int_0^{10} t\, dt$$

$$= 6\int_0^t t\, dt - \frac{6t^2}{2}\Big|_0^{10}$$

$$= 6\int_0^t t\, dt - 150$$

therefore

$$\mathcal{L}\left[\int_{10}^t 6t\, dt\right] = \frac{6}{s^2} - \frac{150}{s}$$

Of course we could have carried the integration out and then performed the transform, such as

$$\int_{10}^t 6t\, dt = \frac{6t^2}{2}\Big|_{10}^t = 3t^2 - 150$$

Then

$$\mathcal{L}[3t^2 - 150] = \frac{6}{s^2} - \frac{150}{s}$$

which agrees.

(g) Find $\mathcal{L}\left[2\displaystyle\int\int\int t^3\, dt\right]$ using Eq. (4-25).

From Eq. (4-25) $h(t) = 2t^3$ and $n = 3$, therefore,

$$H(s) = \mathcal{L}[2t^3] = 2\frac{3!}{s^4} = \frac{12}{s^4}$$

and

$$\frac{H(s)}{s^3} + \sum_{k=0}^{n-1=2} \frac{h^{(-k-1)}(0^+)}{s^{3-k}} = \frac{12}{s^7} + \frac{h^{(-1)}(0^+)}{s^3}$$

$$+ \frac{h^{(-2)}(0^+)}{s^2} + \frac{h^{(-3)}(0^+)}{s}$$

In part (d) $h^{(-1)}(0^+) = C_1$, $h^{(-2)}(0^+) = C_2$, etc.

(h) Find $\mathcal{L}\left[\int\int f(t)\, dt\right]$ if $f(t) = 10e^{-2t}$ and $f^{(-1)}(0^+) = -3$, $f^{(-2)}(0^+) = 4$.

$$\mathcal{L}\left[\int\int f(t)\, dt\right] = \frac{F(s)}{s^2} + \sum_{k=0}^{1} \frac{f^{(-k-1)}(0^+)}{s^{2-k}}$$

since $n = 2$. We see that for $f(t) = 10e^{-2t}$ that

$$F(s) = 10\left(\frac{1}{s+2}\right) = \frac{10}{s+2}$$

therefore,

$$\mathcal{L}[f^{(-2)}(t)\, dt] = \frac{10}{s^2(s+2)} + \frac{f^{(-1)}(0^+)}{s^2} + \frac{f^{(-2)}(0^+)}{s}$$

$$= \frac{10}{s^2(s+2)} - \frac{3}{s^2} + \frac{4}{s}$$

4—11 Shifting

Suppose that it is desirable to shift some general function f b units with respect to the independent variable. Let t represent the independent variable. Then if we shifted the function $f(t)$ by adding b units to t we would have $f(t + b)$. Let us call this new function $g(t)$, then

$$g(t) = f(t + b) \qquad\qquad (4\text{-}27)$$

where $g(t)$ is the shifted function of $f(t)$, as we shall see from Fig. 4–8. Figure 4–8(a) shows the nonshifted function $f(t)$ with reference points at t equal $-a$ and b. Figure 4–8(b) shows by adding b units to t it appears we have shifted $f(t)$ to the left; this is written as $f(t + b)$. Let us check a few of the shifted function points by determining where the reference points of Fig. 4–8(a) are on Fig. 4–8(b). Now, since we have defined the shifted function as $g(t)$, then $g(t) \equiv f(t + b)$ as stated in Eq. (4–27). Then to find the reference point $f(b)$ of Fig. 4–8(a) on Fig. 4–8(b) we must find $g(t)|_{t=0}$ on Fig. 4–8(b) since the point $t = b$ on Fig. 4–8(a) is equal to $t = 0$ on Fig. 4–8(b). Hence, for $f(t + b)|_{t=0}$ we see $f(t + b)\big|_{t=0} = B$ from Fig. 4-8(a). Then evaluating $g(t)$ at $t = 0$ we have $g(t)\big|_{t=0} = B$ as seen from Fig. 4-8(b). Hence $g(0) = f(b) = B$, which is our first reference point. For the second point we shall locate $f(-a)$ of Fig. 4–8(a) on Fig. 4–8(b). Since we want $f(-a)$ of Fig. 4–8(a) $f(t + b)$ of Fig. 4–8(b) must also equal $f(-a)$. Then $f(t + b)\big|_{t=?} = f(-a) = g(t)$ since $g(t) = f(t + b)$. To determine where to evaluate t for $f(t + b)$ we equate $t + b$ and $-a$, thus $t + b = -a$. Solving for t of Fig. 4–8(b) we find that $t = -(a + b)$. Then for Fig. 4–8(b)

$$g(t)\Big|_{t=-(b+a)} = g[-(b + a)] = f[-(b + a) + b] = f(-a) = -A$$

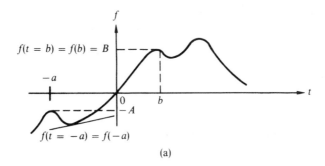

(a)

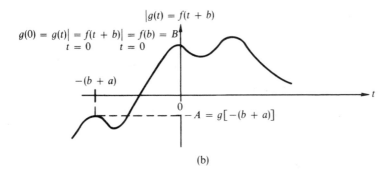

(b)

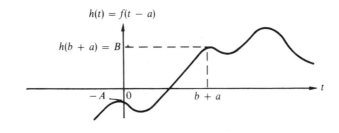

(c)

FIGURE 4–8   (a) Nonshifted function $f(t)$; (b) The function $f(t)$ shifted b units (c); The function $f(t)$ shifted $-a$ units

Therefore,

$$f(t + b) = [f(t)] \qquad\qquad \textbf{(4-28a)}$$

shifted b units in the negative direction of t for $b > 0$.

Figure 4–8(c) illustrates $f(t)$ shifted $-a$ units. Notice $f(t)$ appears to be shifted to the right. Again let us check the reference points of Fig. 4–8(a) on Fig. 4–8(c). To find $f(b)$ of Fig. 4–8(a) on Fig. 4–8(c) we must realize

$$h(t) = f(t - a)$$

To find when $h = f$ for the specific value of

$$f(t - a)\Big|_{(t-a)=b} = h(t)\Big|_{t=?} = B$$

we must equate $t - a = b$ and solve for t. Therefore $t = b + a$
so

$$h(t = b + a) = h(b + a) = f(b) = B$$

Likewise, to find when

$$h(t) = f(t - a) = f(-a) = -A$$

then

$$t - a = -a \quad \text{or} \quad t = 0$$

Hence, $h(0) = -A$. Therefore

$$f(t - a) = [f(t) \text{ shifted } a \text{ units in the positive direction of } t$$
$$\text{for } a > 0] \tag{4-28b}$$

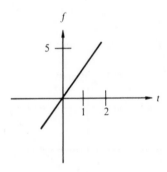

(a)

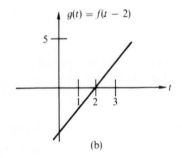

(b)

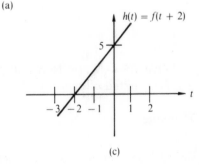

(c)

FIGURE 4–9

As a specific example consider $f = 3t$, which is graphed in Fig. 4–9(a). First suppose we shift this function ② units to the right, which means we perform $f(t - 2)$. Then

$$f(t - 2) = g(t) = 3(t - 2) = 3t - 6$$

which is graphed in Fig. 4–9(b). Next shift $f(t)$ ② units to the left, as shown in Fig. 4–9(c), hence

$$f(t + 2) = h(t) = 3(t + 2) = 3t + 6$$

Other examples of shifted functions follow.

Example 4–7   (a) If $h(x) = 3x^2 + 2x + 5$ then to shift $h(x)$ ③ units in the positive direction $g(x) = h(x - 3) = 3(x - 3)^2 + 2(x - 3) + 5$ from Eq. (4–28b).
(b) If $y(\theta) = \sin \theta$ shift $y(\theta)$ γ units in the negative direction. Hence, $x(\theta) = y(\theta + \gamma) = \sin (\theta + \gamma)$ from Eq. (4–28a).
(c) $z(t) = (6t^2/\tan t) - 2t$, where z is to be shifted ⑤ units in the negative direction. Then

$$\beta(t) = z(t + s) = \frac{6(t + 5)^2}{\tan (t + 5)} - 2(t + 5)$$

4–12 Laplace Transform of Shifted Function

Consider some function $f(t)$, shown in Fig. 4–10(a), which has been shifted a units in the positive direction of the independent variable and then multiplied by $u(t)$. Letting $g(t)$ represent this shifted function, then

$$g(t)u(t) = f(t - a)u(t)$$

Taking the Laplace transform we have

$$\mathcal{L}[g(t)u(t)] = G(s) = \mathcal{L}[f(t - a)u(t)] = \int_0^\infty f(t - a)e^{-st}\, dt \quad (4\text{–}29)$$

where $g(t)u(t)$ is illustrated in Fig. 4–10(b). To evaluate the integral let $x = t - a$, then $dx = dt$ and the limits of the integral become:

$$\text{at } t = 0 \quad x = -a \quad \text{and}$$
$$\text{at } t = \infty \quad x = \infty$$

Solve for t: we find $t = x + a$, therefore Eq. (4–29) becomes

$$G(s) = \int_{-a}^\infty f(x)e^{-s(x+a)}\, dx = e^{-as} \int_{-a}^\infty f(x)e^{-sx}\, dx \quad (4\text{–}30)$$

where $f(x)$ is illustrated in Fig. 4–10(d). Notice that the integral would be simply the Laplace of $f(x)$, which is $F(s)$, if the lower limit were zero rather than $-a$ [check Eq. (4–8) and recall the independent variable under

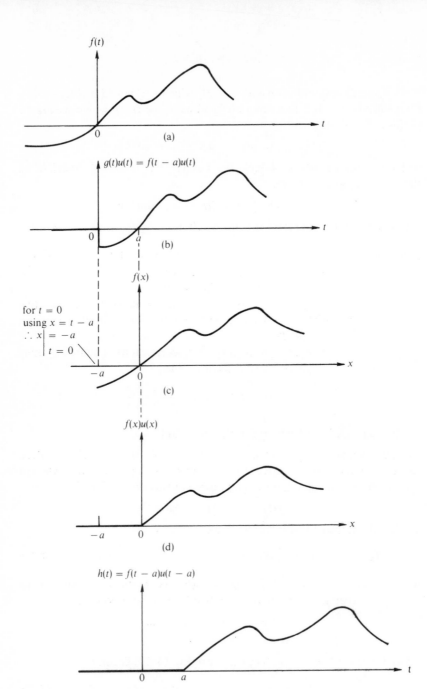

FIGURE 4–10 (a) Graph of $f(t)$; (b) Graph of $f(t - a)u(t)$;
(c) Graph of $f(x)$ where $x = t - a$; (d) Graph of $f(x)u(x)$;
(e) Graph of $f(t - a)u(t - a)$ which is Fig. 4–10(d) where $x = t - a$

an integral is just a dummy variable]. Then let us require that $f(x)$ be altered such that *there is a magnitude of zero until x equals 0*, as shown in Fig. 4–10(d). As we know, we can accomplish this by forming the product $f(x)u(x)$. Hence, writing Eq. (4–30) as $f(x)u(x)$ and *adhering to our new requirements* we have

$$\mathcal{L}[f(x)u(x)] = e^{-as} \int_0^\infty f(x)e^{-sx}\,dx = e^{-as}F(s) \qquad (4\text{-}31)$$

where $u(x)$ was omitted from beneath the integral.

Converting from Eq. (4–31) the independent variable x back to t we have

$$\mathcal{L}[f(t-a)u(t-a)] = e^{-as}F(s) \qquad (4\text{-}32)$$

since $x = t - a$. It is important to understand that the shifted unit step function $u(t-a)$ *must* be present if one is to apply Eq. (4–32), where

$$u(t-a) = \begin{cases} 0 & \text{for } (t-a) < 0, \text{ or } t < a \\ 1 & \text{for } (t-a) > 0, \text{ or } t > a \end{cases}$$

Also realize the difference between Eqs. (4–29) and Eq. (4–32). This can be accomplished by examining Fig. 4–10(b) and (e).

Example 4–8   (a) For this example we shall find the Laplace of the shifted sine wave of Fig. 4–11(a). Note the resultant wave-

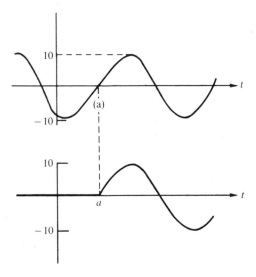

FIGURE 4–11   (a) Graph of $10 \sin \omega(t-a)$; (b) Graph of $10 \sin \omega(t-a)u(t-a)$

form when the shifted Unit Step function becomes part of the waveform as shown in Fig. 4–11(b).

$$\mathcal{L}[10 \sin \omega(t - a)u(t - a)] = ?$$

From Eq. (4–32)

$$\mathcal{L}[f(t - a)u(t - a)] = \mathcal{L}[10 \sin \omega(t - a)u(t - a)]$$
$$= e^{-as}F(s)$$

Now we know $\mathcal{L}[f(t)u(t)] = F(s)$ so we must identify $f(t)$, that is, $f(t - a)$ not shifted. Since $f(t - a) = 10 \sin \omega(t - a)$ then to find $f(t)$ let us add a units to $f(t - a)$, or $f[(t - a) + a] = f(t)$. Then $f[(t - a) + a] = 10 \sin \omega[(t - a) + a] = 10 \sin \omega t$, or $f(t) = 10 \sin \omega t$.
So

$$F(s) = \mathcal{L}[f(t)u(t)] = 10\frac{\omega}{s^2 + \omega^2} = \frac{10\omega}{s^2 + \omega^2}$$

Hence

$$\mathcal{L}[10 \sin \omega(t - a)u(t - a)] = \frac{10\omega}{s^2 + \omega^2}e^{-as}$$

(b) $\mathcal{L}[10(t - 2)u(t - 2)] = ?$
Since $f(t - a) = t - 2$ [one could also state $f(t - a) = 10(t - 2)$] then $f(t) = t$, where $a = 2$. So $F(s) = 1/s^2$ from Eq. (4–19). Hence,

$$\mathcal{L}[10(t - 2)u(t - 2)] = 10[F(s)e^{-as}] = 10\left[\frac{e^{-2s}}{s^2}\right]$$

(c) $\mathcal{L}[10(t - 2)^2u(t - 2)] = ?$

$$f(t) = t^2 \text{ [could also say } f(t) = 10t^2]$$

Therefore,

$$F(s) = \left(\frac{2!}{s^3}\right) = \frac{2}{s^3}$$

so

$$\mathcal{L}[10(t - 2)^2u(t - 2)] = \frac{20}{s^3}e^{-2s}$$

(d) $\mathcal{L}[5e^{-(t + 5/RC)}u(t + 5)] = ?$

$$f(t) = 5e^{-(t/RC)} \text{ [could have said } f(t) = e^{-(t/RC)}]$$

Therefore,

$$F(s) = 5\left[\frac{1}{s + \dfrac{1}{RC}}\right] = \frac{5}{s + \dfrac{1}{RC}}$$

so

$$\mathcal{L}[5e^{-(t + 5/RC)}u(t + 5)] = \frac{5}{s + \dfrac{1}{RC}}e^{5s}$$

(e) $\mathcal{L}[u(t+3)] = ?$

$$f(t) = 1$$

Therefore, $F(s) = 1/s$, so

$$\mathcal{L}[u(t+3)] = \frac{1}{s}e^{3s}$$

4–13 Waveform Construction—Nonperiodic and Periodic

Often the waveforms with which we deal are not continuous waveforms in the normal sense. That is, rather than having a smooth waveform, such as a sinewave, we may have one which exhibits discontinuities. An example of a discontinuous wave is a pulse, where the discontinuity occurs at the abrupt change, such as at $t = a$ and b of Fig. 4–12. It will be demonstrated

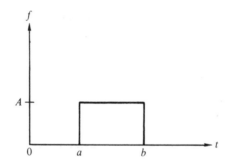

FIGURE 4–12   Discontinuous waveform

that by the use of the Unit Step function, shifted and nonshifted, an expression can be written for a discontinuous waveform.

The technique is to use the Unit Step function as a multiplier as was done for those waveforms of Fig. 4–10. To reiterate, since the Unit Step function has a value of zero or one, then when it is serving as a multiplier of some function f it will either force the product of $f(t)u(t)$ or $f(t-a)u(t-a)$ to zero, when the Unit Step function has a value of zero, or the product will be equal to the function f, when the Unit Step function has a value of unity. To reinforce this concept review Fig. 4–10.

Let us write an expression for the pulse shown in Fig. 4–12. We shall do this by summing several waves, which is demonstrated in sequential steps in Fig. 4–13. From Fig. 4–12 or Fig. 4–13(d), we see that our amplitude is to be A units when $a < t < b$, where we have left $t = a$ and $t = b$ undefined. We are leaving these two points undefined, as was similarly done for the Unit Step function of Fig. 4–2(b) since we may not be certain as to what curve was followed at the discontinuities.

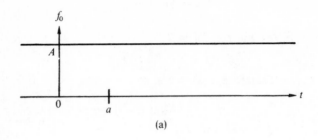

(a)

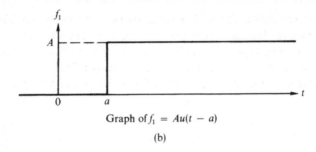

Graph of $f_1 = Au(t - a)$

(b)

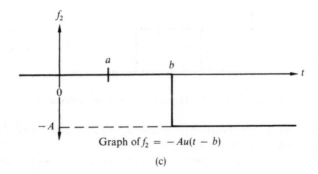

Graph of $f_2 = -Au(t - b)$

(c)

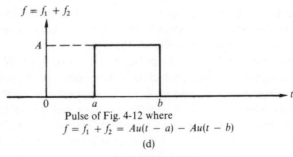

Pulse of Fig. 4-12 where
$f = f_1 + f_2 = Au(t - a) - Au(t - b)$

(d)

FIGURE 4–13

The basic equation with which we will deal is $f_0 = A$, which is illustrated in Fig. 4–13(a). It is from Fig. 4–13(a) that we shall "carve" Fig. 4–13(d).

First, we alter Fig. 4–13(a) by forming the product of $Au(t - a)$ (defined as f_1) in order that we may force the amplitude to zero for $t < a$, as shown in Fig. 4–13(b). From Fig. 4–13(b) we see we need to add negative A units for $t > b$ to Fig. 4–13(b) in order that Fig. 4–13(d) be created. Hence, $f_2 = -Au(t - b)$ is formed [see Fig. 4–13(c)]. Then summing f_1 and f_2 we have our desired results, which are illustrated in Fig. 4–13(d), that is,

$$f = f_1 + f_2 = Au(t - a) - Au(t - b)$$

$$= \begin{cases} 0 \text{ for } t < a, \text{ since } u(t - a) = u(t - b) = 0 \\ A \text{ for } a < t < b \text{ since } u(t - a) = 1 \text{ and } u(t - b) = 0 \\ 0 \text{ for } t < b \text{ since } u(t - a) = u(t - b) = 1 \end{cases} \quad (4\text{–}33)$$

We will now write an expression for the waveform of Fig. 4–14(a). It is recognized that Fig. 4–14(a) is composed of a straight line over the range of $a \leq t \leq b$ for the independent variable t. The equation of a straight line has the form $y = mx + b$, where $m = $ slope, $b = y$-intercept. Hence $e_1 = mt + b$ where $m = \Delta e/\Delta t$ and $b = e$-intercept. In order to determine b we must establish a reference point on the independent variable's axis, hence let us define t_1 to be our reference, or more simply the zero position. Then the straight line intercepts at the origin and $b = 0$. The equation of the straight line is $mt = (\Delta e/\Delta t)t$ under this condition. Since this equation has values for both positive and negative values of t, from Fig. 4–14(a) we see we want a value of zero for $t < t_1 \equiv 0$, we shall multiply mt by $u(t)$, as shown in Fig. 4–14(b). We must now force Fig. 4–14(b) to an amplitude of zero for $t > t_2$. There are two methods to do this. They both add an equal, but opposite, amount of amplitude to e_1 [Fig. 4–14(b)] for $t > t_2$, but differ in that one uses the shifting function as it appears in Eq. (4–32) and the other does not. The first method, which is the better method, will be used first. Let us add the same amplitude to e_1 but make it negative and shift it t_2 units in the positive t direction. Also, let us force the amplitude of this new function, say e_2, to zero until $t > t_2$, as shown in Fig. 4–14(c). The expression for e_2 is $-(\Delta e_2/\Delta t)(t - t_2)u(t - t_2)$. Forming the sum of e_1 and e_2 results in Fig. 4–14(d), that is

$$e_3 = e_1 + e_2 = \frac{\Delta e}{\Delta t}tu(t) - \frac{\Delta e}{\Delta t}(t - t_2)u(t - t_2)$$

To graph e_3 we shall consider when $0 < t < t_2$, where we will leave $t = 0$ and $t = t_2$ undefined. Then for this range of t we have $e_3 = (\Delta e_1/\Delta t)t$ since $u(t) = 1$ and $u(t - t_2) = 0$. For $t > t_2$, $e_3 = (\Delta e_1/\Delta t)[t - (t - t_2)] = (\Delta e_1/\Delta t)t_2 = E$ since: $\Delta e_1 = E$, $\Delta t = t_2 - t_1 = t_2$ for t_1 defined as zero,

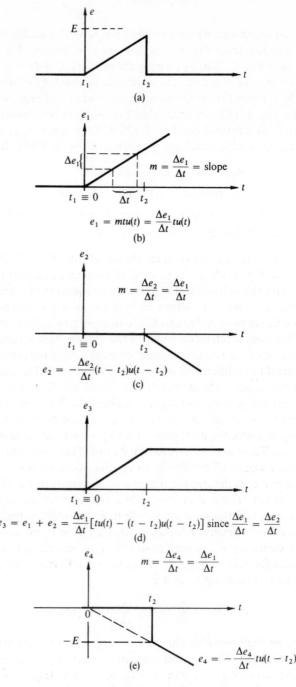

FIGURE 4–14

and $u(t) = u(t - t_2) = 1$ for $t > t_2$. The function e_3 is shown in Fig. 4–14(d). Then to obtain e of Fig. 4–14(a) we must add $-Eu(t - t_2)$ (not shown) to Fig. 4–14(d). Hence,

$$e(t) = e_3(t) + [-Eu(t - t_2)]$$

$$= \frac{\Delta e_1}{\Delta t}[tu(t) - (t - t_2)u(t - t_2)] - Eu(t - t_2)$$

Since $\Delta e_1/\Delta t = E/t_2$ for $t_1 \equiv 0$, then

$$e(t) = \frac{E}{t_2}[tu(t) - (t - t_2)u(t - t_2)] - Eu(t - t_2) \qquad (4\text{-}34)$$

which mathematically describes Fig. 4–14(a). As can be seen from the term $(t - t_2)u(t - t_2)$ of Eq. (4–34) the shifting function applies, as appears in Eq. (4–32).

Now let us take the second approach to writing the equation describing Fig. 4–14(a). Beginning with Fig. 4–14(b) and modifying it by adding $-(\Delta e_1/\Delta t)tu(t - t_2)$, shown in Fig. 4–14(e), we would have Fig. 4–14(a). Hence

$$e(t) = \frac{\Delta e_1}{\Delta t}[tu(t) - tu(t - t_2)] = \frac{E}{t_2}[tu(t) - tu(t - t_2)] \qquad (4\text{-}35)$$

Both Eqs. (4–34) and (4–35) are correct expressions, but Eq. (4–35) does not utilize the shifting function of Eq. (4–32). To demonstrate the problem involved with working with Eq. (4–35) let's find the Laplace transforms of both Eqs. (4–34) and (4–35). Hence

$$\mathscr{L}\left\{\frac{E}{t_2}[tu(t) - (t - t_2)u(t - t_2)] - Eu(t - t_2)\right\}$$

$$= \frac{E}{t_2}\left[\frac{1}{s^2} - \frac{e^{-t_2 s}}{s^2}\right] - \frac{Ee^{-t_2 s}}{s}$$

which presents no problems. Now perform the Laplace transform of Eq. (4–35). Hence

$$\mathscr{L}\left\{\frac{E}{t_2}[tu(t) - tu(t - t_2)]\right\} = \frac{E}{t_2}\frac{1}{s^2} - \frac{E}{t_2}\mathscr{L}[tu(t - t_2)]$$

We have no transform form which fits $\mathscr{L}[tu(t - t_2)]$, therefore we would have to actually integrate, that is

$$\mathscr{L}[tu(t - t_2)] = \int_{t_2}^{\infty} te^{-st}\, dt$$

Notice the lower limit is now t_2 rather than 0; this is due to $u(t - t_2)$.

In conclusion always attempt to write the expression such that standard transforms (ones from a table of transforms) may be applied, and this usually means applying the shifting function, when needed, such that it complies with Eq. (4–32).

Example 4–9   (a) Write an expression for $e(t)$ shown in Fig. 4–15 and then determine $E(s)$.

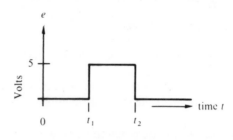

FIGURE 4–15

$$e_1(t) = 5u(t - t_1)$$
$$e_2(t) = -5u(t - t_2)$$
$$e(t) = e_1(t) + e_2(t) = 5[u(t - t_1) - u(t - t_2)]$$

Now

$$E(s) = \mathcal{L}[e(t)] = 5\mathcal{L}[u(t - t_1) - u(t - t_2)]$$
$$E(s) = 5\left[\frac{e^{-t_1 s}}{s} - \frac{e^{-t_2 s}}{s}\right] = \frac{5}{s}[e^{-t_1 s} - e^{-t_2 s}]$$

(b) Write an expression for $y(x)$ of Fig. 4–16(a) and then find $Y(s)$. In order to properly express $y(x)$ view y_1 and y_2 of Fig. 4–16(b) and (c). Therefore

$$y(x) = y_1(x) + y_2(x) = 2\left[\sin \frac{2\pi}{5}(x - 5)u(x - 5)\right.$$
$$\left. - \sin \frac{2\pi}{5}(x - 10)u(x - 10)\right]$$

So,

$$Y(s) = \mathcal{L}[y(x)] = 2\left[\frac{\left(\frac{2\pi}{5}\right)e^{-5s}}{s^2 + \left(\frac{2\pi}{5}\right)^2} - \frac{\left(\frac{2\pi}{5}\right)e^{-10s}}{s^2 + \left(\frac{2\pi}{5}\right)^2}\right]$$
$$= \frac{4\pi}{5\left(s^2 + \frac{4\pi^2}{25}\right)}(e^{-5s} - e^{-10s})$$

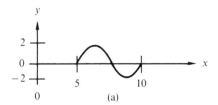

(a)

$$y_1 = 2 \sin \tfrac{2}{5}\pi(x - 5)u(x - 5)$$

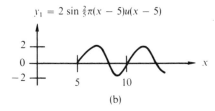

(b)

$$y_2 = -2 \sin \tfrac{2}{5}\pi(x - 10)u(x - 10)$$

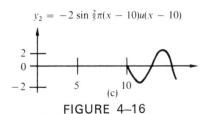

(c)

FIGURE 4–16

(c) Write an expression for $r(y)$, as shown in Fig. 4–17, and then determine $R(s)$.

$$r(y) = \left[-\frac{E}{y_d}y + E \right]u(y) + \left[\frac{E}{y_d}(y - y_d)u(y - y_d) \right]$$

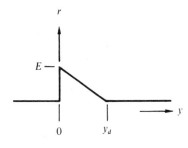

FIGURE 4–17

check on $r(y)$:

For $0 < y < y_d$: $u(y) = 1$ and $u(y - y_d) = 0$, there-fore

$$r(y) = -\frac{E}{y_d}y + E$$

which is correct.

For $y_d < y$: $u(y) = u(y - y_d) = 1$, therefore

$$r(y) = -\frac{E}{y_d}y + E + \frac{E}{y_d}y - E = 0$$

which is correct. Hence,

$$R(s) = \mathcal{L}[r(y)] = -\frac{E}{y_d}\frac{1}{s^2} + \frac{E}{s} + \frac{E}{y_d}\frac{e^{-y_ds}}{s^2}$$

$$= -\frac{E}{y_ds^2}(1 - e^{-y_ds}) + \frac{E}{s}$$

4–14   Laplace Transform of Periodic Functions

Consider the waveform of Fig. 4–18, which is meant to represent some general periodic waveform. Since the waveform is periodic then the

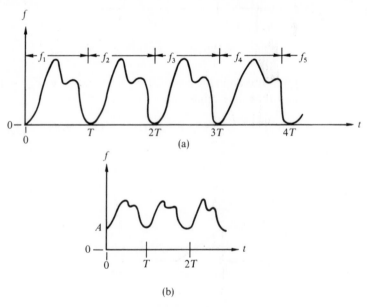

FIGURE 4–18

waveform in the time intervals $0 \leq t \leq T, T \leq t \leq 2T, 2T \leq t \leq 3T, \ldots,$ $(n-1)T \leq t \leq nT, \ldots,$ is the same in physical construction. Therefore we can state the periodic function f can be written as

$$f(t) = f_1(t) + f_2(t) + f_3(t) + \cdots + f_n(t) + \cdots. \qquad (4\text{-}36)$$

Since f_1, f_2, f_3, etc., have the same physical construction, but differ only at the time interval in which they occur, we may use the shifting concept and state

$$f_2(t) = f_1(t - T)u(t - T)$$
$$f_3(t) = f_1(t - 2T)u(t - 2T)$$
$$f_4(t) = f_1(t - 3T)u(t - 3T)$$
$$\cdot$$
$$\cdot \qquad\qquad\qquad\qquad (4\text{-}37)$$
$$\cdot$$
$$f_n(t) = f_1[t - (n-1)T]u[t - (n-1)T]$$
$$f_{n+1}(t) = f_1(t - nT)u(t - nT)$$

where we will ignore those points at $t = T, 2T, 3T, 4T \cdots nT$ since they are undefined for $f(t - nT)u(t - nT)$ because of $u(t - nT)$. Then from Eqs. (4–36) and (4–37) we may write

$$f(t) = \sum_{n=0}^{m} f_1(t - nT)u(t - nT)$$
$$= f_1(t)u(t) + f_1(t - T)u(t - T) + \cdots + f_1(t - mT)u(t - mT) \qquad (4\text{-}38)$$

which is the mathematical expression for Fig. 4–18(a).

Next let us determine the Laplace transform of Eq. (4–38). Hence

$$\mathcal{L}[f(t)u(t)] = \mathcal{L}\left[\sum_{n=0}^{m} f_1(t - nT)u(t - nT)\right]$$
$$= \mathcal{L}[f_1(t)u(t)] + \mathcal{L}[f_1(t - T)u(t - T)]$$
$$\quad + \mathcal{L}[f_1(t - 2T)u(t - 2T)]$$
$$\quad + \mathcal{L}[f_1(t - 3T)u(t - 3T)] + \cdots$$
$$\quad + \mathcal{L}[f_1(t - mT)u(t - mT)]$$
$$= F_1(s) + F_1(s)e^{-Ts} + F_1(s)e^{-2Ts} + F_1(s)e^{-3Ts} + \cdots$$
$$\quad + F_1(s)e^{-mTs}$$
$$= F_1(s) \sum_{n=0}^{m} e^{-nTs}$$

or

$$\mathcal{L}[f(t)u(t)] = F(s) = F_1(s) \sum_{n=0}^{m} e^{-nTs} \qquad (4\text{-}39)$$

where $f(t)$ is periodic and $F_1(s)$ is the transform of $f_1(t)$, which is the expression for *the first period*.

If the waveform is to have a reference other than zero for the dependent variable, such as Fig. 4–18(b), then we must add that reference level to Eq. (4–38). Hence, for Fig. 4–18(b)

$$f(t) = Au(t) + \sum_{n=0}^{m} f_1(t - nT)u(t - nT)$$

Taking the Laplace we find

$$F(s) = \frac{A}{s} + F_1(s) \sum_{n=0}^{m} e^{-nTs} \qquad \textbf{(4–39a)}$$

In electrical terminology the term $Au(t)$ represents the dc level.

For a specific example let us find $\mathcal{L}[\sin \omega t\, u(t)]$ using Eq. (4–39) and see if it agrees with Eq. (4–15).

Example 4–10   (a) Find $\mathcal{L}[\sin \omega tu(t)]$, illustrated in Fig. 4–19, using Eq. (4–39).

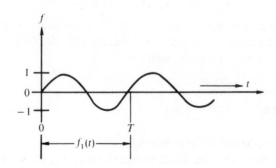

FIGURE 4–19

$f_1(t)$ can be expressed as

$$f_1(t) = \sin \omega tu(t) - \sin \omega(t - T)u(t - T)$$

Then

$$F_1(s) = \frac{\omega}{s^2 + \omega^2} - \frac{\omega e^{-Ts}}{s^2 + \omega^2}$$

or

$$F_1(s) = \frac{\omega(1 - e^{-Ts})}{s^2 + \omega^2}$$

So from Eq. (4–39) we have

$$\mathcal{L}[f(t)u(t)] = \mathcal{L}[\sin \omega tu(t)] = F_1(s) \sum_{n=0}^{m} e^{-nTs}$$

$$= \frac{\omega(1 - e^{-Ts})}{s^2 + \omega^2} \sum_{n=0}^{m} e^{-nTs}$$

Now

$$\sum_{n=0}^{m} e^{-nTs} = 1 + e^{-Ts}e^{-2Ts} + \cdots + e^{-mTs}$$

and from the series

$$\sum_{n=0}^{\infty} e^{nx} = 1 + e^{x} + e^{2x} + e^{3x} + \cdots = \frac{1}{1 - e^{x}}$$

$$\text{for } x < 0$$

we have

$$\sum_{n=0}^{\infty} e^{-nTs} = \frac{1}{1 - e^{-Ts}}$$

by letting $x = -Ts$ and having m approach ∞ (some large number). Thus

$$\mathscr{L}[\sin \omega t u(t)] = \frac{\omega(1 - e^{-Ts})}{s^2 - \omega^2} \frac{1}{1 - e^{-Ts}} = \frac{\omega}{s^2 + \omega^2}$$

which agrees with Eq. (4–15). Notice that since $\sum_{n=0}^{\infty} e^{-nTs}$ $= (1/1 - e^{-Ts})$ then Eq. (4–39) could have been written as

$$\mathscr{L}[f(t)u(t)] = F(s) \frac{1}{1 - e^{-Ts}} \qquad \textbf{(4-40)}$$

where f is periodic and m is large.

(b) Let us consider another example, that of a pulse train shown in Fig. 4–20. Writing e_1, that is, the first period, we have $e_1(t) = Au(t) - Au(t - t_d)$.

Finding $E_1(s)$

$$E_1(s) = \mathscr{L}[e_1(t)] = \mathscr{L}[Au(t) - Au(t - t_d)]$$

$$= \frac{A}{s} - \frac{A}{s}e^{-t_d s} = \frac{A}{s}(1 - e^{-t_d s})$$

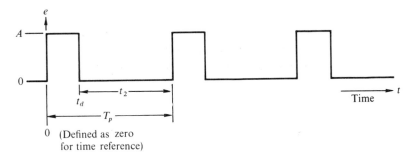

FIGURE 4–20

Therefore,

$$E(s) = E_1(s) \sum_{n=0}^{m} e^{-nT_p s} = \frac{A}{s}(1 - e^{-t_d s}) \sum_{n=0}^{m} e^{-nT_p s}$$

from Eq. (4–39), or

$$E(s) = \frac{A}{s} \frac{(1 - e^{-t_d s})}{1 - e^{-T_p s}}$$

from Eq. (4–40) if m is large. Supposing that the pulse amplitude A is 2 V, the duration $t_d = 5 \times 10^{-3}$ s, and the period $T_p = 30 \times 10^{-3}$ s. Then

$$E(s) = \frac{2}{s}(1 - e^{-5 \times 10^{-3} s}) \sum_{n=0}^{m} e^{-n30 \times 10^{-3} s}$$

(c) Find $I(s)$ if $i(t)$ appears as shown in Fig. 4–21.

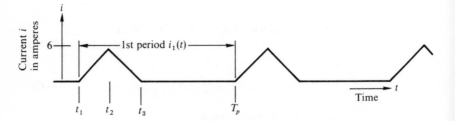

FIGURE 4–21

The basic straight-line equation is $i(t) = \pm mt$ where $|m| = $ absolute value of the slope $m = 6/(t_2 - t_1) = 6/(t_3 - t_2) = 6/\Delta t$.

Writing the necessary equations to construct $i(t)$, we begin with the straight line in the range $t_1 < t < t_2$, which is

$$i_{1'}(t) = \frac{6}{\Delta t}(t - t_1)u(t - t_1)$$

where we primed the one to distinguish it from the first period $i_1(t)$. For $t_2 < t < t_3$ we need an equation of the form

$$i_2(t) = -\frac{6}{\Delta t}(t - t_2)u(t - t_2)$$

Now

$$i_{1'}(t) + i_2(t) = \frac{6}{\Delta t}(t_2 - t_1) = 6$$

for $t > t_2$, which from the graph is the amplitude of $i(t)$ for $t = t_2$. Since $i_1(t) + i_2(t)$ equals a constant for $t > t_2$ we will need to write an equation forcing this constant to zero. Hence, $i_3(t) = -(6/\Delta t)(t - t_2)u(t - t_2)$.

Lastly let $i_4(t) = (6/\Delta t)(t - t_3)u(t - t_3)$ to cancel the effects of $i_3(t)$ for $t > t_3$. Thus, the first period for $i(t)$ is expressed as

$$i_1(t) = i_1(t) + i_2(t) + i_3(t) + i_4(t)$$

$$= \frac{6}{\Delta t}(t - t_1)u(t - t_1) - \frac{6}{\Delta t}(t - t_2)u(t - t_2)$$

$$- \frac{6}{\Delta t}(t - t_2)u(t - t_2) + \frac{6}{\Delta t}(t - t_3)u(t - t_3)$$

Therefore

$$i_1(t) = \frac{6}{\Delta t}[(t - t_1)u(t - t_1) - 2(t - t_2)u(t - t_2)$$

$$+ (t - t_3)u(t - t_3)]$$

Let us check $i_1(t)$ by graphing it. The equations from which we shall graph are determined by the ranges of t for which the unit step functions have a value of unity. From the expression for $i_1(t)$ we see that five time intervals are involved due to $u(t - t_n)$, where $n = 1, 2, 3$. Those are $t < t_1$, $t_1 < t < t_2$, $t_2 < t < t_3$, $t_3 < t < T_p$, and $t > T_p$. We will look at $i_1(t)$ in view of these time intervals. Hence,

For $t < t_1$: $u(t - t_1) = u(t - t_2) = u(t - t_3) = 0$
therefore $i_1(t) = 0$
For $t_1 < t < t_2$: $u(t - t_1) = 1$ and $u(t - t_2) = u(t - t_3)$
$= 0$, therefore,

$$i_1(t) = \frac{6}{\Delta t}(t - t_1) = \frac{6}{\Delta t}t - \frac{6t_1}{\Delta t}$$

which is correct. Check: at $t = t_1$

$$i_1(t = t_1) = \frac{6}{\Delta t}(t_1 - t_1) = 0$$

and at $t = t_2$

$$i_1(t = t_2) = \frac{6}{\Delta t}(t_2 - t_1) = 6$$

which agrees with the graph of $i_1(t)$.
For $t_2 < t < t_3$: $u(t - t_1) = u(t - t_2) = 1$ and $u(t - t_3)$
$= 0$, therefore,

$$i_1(t) = \frac{6}{\Delta t}[(t - t_1) - 2(t - t_2)]$$

$$= \frac{6}{t_2 - t_1}(t - t_1) - \frac{12}{t_2 - t_1}(t - t_2)$$

$$= -\frac{6}{t_2 - t_1}t + \frac{12t_2 - 6t_1}{t_2 - t_1}$$

$$= -\frac{6}{t_2 - t_1}t + \frac{6(2t_2 - t_1)}{t_2 - t_1}$$

To evaluate this equation let $t = t_2$, hence,

$$i_1(t)\Big|_{t=t_2} = -\frac{6t_2}{t_2 - t_1} + \frac{6(2t_2 - t_1)}{t_2 - t_1} = \frac{6(t_2 - t_1)}{t_2 - t_1} = 6$$

which checks with our graph for $t = t_2$. Also checking for $t = t_3$ we have

$$i_1(t = t_3) = -\frac{6t_3}{t_2 - t_1} + \frac{6(2t_2 - t_1)}{t_2 - t_1}$$

but since $\Delta t = t_2 - t_1 = t_3 - t_2$ then $t_3 = 2t_2 - t_1$. So

$$i_1(t_3) = -\frac{6t_3}{t_2 - t_1} + \frac{6t_3}{t_2 - t_1} = 0$$

which agrees with our graph of $i(t)$ also.

For $t_3 < t < T_p$ and $t > T_p$: $u(t - t_1) = u(t - t_2)$
$= u(t - t_3) = u(t - t_3) = 1$

$$i_1(t) = \frac{6}{\Delta t}(t - t_1) - \frac{12}{\Delta t}(t - t_2) + \frac{6}{\Delta t}(t - t_3)$$

$$= -\frac{6t_1}{\Delta t} + \frac{12t_2}{\Delta t} - \frac{6t_3}{\Delta t}$$

$$= -\frac{6t_3}{\Delta t} + \frac{6(2t_2 - t_1)}{\Delta t} = 0$$

since $t_3 = 2t_2 - t_1$. Then our equation for $i_1(t)$ is correct. Thus

$$I(s) = \mathcal{L}[i(t)u(t)] = I_1(s) \sum_{n=0}^{m} e^{-nT_p s}$$

from Eq. (4–39). And

$$I_1(s) = \mathcal{L}[i_1(t)] = \frac{6}{\Delta t}\mathcal{L}[(t - t_1)u(t - t_1)]$$

$$- \frac{12}{\Delta t}\mathcal{L}[(t - t_2)u(t - t_2)]$$

$$+ \frac{6}{\Delta t}\mathcal{L}[(t - t_3)u(t - t_3)]$$

$$= \frac{6}{\Delta t}\frac{e^{-t_1 s}}{s^2} - \frac{12}{\Delta t}\frac{e^{-t_2 s}}{s^2} + \frac{6}{\Delta t}\frac{e^{-t_3 s}}{s^2}$$

Hence

$$\mathcal{L}[i(t)u(t)] = \frac{6}{\Delta t s^2}[e^{-t_1 s} - 2e^{-t_2 s} + e^{-t_3 s}] \sum_{n=0}^{m} e^{-Tps}$$

(d) Write an equation for $e_{in}(t)$ in Fig. 4–22.

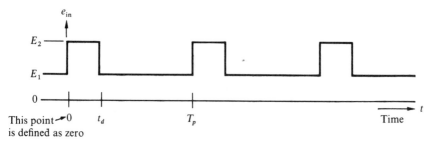

FIGURE 4–22

Defining $E_2 - E_1$ as ΔE we have $\Delta Eu(t) - \Delta Eu(t - t_d)$, for the first period, where the dc E_1 level was not considered. Let us define this as $e_{in_{ac}}(t)$, where the subscript ac means "no dc term considered." Hence, $e_{in_{ac}}(t) = \Delta Eu(t) - \Delta Eu(t - t_d)$. Then the equation for the ac portion of this waveform is

$$e_{in_{ac}}(t) = \Delta E \sum_{n=0}^{m} \{u(t - nTp) - u[t - (t_d + nTp)]\}$$

Adding the dc term we have $e_{in}(t)$, which is

$$e_{in}(t) = E_1 u(t) + \Delta E \sum_{n=0}^{m} \{u(t - nTp) - u[t - (t_d + nTp)]\}$$

Taking the Laplace transform

$$e_{in}(s) = \frac{E_1}{s} + \frac{\Delta E}{s} \sum_{n=0}^{m} [e^{-nTps} - e^{-(t_d + nTp)s}]$$

$$= \frac{E_1}{s} + \frac{\Delta E}{s}(1 - e^{-t_d s}) \sum_{n=0}^{m} e^{-nTps}$$

Notice that

$$\frac{\Delta E}{s}(1 - e^{-t_d s}) = \mathcal{L}[e_{in_{ac}}(t)]$$

So we could also state

$$E_{in}(s) = \frac{E_1}{s} + E_{in_{ac}}(s) \sum_{n=0}^{m} e^{-nTps}$$

4–15   Laplace Transform of the Unit Impulse

The Unit Impulse, designated as δ, is an important function for it helps in explaining instantaneous events, that is, the unit impulse has a value only for one specific value of the independent variable and is zero elsewhere. To develop this concept consider Fig. 4–23(a). We may express the waveform of Figure 4–23(a) as

$$f = \frac{1}{d}[u(t - a) - u(t - b)] \tag{4-41}$$

where $d = b - a$. Equation (4–41) may be made to define an instantaneous event by forcing a to approach b or vice versa. The choice is dependent on where the instantaneous event occurs. Let us suppose the event is to occur at $t = a$. Then let b's value approach a's. From Eq. (4–41) this would be expressed as

$$\underset{b \to a}{\text{limit}} f = \underset{d \to 0}{\text{limit}} f = \underset{b \to a}{\text{limit}} \frac{1}{d}[u(t - a) - u(t - b)],$$

since $d = b - a$. The expression $\text{limit}_{b \to a} f$ is illustrated in Fig. 4–23(b). If we would have wished to express the event to occur when $t = b$ then we would have written

$$\underset{a \to b}{\text{limit}} f = \underset{d \to 0}{\text{limit}} f = \underset{a \to b}{\text{limit}} \frac{1}{d}[u(t - a) - u(t - b)]$$

which is illustrated in Fig. 4–23(c). In each of the two cases we have created a dependent function ($\text{limit}_{d \to 0} f$) which has a value only at a specific value of the independent variable. Let us define the unit impulse from these concepts, that is, let us designate the unit impulse as δ and define it as

$$\text{Unit Impulse} \equiv \underset{d \to 0}{\text{limit}} f \tag{4-42}$$

where f is expressed in Eq. (4–41). Now, notice Eq. (4–42) is a general expression and does not indicate where $b \to a$ or $a \to b$. We will use the notation used for shifted functions to indicate at what value of the independent variable δ is to occur. For Fig. 4–23(b) we would write $\delta(t - a)$ and for Fig. 4–23(c) $\delta(t - b)$ would be appropriate. If the instantaneous event is to occur at $t = 0$ we would write $\delta(t)$.

There are a couple of characteristics of the unit impulse which should be pointed out. The first is that the amplitude of the unit impulse is infinite at the value of the independent variable for which it exists. This can be seen from Eqs. (4–41) and (4–42), realizing $d = b - a$. The second characteristic being that the area of the unit impulse is always unity. This is best seen from Fig. 4–23(a). Also we should realize that $\delta(t)$ is a concept which can only be approached physically, that is, no physical phenomena occur which have zero duration, infinite amplitude, with an area of unity.

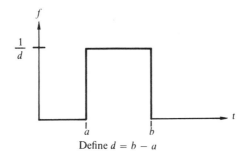

Define $d = b - a$

(a)

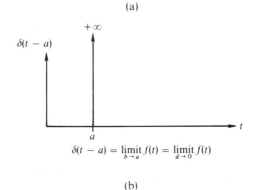

$\delta(t - a) = \underset{b \to a}{\text{limit}}\, f(t) = \underset{d \to 0}{\text{limit}}\, f(t)$

(b)

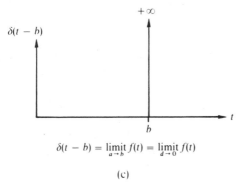

$\delta(t - b) = \underset{a \to b}{\text{limit}}\, f(t) = \underset{d \to 0}{\text{limit}}\, f(t)$

(c)

FIGURE 4–23

At this time the next logical step would be to demonstrate the circuit analysis use of the unit impulse; however, we will reserve demonstrating its use until later.

An immediate value of the unit impulse stems from the form of its Laplace transform. The Laplace transform of $\delta(t)$ requires the evaluation of

$$\mathcal{L}[\delta(t)] = \int_0^\infty \delta(t)e^{-st}\, dt \qquad (4\text{-}43)$$

We realize that $\delta(t)$ has a value only at $t = 0$ and nowhere else. Then Eq. (4–43) can be written as

$$\mathcal{L}[\delta(t)] = \int_0^\infty \delta(t)e^{-s\cdot 0}\, dt = \int_0^\infty \delta(t)\, dt$$

The integral $\int_0^\infty \delta(t)\, dt$ is simply the area under δ, which is unity as we have already observed, hence

$$\mathcal{L}[\delta(t)] = \int_0^\infty \delta(t)\, dt = \text{area under } \delta = 1 \qquad (4\text{-}44)$$

Next, let us evaluate $\mathcal{L}[\delta(t - a)]$:

$$\mathcal{L}[\delta(t - a)] = \int_0^\infty \delta(t - a)e^{-st}\, dt$$

Now δ is zero except at $t = a$, then

$$\mathcal{L}[\delta(t - a)] = \int_0^\infty \delta(t - a)e^{-sa}\, dt = e^{-as}\int_0^\infty \delta(t - a)\, dt$$

Again,

$$\int_0^\infty \delta(t - a)\, dt = \text{area under } \delta = 1$$

so

$$\mathcal{L}[\delta(t - a)] = (\text{area under } \delta)\cdot e^{-as} = e^{-as} \qquad (4\text{-}45)$$

As in other shifted functions e^{-as} indicates the function was shifted a units of the independent variable t.

There is another means to arrive at the unit impulse and its transform. It is not as straightforward from a physical understanding viewpoint; however, it results in a mathematical form which is beneficial and also readily indicates the units of the unit impulse. For these reasons we shall undertake this second derivation of the unit impulse and its transform. Let us begin by considering Fig. 4–24(a). As before let (d) approach zero, which means Fig. 4–24(a) will *approach* a unit step function $u(t)$. Expressing this mathematically we have

$$\underset{d\to 0}{\text{Limit}}\ g(t) \longrightarrow u(t) \qquad (4\text{-}46)$$

as seen from Fig. 4–24(a).

Now let us differentiate the function g, which will yield the function f of Fig. 4–23(a), that is,

$$\frac{d}{dt}g(t) = f(t) = \begin{cases} \dfrac{1}{d} & \text{for } a < t < b \\[2mm] 0 & \text{for } t > b \end{cases} \qquad (4\text{-}47)$$

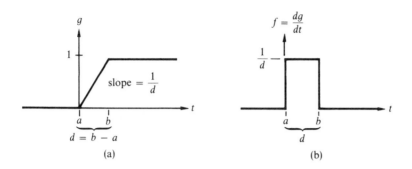

FIGURE 4–24

which is also illustrated in Fig. 4–24(b). Now let d approach zero, which yields the unit impulse δ of Fig. 4–23(b) or (c). We may express this as

$$\underset{d \to 0}{\text{Limit}} \frac{d}{dt} g(t) = \delta(t) \qquad \textbf{(4-48)}$$

or we may write Eq. (4–48) as

$$\frac{d}{dt} \underset{d \to 0}{\text{limit}} \, g(t) = \delta(t) \qquad \textbf{(4-48a)}$$

since the order of operation is of no importance. Substituting Eq. (4–46) into Eq. (4–48a) we have

$$\delta(t) = \frac{d}{dt} \underset{d \to 0}{\text{limit}} \, g(t) \longrightarrow \frac{d}{dt} u(t)$$

Thus,

$$\delta(t) = \frac{d}{dt} u(t) \qquad \textbf{(4-49)}$$

Then the unit impulse may be expressed as the derivative of the unit step function. This physically agrees with the unit impulse since the unit step's derivative is zero everywhere except at its point of discontinuity and at this point it is infinite since the slope of the unit step is infinite at that point. Notice Eq. (4–49) is a more convenient way of expressing δ than is Eq. (4–42), but Eq. (4–42) gives a better "feel" for what the unit impulse is, especially in terms of its area.

Now that we have Eq. (4–49) we have a means to determine the units of the unit impulse. From Eq. (4–49)

$$u(t) = \int_{t=a}^{t=b} \delta(t) \, dt \qquad \textbf{(4-50)}$$

Now we stated that the unit step function u is to be unitless. Then Eq.

(4–50) must be unitless, or

$$u(t) = \text{unitless} = \int_a^b \delta(t)\, dt = \text{area under } \delta \qquad \textbf{(4-51)}$$

But the integral $\int_a^b \delta(t)\, dt$ is being integrated over the independent variable t, which has units. Therefore, to make this integration result in a unitless function we must make δ have the inverse units of the independent variable, which in this analysis is t. Therefore,

$$\delta(t) = \frac{1}{\text{units of } t} \qquad \textbf{(4-52)}$$

which mathematically demonstrates its units.

Next let us multiply the amplitude of Figure 4–23(a) and Fig. 4–24(a) by a constant factor of k and determine its transform. Then Eq. (4–41) would be expressed as

$$kf = \frac{k}{d}[u(t-a) - u(t-b)]$$

Taking the limit as d approaches zero we have

$$\underset{d\to 0}{\text{Limit }} kf = k \underset{d\to 0}{\text{ limit }} f \qquad \textbf{(4-53)}$$

since k is not a function of d. From Eq. (4–42) we see that $\text{limit}_{d\to 0}\, f$ defines the unit impulse, hence Eq. (4–53) is

$$k \underset{d\to 0}{\text{ limit }} f = k\,\delta(t) \qquad \textbf{(4-54)}$$

It follows then that

$$\mathcal{L}[k\,\delta(t)] = k\mathcal{L}[\delta(t)] = k\cdot[\text{area of } \delta(t)] = k \qquad \textbf{(4-55)}$$

Since the coefficient k acts as a "weighting factor" let us term any coefficient of δ as the *strength* of the unit impulse.

To gain some feel for using the unit impulse function suppose we wish to find the Laplace transform of some general function f for a specific value of its independent variable as shown in Fig. 4–25(a). Suppose the independent

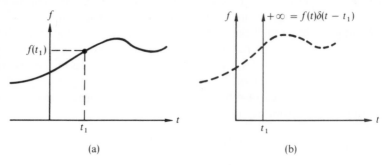

(a)   (b)

FIGURE 4–25

variable is t and we wish to find the Laplace transform of f at some specific value of t, say $t = t_1$. Then we will use $\delta(t - t_1)$ as a multiplier, since $\delta(t - t_1)$ is zero everywhere except at $t = t_1$. Hence,

$$\text{point of interest} = f(t)\,\delta(t - t_1) \tag{4-56}$$

This concept is illustrated in Fig. 4–25(b). Finding the Laplace transform of Eq. (4–56) yields

$$\mathcal{L}[f(t)\,\delta(t - t_1)] = \int_0^\infty f(t)\,\delta(t - t_1)]e^{-st}\,dt$$

$$= f(t - t_1)e^{-st_1}\int_0^\infty \delta(t - t_1)\,dt$$

or

$$\mathcal{L}[f(t)\,\delta(t - t_1)] = [f(t - t_1)e^{-st_1}]\cdot[\text{area of } \delta] = f(t_1)e^{-st_1} \tag{4-57}$$

since

$$f(t)\,\delta(t - t_1) = f(t_1)$$

Recall that only at $t = t_1$ will the product $f(t)\,\delta(t - t_1)$ have a value other than zero, and $f(t_1) = $ constant. Comparing Eq. (4–57) with Eq. (4–55) we see that $f(t_1)$ is the strength of the unit impulse for this particular case.

Notice there is a difference from Eq. (4–57) and the results if we would have first found the value of f at $t = t_1$ and then would have taken the Laplace transform. That is, we would then have

$$\mathcal{L}[f(t = t_1)u(t)] = \mathcal{L}[(\text{constant})\cdot u(t)] = \frac{f(t_1)}{s} \tag{4-58}$$

The difference between Eqs. (4–57) and (4–58) is the time for which we are saying $f(t = t_1)$ exists. For Eq. (4–57) we are saying we want the transform of f for when $t = t_1$ only, hence we used $\delta(t - t_1)$, and for Eq. (4–58) we are saying the value of f, evaluated at $t = t_1$, is to exist from when t is zero to infinity, thus $u(t)$ is used. We will see other uses for δ later.

4–16   Inverse of the Laplace Transform

Up to this point we have concerned ourselves with the Laplace transforms of various functions, which meant we would transfer the dependence of the dependent variable from some independent variable (the independent for most of our cases has been t) to the independent variable s. Another way to state this is that we transformed the dependent variable from the t-plane (assuming t was the independent variable) to the s-plane using Laplace transform. Henceforth we will develop means to transfer from the s-plane back to the original independent variable plane. When we perform this reverse transformation we speak of taking the inverse Laplace transform and designate it as $\mathcal{L}^{-1}$.

One method to determine the inverse Laplace transform of some function $F(s)$ is to evaluate

$$f(t) = \frac{1}{2\pi j} \int_{\sigma - j\infty}^{\sigma + j\infty} F(s) e^{ts} \, ds$$

However, there is an easier way. The manner in which we shall find an inverse Laplace transform shall be by using a table of transforms. The table is composed of the untransformed functions and their Laplace transforms, such as those derived in Eqs. (4–10), (4–12), (4–13), (4–15), (4–16), (4–18), (4–19), etc., but are written in a more general form in Table 4–2, which appears at the end of this chapter. These equations are known as transform pairs. Our approach shall be to take the transformed function, say $H(s)$, and "search" Table 4–2 until we find an equation in the s-plane which matches it. Once we have determined which equation matches in the s-plane we merely look on the other side of the equation for the other part of the pair, which is the dependent variable as a function of the original independent variable (the table is in the t-plane but one may substitute x, y, z, etc., for the independent variable). Before actually using Table 4–2 let us work some examples using the derived Eqs. (4–10), (4–12), etc., so that we can better understand the form of Table 4–2. Suppose we were given

$$G(s) = \frac{10}{s^2 + 100}$$

and asked to find $g(x)$, which is written as $\mathcal{L}^{-1}[10/(s^2 + 100)] = \mathcal{L}^{-1}[G(s)] = g(x) = ?$. Now, we know that we must search to find an equation in the s-plane which has the same general form as $10/(s^2 + 100)$. As we search our derived equations we see that Eq. (4–15) is suitable since $10/(s^2 + 100)$ and $\omega/(s^2 + \omega^2)$; both have numerator and denominator in the same general form. Now Eq. (4–15) appears as

$$\mathcal{L}[\sin \omega t \, u(t)] = \frac{\omega}{s^2 + \omega^2}$$

but it would appear as

$$\mathcal{L}[\sin \omega x \, u(x)] = \frac{\omega}{s^2 + \omega^2}$$

if in our original derivation the independent variable was x rather than t, which amounts to substituting $t = x$. Taking the inverse Laplace of both sides of the equation we have

$$\mathcal{L}^{-1}\{\mathcal{L}[\sin \omega x \, u(x)]\} = \mathcal{L}^{-1}\left[\frac{\omega}{s^2 + \omega^2}\right] = \sin \omega x \, u(x)$$

since

$$\mathcal{L}^{-1}\{\mathcal{L}[\sin \omega x \, u(x)]\} = \sin \omega x \, u(x)$$

Thus

$$\sin \omega x \, u(x) = \mathcal{L}^{-1}\left[\frac{\omega}{s^2 + \omega^2}\right]$$

Now we equate $\omega/(s^2 + \omega^2)$ and $10/(s^2 + 100)$ to determine the value of the constant ω, $\omega/(s^2 + \omega^2) = 10/(s^2 + 100)$, which yields $\omega = 10$. Therefore,

$$\mathcal{L}^{-1}[G(s)] = g(x) = \mathcal{L}^{-1}\left[\frac{10}{s^2 + 100}\right] = \sin 10x \, u(x)$$

One question which may have arisen earlier was "in the statement of the problem we were asked to find $g(x)$ given $G(s)$; how was it known that g was a function of x when all that was given was $G(s)$?" The answer is that there is no way of knowing if given just $G(s)$ whether g will be a function of x, y, z, t, etc. The determination of what independent variable to transform back to comes from knowing the variable of the problem. The proper independent variable choice will be apparent as shown in a later chapter.

In the examples to follow try to notice characteristics and patterns which exist in attempting to find an inverse Laplace transform. It is from these characteristics and patterns we shall understand the form of Table 4–2 and also develop a set of rules and procedures to follow.

Example 4–11   (a) Given $H(s) = 50/(s^2 + 100)$ find $h(y)$. Before searching for the equation in the s-plane which has the same form as $50/(s^2 + 100)$ let us generalize $50/(s^2 + 100)$. Looking at the numerator and denominator we have:

$$50 = \text{constant}$$

and

$$s^2 + 100 = s^2 + \text{constant}$$

Thus $50/(s^2 + 100)$ looks like [constant/$(s^2 + \text{constant})$]. We have now generalized $50/(s^2 + 100)$, so let us search for some transform pair which has the general form of constant/$(s^2 + \text{constant})$. As we search we find Eq. (4–15) is suitable since $\omega/(s^2 + \omega^2) = \text{constant}/(s^2 + \text{constant})$, where $\omega = \text{constant}$. We realize we must manipulate $50/(s^2 + 100)$ in order that it be in the *specific form* as $\omega/(s^2 + \omega^2)$. Thus $50/(s^2 + 100) = K\omega/(s^2 + \omega^2)$ where K is a "catchall" constant we may need in the manipulation. Then equating numerator and denominator we see $K\omega = 50$ and $\omega^2 = 100$. Hence $\omega = \sqrt{100} = 10$ (interested only in positive values), and $K = 50/\omega = 50/10 = 5$.

Therefore

$$h(y) = \mathcal{L}^{-1}\left[\frac{50}{s^2 + 100}\right] = \mathcal{L}^{-1}\left[\frac{5 \cdot 10}{s^2 + 100}\right]$$

$$= 5\mathcal{L}^{-1}\left[\frac{10}{s^2 + 100}\right] = 5 \sin 10y\, u(y)$$

since from Eq. (4–15) we realize

$$\mathcal{L}^{-1}\left[\frac{K\omega}{s^2 + \omega^2}\right] = K\mathcal{L}^{-1}\left[\frac{\omega}{s^2 + \omega^2}\right] = K \sin \omega t\, u(t)$$

(b) Given $Y(s) = 10/s^3$ find $y(z)$. First generalize $Y(s)$ so we may search for a similar form. Thus

$$\frac{10}{s^3} = \frac{\text{constant}}{s^{\text{constant}}}$$

Second, we search the equations and find that Eq. (4–19) is similar. That is

$$\frac{mn!}{s^{n+1}} = \frac{\text{constant}}{s^{\text{constant}}}$$

where m will serve as our "catch-all" constant. Third, to put $10/s^3$ in a specific form we will manipulate the transformed function and solve for the constants by equating numerator and denominator. Thus $10/s^3 = mn!/s^{n+1}$. From the denominator we see that $n + 1 = 3$ and from the numerator $mn! = 10$. Then from $n + 1 = 3$ we know $n = 2$, so

$$m = \frac{10}{n!} = \frac{10}{2!} = \frac{10}{1 \cdot 2} = 5$$

Fourth, take the inverse Laplace transform using Eq. (4–19), which is

$$\mathcal{L}^{-1}\left[\frac{mn!}{s^{n+1}}\right] = mz^n u(z)$$

or

$$y(z) = \mathcal{L}^{-1}\left[\frac{10}{s^3}\right] = 5z^2 u(z)$$

since $m = 5$ and $n = 2$.

Example 4–12 Given $V(s) = 7/(6s + 12)$ find $v(t)$. We notice for the first time we have a coefficient of s, which is something other than unity. Let us force the coefficient of s to unity, hence

$$V(s) = \frac{7}{6s + 12} = \frac{7}{6(s + 2)} = \frac{\dfrac{7}{6}}{s + 2}$$

Next let us generalize the equation, that is,

$$V(s) = \frac{\frac{7}{6}}{s+2} = \frac{\text{constant}}{s+\text{constant}}$$

Now we are in a position to search for a similar transform. We find Eq. (4–13) has the same general form. So let us manipulate the constants to obtain the specific form. We notice Eq. (4–13) has no "catch-all" constant so let us put in the constant K to serve this purpose. Then

$$K\left[\frac{1}{s-\alpha}\right] = \frac{K}{s-\alpha} = \frac{\frac{7}{6}}{s+2}$$

Equating numerator and denominator we have

$$K = \frac{7}{6} \quad \text{and} \quad s+2 = s-\alpha, \text{ or } \alpha = -2$$

Thus

$$v(t) = \mathcal{L}^{-1}\left[\frac{7}{6(s+2)}\right] = \frac{7}{6}\mathcal{L}^{-1}\left[\frac{1}{s+2}\right] = \frac{7}{6}e^{-2t}u(t)$$

Next let us formulate some general rules and procedures to follow when attempting to find an inverse Laplace transform using Table 4–2 at the end of this chapter.

Procedure 1:

Rule 1: Begin by forcing the coefficient of s with the highest power to be unity. This is usually accomplished by factoring as was done in Example 4–12. It may be necessary to put the term under common denominator in order to determine this coefficient.

Procedure 2:

Rule 2: Generalize the function by writing in "constant" (or some equivalent) wherever a constant exists in the transformed function. This allows easier comparison when searching Table 4–2.

Procedure 3:

Search Table 4–2 to identify the transform pair.

Procedure 4:

If the transform pair cannot be identified then manipulation of the s-plane function may be required. This manipulation is usually algebraic and is done just to get the function for which we wish the inverse in a recognizable form. This also usually requires some constant(s) be put in the equation. This procedure may occur anyplace, depending on when you recognize the need for manipulation of the equation.

Procedure 5:

Solve for the constants by equating numerator and denominator of the transform from Table 4–2 and the function for which the inverse is sought. Substitute these values into the inverse Laplace transform function of the transform pair, which is the solution.

These procedures are offered as an aid and are not to be looked upon as "commandments" to be followed religiously.

In view of the rules and procedures given let us examine Table 4–2, which is a table of transform pairs. Notice the coefficient of s raised to the highest power is unity; this is the reason for Rule 1. In order not to allow constants to confuse us we generalize our functions, hence Rule 2 and the reason for the "Generalized form of transformed function" column of Table 4–2. We spoke of a "catch-all" constant K in our examples, which is one of the possible constants in procedure 4; hence to our transform pairs we put the constant K.

Notice in Table 4–2 some of the transform pairs which we did not derive, but which are just stated. This is a realistic approach since we are interested in Laplace transforms as a tool. There are many more tables which are better and more complete, but this one will serve our purposes.

Now let us consider some more examples using the procedures and rules given.

Example 4–13   Given $X(s) = 20s/(5s^2 + 6)$ find $x(y)$.

Procedure 1:

$$X(s) = \frac{20s}{5\left(s^2 + \dfrac{6}{5}\right)} = \frac{4s}{s^2 + \dfrac{6}{5}}$$

Procedure 2:

$$\frac{4s}{s^2 + \dfrac{6}{5}} = \frac{\text{constant} \cdot s}{s^2 + \text{constant}}$$

Procedure 3:

From Table 4–2 [Eq. (8)] we find

$$\frac{\text{constant} \cdot s}{s^2 + \text{constant}} = \frac{Ks}{s^2 + \omega^2}$$

Therefore, we have identified the transform pair as

$$\mathcal{L}^{-1}\left[\frac{Ks}{s^2 + \omega^2}\right] = K \cos \omega t\, u(t)$$

where t represents any independent variable.

Procedure 4:
Not applicable

Procedure 5:

$$\frac{Ks}{s^2 + \omega^2} = \frac{4s}{s^2 + \dfrac{6}{5}} \quad \text{so } K = 4 \text{ and } \omega^2 = \frac{6}{5}$$

Then $\omega = \sqrt{\frac{6}{5}}$, so

$$x(y) = \mathcal{L}^{-1}\left[\frac{20s}{5s^2 + 6}\right] = 4\mathcal{L}^{-1}\left[\frac{s}{s^2 + \dfrac{6}{5}}\right]$$

$$= 4\cos\sqrt{\frac{6}{5}}\,yu(y)$$

Another way we could have found $x(y)$ was to view $4s/(s^2 + \frac{6}{5}) = (\text{constant}/s^2 + \text{constant})\cdot s$ as being similar to Eq. (15) of Table 4–2, where $f(0^+) = \text{constant} = 0$. Then proceeding with Procedure 4 we have

Procedure 4:
$X(s) = KsF(s)$, therefore

$$x(y) = \mathcal{L}^{-1}[KsF(s)] = K\frac{df(y)}{dy} = \mathcal{L}^{-1}\left[\frac{4s}{s^2 + \dfrac{6}{5}}\right]$$

Procedure 5:

$$KsF(s) = \frac{4s}{s^2 + \dfrac{6}{5}}$$

therefore

$$KF(s) = \frac{4}{s^2 + \dfrac{6}{5}}$$

We must now return to Procedure 2 for we will have to search Table 4–2 again to find the transform pair which is similar to $4/(s^2 + \frac{6}{5})$. Hence,

$$\frac{4}{s^2 + \dfrac{6}{5}} = \frac{\text{constant}}{s^2 + \text{constant}}$$

This form is similar to Eq. (7), hence

$$KF(s) = \frac{4}{s^2 + \dfrac{6}{5}} = \frac{K\omega}{s^2 + \omega^2}$$

Then $K\omega = 4$ and $\omega^2 = 6/5$, or $\omega = \sqrt{6/5}$ since we are interested only in positive ω's. Thus

$$K = \frac{4}{\omega} = \frac{4}{\sqrt{\dfrac{6}{5}}}$$

From Eq. (7) of Table 4-2 we have

$$f(y) = \mathcal{L}^{-1}[F(s)] = \mathcal{L}^{-1}\left[\frac{\sqrt{\dfrac{6}{5}}}{s^2 + \dfrac{6}{5}}\right] = \sin\sqrt{\frac{6}{5}}\,yu(y)$$

Now,

$$x(y) = \mathcal{L}^{-1}[KsF(s)] = K\frac{df(y)}{dy}$$

$$= \frac{4}{\sqrt{\dfrac{6}{5}}}\frac{d}{dy}\left[\sin\sqrt{\frac{6}{5}}\,yu(y)\right]$$

$$= \frac{4}{\sqrt{\dfrac{6}{5}}}\left[\sin\sqrt{\frac{6}{5}}\,y\,\frac{du(y)}{dt}\right.$$

$$\left. + u(y)\frac{d\sin\sqrt{\dfrac{6}{5}}\,y}{dy}\right]$$

Recall $\delta(y) = \dfrac{du(y)}{dy}$, so

$$x(y) = \frac{4}{\sqrt{\dfrac{6}{5}}}\left[\sin\sqrt{\frac{6}{5}}\,y\,\delta(y) + \sqrt{\frac{6}{5}}\cos\sqrt{\frac{6}{5}}\,yu(y)\right]$$

Now we are interested only in positive values of y. That is, for $y \geq 0^+$. Then $\sin\sqrt{6/5}\,y\,\delta(y) = \sin(\sqrt{6/5}\,0^+)\cdot 0$ since for $y = 0^+$ the term $\delta(y = 0^+) = 0$. Then $x(y) = 4\cos\sqrt{6/5}\,yu(y)$, which agrees with the solution previously found.

Example 4-13 was offered to demonstrate that there usually is no unique transform pair to use; however, there is usually one which is more convenient than the others.

Example 4-14   Given $H(s) = 6/(5s + 10)^2 + 7/2s^2$ find $h(t)$.
Procedure 1:

$$\frac{6}{(5s + 10)^2} = \frac{6}{[5(s + 2)]^2} = \frac{6}{25(s + 2)^2} = \frac{\dfrac{6}{25}}{(s + 2)^2}$$

Therefore,

$$H(s) = \frac{\frac{6}{25}}{(s+2)^2} + \frac{\frac{7}{2}}{s^2}$$

Since we manipulated the function $H(s)$ we are also doing Procedure 4.

Procedure 2:

$$H(s) = \frac{\frac{6}{25}}{(s+2)^2} + \frac{\frac{7}{2}}{s^2} = \frac{\text{const.}}{(s+\text{const.})^{\text{const.}}} + \frac{\text{const.}}{s^{\text{const.}}}$$

Procedure 3:
From Eq. (4–14) we know

$$h(t) = \mathcal{L}^{-1}\left[\frac{\frac{6}{25}}{(s+2)^2}\right] + \mathcal{L}^{-1}\left[\frac{\frac{7}{2}}{s^2}\right]$$

therefore we will search Table 4–2 for constant/$(s + $ constant$)^{\text{constant}}$ and constant/s^{constant} separately. From Table 4–2 we see Eq. (6) matches constant/$(s + $ constant$)^{\text{constant}}$ where $n = 2$, and that Eq. (2) matches constant/s^{constant}. Just in passing, Eq. (18) also matches if $KF(s) = (7/2)/s$.

Procedure 4:
Used in Procedure 1.

Procedure 5:
Using Eqs. (2) and (6) of Table 4–2 we have

$$\frac{K}{(s+\alpha)^n} = \frac{\frac{6}{25}}{(s+2)^2} \quad \text{and} \quad \frac{K}{s^2} = \frac{\frac{7}{2}}{s^2}$$

where K will have a different value in each case. Considering $K/(s + \alpha)^n = (6/25)/(s + 2)^2$ we find $K = (6/25)$, $n = 2$ and $\alpha = -2$. We next consider $K/s^2 = (7/2)/s^2$ from which we find $K = (7/2)$. Then

$$h(t) = \frac{\frac{6}{25}}{(2-1)!}t^2 e^{-2t}u(t) + \frac{7}{2}tu(t)$$

or

$$h(t) = \left[\frac{6}{25}t^2 e^{-2t} + \frac{7}{2}t\right]u(t)$$

Example 4–15   Given $Y(s) = 5/(9s + 3s^2 + 10)$ find $y(x)$.

Procedure 1:

$$Y(s) = \frac{5}{3\left(s^2 + 3s + \dfrac{10}{3}\right)}$$

Procedure 2:

$$\frac{5}{3\left(s^2 + 3s + \dfrac{10}{3}\right)} = \frac{\text{const.}}{\text{const.}(s^2 + \text{const.} \cdot s + \text{const.})}$$

Procedure 3:

We see we can write $Y(s)$ as

$$\frac{\dfrac{5}{3}}{s^2 + 3s + \dfrac{10}{3}} = \frac{\text{constant}}{s^2 + \text{constant} \cdot s + \text{constant}}$$

which matches with Eq. (9) of Table 4–2. In this last step we applied Procedure 4. We now see that whether we use Eq. (9) or (10) depends on ζ's value. We can determine the value of ζ by equating denominators and solve for like coefficients; hence

$$s^2 + 3s + \frac{10}{3} = s^2 + 2\zeta\omega_n s + \omega_n^2$$

therefore $2\zeta\omega_n = 3$ and $\omega_n^2 = (10/3)$. So $\omega_n = \sqrt{(10/3)}$ and $\zeta = 3/2\omega_n = 3/[2\sqrt{(10/3)}] = \sqrt{(27/40)} < 1$. Since $\zeta < 1$ we are instructed to use Eq. (9) of Table 4–2. Thus

$$\frac{\dfrac{5}{3}}{s^2 + 3s + \dfrac{10}{3}} = \frac{K}{s^2 + 2\zeta\omega_n s + \omega_n^2}$$

Solving for K we have $K = (5/3)$. Then from Eq. (9)

$$y(x) = \mathcal{L}^{-1}\left[\frac{K}{s^2 + 2\zeta\omega_n s + \omega_n^2}\right]$$

$$= \frac{K}{\omega_n\sqrt{1 - \zeta^2}} e^{-\zeta\omega_n t} \sin \omega_n\sqrt{1 - \zeta^2} t u(t)$$

so

$$y(x) = \frac{\dfrac{5}{3}}{\sqrt{\dfrac{10}{3}}\sqrt{1 - \left(\dfrac{27}{40}\right)}} e^{-\sqrt{27/40}\sqrt{10/3}t}$$

$$\times \sin \sqrt{\frac{10}{3}}\sqrt{1 - \frac{27}{40}} t u(t)$$

which of course can be reduced to a much nicer form.

Example 4–16   Given $H(s) = 10/(s^2 + 7s + 10) + 6$ find $h(t)$. Using Eq. (4–14) we know·

$$h(t) = \mathcal{L}^{-1}\left[\frac{10}{s^2 + 7s + 10}\right] + \mathcal{L}^{-1}[6]$$

Procedure 1:
Not applicable

Procedures 2 and 3:

$$\frac{10}{s^2 + 7s + 10} = \frac{\text{constant}}{s^2 + \text{constant} \cdot s + \text{constant}}$$

which matches Eq. (9). Then we must determine ζ in order to know whether to use Eq. (9) or (10) of Table 4–2. Hence,

$$s^2 + 7s + 10 = s^2 + 2\zeta\omega_n s + \omega_n^2$$

from which $2\zeta\omega_n = 7$ and $\omega_n^2 = 10$. So $\omega_n = \sqrt{10}$ and

$$\zeta = \frac{7}{2\omega_n} = \frac{7}{2\sqrt{10}} = \sqrt{\frac{49}{40}} > 1$$

therefore we shall use Eq. (10). Equation (10) says that we must factor $s^2 + 7s + 10$ in order to get the form $(s + \alpha)(s + \beta)$. Using the quadric equation form $ax^2 + bx + c$ where $x_1, x_2 = -(b/2a) \pm (1/2a)\sqrt{b^2 - 4ac}$ to solve for the roots we have

$$s_1, s_2 = -\frac{7}{2} \pm \frac{1}{2}\sqrt{(7)^2 - 4(10)} = -\frac{7}{2} \pm \frac{3}{2}$$

or

$$s_1 = -5 \quad \text{and} \quad s_2 = -2$$

We know that

$$(s + \alpha)\Big|_{s=s_1} = 0 \quad \text{and} \quad (s + \beta)\Big|_{s=s_2} = 0$$

hence

$$s_1 + \alpha = 0, \text{ or } \alpha = -s_1 \quad \text{and} \quad \beta = -s_2$$

Then

$$\alpha = -(-5) = 5 \quad \text{and} \quad \beta = 2$$

Of course, it was arbitrary whether $\alpha \equiv -s_1$ or $\alpha \equiv -s_2$ and likewise for β. Then we can write

$$\frac{10}{s^2 + 7s + 10} = \frac{10}{(s + 2)(s + 5)} = \frac{K}{(s + \alpha)(s + \beta)}$$

Procedure 5:

$$K = 10, \alpha = 2, \quad \text{and} \quad \beta = 5$$

Then

$$\mathcal{L}^{-1}\left[\frac{10}{(s+2)(s+5)}\right] = \frac{10}{(5-2)}(e^{-2t} - e^{-5t})u(t)$$

$$= \frac{10}{3}(e^{-2t} - e^{-5t})u(t)$$

Now we shall find $\mathcal{L}^{-1}[6]$

Procedure 1:
Not applicable

Procedure 2:
6 = constant

Procedure 3:
Equation (14) is identified as the transform pair.

Procedure 4:
Not applicable

Procedure 5:
$K = 6$, therefore

$$\mathcal{L}^{-1}[K] = K\delta(t)$$

or

$$\mathcal{L}^{-1}[6] = 6\delta(t)$$

The solution to $\mathcal{L}^{-1}\{[10/(s^2 + 7s + 10)] + 6\}$ is

$$h(t) = \frac{10}{3}(e^{-2t} - e^{-5t})u(t) + 6\delta(t)$$

4–17 Partial Fractions

Many times when a function appears such as $1/s(s + 10)$ it is a great temptation to perform $\mathcal{L}^{-1}[1/s(s + 10)] = \mathcal{L}^{-1}[1/s] \cdot \mathcal{L}^{-1}[1/(s + 10)]$, *which is wrong.* We can see this is incorrect by recalling the integral for the inverse Laplace transform and applying it, that is,

$$\mathcal{L}^{-1}\left[\frac{1}{s(s+10)}\right] = \int_{\sigma-j\infty}^{\sigma+j\infty} \frac{1}{s(s+10)}e^{ts}\,ds$$

From calculus we know

$$\int_{-\sigma-j\infty}^{\sigma+j\infty} \frac{1}{s(s+10)}e^{ts}\,ds \neq \left[\int_{\sigma-j\infty}^{\sigma+j\infty} \frac{1}{s}e^{ts}\,ds\right] \cdot \left[\int_{\sigma-j\infty}^{\sigma+j\infty} \frac{1}{s+10}e^{ts}\,ds\right]$$

$$= \mathcal{L}^{-1}\left[\frac{1}{s}\right] \cdot \mathcal{L}^{-1}\left[\frac{1}{s+10}\right]$$

therefore

$$\mathcal{L}^{-1}\left[\frac{1}{s(s+10)}\right] \neq \mathcal{L}^{-1}\left[\frac{1}{s}\right] \cdot \mathcal{L}^{-1}\left[\frac{1}{s+10}\right]$$

We will develop an inverse Laplace transform which can handle a product of two functions, but for now we will investigate other means to handle these products.

Taking another look at $1/s(s+10)$ we realize that we could view it as having originally been two fractions, one with a denominator of s and the other a denominator of $s+10$, that is

$$\frac{1}{s(s+10)} = \frac{K_1}{s} + \frac{K_2}{s+10}$$

The right-hand side of this equation is the partial fractional form of $1/s(s+10)$. We put the constants K_1 and K_2 in the numerator since we do not know what goes there explicitly. One way to find the values of K_1 and K_2 is to form a common denominator of the two fractions and equate this numerator to the numerator of $1/s(s+10)$. Then

$$\frac{1}{s(s+10)} = \frac{K_1(s+10) + K_2 s}{s(s+10)} = \frac{(K_1 + K_2)s + 10K_1}{s(s+10)}$$

Equating numerators we have $1 = (K_1 + K_2)s + 10K_1$, therefore $10K_1 = 1$ and $(K_1 + K_2)s = 0$ since the coefficient of s is zero in the left-hand side of the equation. Hence, $K_1 = \frac{1}{10} = 0.1$ and from $(K_1 + K_2)s = 0$ we find $K_2 = -K_1 = -0.1$. Substituting these values for K_1 and K_2 we have

$$\frac{1}{s(s+10)} = \frac{0.1}{s} - \frac{0.1}{s+10}$$

which yields a "nice" form for finding the inverse Laplace transform. To demonstrate let us take the inverse Laplace transform which is

$$\mathcal{L}^{-1}\left[\frac{1}{s(s+10)}\right] = \mathcal{L}^{-1}\left[\frac{0.1}{s} - \frac{0.1}{s+10}\right] = \mathcal{L}^{-1}\left[\frac{0.1}{s}\right] - \mathcal{L}^{-1}\left[\frac{0.1}{s+10}\right]$$

Generalizing the right-hand side we have

$$\frac{0.1}{s} = \frac{\text{constant}}{s} \quad \text{and} \quad \frac{0.1}{s+10} = \frac{\text{constant}}{s+\text{constant}}$$

Searching Table 4–2 we identify Eqs. (1) and (4) as being the transform pairs of interest. Then from Eq. (1) $K/s = 0.1/s$ and from Eq. (4)

$$\frac{K}{s+\alpha} = \frac{0.1}{s+10}$$

Solving for the K's of Eqs. (1) and (4), which are equal in this particular case, we have respectively $K = 0.1$ and $K = 0.1$.

α of Eq. (4) is found to be $\alpha = 10$, so

$$\mathcal{L}^{-1}\left[\frac{1}{s(s+10)}\right] = \mathcal{L}^{-1}\left[\frac{0.1}{s}\right] - \mathcal{L}^{-1}\left[\frac{0.1}{s+10}\right] = 0.1u(t) - 0.1e^{-10t}u(t)$$

$$= 0.1(1 - e^{-10t})u(t)$$

where we have assumed t as the independent variable. To verify this inverse let us perform $\mathcal{L}^{-1}[1/s(s+10)]$ without forming two fractions. Thus

$$\frac{1}{s(s+10)} = \frac{\text{constant}}{s(s+\text{constant})}$$

which is identified as Eq. (5). It could also be identified as Eq. (10) where either α or β is zero and the remaining one is equal to 10. Using Eq. (5) $K/s(s+\alpha) = 1/s(s+10)$, from which we find $K = 1$ and $\alpha = 10$. Then

$$\mathcal{L}^{-1}\left[\frac{1}{s(s+10)} = \frac{1}{10}(1 - e^{-10t})ut\right.$$

which agrees with our previous solution.

The technique of separating the original function into fractions is known as partial fractions. Partial fractions can be a very helpful aid for they take a complex expression and put it in a simpler form. The example we used to demonstrate partial fractions does not point this out since in Table 4–2 we had a transform pair, $K/s(s+\alpha)$, which matches $1/s(s+10)$ directly. However, suppose we were given $(s+2)/s(s+10)$ and were asked to find its inverse? By using partial fractions $s+2/s(s+10)$ we can write $s+2/s(s+10) = (K_1/s) + (K_2/s+10)$ and then perform

$$\mathcal{L}^{-1}\left[\frac{K_1}{s}\right] + \mathcal{L}^{-1}\left[\frac{K_2}{s+10}\right]$$

which is easily performed since these forms appear in Table 4–2. Then let us formulate some concepts in order to utilize partial fractions to aid in finding inverse Laplace transforms.

Functions which can be written as the ratio of two polynomials, that is, numerator and denominator expressible as integral powers of s, can be written as the sum of partial fractions. Partial fractions may be classified into two categories; nonrepeated roots and repeated roots. Which of these two categories a partial fraction would fall into is solely determined by the denominator of that partial fraction. If the partial fraction contains a single root it is a nonrepeated root. Examples of nonrepeated roots are:

1. $\dfrac{A(s)}{s + 10}$, the root is at $s = -10$, which is determined from $s + 10 = 0$.

2. $\dfrac{B(s)}{s - 5}$, the root is at $s = 5$.

3. $\dfrac{C(s)}{s}$, the root is at $s = 0$.

If the denominator of the partial fraction has a single-value multi-root, it is a repeated root. Examples of repeated roots are:

1. $\dfrac{A(s)}{(s + 10)^n}$, which has n roots at the value $s = -10$.

2. $\dfrac{B(s)}{(s - 5)^2}$, has two roots at the value $s = 5$.

3. $\dfrac{C(s)}{s^3}$, has three roots at the value $s = 0$.

We shall first investigate nonrepeated roots.

Consider some function $F(s)$ which can be written as the ratio of two polynomials $N(s)$ and $D(s)$. We shall consider $D(s)$ to be factorable into quantities of the form $(s + \alpha)^n$ where $n = 1$. This yields partial fractions of the nonrepeated case. Writing $F(s)$ in general terms we have

$$F(s) = \frac{N(s)}{D(s)} = \frac{a_n s^n + a_{n-1} s^{n-1} + a_{n-2} s^{n-2} + \cdots + a_1 s + a_0}{b_m s^m + b_{m-1} s^{m-1} + b_{m-2} s^{m-2} + \cdots + b_1 s + b_0}$$

$$(4\text{-}59)$$

where $m > n$ for $F(s)$ to be a proper fraction. By factoring $D(s)$ we write Eq. (4–59) as

$$F(s) = \frac{N(s)}{D(s)} = \frac{a_n s^n + a_{n-1} s^{n-1} + a_{n-2} s^{n-2} + \cdots + a_1 s + a_0}{(s - s_1)(s - s_2)(s - s_3) \cdots (s - s_m)} \quad (4\text{-}60)$$

From Eq. (4–60) we may express $F(s)$ as the sum of partial fractions, hence

$$F(s) = \frac{a_n s^n + a_{n-1} s^{n-1} + a_{n-2} s^{n-2} + \cdots + a_1 s + a_0}{(s - s_1)(s - s_2)(s - s_3) \cdots (s - s_m)}$$

$$= \frac{K_1}{s - s_1} + \frac{K_2}{s - s_2} + \frac{K_3}{s - s_3} + \cdots + \frac{K_m}{s - s_m} = \sum_{r=1}^{m} \frac{K_r}{s - s_r}$$

$$(4\text{-}61)$$

where s_r represents the roots taken one at a time and K_r is a constant associated with the partial formed from the rth root.

To determine the constant K_m we merely have to multiply both sides of

Eq. (4–61) by $(s - s_m)$ and then evaluate those products at the root of that quantity, which is found from $(s - s_m) = 0$, or more simply evaluate the product at $s = s_m$. Then solving for K_m from Eq. (4–61) we first multiply by $(s - s_m)$:

$$(s - s_m)F(s) = \frac{s - s_m}{s - s_1}K_1 + \frac{s - s_m}{(s - s_2)}K_2 + \cdots + \frac{s - s_m}{(s - s_m)}K_m$$

$$= \frac{s - s_m}{s - s_1}K_1 + \frac{s - s_m}{s - s_2}K_2 + \cdots + K_m$$

since $(s - s_m)/(s - s_m) = 1$. Next we are to evaluate s at the root s_m, therefore

$$[(s - s_m)F(s)]\Big|_{s = s_m} = \frac{s_m - s_m}{s_m - s_1}K_1 + \frac{s_m - s_m}{s_m - s_2}K_2 + \cdots + K_m$$

Now $s_m - s_m = 0$ so $[(s - s_m)F(s)]\Big|_{s = s_m} = K_m$, which is what we sought.

Putting this in mathematical form using Eq. (4–61) we have

$$K_m = [(s - s_m)F(s)]\Big|_{s = s_m} = \left[(s - s_m) \sum_{n=1}^{m} \frac{K_r}{(s - s_r)}\right]\Big|_{s = s_m} \qquad \textbf{(4-62)}$$

where the operation inside the brackets is to be performed before it is evaluated at s_m.

Before proceeding to repeated roots let us consider some examples of the nonrepeated roots where we will utilize Eq. (4–62).

Example 4–17   Given $F(s) = (s + 6)/[(s + 2)(s + 3)]$ find the partial fractions of $F(s)$. Then

$$F(s) = \frac{s + 6}{(s + 2)(s + 3)} = \frac{K_1}{s + 2} + \frac{K_2}{s + 3}$$

which is the same form as Eq. (4–61). To determine K_1 we perform

$$K_1 = [(s + 2)F(s)]\Big|_{s=-2} = \left\{(s + 2)\left[\frac{s + 6}{(s + 2)(s + 3)}\right]\right\}\Big|_{s=-2}$$

$$= \frac{s + 6}{s + 3}\Big|_{s=-2} = \frac{-2 + 6}{-2 + 3}$$

or $K_1 = 4$, which are the operations indicated in Eq. (4–62). We determine K_2 in a similar manner, that is, from Eq. (4–62)

$$K_2 = \left\{(s + 3)\left[\frac{s + 6}{(s + 2)(s + 3)}\right]\right\}\Big|_{s=-3} = \frac{s + 6}{s + 2}\Big|_{s=-3}$$

$$= \frac{-3 + 6}{-3 + 2} = -3$$

Therefore,

$$F(s) = \frac{s + 6}{(s + 2)(s + 3)} = \frac{4}{s + 2} - \frac{3}{s + 3}$$

which is the solution we sought. Let us check this solution by forming a fraction with a common denominator from the two partial fractions, hence

$$\frac{4}{s + 2} - \frac{3}{s + 3} = \frac{4(s + 3) - 3(s + 2)}{(s + 2)(s + 3)}$$

$$= \frac{4s - 3s + 12 - 6}{(s + 2)(s + 3)} = \frac{s + 6}{(s + 2)(s + 3)}$$

which agrees with our original form of $F(s)$.

Keep in mind that the value of partial fractions was to aid in finding the inverse Laplace transform. It aids by taking the form $(s + 6)/[(s + 2)(s + 3)]$, which matches none of the transform pairs of Table 4–2, and allows $(s + 6)/[(s + 2)(s + 3)]$ to be written in the form $4/(s + 2) - 3/(s + 3)$. Now $4/(s + 3)$ and $3/(s + 3)$ are easily identified with transform pairs of Table 4–2.

Example 4–18   Given $H(s) = (s + 5)/(2s^2 + 20s + 48)$ find the partial fraction form of $H(s)$, that is, $H(s) = \sum_{r=1}^{m} K_r/(s - s_r)$ of Eq. (4–61). First we must get the coefficient of the highest power of s, that is s^2, equal to unity and then we will factor the quadratic. Hence,

$$H(s) = \frac{s + 5}{2(s^2 + 10s + 24)} = \frac{1}{2} \frac{s + 5}{(s + 4)(s + 6)}$$

$$= \frac{K_1}{s + 4} + \frac{K_2}{s + 6}$$

Determining K_1 and K_2 we have

$$K_1 = \frac{s + 5}{2(s + 6)}\bigg|_{s=-4} = \frac{-4 + 5}{2(-4 + 6)} = \frac{1}{4}$$

and

$$K_2 = \frac{s + 5}{2(s + 4)}\bigg|_{s=-6} = \frac{-6 + 5}{2(-6 + 4)} = \frac{1}{4}$$

Thus

$$H(s) = \frac{1}{4} \frac{1}{(s + 4)} + \frac{1}{4} \frac{1}{(s + 6)} = \frac{1}{4}\left(\frac{1}{s + 4} + \frac{1}{s + 6}\right)$$

Again, let us check the validity of the values we determined for K_1 and K_2 by putting the partial fractions back under common denominator. Thus

$$H(s) = \frac{1}{4}\left(\frac{1}{s+4} + \frac{1}{s+6}\right) = \frac{1}{4}\left[\frac{(s+6)+(s+4)}{(s+4)(s+6)}\right]$$

$$= \frac{1}{4}\left[\frac{2s+10}{(s+4)(s+6)}\right] = \frac{2}{4}\frac{(s+5)}{(s+4)(s+6)}$$

$$= \frac{1}{2}\frac{s+5}{(s+4)(s+6)}$$

which is our original function. If we were asked for $h(t)$ where $h(t) = \mathcal{L}^{-1}[H(s)]$ we would have

$$h(t) = \frac{1}{2}\mathcal{L}^{-1}\left[\frac{s+5}{(s+4)(s+6)}\right]$$

$$= \frac{1}{4}\left[\mathcal{L}^{-1}\left(\frac{1}{s+4}\right) + \mathcal{L}^{-1}\left(\frac{1}{s+6}\right)\right]$$

$$h(t) = \frac{1}{4}(e^{-4t} + e^{-6t})u(t)$$

Example 4—19   Given $Y(s) = (5s^3 + 2)/(s^3 + 6s^2 + 11s + 6)$ find $y(x)$. We must first make $Y(s)$ a proper fraction, hence

$$
\begin{array}{r}
5 \\
s^3 + 6s^2 + 11s + 6\overline{\smash{)}5s^3 + 2} \\
5s^3 + 30s^2 + 55s + 30 \\
\hline
-30s^2 - 55s - 28
\end{array}
$$

So,

$$Y(s) = \frac{5s^3 + 2}{s^3 + 6s^2 + 11s + 6} = 5 - \frac{30s^2 + 55s + 28}{s^3 + 6s^2 + 11s + 6}$$

where $(30s^2 + 55s + 28)/(s^3 + 6s^2 + 11s + 6)$ is a proper fraction. Writing $(30s^2 + 55s + 28)/(s^3 + 6s^2 + 11s + 6)$ in partial fractional form we have

$$\frac{30s^2 + 55s + 28}{s^3 + 6s^2 + 11s + 6} = \frac{30s^2 + 55s + 28}{(s+1)(s+2)(s+3)}$$

$$= \frac{K_1}{s+1} + \frac{K_2}{s+2} + \frac{K_3}{s+3}$$

LINS method of factoring is one means which could be used. In determining the constants K_1, K_2, and K_3 we perform:

$$K_1 = [(s+1)Y(s)]\Big|_{s=-1} = \left[\frac{30s^2 + 55s + 28}{(s+2)(s+3)}\right]\Big|_{s=-1} = \frac{3}{2}$$

$$K_2 = \left[\frac{30s^2 + 55s + 28}{(s+2)(s+3)}\right]\Big|_{s=-2} = -38$$

and

$$K_3 = \left[\frac{30s^2 + 55s + 28}{(s + 1)(s + 2)}\right]\Bigg|_{s=-3} = \frac{133}{2}$$

Therefore,

$$Y(s) = 5 - \left(\frac{\frac{3}{2}}{s + 1} - \frac{38}{s + 2} + \frac{\frac{133}{2}}{s + 3}\right)$$

Before finding $y(x)$ let us check the partial fraction's validity by forming a common denominator of the three partial fractions and see if we get $(30s^2 + 55s + 28)/[(s + 1)(s + 2)(s + 3)]$. Thus,

$$\frac{\frac{3}{2}}{s + 1} - \frac{38}{s + 2} + \frac{\frac{133}{2}}{s + 3}$$

$$= \frac{\frac{3}{2}(s+2)(s+3) - 38(s+1)(s+3) + \frac{133}{2}(s+1)(s+2)}{(s + 1)(s + 2)(s + 3)}$$

$$= \frac{68s^2 + 207s + 142 - 38s^2 - 152s - 114}{(s + 1)(s + 2)(s + 3)}$$

$$= \frac{30s^2 + 55s + 28}{(s + 1)(s + 2)(s + 3)}$$

which agrees with the original fraction.

Let us return to determining $y(x)$ by performing $\mathcal{L}^{-1}[Y(s)]$. Hence,

$$y(x) = \mathcal{L}^{-1}\left[\frac{5s^3 + 2}{s^3 + 6s^2 + 11s + 6}\right]$$

$$= \mathcal{L}^{-1}\left[5 - \frac{\frac{3}{2}}{s + 1} + \frac{38}{s + 2} - \frac{\frac{133}{2}}{s + 3}\right]$$

so

$$y(x) = 5\delta(x) - \frac{3}{2}e^{-x}u(x) + 38e^{-2x}u(x) - \frac{133}{2}e^{-3x}u(x)$$

$$y(x) = 5\delta(x) - \left(\frac{3}{2}e^{-x} - 38e^{-2x} + 133e^{-3x}\right)u(x)$$

Example 4—20 Given $F(s) = (s^2 + 1)/(4s^3 + 24s^2 + 32s)$ find $f(t)$. We notice that according to Procedure 1 we must make s^3 have a coefficient of unity. Then

$$F(s) = \frac{s^2 + 1}{4(s^3 + 6s^2 + 8s)}$$

We are now ready to factor the denominator in preparation for forming $F(s)$'s partial fraction, that is,

$$F(s) = \frac{s^2 + 1}{4[s(s^2 + 6s + 8)]} = \frac{s^2 + 1}{4s(s + 2)(s + 4)}$$

The partial fraction then is

$$F(s) = \frac{s^2 + 1}{4s(s + 2)(s + 4)} = \frac{K_1}{s} + \frac{K_2}{s + 2} + \frac{K_3}{s + 4}$$

Evaluating K_1, K_2, and K_3 we find

$$K_1 = \left[\frac{s^2 + 1}{4(s + 2)(s + 4)}\right]\Bigg|_{s=0} = \frac{1}{32}$$

$$K_2 = \left[\frac{s^2 + 1}{4s(s + 4)}\right]\Bigg|_{s=-2} = -\frac{5}{16}$$

and

$$K_3 = \left[\frac{s^2 + 1}{4s(s + 2)}\right]\Bigg|_{s=-4} = \frac{17}{32}$$

Hence,

$$F(s) = \frac{\dfrac{1}{32}}{s} - \frac{\dfrac{5}{16}}{s + 2} + \frac{\dfrac{17}{32}}{s + 4}$$

so

$$f(t) = \left(\frac{1}{32} - \frac{5}{16}e^{-2t} + \frac{17}{32}e^{-4t}\right)u(t)$$

Next we will investigate partial fractions containing repeated roots. As in the case of a nonrepeated root case consider some function $F(s)$ which can be written as the ratio of two polynomials $N(s)$ and $D(s)$. As before we shall consider $D(s)$ to be factorable into quantities of the form $(s + \alpha)^n$, but now the integer n will be greater than 1. This yields partial fractions of the repeated root case.

To begin, consider the fraction of Eq. (4–59) written as

$$F(s) = \frac{N(s)}{D(s)} = \frac{a_n s^n + a_{n-1} s^{n-1} + a_{n-2} s^{n-2} + \cdots + a_1 s + a_0}{(s - s_1)^k} \quad \textbf{(4–63)}$$

Expanding Eq. (4–63) to the partial fraction form for functions with repeated roots we have

$$F(s) = \frac{N(s)}{(s - s_1)^k}$$

$$= \frac{K_{11}}{(s - s_1)^1} + \frac{K_{12}}{(s - s_1)^2} + \frac{K_{13}}{(s - s_1)^3} + \cdots + \frac{K_{1k}}{(s - s_1)^k}$$

$$= \sum_{m=1}^{k} \frac{K_{1m}}{(s - s_1)^m} \quad \textbf{(4–64)}$$

Now, we can determine K_{1k} using the same techniques used for the non-repeated root case, that is,

$$[(s - s_1)^k F(s)]\Big|_{s=s_1} = \frac{(s - s_1)^k}{(s - s_1)^1}\Big|_{s=s_1} K_{11} + \frac{(s - s_1)^k}{(s - s_1)^2}\Big|_{s=s_1} K_{12} + \cdots$$
$$+ \frac{(s - s_1)^k}{(s - s_1)^{k-1}}\Big|_{s=s_1} K_{1(k-1)} + \frac{(s - s_1)^k}{(s - s_1)^k}\Big|_{s=s_1} K_{1k}$$
$$= \left[(s - s_1)^k \sum_{m=1}^{k} \frac{K_{1m}}{(s - s_1)^m}\right]\Big|_{s=s_1} \tag{4-64a}$$

or

$$[(s - s_1)^k F(s)]\Big|_{s=s_1} = (s - s_1)^{k-1}\Big|_{s=s_1} K_{11} + (s - s_1)^{k-2}\Big|_{s=s_1} K_{12} + \cdots$$
$$+ (s - s_1)\Big|_{s=s_1} K_{1(k-1)} + K_{1k} \tag{4-65}$$

after carrying out the division.

Now since $(s - s_1)^n\Big|_{s=s_1} = (s_1 - s_1)^n = 0$ Eq. (4-65) becomes

$$[(s - s_1)^k F(s)]\Big|_{s=s_1} = 0 \cdot K_{11} + 0 \cdot K_{12} + \cdots + 0 \cdot K_{1(k-1)} + K_{1k}$$

Therefore

$$K_{1k} = [(s - s_1)^k F(s)]\Big|_{s=s_1} \tag{4-66}$$

Notice we cannot find $K_{1(k-1)}$ using the techniques of the nonrepeated roots, that is,

$$K_{1(k-1)} \neq [(s - s_1)^{k-1} F(s)]\Big|_{s=s_1} = (s - s_1)^{k-2} K_{11} + (s - s_1)^{k-3}\Big|_{s=s_1} K_{12} + \cdots$$
$$+ K_{1(k-1)} + (s - s_1)^{-1}\Big|_{s=s_1} K_{1k}$$

of which

$$(s - s_1)^{-1}\Big|_{s=s_1} K_{1k} = \frac{K_{1k}}{s_1 - s_1} = \frac{K_{1k}}{0}$$

is undefined. We will have to determine another way for finding $K_{1(k-1)}$, $K_{1(k-2)}, \ldots, K_{13}, K_{12}, K_{11}$. Let us return to Eq. (4-64) and again multiply it by $(s - s_1)^k$ as if we were trying to determine K_{1k} of Eq. (4-66), except we will not substitute $s = s_1$. Then

$$(s - s_1)^k F(s) = (s - s_1)^{k-1} K_{11} + (s - s_1)^{k-2} K_{12} + \cdots$$
$$+ (s - s_1)^2 K_{1(k-2)} + (s - s_1) K_{1(k-1)} + K_{1k}$$
$$= \sum_{m=1}^{k} (s - s_1)^{k-m} K_{1m} \tag{4-67}$$

which is essentially Eq. (4-66) without s being evaluated at the root s_1. Notice from Eq. (4-67) if we will differentiate Eq. (4-67) the constant

$K_{1(k-1)}$ can be determined by evaluating s at the root s_1. Thus

$$\frac{d}{ds}[(s-s_1)^k F(s)] = K_{11}\frac{d}{ds}(s-s_1)^{k-1} + K_{12}\frac{d}{ds}(s-s_1)^{k-2} + \cdots$$

$$+ K_{1(k-2)}\frac{d}{ds}(s-s_1)^2 + K_{1(k-1)}\frac{d}{ds}(s-s_1) + \frac{dK_{1k}}{ds}$$

$$= \frac{d}{ds}\sum_{m=1}^{k}(s-s_1)^{k-m}K_{1m}$$

or

$$\frac{d}{ds}[(s-s_1)^k F(s)] = (k-1)K_{11}(s-s_1)^{k-2}$$

$$+ (k-2)K_{12}(s-s_1)^{k-3} + \cdots$$

$$+ 2K_{1(k-2)}(s-s_1) + K_{1(k-1)}$$

$$= \sum_{m=1}^{k}(k-m)(s-s_1)^{(k-m-1)}K_{1m} \qquad (4\text{-}68)$$

since $dK_{1k}/ds = 0$.

Now evaluating s at the root s_1 we find Eq. (4–68) yields

$$K_{1(k-1)} = \left\{\frac{d}{ds}[(s-s_1)^k F(s)]\right\}\bigg|_{s=s_1} \qquad (4\text{-}69)$$

Notice $[\sum_{m=1}^{k}(k-m)(s-s_1)^{[(k-m)-1]}K_{1m}]|_{s=s_1}$ has a value only for $m = k-1$, and that value is $K_{1(k-1)}$.

To determine the value of $K_{1(k-2)}$ let us differentiate Eq. (4–68),

$$\frac{d^2}{ds^2}[(s-s_1)^k F(s)] = (k-1)K_{11}\frac{d}{ds}(s-s_1)^{k-2}$$

$$+ (k-2)K_{12}\frac{d}{ds}(s-s_1)^{k-3} + \cdots$$

$$+ 2K_{1(k-2)}\frac{d}{ds}(s-s_1) + \frac{d}{ds}K_{1(k-1)}$$

$$= \frac{d}{ds}\sum_{m=1}^{k}(k-m)(s-s_1)^{[(k-m)-1]}K_{1m}$$

or

$$\frac{d^2}{ds^2}[(s-s_1)^k F(s)] = (k-1)(k-2)K_{11}(s-s_1)^{k-3}$$

$$+ (k-2)(k-3)K_{12}(s-s_1)^{k-4} + \cdots + 2K_{1(k-2)}$$

$$= \sum_{m=1}^{k-1}(k-m)[(k-m)-1](s-s_1)^{[(k-m)-2]}K_{1m}$$

$$(4\text{-}70)$$

Now, let us evaluate s at s_1 using Eq. (4–70), thus

$$2K_{1(k-2)} = \left\{\frac{d^2}{ds^2}[(s-s_1)^k F(s)]\right\}\bigg|_{s=s_1}$$

$$= \left[\sum_{m=1}^{k}(k-m)[(k-m)-1](s-s_1)^{[(k-m)-2]}K_{1m}\right]\bigg|_{s=s_1}$$

for which only the term for $m = k - 2$ exists. Then $2K_{1(k-2)} = (k - m)! K_{1m}|_{m=k-2}$, therefore

$$K_{1m} = \frac{1}{2!}\left\{\frac{d^2}{ds^2}[(s - s_1)^k F(s)]\right\}\Bigg|_{s=s_1} \tag{4-71}$$

since $(k - m)! = 2!$. To determine values for the remaining constants we could continue to differentiate as we have done and then evaluate the differentiated equation at the root s_1. This will result in the general expression

$$K_{1m} = \frac{1}{(k - m)!}\left\{\frac{d^{k-m}}{ds^{k-m}}[(s - s_1)^k F(s)]\right\}\Bigg|_{s=s_1} \tag{4-72}$$

where $k =$ degree of $D(s)$ according to Eqs. (4–63) and (4–64)
      $m =$ the degree of root under consideration

which is valid for evaluating all of the constants K_{11}, K_{12}, K_{13}, etc., etc., for repeated roots.

Next let us utilize Eq. (4–72) by considering some examples.

Example 4–21   Given $G(s) = 5s/(s + 10)^2$ find $g(t)$.
Using Eq. (4–64) to put $G(s)$ in partial fraction form we have

$$G(s) = \frac{5s}{(s + 10)^2} = \frac{K_{11}}{s + 10} + \frac{K_{12}}{(s + 10)^2}$$

where $k = 2$. Now we will use Eq. (4–72) to evaluate K_{11} and K_{12}, thus

$$K_{11} = K_{1m}|_{m=1}$$

$$= \frac{1}{(2 - 1)!}\left\{\frac{d^{2-1}}{ds^{2-1}}\left[(s + 10)^2 \frac{5s}{(s + 10)^2}\right]\right\}\Bigg|_{s=-10}$$

$$= \left\{\frac{d}{ds}[5s]\right\}\Bigg|_{s=-10} = 5$$

and

$$K_{12} = K_{1m}|_{m=2}$$

$$= \frac{1}{(2 - 2)!}\left\{\frac{d^{2-2}}{ds^{2-2}}\left[(s + 10)^2 \frac{5s}{(s + 10)^2}\right]\right\}\Bigg|_{s=-10}$$

$$= \frac{1}{0!}\left\{\frac{d^0}{ds^0}[5s]\right\}\Bigg|_{s=-10} = -5s\Big|_{s=-10} = -50$$

since $0! = 1$ and d^0/ds^0 means *take no derivative*. Therefore,

$$G(s) = \frac{5s}{(s + 10)^2} = \frac{5}{s + 10} - \frac{50}{(s + 10)^2}$$

Before performing $\mathcal{L}^{-1}[G(s)]$ let us put the partial fraction under common denominator to see if we get $5s/(s + 10)^2$

again. Hence

$$\frac{5}{s + 10} - \frac{50}{(s + 10)^2} = \frac{5(s + 10) - 50}{(s + 10)^2} = \frac{5s}{(s + 10)^2}$$

which agrees with the original form of $G(s)$. Then

$$g(t) = \mathcal{L}^{-1}\left[\frac{5s}{(s + 10)^2}\right] = \mathcal{L}^{-1}\left(\frac{5}{s + 10}\right)$$

$$- \mathcal{L}^{-1}\left[\frac{50}{(s + 10)^2}\right]$$

$$= 5e^{-10t}u(t) - 50te^{-10t}u(t) = 5e^{-10t}(1 - t)u(t)$$

using Eq. (6) of Table 4–2 exclusively by letting $n = 1$ and then 2, or using Eq. (6) for $\mathcal{L}^{-1}[50/(s + 10)^2]$ and Eq. (4) for $\mathcal{L}^{-1}[5/(s + 10)]$.

Example 4–22   Given $H(s) = (2s + 5)/(s + 6)^2$ find $h(x)$. From Eq. (4–64)

$$H(s) = \frac{2s + 5}{(s + 6)^3} = \frac{K_{11}}{s + 6} + \frac{K_{12}}{(s + 6)^2} + \frac{K_{13}}{(s + 6)^3}$$

where $k = 3$.
Using Eq. (4–72) to evaluate K_{11}, K_{12}, and K_{13}, hence

$$K_{11} = K_{1m}\Big|_{m=1} = \frac{1}{2!}\left\{\frac{d^2}{ds^2}\left[(s + 6)^3\frac{2s + 5}{(s + 6)^3}\right]\right\}\Big|_{s=-6}$$

so

$$K_{11} = \frac{1}{2}\left[\frac{d^2}{ds^2}(2s + 5)\right]\Big|_{s=-6} = \frac{1}{2}[0]\Big|_{s=-6} = 0$$

$$K_{12} = \frac{1}{1!}\left[\frac{d}{ds}(2s + 5)\right]\Big|_{s=-6} = [2]\Big|_{s=-6} = 2$$

and

$$K_{13} = [(2s + 5)]\Big|_{s=-6} = -7$$

Therefore

$$H(s) = \frac{2s + 5}{(s + 6)^3} = \frac{2}{(s + 6)^2} - \frac{7}{(s + 6)^3}$$

Then

$$h(x) = \mathcal{L}^{-1}\left[\frac{2}{(s + 6)^2}\right] - \mathcal{L}^{-1}\left[\frac{7}{(s + 6)^3}\right]$$

$$= \frac{2}{(2 - 1)!}t^{2-1}e^{-6t}u(t) - \frac{7}{(3 - 1)!}t^{3-1}e^{-6t}u(t)$$

$$= 2te^{-6t}u(t) - \frac{7}{2}t^2e^{-6t}u(t)$$

$$= te^{-6t}\left(2 - \frac{7}{2}t\right)u(t)$$

We may use partial fractions for functions which have multirepeated roots, that is, functions which appear as

$$F(s) = \frac{N(s)}{(s - s_1)^k(s - s_2)^q(s - s_3)^r \cdots (s - s_y)^p}$$

Writing $F(s)$ in partial fraction form we have,

$$
\begin{aligned}
F(s) &= \frac{N(s)}{(s - s_1)^k(s - s_2)^q(s - s_3)^r \cdots (s - s_y)^p} \\
&= \left[\frac{k_{11}}{(s - s_1)^1} + \frac{k_{12}}{(s - s_1)^2} + \cdots + \frac{k_{1k}}{(s - s_1)^k} \right] \\
&\quad + \left[\frac{K_{21}}{(s - s_2)^1} + \frac{K_{22}}{(s - s_2)^2} + \frac{K_{23}}{(s - s_2)^3} + \cdots + \frac{K_{2q}}{(s - s_2)^q} \right] \\
&\quad + \left[\frac{K_{31}}{(s - s_3)^1} + \frac{K_{32}}{(s - s_3)^2} + \frac{K_{33}}{(s - s_3)^3} + \cdots + \frac{K_{3r}}{(s - s_3)^r} \right] \\
&\quad + \left[\frac{K_{y1}}{(s - s_y)^1} + \frac{K_{y2}}{(s - s_y)^2} + \frac{K_{y3}}{(s - s_y)^3} + \cdots + \frac{K_{yp}}{(s - s_y)^p} \right] \\
&= \sum_{m=1}^{k} \frac{K_{1m}}{(s - s_1)^m} + \sum_{y=1}^{q} \frac{k_{2y}}{(s - s_2)^y} + \sum_{z=1}^{r} \frac{K_{3z}}{(s - s_3)^z} + \cdots \\
&\quad + \sum_{x=1}^{p} \frac{K_{yx}}{(s - s_y)^x} \quad\quad\quad\quad \textbf{(4-73)}
\end{aligned}
$$

An example of Eq. (4-73) is

$$F(s) = \frac{10s + 6}{(s + 6)^2(s + 2)^4} = \frac{N(s)}{(s + 6)^2(s + 2)^4} = \frac{N(s)}{(s - s_1)^2(s - s_2)^4}$$

defining $s_1 = -6$ and $s_2 = -2$. Then $F(s)$ may be written as

$$
\begin{aligned}
F(s) &= \frac{K_{11}}{s + 6} + \frac{K_{12}}{(s + 6)^2} + \frac{K_{21}}{s + 2} + \frac{K_{22}}{(s + 2)^2} + \frac{K_{23}}{(s + 2)^3} + \frac{K_{24}}{(s + 2)^4} \\
&= \sum_{m=1}^{2} \frac{K_{1m}}{(s + 6)^m} + \sum_{y=1}^{4} \frac{K_{2y}}{(s + 2)^y}
\end{aligned}
$$

Returning to Eq. (4-73), if we wish to evaluate the constants generated from K_{1m} we see that by multiplying $F(s)$ by $(s - s_1)^k$ and evaluating that product at $s = s_1$ we have essentially Eq. (4-64a) since $[(s - s_1)^k]\big|_{s=s_1} = 0$, that is

$$
\begin{aligned}
\left[(s - s_1)^k F(s)\right]\bigg|_{s=s_1} &= \left[(s - s_1)^k \sum_{m=1}^{k} \frac{K_{1m}}{(s - s_1)^m}\right]\bigg|_{s=s_1} \\
&\quad + \left[(s - s_1)^k \sum_{y=1}^{q} \frac{K_{2y}}{(s - s_2)^y}\right]\bigg|_{s=s_1} + \cdots \\
&\quad + \left[(s - s_1)^k \sum_{x=1}^{p} \frac{K_{yx}}{(s - s_y)^x}\right]\bigg|_{s=s_1} \quad\quad \textbf{(4-74)}
\end{aligned}
$$

or

$$\left[(s - s_1)^k F(s)\right]\bigg|_{s=s_1} = \left[(s - s_1)^k \sum_{m=1}^{k} \frac{K_{1m}}{(s - s_1)^m}\right]\bigg|_{s=s_1} \quad\quad \textbf{(4-74a)}$$

since only the term with $(s - s_1)$ in its denominator has any chance of having a value, other than zero, after s is evaluated at s_1. Let us show that this is true by looking at any one of the terms which are forced to zero. Choosing the term

$$\left[(s - s_1)^k \sum_{y=1}^{q} \frac{K_{2y}}{(s - s_2)^y} \right]\Bigg|_{s=s_1}$$

from Eq. (4–74). Expanding that term we have

$$\left[(s - s_1)^k \sum_{y=1}^{q} \frac{K_{2y}}{(s - s_2)^y} \right]\Bigg|_{s=s_1} = \left[\frac{(s - s_1)^k}{(s - s_2)} K_{21} + \frac{(s - s_1)^k}{(s - s_2)^2} K_{22} \right.$$

$$\left. + \frac{(s - s_1)^k}{(s - s_2)^3} K_{23} + \cdots + \frac{(s - s_1)^k}{(s - s_2)^q} K_{2q} \right]\Bigg|_{s=s_1} = 0$$

since $(s - s_1)^k \big|_{s=s_1} = 0$, which demonstrates Eq. (4–75) is true. Then, since Eq. (4–74a) and Eq. (4–64a) are the same we may evaluate $K_{11}, K_{12}, K_{13},$ $\ldots, K_{1k}$ from Eq. (4–72). If we wish to determine the values for those constants generated by K_{2y} we may use the same reasoning and perform

$$[(s - s_2)F(s)]\Big|_{s=s_2} = \left[(s - s_2)^q \sum_{y=1}^{q} \frac{K_{2y}}{(s - s_2)^y} \right]\Bigg|_{s=s_2}$$

using Eq. (4–73). Again we have the same form as Eq. (4–64a) and therefore may use Eq. (4–72) to determine the values for $K_{21}, K_{22}, \ldots, K_{2y}$. Hence, Eq. (4–72) would appear as

$$K_{2y} = \frac{1}{(q - y)!} \left\{ \frac{d^{q-y}}{ds^{q-y}} [(s - s_2)^q F(s)] \right\} \Bigg|_{s=s_2}$$

We could do the same for determining the value for the constants generated from K_{3z} from Eq. (4–73) and find Eq. (4–72) to appear as

$$K_{3z} = \frac{1}{(r - z)!} \left\{ \frac{d^{r-z}}{ds^{r-z}} [(s - s_3)^r F(s)] \right\} \Bigg|_{s=s_3}$$

Let us generalize Eq. (4–72). Let Eq. (4–72) be modified to appear as

$$K_{nm} = \frac{1}{(k - m)!} \left\{ \frac{d^{k-m}}{ds^{k-m}} [(s - s_n)^k F(s)] \right\} \Bigg|_{s=s_n} \tag{4-75}$$

where n indicates that the constants for the partial fraction of the repeated roots s_n are being solved for; m and k represent the same as in Eq. (4–72).

At this point let us work some examples in order to gain experience with Eq. (4–75).

Example 4–23   Given $X(s) = (3s^2 + 2)/[s^2(s + 3)^2]$ find $x(y)$. From Eq. (4–73) we may write $X(s)$ as

$$X(s) = \frac{3s^2 + 2}{s^2(s + 3)^2} = \left[\frac{K_{11}}{s} + \frac{K_{12}}{s^2} \right]$$

$$+ \left[\frac{K_{21}}{(s + 3)^1} + \frac{K_{22}}{(s + 3)^2} \right]$$

Using Eq. (4–75)

$$K_{11} = K_{nm}\Big|_{\substack{n=m=1 \\ k=2}} = \frac{1}{1!}\left\{\frac{d}{ds}\left[s^2 \cdot \frac{3s^2 + 2}{s^2(s + 3)^2}\right]\right\}\Big|_{s=0}$$

$$= \left\{\frac{d}{ds}\left[\frac{3s^2 + 2}{(s + 3)^2}\right]\right\}\Big|_{s=0}$$

$$= \frac{(s + 3)^2 6s - (3s^2 + 2)2(s + 3)}{[(s + 3)^2]^2}\Big|_{s=0}$$

using Eq. (26) of Table 4–2. Then $K_{11} = -(12/81) = -(4/27)$. Evaluating K_{12} next using Eq. (4–75) we have

$$K_{12} = \frac{1}{0!}\left\{\frac{d^0}{ds^0}\left[\frac{3s^2 + 2}{(s + 3)^2}\right]\right\}\Big|_{s=0} = \left[\frac{3s^2 + 2}{(s + 3)^2}\right]\Big|_{s=0} = \frac{2}{9}$$

To determine the constants for the root $s_2 = -3$ we have

$$K_{21} = K_{nm}\Big|_{\substack{n=2 \\ m=1 \\ k=2}} = \frac{1}{1!}\left\{\frac{d}{ds}\left[\frac{3s^2 + 2}{s^2}\right]\right\}\Big|_{s=-3}$$

$$= \left[\frac{s^2(6s) - 2s(3s^2 + 2)}{s^4}\right]\Big|_{s=-3} = \frac{12}{81} = \frac{4}{27}$$

and

$$K_{22} = \left[\frac{3s^2 + 2}{s^2}\right]\Big|_{s=-3} = \frac{29}{9}$$

Therefore,

$$X(s) = -\frac{4}{27}\frac{1}{s} + \frac{2}{9}\frac{1}{s^2} + \frac{4}{27}\frac{1}{(s + 3)} + \frac{29}{9}\frac{1}{(s + 3)^2}$$

(This answer may be checked for its validity by putting the partial fractions of $X(s)$ under common denominator as we did previously.)

Then

$$x(y) = \mathcal{L}^{-1}\left[\frac{3s^2 + 2}{s^2(s + 3)^2}\right] = -\frac{4}{27}\mathcal{L}^{-1}\left[\frac{1}{s}\right] + \frac{2}{9}\mathcal{L}^{-1}\left[\frac{1}{s^2}\right]$$

$$+ \frac{4}{27}\mathcal{L}^{-1}\left[\frac{1}{s + 3}\right] + \frac{29}{9}\mathcal{L}^{-1}\left[\frac{1}{(s + 3)^2}\right]$$

$$= -\frac{4}{27}u(t) + \frac{2}{9}tu(t) + \frac{4}{27}e^{-3t}u(t)$$

$$+ \frac{29}{9}\left[\frac{1}{(2 - 1)!}te^{-3t}\right]u(t)$$

Therefore,

$$x(y) = \left[\left(t - \frac{2}{3}\right)\frac{2}{9} + \left(29t + \frac{4}{3}\right)\frac{e^{-3t}}{9}\right]u(t)$$

Example 4–24 Given $F(s) = 2/(s+1)^2(s+2)^3$ find $f(t)$. From Eq. (4–73)

$$F(s) = \frac{2}{(s+1)^2(s+2)^3} = \frac{K_{11}}{s+1} + \frac{K_{12}}{(s+1)^2} + \frac{K_{21}}{s+2}$$
$$+ \frac{K_{22}}{(s+2)^2} + \frac{K_{23}}{(s+2)^3}$$

and from Eq. (4–75)

$$K_{11} = \frac{1}{1!} \left\{ \frac{d}{ds} \left[\frac{2}{(s+2)^3} \right] \right\} \bigg|_{s=-1}$$
$$= \frac{(s+3)^3 0 - 3(s+2)^2 2}{(s+2)^6} \bigg|_{s=-1} = -6,$$

$$K_{12} = \left[\frac{2}{(s+2)^3} \right] \bigg|_{s=-1} = 2$$

$$K_{21} = \frac{1}{2!} \left\{ \frac{d^2}{ds^2} \left[\frac{2}{(s+1)^2} \right] \right\} \bigg|_{s=-3}$$

Now

$$\frac{d}{ds} \left[\frac{2}{(s+1)^2} \right] = \frac{-2(s+1)2}{(s+1)^4} = -\frac{4}{(s+1)^3}$$

so

$$\frac{d^2}{ds^2} \left[\frac{2}{(s+1)^2} \right] = -\frac{d}{ds} \left[\frac{4}{(s+1)^3} \right] = \frac{12}{(s+1)^4}$$

Therefore

$$K_{21} = \frac{1}{2!} \left[\frac{12}{(s+1)^4} \right] \bigg|_{s=-2} = 6$$

Also,

$$K_{22} = \frac{1}{1!} \frac{d}{ds} \left[\frac{2}{(s+1)^2} \right] \bigg|_{s=-2} = -\frac{4}{(s+1)^3} \bigg|_{s=-2} = 4$$

and

$$K_{23} = \frac{1}{0!} \left[\frac{2}{(s+1)^2} \right] \bigg|_{s=-2} = 2$$

Hence,

$$F(s) = -\frac{6}{(s+1)} + \frac{2}{(s+1)^2} + \frac{6}{(s+2)} + \frac{4}{(s+2)^2}$$
$$+ \frac{2}{(s+2)^3}$$

Therefore

$$f(t) = \mathcal{L}^{-1}\left[\frac{2}{(s+1)^2(s+2)^3}\right]$$

$$= -\mathcal{L}^{-1}\left[\frac{6}{s+1}\right] + \mathcal{L}^{-1}\left[\frac{2}{(s+1)^2}\right] + \mathcal{L}^{-1}\left[\frac{6}{s+2}\right]$$

$$+ \mathcal{L}^{-1}\left[\frac{4}{(s+2)^2}\right] + \mathcal{L}^{-1}\left[\frac{2}{(s+2)^3}\right]$$

so

$$f(t) = \left[-6e^{-t} + \frac{2}{1!}te^{-t} + 6e^{-2t} + \frac{4}{1!}te^{-2t}\right.$$

$$\left. + \frac{2}{2!}t^2e^{-2t}\right]u(t)$$

$$f(t) = [(t-3)e^{-t} + (3+2t+t^2)e^{-2t}]u(t)$$

Our last consideration of partial fractions shall be when the function, which is to be written as the sum of partial fractions, is a hybrid of repeated and nonrepeated roots. That is, where $F(s)$ can be written as

$$F(s) = \frac{N(s)}{(s-s_1)(s-s_2)\cdots(s-s_m)(s-s_a)^k(s-s_b)^r\cdots(s-s_y)^p}$$

$$(4-76)$$

which is a hybrid of Eqs. (4-60) and (4-73). Notice the denominator of Eq. (4-76) is simply the product of Eqs. (4-60) and (4-73). Equation (4-76) may be written as the sum of partial fractions composed of nonrepeated roots and repeated roots as given in Eqs. (4-61) and (4-73) respectively. Thus we may write

$$F(s) = \frac{N(s)}{\underbrace{(s-s_1)(s-s_2)\cdots(s-s_m)}_{\text{nonrepeated roots}}\underbrace{(s-s_a)^k(s-s_b)^r\cdots(s-s_y)^p}_{\text{repeated roots}}}$$

$$= \frac{K_1}{s-s_1} + \frac{K_2}{s-s_2} + \cdots + \frac{K_m}{s-s_m} + \frac{K_{a1}}{s-s_a} + \frac{K_{a2}}{(s-s_a)^2}$$

$$+ \cdots + \frac{K_{ak}}{(s-s_a)^k} + \frac{K_{b1}}{s-s_b} + \frac{K_{b2}}{(s-s_b)^2}$$

$$+ \cdots + \frac{K_{br}}{(s-s_b)^r} + \frac{K_{y1}}{s-s_y} + \cdots + \frac{K_{yp}}{(s-s_y)^p} \qquad (4-77)$$

Since $F(s)$ is expressible in terms of Eqs. (4-61) and (4-73) we can use Eqs. (4-62) and (4-75) to determine the value for K_m and K_{nm} just as we have done previously. Then for some function composed of nonrepeated and repeated roots we shall write it in the form of Eq. (4-77), and solve for the constants $K_1, K_2, K_3, \ldots K_m, K_{a1}, K_{a2}$, etc. using Eqs. (4–62) and (4–75). To better demonstrate what has been stated consider the following examples.

Example 4–25   Given $P(s) = (3s + 1)/s(s + 1)(s + 2)^2$ find $p(x)$. From the form of Eq. (4–77) we may write $P(s)$ as

$$P(s) = \frac{3s + 1}{s(s + 1)(s + 2)^2} = \frac{K_1}{s} + \frac{K_2}{s + 1} + \frac{K_{a1}}{s + 2} + \frac{K_{a2}}{(s + 2)^2}$$

Now we are only using the symbol a of the subscript K_{a1} and K_{a2} as an index so as to distinguish between K_1 and K_2. So, let us set $a = 1$ since K_{11} and K_{12} are more logical writings than K_{a1} and K_{a2}. Hence,

$$P(s) = \frac{K_1}{s} + \frac{K_2}{s + 1} + \frac{K_{11}}{s + 2} + \frac{K_{12}}{(s + 2)^2}$$

Solving for the nonrepeated root constants K_1 and K_2 first we use Eq. (4–62). Thus

$$K_1 = \left[s \cdot \frac{3s + 1}{s(s + 1)(s + 2)^2}\right]\bigg|_{s=0} = \left[\frac{3s + 1}{(s + 1)(s + 2)^2}\right]\bigg|_{s=0}$$
$$= \frac{1}{4}$$

$$K_2 = \left[\frac{3s + 1}{s(s + 2)^2}\right]\bigg|_{s=-2} = 2$$

Next, solving for the repeated root constants using Eq. (4–75) we have

$$K_{11} = K_{nm}\bigg|_{\substack{k=2 \\ n=1 \\ m=1}} = \frac{1}{1!}\left\{\frac{d}{ds}\left[(s + 2)^2 \frac{3s + 1}{s(s + 1)(s + 2)^2}\right]\right\}\bigg|_{s=-2}$$

$$= \left\{\frac{d}{ds}\left[\frac{3s + 1}{s(s + 1)}\right]\right\}\bigg|_{s=-2}$$

$$= \frac{3[s(s + 1)] - \left\{\frac{d}{ds}[s(s + 1)]\right\}(3s + 1)}{[s(s + 1)]^2}\bigg|_{s=-2}$$

Now

$$\frac{d}{ds}[s(s + 1)] = \frac{d}{ds}(s^2 + s) = 2s + 1$$

so

$$K_{11} = \frac{3s(s + 1) - (2s + 1)(3s + 1)}{s^2(s + 1)^2}\bigg|_{s=-2} = -\frac{9}{4}$$

and

$$K_{12} = \left[\frac{3s + 1}{3(s + 1)} \right]\Big|_{s=-2} = -\frac{5}{2}$$

Therefore

$$P(s) = \frac{1}{4s} + \frac{2}{s + 1} - \frac{9}{4(s + 2)} - \frac{5}{2(s + 2)^2}$$

Before finding $p(x)$ let us check the validity of our partial fractions by returning the partial fractions to a common denominator. That is

$$P(s) = \frac{(s + 1) + 2(4s)}{4s(s + 1)} - \frac{9(s + 2) + 10}{4(s + 2)^2}$$

$$= \frac{1}{4}\left[\frac{(9s + 1)(s + 2)^2 - (s^2 + s)(9s + 28)}{s(s + 1)(s + 2)^2} \right]$$

$$= \frac{1}{4}\left[\frac{12s + 4}{s(s + 1)(s + 2)^2} \right] = \frac{3s + 1}{s(s + 1)(s + 2)^2}$$

which is correct. Then,

$$p(x) = \mathcal{L}^{-1}\left[\frac{1}{4s} + \frac{2}{s + 1} - \frac{9}{4(s + 2)} - \frac{5}{2(s + 2)^2} \right]$$

$$= \frac{1}{4}u(x) + 2e^{-x}u(x) - \frac{9}{4}e^{-2x}u(x) - \frac{5}{2}xe^{-2x}u(x)$$

or,

$$p(x) = \left[\frac{1}{4} + 2e^{-x} - \frac{1}{2}\left(\frac{9}{2} + 5x \right)e^{-2x} \right]u(x)$$

Example 4–26 Given $F(s) = (s + 1)e^{-3s}/s^2(s + 5)$ find $f(t)$. From the denominator we realize that $F(s)$ is a good candidate for partial fractions except we notice a difference between this example and the others. That difference is e^{-3s} of the numerator. From Table 4–2 we see that Eq. (21) is the only transform pair which has $e^{\text{constant} \cdot s}$. Then Eq. (21) must be the transform pair we wish. Hence,

$$F(s) = \frac{(s + 1)e^{-3s}}{s^2(s + 5)} = Ke^{-as}G(s)$$

where the $F(s)$ of Eq. (21), Table 4–2, was changed to $G(s)$ since the $F(s)$ of Example 4–26 and the $F(s)$ of Eq. (21) are not the same. Thus $e^{-3s} = e^{-as}$ or $a = 3$, and $(s + 1)/s^2(s + 5) = KG(s)$. Then $K = 1$ and

$$G(s) = \frac{s + 1}{s^2(s + 5)}$$

Using partial fractions

$$G(s) = \frac{s+1}{s^2(s+5)} = \frac{K_{11}}{s} + \frac{K_{12}}{s^2} + \frac{K_1}{s+5}$$

of which

$$K_{11} = \left\{ \frac{d}{ds}\left[\frac{s+1}{s+5}\right] \right\}\bigg|_{s=0} = \frac{(s+5)-(s+1)}{(s+5)^2}\bigg|_{s=0} = \frac{4}{25}$$

$$K_{12} = \left[\frac{s+1}{s+5}\right]\bigg|_{s=0} = \frac{1}{5}$$

and

$$K_1 = \left[\frac{s+1}{s^2}\right]\bigg|_{s=-5} = -\frac{4}{25}$$

Therefore,

$$G(s) = \frac{4}{25s} + \frac{1}{5s^2} - \frac{4}{25(s+5)}$$

or

$$g(t) = \left(\frac{4}{25} + \frac{1}{5}t - \frac{4}{25}e^{-5t}\right)u(t)$$

Now Eq. (21) of Table 4–2 states

$$\mathcal{L}[Kg(t-a)u(t-a)] = Ke^{-as}G(s)$$

which in our example means

$$F(s) = Ke^{-as}G(s) = \mathcal{L}[Kg(t-a)u(t-a)]$$

So

$$f(t) = \mathcal{L}^{-1}[F(s)] = \mathcal{L}^{-1}[Ke^{-as}G(s)]$$
$$= Kg(t-a)u(t-a)$$

or more simply

$$f(t) = Kg(t-a)u(t-a)$$

Well, since

$$g(t) = \left(\frac{4}{25} + \frac{1}{5}t - \frac{4}{25}e^{-5t}\right)u(t)$$

then

$$g(t-a) = \left[\frac{4}{25} + \frac{1}{5}(t-a) - \frac{4}{25}e^{-5(t-a)}\right]u(t-a)$$

We determined that $a = 3$, therefore

$$g(t-3) = \left[\frac{4}{25} + \frac{1}{5}(t-3) - \frac{4}{25}e^{-5(t-3)}\right]u(t-3)$$

Hence

$$g(t - 3)u(t - 3) = \left[\frac{4}{25} + \frac{1}{5}(t - 3)\right.$$
$$\left. - \frac{4}{25}e^{-5(t-3)}\right]u(t - 3)$$

since $u(t - 3) \cdot u(t - 3) = u(t - 3)$
Therefore

$$f(t) = \left[\frac{4}{25} + \frac{1}{5}(t - 3) - \frac{4}{25}e^{-5(t-3)}\right]u(t - 3)$$
$$= \left[-\frac{11}{25} + \frac{1}{5}t - \frac{4}{25}e^{-5(t-3)}\right]u(t - 3)$$

Example 4–27   Given $H(s) = 6se^{-5s}/(s + 2)^2(s + 3)$ find $h(t)$. From Table 4–2 the transform pair is again identified as Eq. (21) because of e^{-5s}. Then

$$h(t) = \mathcal{L}^{-1}[H(s)] = Kf(t - a)u(t - a)$$
$$= \mathcal{L}^{-1}[Ke^{-as}F(s)]$$

so,

$$H(s) = Ke^{-as}F(s) = \frac{6se^{-5s}}{(s + 2)^2(s + 3)}$$

Then $K = 6$, $a = 5$ and

$$F(s) = \frac{s}{(s + 2)^2(s + 3)}$$

Using partial fractions to find $f(t)$, hence

$$F(s) = \frac{s}{(s + 2)^2(s + 3)} = \frac{K_{11}}{s + 2} + \frac{K_{12}}{(s + 2)^2} + \frac{K_1}{s + 3}$$

and

$$K_{11} = \left\{\frac{d}{ds}\left[\frac{s}{s + 3}\right]\right\}\bigg|_{s=-2} = \frac{(s + 3) - s}{(s + 3)^2}\bigg|_{s=-2} = 3$$

$$K_{12} = \left[\frac{s}{s + 3}\right]\bigg|_{s=-2} = -2$$

and

$$K_1 = \left[\frac{s}{(s + 2)^2}\right]\bigg|_{s=-3} = -3$$

Then

$$F(s) = \frac{3}{s + 2} - \frac{2}{(s + 2)^2} - \frac{3}{s + 3}$$

so

$$f(t) = (3e^{-2t} - 2te^{-2t} - 3e^{-3t})u(t)$$

Hence,

$$f(t - a)u(t - a) = f(t - 5)u(t - 5)$$
$$= [3e^{-2(t-5)} - 2(t - 5)e^{-2(t-5)}$$
$$- 3e^{-3(t-5)}]u(t - 5)$$

so

$$h(t) = Kf(t - a)u(t - a) = 6[3e^{-2(t-5)}$$
$$- 2(t - 5)e^{-2(t-5)} - 3e^{-3(t-5)}]u(t - 5)$$
$$= 6[(13 - 2t)e^{10}e^{-2t} - 3e^{15}e^{-3t}]u(t - 5)$$

Example 4–28 Using Ex. 4–25 find $f(x)$ given $F(s) = P(s)e^{-4s}$. From Eq. (21) of Table 4–2 we know

$$f(x) = \mathcal{L}^{-1}[P(s)e^{-4s}] = p(x - 4)u(x - 4)$$

where $K = 1$.
Also from Ex. 4–25 we know

$$p(x) = \left[\frac{1}{4} + 2e^{-x} - \frac{1}{2}\left(\frac{9}{2} + 5x\right)e^{-2x}\right]u(x)$$

therefore,

$$f(x) = \left\{\frac{1}{4} + 2e^{-(x-4)}\right.$$
$$\left. - \frac{1}{2}\left[\frac{9}{2} + 5(x - 4)e^{-2(x-4)}\right]\right\}u(x - 4)$$

4–18 The Convolution Integral

When we were investigating partial fractions we saw that

$$\mathcal{L}^{-1}[G(s)F(s)] \neq \mathcal{L}^{-1}[G(s)] \cdot \mathcal{L}^{-1}[F(s)] = g(t) \cdot f(t)$$

However, it was mentioned at that time that a transform pair would be given for just such a case. The transform pair will not be derived here, but will simply be stated and applied to some examples. The reason that any discussion is avoided for now is that learning how to apply the transform will be task enough. The transform pair appears as

$$\mathcal{L}\left[\int_0^t g(t - \tau)f(\tau)\,d\tau\right] = \mathcal{L}\left[\int_0^t g(\tau)f(t - \tau)\,d\tau\right]$$
$$= \mathcal{L}[g(t) * f(t)] = G(s)F(s) \qquad \textbf{(4–78)}$$

The integral portion of Eq. (4–78) is known as the convolution integral and is commonly written as $g(t) * f(t)$. Let us now gain some experience applying Eq. (4–78) by working some examples.

Example 4–29 Given $H(s) = 10/s(s + 5)$ find $h(t)$. We know that we already have several means with which to find $h(t)$. One would be to use Eq. (5) of Table 4–2 directly, another

would be to use partial fractions. However, we will use
Eq. (4–78). Then

$$H(s) = G(s)F(s) = \frac{10}{s(s + 5)}$$

We must now identify $G(s)$ and $F(s)$, which could be:

$$G(s) = \frac{10}{s} \quad \text{and} \quad F(s) = \frac{1}{s + 5}$$

or

$$G(s) = \frac{1}{s + 5} \quad \text{and} \quad F(s) = \frac{10}{s}$$

or

$$G(s) = \frac{1}{s} \quad \text{and} \quad F(s) = \frac{10}{s + 5}$$

and so on.

As we see it is arbitrary as to how we define $G(s)$ and
$F(s)$ so long as $G(s)F(s) = H(s)$. Now, it may be more
convenient in performing the integration of $g(t) * f(t)$ to
identify $G(s)$ and $F(s)$ in a particular manner, but to
recognize which is best comes with experience. Let us
define

$$G(s) = \frac{10}{s} \quad \text{and} \quad F(s) = \frac{1}{s + 5}$$

and use

$$\int_0^t g(t - \tau)f(\tau)\,d\tau = g(t) * f(t) = \mathcal{L}^{-1}[G(s)F(s)] = h(t)$$

from Eq. (4–78). Then

$$g(x) = \mathcal{L}^{-1}[G(s)] = \mathcal{L}^{-1}\left[\frac{10}{s}\right] = 10u(x)$$

where x is used as a dummy variable. Then $g(t - \tau) =
10u(t - \tau)$, where $x = t - \tau$. And

$$f(x) = \mathcal{L}^{-1}[F(s)] = \mathcal{L}^{-1}\left[\frac{1}{s + 5}\right] = e^{-5x}u(x)$$

so $f(\tau) = e^{-5\tau}u(\tau)$ if we let $x = \tau$. From the convolution
integral

$$\int_0^t [10u(t - \tau)e^{-5\tau}u(\tau)]\,d\tau = \mathcal{L}^{-1}[G(s)F(s)] = h(t)$$

So

$$h(t) = 10 \int_0^t e^{-5\tau}u(t - \tau)u(\tau)\,d\tau$$

but

$$u(\tau) = \begin{cases} 0 \text{ for } \tau < 0 \\ 1 \text{ for } \tau > 0 \end{cases}$$

and

$$u(t - \tau) = \begin{cases} 0 \text{ for } \tau > t \\ 1 \text{ for } \tau < t \end{cases}$$

where the boundaries for $u(t - \tau)$ are determined by setting the quantity $(t - \tau)$ to some dummy variable, as we had x, and then investigate x as a function of t and τ. That is,

$$u(t - \tau)\Big|_{(t-\tau)=x} = u(x) = \begin{cases} 0 \text{ for } x < 0 \\ 1 \text{ for } x > 0 \end{cases}$$

We now take the conditions of $x < 0$ and $x > 0$ and determine what this means in terms of t and τ. That is, since $x < 0$ then $(t - \tau) < 0$, or $t < \tau$. Also, from $x = (t - \tau) > 0$, which says $\tau < t$. Taking the product of $u(\tau)$ and $u(t - \tau)$ we have

$$u(t - \tau)u(\tau) = \begin{cases} 0 \text{ for } 0 > \tau > t \\ 1 \text{ for } 0 < \tau < t \end{cases}$$

as can be seen from the illustrations of Fig. 4–26. We see from Fig. 4–26(c) that the product $u(\tau)u(t - \tau)$ cor-

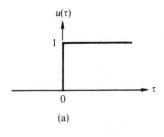

(a)

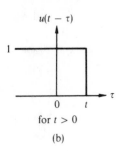

for $t > 0$

(b)

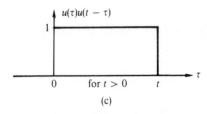

(c)

FIGURE 4–26

responds to the limits of our integral of Eq. (4–78); hence, we may omit them. Thus,

$$h(t) = 10 \int_0^t e^{-5\tau}\, d\tau = -\frac{10}{5}e^{-5\tau}\Big|_{\tau=0}^{\tau=t} u(t)$$

$$= -2(e^{-5t} - e^0)u(t) = 2(1 - e^{-5t})u(t)$$

where $u(t)$ was derived from the limits of the convolution integral. Let us verify our solution using Eq. (5) of Table 4–2. Thus

$$\mathcal{L}^{-1}\left[\frac{10}{s(s+5)}\right] = \frac{10}{5}(1 - e^{-5t})u(t) = 2(1 - e^{-5t})$$

We will now work the same problem but use

$$\int_0^t g(t)f(t - \tau)\, d\tau = \mathcal{L}^{-1}[G(s)F(s)]$$

of Eq. (4–78). Still using $G(s) = 10/s$ and $F(s) = 1/(s + 5)$, from which we determine $g(x) = 10\, u(x)$ and $f(x) = e^{-5x}u(x)$. For $g(x)$ we now let $x = \tau$ and for $f(x)$ we let $x = (t - \tau)$. Then

$$h(t) = \int_0^t 10u(\tau)e^{-5(t-\tau)}u(t - \tau)\, d\tau$$

$$= 10e^{-5t}\int_0^t e^{5\tau}u(\tau)u(t - \tau)\, d\tau$$

$$= 10e^{-5t}\int_0^t e^{5\tau}\, d\tau = 10e^{-5t}\left[\frac{1}{5}e^{5\tau}\right]\Big|_{\tau=0}^{t}$$

$$= 2e^{-5t}(e^{5t} - 1)u(t) = 2(1 - e^{-5t})u(t)$$

which agrees with our previous answers.

Example 4–30   Given $G(s) = 2/s^2(s^2 + \omega_n^2)$ find $g(t)$, where ω_n is a constant.

From Eq. (4–78) we will use

$$\int_0^t h(\tau)f(t - \tau)\, d\tau = h(t) * f(t) = \mathcal{L}^{-1}[H(s)F(s)] = g(t)$$

We changed the $G(s)$ of Eq. (4–78) to $H(s)$ since our given problem was defined as $G(s)$. Let $F(s) = 2/s$ and

$$H(s) = \frac{1}{s(s^2 + \omega_n^2)}$$

Hence $f(x) = 2u(x)$, and

$$H(x) = \frac{1}{\omega_n^2}(1 - \cos \omega_n x)u(x)$$

using Eqs. (1) and (13) of Table 4-2. Then

$$f(t - \tau) = 2u(t - \tau) \quad \text{if } x = t - \tau$$

and

$$h(\tau) = \frac{1}{\omega_n^2}(1 - \cos \omega_n \tau)u(\tau) \quad \text{for } x = \tau$$

Then

$$\int_0^t h(\tau)f(t - \tau)\,d\tau = \int_0^t \frac{1}{\omega_n^2}(1 - \cos \omega_n \tau)$$
$$\times 2u(\tau)u(t - \tau)\,d\tau$$
$$= \frac{2}{\omega_n^2}\int_0^t (1 - \cos \omega_n \tau)\,d\tau$$

since

$$u(\tau)u(t - \tau) = \begin{cases} 0 \text{ for } 0 > \tau > t \\ 1 \text{ for } 0 < \tau < t \end{cases}$$

as we saw in Example 4-29. Thus

$$g(t) = \frac{2}{\omega_n^2}\int_0^t (1 - \cos \omega_n\, d\tau)$$
$$= \frac{2}{\omega_n^2}\left[\int_0^t d\tau - \int_0^t \cos \omega_n \tau\, d\tau\right]$$
$$= \frac{2}{\omega_n^2}\left[\tau\big|_0^t - \frac{1}{\omega_n}\sin \omega_n \tau\Big|_0^t\right]$$
$$= \frac{2}{\omega_n^2}\left[t - \frac{1}{\omega_n}\sin \omega_n t\right]u(t)$$

It is recommended that the reader solve this same problem by letting $H(s) = 2/s$ and $F(s) = 1/s(s^2 + \omega_n^2)$. Another choice would have been to define $F(s) = 1/s^2$ and $H(s) = 1/(s^2 + \omega_n^2)$, which would require using integration-by-parts to solve for $h(t)$. This should demonstrate that while it makes no difference as to how $H(s)$ and $F(s)$ are chosen insofar as arriving at a correct solution, it does make a practical difference in the amount of ease at arriving at that solution.

4-19 Initial and Final Value Theorems

Many times the function we are attempting to find the inverse Laplace transform of is the result of many algebraic manipulations. It is very possible that some error could have been committed in our algebraic manipulations, and since taking the inverse Laplace is sometimes a tedious job we would like some means to verify that the function is correct before trying to find its inverse. The Initial Value Theorem will aid in our determining if a function is correct by allowing us to quickly evaluate the initial value of the function from the function and since we usually know this value the validity of the function is determined.

Let us consider

$$\mathcal{L}\left[\frac{df(t)}{dt}u(t)\right] = sF(s) - f(0^+)$$

which by definition is

$$\int_0^\infty \left[\frac{df(t)}{dt}\right]e^{-st}\,dt = \int_0^\infty e^{-st}\,df = e^{-st}\int_0^\infty df$$

So

$$e^{-st}\int_0^\infty df = sF(s) - f(0^+) \qquad (4\text{-}79)$$

Now let us take the limit of

$$e^{-st}\int_0^\infty df$$

as s approaches infinity. Thus

$$\lim_{s\to\infty} e^{-st}\int_0^\infty df = 0$$

since

$$\lim_{s\to\infty} e^{-st} = e^{-\infty} = 0$$

Then from Eq. (4–79)

$$0 = \lim_{s\to\infty}[sF(s) - f(0^+)] = \lim_{s\to\infty} sF(s) - f(0^+) \qquad (4\text{-}80)$$

Solving for $f(0^+)$ from Eq. (4–80) and realizing $f(0^+)$ is the initial conditions of $f(t)$, which can be written as

$$f(0^+) = \lim_{t\to0^+} f(t)$$

then Eq. (4–80) can be written as

$$f(0^+) = \lim_{t\to0^+} f(t) = \lim_{s\to\infty} sF(s) \qquad (4\text{-}81)$$

Equation (4–81) is the initial value theorem.

We shall now consider some examples using Eq. (4–81).

Example 4–31　Verify that $I(s)$ is correct if

$$i(0^+) = \frac{E - v(0^+)}{R}$$

when given

$$I(s) = \frac{E - v(0^+)}{R\left(s + \dfrac{1}{RC}\right)}$$

From Eq. (4–81)

$$i(0^+) = \lim_{t \to 0^+} i(t) = \lim_{s \to \infty} sI(s) = \lim_{s \to \infty} s \frac{E - v(0^+)}{R\left(s + \dfrac{1}{RC}\right)}$$

If we use this form without algebraic manipulation we see that we have

$$\lim_{s \to \infty} \frac{s[E - v(0^+)]}{R\left(s + \dfrac{1}{RC}\right)} = \frac{\infty}{\infty}$$

which is undefined. So let us manipulate the function, hence

$$\frac{s[E - v(0^+)]}{R\left(s + \dfrac{1}{RC}\right)} = \frac{s[E - v(0^+)]}{sR\left(1 + \dfrac{1}{RCs}\right)}$$

therefore

$$\lim_{s \to \infty} \frac{E - v(0^+)}{R\left(1 + \dfrac{1}{RCs}\right)} = \frac{E - v(0^+)}{R}$$

since

$$\lim_{s \to \infty} \frac{1}{RCs} = 0$$

Then

$$i(0^+) = \frac{E - v(0^+)}{R}$$

Example 4–32   Given

$$I(s) = \frac{\dfrac{E}{s} + Li(0^+)}{Ls + R}$$

verify $I(s)$ is correct.
From Eq. (4–81)

$$i(0^+) = \lim_{s \to \infty} \frac{s\left[\dfrac{E}{s} + Li(0^+)\right]}{Ls + R}$$

$$= \lim_{s \to \infty} \frac{\dfrac{E}{s} + Li(0^+)}{L + \dfrac{R}{s}} = \frac{Li(0^+)}{L} = i(0^+)$$

As we saw from both Examples 4–31 and 4–32 we want to algebraically manipulate the function such that the s in the product of $sF(s)$ is divided out, and also attempt to get terms to appear as [constant/s] for they approach zero as s approaches infinity.

Equation (4–81) can be used to determine initial values if the transformed function is known.

Example 4–33   Given

$$E_o(s) = \frac{E - K}{s + \dfrac{1}{RC}}$$

find $e_0(0^+)$. From Eq. (4–81)

$$e_0(0^+) = \lim_{s \to \infty} sE_0(s) = \lim_{s \to \infty} \frac{s(E - K)}{s\left(1 + \dfrac{1}{RCs}\right)} = E - K$$

We also may use Eq. (4–81) to determine derivatives of a function. This can be shown by letting $f(t)$ of Eq. (4–81) equal $dg(t)/dt$. Then from Eq. (4–81)

$$f(0^+) = \lim_{t \to 0^+} f(t) = \lim_{s \to \infty} sF(s) = \lim_{t \to 0^+} \frac{dg(t)}{dt} = g'(0^+) \quad \textbf{(4-82)}$$

where

$$g'(t) = \frac{dg(t)}{dt}$$

Now since

$$f(t) = \frac{dg(t)}{dt}$$

then

$$F(s) = sG(s) - g(0^+)$$

Returning to Eq. (4–82) and substituting

$$F(s) = sG(s) - g(0^+)$$

we have

$$g'(0^+) = \lim_{t \to 0^+} \frac{dg(t)}{dt} = \lim_{s \to \infty} s[sG(s) - g(0^+)] \quad \textbf{(4-83)}$$

which is what we sought.

Example 4–34   Given $H(s) = 5/s + 0.1$ find $h'(0^+)$. From Eq. (4–83) we see we must find $g(0^+)$, hence, applying Eq. (4–81)

$$g(0^+) = \lim_{s \to \infty} \frac{s5}{s + 0.1} = \lim_{s \to \infty} \frac{5}{1 + \dfrac{0.1}{s}} = 5$$

Then

$$g'(0^+) = \lim_{s \to \infty} s\left[\frac{s5}{s + 0.1} - 5\right]$$

$$= \lim_{s \to \infty} s\left[\frac{5s - 5(s + 0.1)}{s + 0.1}\right] = \lim_{s \to \infty} s\left[-\frac{0.5}{s + 0.1}\right]$$

$$= \lim_{s \to \infty}\left[-\frac{0.5}{1 + \frac{0.1}{s}}\right] = -0.5$$

Let us check our answer $g'(0^+) = -0.5$ by actually finding $g'(t)$ and then evaluating this at $t = 0^+$. Finding $g(t)$

$$g(t) = \mathcal{L}^{-1}\left[\frac{5}{s + 0.1}\right] = 5e^{-0.1t}u(t)$$

So

$$g'(t) = 5(-0.1)e^{-0.1t}u(t) + 5e^{-0.1t}\frac{du(t)}{dt}$$

using Eq. (26) of Table 4–2. Then

$$g'(t) = -0.5e^{-0.1t}u(t) + 5e^{-0.1t}\delta(t)$$

Now we wish to evaluate $g'(t)$ at $t = 0^+$ and it is important we understand that we are at $t = 0^+$ rather than $t = 0$. The reason for emphasizing the point at which t is evaluated is because

$$\delta(t) = \begin{cases} 0 \text{ for } 0 < t < 0 \\ \infty \text{ for } t = 0 \end{cases}$$

Then

$$5e^{0.1t}\delta(t)\Big|_{t=0^+} = 5e^{0.1(0^+)}\delta(0^+) = 0$$

since

$$\delta(0^+) = 0$$

Therefore,

$$g'(t) = -0.5e^{-0.1t}u(t) \text{ for } t > 0$$

To evaluate $g'(t)$ at $t = 0^+$ we simply substitute in $t = 0^+$ for t. We will numerically treat 0^+ as if it were 0. The reason we can treat $t = 0^+$ as if it were $t = 0$, especially after all the emphasis we placed on the fact that we were evaluating t at $t = 0^+$ rather than $t = 0$, is that the numerical value 0 or 0^+ is for all practical purposes the same, except when the unit impulse is being evaluated. So

$$g'(0^+) = g'(t)\Big|_{t=0^+} = -0.5e^{-0.1(0)} = -0.5$$

This agrees with our previous answer.

It might be interesting to evaluate $g'(t)$ at $t = 0$ and see if our equation

$$g'(t) = -0.5e^{-0.1t}u(t) + 5e^{-0.1t}\delta(t)$$

still holds valid. Thus

$$g'(t)\Big|_{t=0} = g'(0) = -0.5 + 5(\infty) = \infty$$

Now, at $t = 0$ a discontinuity exists due to $u(t)$ in the product $5e^{-0.1t}u(t)$. The slope (and remember the first derivative is the slope) at the discontinuity is infinite, therefore the equation for $g'(t)$ does agree with the physical graph of $5e^{-0.1t}u(t)$.

Many times it would be convenient to be able to determine the final value of a function in the t-plane from its s-plane transform. The theorem which allows us to do this is the Final Value Theorem. As was done for the Initial Value Theorem let us begin with

$$\mathcal{L}\left[\frac{df(t)}{dt}u(t)\right] = \int_0^\infty \left[\frac{df(t)}{dt}\right]e^{-st}\,dt = e^{-st}\int_0^\infty df$$

which gives us Eq. (4–79) as previously written.

$$e^{-st}\int_0^\infty df = sF(s) - f(0^+) \qquad (4\text{-}79)$$

Now the integral may be written as

$$\lim_{t\to\infty}\int_0^t df$$

Then Eq. (4–79) becomes

$$e^{-st}\lim_{t\to\infty}\int_0^t df = sF(s) - f(0^+) \qquad (4\text{-}83)$$

Performing the integration of Eq. (4–83) we have

$$e^{-st}\lim_{t\to\infty}[f(t) - f(0^+)] = sF(s) - f(0^+)$$

where $f(0^+)$ is due to the lower limit of the integral. Now $f(0^+)$ is not affected by the limiting process so

$$e^{-st}[\lim_{t\to\infty} f(t) - f(0^+)] = sF(s) - f(0^+)$$

or

$$e^{-st}\lim_{t\to\infty} f(t) = sF(s) - f(0^+)(1 - e^{-st}) \qquad (4\text{-}84)$$

Let us now take the limit of Eq. (4–84) as s approaches zero. Then

$$\lim_{s\to 0}[e^{-st}\lim_{t\to\infty} f(t)] = \lim_{s\to 0}[sF(s) - f(0^+)(1 - e^{-st})]$$

Therefore,

$$f(\infty) = \lim_{t\to\infty} f(t) = \lim_{s\to 0} sF(s) \qquad (4\text{-}85)$$

Equation (4–85) is the final value theorem. We shall now apply this theorem.

Example 4–35   Given

$$I(s) = \frac{E - v(0^+)}{R\left(s + \dfrac{1}{RC}\right)}$$

find $i(\infty)$. From Eq. (4–85)

$$i(\infty) = \lim_{t \to \infty} i(t) = \lim_{s \to 0} sI(s) = \lim_{s \to 0} \frac{s[E - v(0^+)]}{R\left(s + \dfrac{1}{RC}\right)}$$

$$= \lim_{s \to 0} \frac{E - v(0^+)}{R\left(1 + \dfrac{1}{RCs}\right)}$$

therefore

$$i(\infty) = 0$$

Let us check this by actually finding and evaluating it as $t \to \infty$. Hence

$$i(t) = \mathcal{L}^1\left[\frac{E - v(0^+)}{R\left(s + \dfrac{1}{RC}\right)}\right] = \frac{E - v(0^+)}{R} e^{-t/RC} u(t)$$

Then

$$i(\infty) = \lim_{t \to \infty} i(t) = \lim_{t \to \infty} \frac{E - v(0^+)}{R} e^{-t/RC}$$

$$= \frac{E - v(0^+)}{R} \frac{1}{e^\infty} = 0$$

which agrees with the value arrived at using the final value theorem.

Example 4–36   Given

$$H(s) = \frac{\omega}{s^2 + \omega^2}$$

find $h(\infty)$.

$$h(\infty) = \lim_{t \to \infty} h(t) = \lim_{s \to 0} sH(s) = \lim_{s \to 0} \frac{s\omega}{s^2 + \omega^2}$$

$$= \lim \frac{\omega}{s\left(1 + \dfrac{\omega^2}{s^2}\right)} = \infty$$

This says it is indeterminate. Let us see why. Now $h(t) = \mathcal{L}^{-1}[\omega/s^2 + \omega^2] = \sin \omega t\, u(t)$, which is periodic. Then $h(\infty) = \lim_{t \to \infty} \sin \omega t = ?$. From this we can generalize and state that the final value theorem *does not* apply to periodic functions.

TABLE 4-2 Transform Pairs

Equation Number	Transform Pairs in Specific Form	Generalized Form of Transformed Function
1	$\mathcal{L}[Ku(t)] = \dfrac{K}{s}$	$\dfrac{\text{constant}}{s}$
2	$\mathcal{L}[Ktu(t)] = \dfrac{K}{s^2}$	$\dfrac{\text{constant}}{s^{\text{constant}}}$
3	$\mathcal{L}[Kt^n u(t)] = K\dfrac{n!}{s^{n+1}}$	$\dfrac{\text{constant}}{s^{\text{constant}}}$
4	$\mathcal{L}[Ke^{-\alpha t}u(t)] = \dfrac{K}{s+\alpha}$	$\dfrac{\text{constant}}{s+\text{constant}}$
5	$\mathcal{L}\left[\dfrac{K}{\alpha}(1-e^{-\alpha t})u(t)\right] = \dfrac{K}{s(s+\alpha)}$	$\dfrac{\text{constant}}{s(s+\text{constant})}$
6	$\mathcal{L}\left[\dfrac{K}{(n-1)!}t^{n-1}e^{-\alpha t}u(t)\right] = \dfrac{K}{(s+\alpha)^n}$	$\dfrac{\text{constant}}{(s+\text{constant})^{\text{constant}}}$
7	$\mathcal{L}[K\sin\omega t u(t)] = \dfrac{K\omega}{s^2+\omega^2}$	$\dfrac{\text{constant}}{s^2+\text{constant}}$
8	$\mathcal{L}[K\cos\omega t u(t)] = \dfrac{Ks}{s^2+\omega^2}$	$\dfrac{\text{constant}\cdot s}{s^2+\text{constant}}$

TABLE 4-2 cont'd

Equation Number		Transform Pairs in Specific Form	Generalized Form of Transformed Function
Quadratic Equations	9 — To be used if $\zeta < 1$	$\mathcal{L}\left[\dfrac{K}{\omega_n\sqrt{1-\zeta^2}}e^{-\delta\omega_n t}\sin\omega_n\sqrt{1-\zeta^2}\,tu(t)\right]$ $=\dfrac{K}{s^2+2\zeta\omega_n s+\omega_n^2}$	$\dfrac{constant}{s^2+constant\cdot s+constant}$
	10 — To be used if $\zeta > 1$ for Eq. 9	$\mathcal{L}\left[\dfrac{K}{\beta-\alpha}(e^{-\alpha t}-e^{-\beta t})u(t)\right]=\dfrac{K}{(s+\alpha)(s+\beta)}$	$\dfrac{constant}{(s+constant)(s+constant)}$
	Note:	If $\zeta = 1$ of Eq. 9 then use Eq. 6, where $n = 2$. If $\zeta = 0$ of Eq. 9 then use Eq. 7, where $\omega = \omega_n$.	
Modified Quadratic Equations	11 — To be used if $\zeta < 1$	$\mathcal{L}\left\{K\left[\dfrac{1}{\omega_n^2}-\dfrac{1}{\omega_n^2\sqrt{1-\zeta^2}}e^{-\zeta\omega_n t}\sin(\omega_n\sqrt{1-\zeta^2}\,t+\phi)\right]u(t)\right\}$ where $\phi=\cos^{-1}\zeta$ $=\dfrac{K}{s(s^2+2\zeta\omega_n s+\omega_n^2)}$	$\dfrac{constant}{s(s^2+constant\cdot s+constant)}$
	12 — To be used if $\zeta > 1$ for Eq. 11	$\mathcal{L}\left[\dfrac{K}{\alpha\beta}\left(1-\dfrac{\beta}{\beta-\alpha}e^{-\alpha t}+\dfrac{\alpha}{\beta-\alpha}e^{-\beta t}\right)u(t)\right]$ $=\dfrac{K}{s(s+\alpha)(s+\beta)}$	$\dfrac{constant}{s(s+constant)(s+constant)}$
	13 — To be used if $\zeta = 0$ for Eq. 11	$\mathcal{L}\left[\dfrac{K}{\omega_n^2}(1-\cos\omega_n t)u(t)\right]=\dfrac{K}{s(s^2+\omega_n^2)}$	$\dfrac{constant}{s(s^2+constant)}$

TABLE 4-2 cont'd

Equation Number	Transform Pairs in Specific Form	Generalized Form of Transformed Function
14	$\mathscr{L}[K\delta(t)] = \mathscr{L}\left[K\dfrac{du(t)}{dt}\right] = K$	constant
15	$\mathscr{L}\left[K\dfrac{df(t)}{dt}u(t)\right] = K[sF(s) - f(0^+)]$	constant $s\cdot F(s)$ − constant
16	$\mathscr{L}\left[K\dfrac{d^n f(t)}{dt^n}u(t)\right] = K\left[s^n F(s) - \displaystyle\sum_{k=1}^{n} s^{n-k}f(0^+)^{(k-1)}\right]$ See Eq (4-21) for nomenclature	
17	$\mathscr{L}\left[K\displaystyle\int_0^t f(t)\,dt\right] = \dfrac{K}{s}F(s)$	$\dfrac{constant}{s}\cdot F(s)$
18	$\mathscr{L}\left[K\underbrace{\displaystyle\int_0^t\int_0^t\cdots\int_0^t}_{n\ \text{integrals}} f(t)\,dt\right] = \dfrac{K}{s^n}F(s)$	$\dfrac{constant}{s^{constant}}\cdot F(s)$
19	$\mathscr{L}\left[K\displaystyle\int f(t)u(t)\,dt\right] = K\left[\dfrac{1}{s}F(s) + \dfrac{f^{(-1)}(0^+)}{s}\right]$ See Eq. (4-24) for nomenclature	$\dfrac{constant}{s}\cdot F(s) + \dfrac{constant}{s}$
20	$\mathscr{L}\left[K\underbrace{\displaystyle\int\int\cdots\int}_{n\ \text{integrals}} f(t)u(t)\,dt\right] = K\left[\dfrac{1}{s^n}F(s) + \displaystyle\sum_{k=0}^{n-1}\dfrac{f^{(-k-1)}(0^+)}{s^{n-k}}\right]$ See Eq. (4-25) for nomenclature	

TABLE 4–2 cont'd

Equation Number	Transform Pairs in Specific Form	Generalized Form of Transformed Function
21	$\mathcal{L}[Kf(t-a)u(t-a)] = Ke^{-as}F(s)$ Laplace of a shifted function	constant $\cdot e^{-\text{constant}\cdot s}\cdot F(s)$
22	$\mathcal{L}[\text{Periodic function } f(t)] = \mathcal{L}[f(t)u(t)] = \mathcal{L}\left[\sum_{n=0}^{m} f_1(t-nT)u(t-nT)\right] = F_1(s)\sum_{n=0}^{m} e^{-nTs}$ if no dc level is present $\mathcal{L}\left[Au(t) + \sum_{n=0}^{m} f_1(t-nT)u(t-nT)\right] = \frac{A}{S} + F_1(s)\sum_{n=0}^{m} e^{-nTs}$ if dc level A is present where f_1 is the first period. If m is very large then $\sum_{n=0}^{m} e^{-nTs} \longrightarrow \frac{1}{1-e^{-Ts}}$.	
23	$\mathcal{L}\left[\int_0^t g(t-\tau)f(\tau)\,d\tau\right] = \mathcal{L}\left[\int_0^t g(t)f(t-\tau)\,d\tau\right] = G(s)F(s) = \mathcal{L}[g(t)*f(t)]$	
24	$f(0^+) = \lim_{t\to 0^+} f(t) = \lim_{s\to\infty} sF(s)$ Not valid if $f(t)$ is periodic	
25	$f(\infty) = \lim_{t\to\infty} f(t) = \lim_{s\to 0} sF(s)$ Not valid if $f(t)$ is periodic	
26	$\frac{d}{dx}\left[\frac{u(x)}{v(x)}\right] = \frac{v\frac{du}{dx} - u\frac{dv}{dx}}{v^2}$ and $\frac{d}{dx}[u(x)v(x)] = u(x)\frac{dv}{dx} + v(x)\frac{du}{dx}$	
(4-62)	$K_m = [(s-s_m)F(s)]\big|_{s=s_m}$ For nonrepeated roots	
(4-75)	$K_{nm} = \frac{1}{(k-m)!}\left\{\frac{d^{k-m}}{ds^{k-m}}[(s-s_n)^k F(s)]\right\}\Big|_{s=s_n}$ For repeated roots	

5 Applications of Laplace Transforms to Circuit Analysis

5-1 Introduction

In chapter 3 we wrote differential equations which were descriptive of the dynamic behavior of a circuit. These equations resulted from loop and nodal analysis. Then in chapter 4 we developed the Laplace transform which transformed the operational mathematics of the differential equations into algebra. We will begin this chapter by demonstrating that this transformation will allow us to find a solution to a differential equation by simple algebraic manipulation. However, this solution is in the s-plane, which is unfamiliar to us. To express the unknown in more familiar terms we will take the inverse Laplace transform, which results in the solution's being expressed in the t-plane (assuming t is the independent variable). We then will have the mathematical solution we sought.

Often mathematical expressions are rather abstract to us. This is due to a lack of experience in interpretation of these equations. To help remedy this we will address ourselves to graphical interpretation of our solutions. This will develop a knack for "letting the mathematics talk to you." After some practice one will find he can get a fairly good idea of how a graph of an equation will look just by visual inspection of the equation. It is then that mathematics will no longer be abstract. And during the process of developing this knack for interpreting equations one will find he has also developed the ability to adjust parameters to obtain a desired graph. In terms of circuit application this ability will aid in component selection so that the desired effects of the circuit are achieved.

As a side benefit from our circuit analysis and equation interpretation we will develop some curves, which we will term universal curves, to aid us when we wish to make a point-by-point plot of an equation. It is not only important that the reader understand the use of these curves, but he should also understand the concepts behind their construction. If he understands this he will be able to develop his own universal curves, for obviously this text cannot cover every possible equation he might encounter.

Most of the concepts of this chapter are developed and demonstrated through examples. As a result it is most important that the reader work each example. It is suggested that no example be undertaken without the reader actually working that example in parallel with the author. It should also be mentioned that all numerical calculations are to slide-rule accuracy.

5–2 Basic Steps of Circuit Analysis

It will be demonstrated that there are five general steps to be followed when using Laplace transforms in circuit analysis. These steps are:

Step 1: Assume the polarities of those voltage sources for which the polarities are not known. Also assume current directions for any current sources for which the current direction is unknown. If we are making a nodal analysis we will also *assume* voltage polarities for all nodal voltages. If we are making a loop analysis we will *assume* loop current directions.

Step 2: Write the differential equations describing the circuit to be analyzed. Also write the equation describing the driving function.

Step 3: Take the Laplace transform of those equations written in step 2.

Step 4: Using algebraic manipulation solve for the unknown (or unknowns) leaving the driving function, or functions, in implicit form. This will give an implicit equation for the unknown which is valid for any driving force. Then substitute the explicit transformed expression for the driving function in this equation, resulting in our unknown being in explicit form.

Step 5: Take the inverse Laplace transform of our explicit equation arrived at in step 4. This step will transform our unknown dependent variable from the s-plane back to the t-plane, assuming t is the independent variable. To find the inverse Laplace transform we can apply those procedures established in section 4–16.

Some example problems will now be considered to demonstrate the use of these steps.

Example 5-1   Consider the circuit given in Fig. 5–1, where we are asked to determine v_o when the driving force, e_{in}, is as illustrated. The switch is closed at $t = 0$.

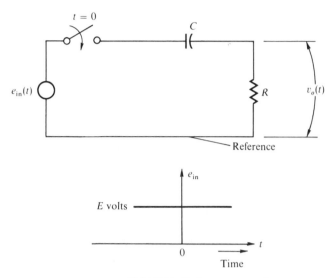

FIGURE 5-1

Solution   We are seeking the solution for v_o, which indicates nodal analysis is in order. Therefore the steps we have outlined will be utilized for nodal analysis.

Step 1: In this simple circuit we can easily determine the polarities of both the driving force e_{in} and the nodal voltage v_o. However, for more complex problems this may not be the case; therefore, to keep our analysis general we will arbitrarily assume polarities for these two voltages. It is the *habit* of the author to usually choose the negative side of the voltage as being common with the reference node. Our circuit under this condition, and for $t > 0$, appears as shown in Fig. 5–2.

Step 2:   Summing the currents at the node of v_o we have

$$C\frac{d}{dt}[e_{in}(t) - v_o(t)] - \frac{v_o(t)}{R} = 0 \qquad (5\text{-}1)$$

The driving function is the voltage source e_{in} and the equation for e_{in} is

$$e_{in}(t) = Eu(t) \qquad (5\text{-}2)$$

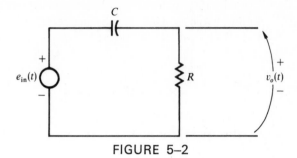

FIGURE 5-2

where the unit step function will force the driving function to comply with the time at which the switch was closed. That is, when the switch is open the driving function e_{in} does not affect the circuit, so for $t < 0$ we want the effects of e_{in} to be zero. However, at $t = 0$ the switch is closed and the driving force e_{in} applies its force. Then for $t > 0$ (the time the switch is closed) we want E volts applied to the circuit. Notice we are avoiding $t = 0$ for reasons discussed when we defined the unit step function. Hence, we are saying that insofar as the circuit is concerned e_{in} appears as shown in Fig. 5-3, which agrees with Eq. (5-2).

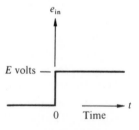

FIGURE 5-3

Step 3: Taking the Laplace transform of the circuit's differential equation given in Eq. (5-1) we have

$$C\{[sE_{in}(s) - e_{in}(0^+)] - [sV_o(s) - v_o(0^+)]\} - \frac{V_o(s)}{R} = 0$$

The transformed driving function $E_{in}(s)$ is

$$E_{in}(s) = \frac{E}{s}$$

Step 4:   Solving for the unknown nodal voltage

$$V_o(s)\left(\frac{1}{R} + Cs\right) = C\{sE_{in}(s) - [e_{in}(0^+) - v_o(0^+)]\}$$

then

$$V_o(s) = \frac{C\{sE_{in}(s) - [e_{in}(0^+) - v_o(0^+)]\}}{Cs + \dfrac{1}{R}} \qquad (5\text{-}3)$$

Substituting the transformed driving function's equation into the equation for $V_o(s)$ we have,

$$V_o(s) = \frac{C\left\{s\left(\dfrac{E}{s}\right) - [e_{in}(0^+) - v_0(0^+)]\right\}}{Cs + \dfrac{1}{R}}$$

$$= \frac{C\{E - [e_{in}(0^+) - v_o(0^+)]\}}{Cs + \dfrac{1}{R}}$$

Step 5:   From procedure 1 of section 4–16 we must force the coefficient of s with the highest power to be unity, so

$$V_o(s) = \frac{C\{E - [e_{in}(0^+) - v_o(0^+)]\}}{C\left(s + \dfrac{1}{RC}\right)}$$

or

$$V_o(s) = \frac{E - [e_{in}(0^+) - v_o(0^+)]}{s + \dfrac{1}{RC}} \qquad (5\text{-}4)$$

Generalizing the function

$$V_o(s) = \frac{\text{constant}}{s + \text{constant}}$$

From Table 4–2 we find Eq. (4) applies. Hence,

$$v_o(t) = \mathcal{L}'[V_o(s)] = \{E - [e_{in}(0^+) - v_o(0^+)]\}e^{-t/RC}u(t)$$
$$(5\text{-}5)$$

which is the solution we sought.

At this point it might be profitable for us to summarize our efforts of Ex. 5–1. We were given a circuit and asked to solve for the unknown nodal voltage v_o. We began by assuming polarities for the voltages e_{in} and v_o, which was applying step 1. Next we applied step 2 by writing a differential equation which mathematically described the circuit's behavior. We also wrote an equation for the driving force e_{in}. These equations are Eqs. (5–1) and (5–2) respectively. We then applied step 3 by taking the Laplace transforms of Eqs. (5–1) and (5–2). The unknown nodal voltage could now be solved for algebraically, which is the application of step 4 and is expressed in Eq. (5–3). Equation (5–3) is a general expression since it is valid for any shape of waveform for the driving force e_{in}. Also Eq. (5–3) is an expression of the nodal voltage in the s-plane, which is not a familiar plane to us. Therefore we wish to transform Eq. (5–3) back to the t-plane or, more simply, take the inverse Laplace transform of Eq. (5–3) in explicit form, which means substituting an explicit equation for $E_{in}(s)$. This was done and resulted in Eq. (5–4). Step 5 was then applied, resulting in Eq. (5–5). Notice it was not necessary to know the exact numerical value of the initial condition in order to determine the inverse Laplace transform. This is because initial conditions are constants.

It is advised that the reader be certain he understands the logic and concepts of Ex. 5–1. Example 5–1 is indicative of the solution to all circuit analysis using Laplace transforms.

Let us now consider another example.

Example 5–2   Given e_{in} and the circuit in Fig. 5–4 find v_o.

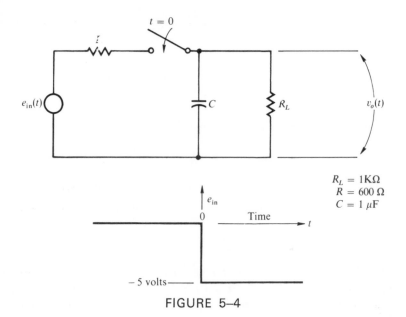

FIGURE 5–4

Solution   *Step 1:*   The circuit appears as in Fig. 5–5 with assumed polarities shown. Notice the assumed polarities are not correct. This is done to demonstrate that it does not matter.

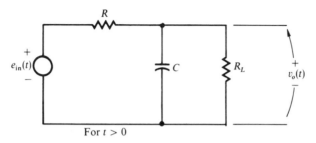

For $t > 0$

FIGURE 5–5

Step 2: Use nodal analysis since we wish to solve for v_o.

$$\frac{e_{\text{in}}(t) - v_0(t)}{R} - C\frac{dv_o(t)}{dt} - \frac{v_o(t)}{R_L} = 0$$

$$e_{\text{in}}(t) = -5u(t)$$

Step 3:

$$\frac{E_{\text{in}}(s) - V_o(s)}{R} - C[sV_o(s) - v_o(0^+)] - \frac{V_o(s)}{R_L} = 0$$

$$E_{\text{in}}(s) = -\frac{5}{s}$$

Step 4:

$$V_o(s)\left(\frac{1}{R} + \frac{1}{R_L} + C_s\right) = \frac{E_{\text{in}}(s)}{R} + Cv_o(0^+)$$

$$V_o(s) = \frac{\dfrac{E_{\text{in}}(s)}{R} + Cv_o(0^+)}{\dfrac{1}{R_{\text{eq}}} + Cs}$$

where $R_{\text{eq}} = \dfrac{RR_L}{R + R_L}$

Then

$$V_o(s) = -\frac{\dfrac{5}{sR} + Cv_o(0^+)}{\dfrac{1}{R_{\text{eq}}} + Cs}$$

since

$$E_{\text{in}}(s) = -\frac{5}{s}$$

Step 5:

$$V_o(s) = \frac{-\dfrac{5}{sR} + Cv_o(0^+)}{C\left(s + \dfrac{1}{R_{eq}C}\right)}$$

$$= -\frac{5}{RC}\frac{1}{s\left(s + \dfrac{1}{R_{eq}C}\right)} + \frac{v_o(0^+)}{s + \dfrac{1}{R_{eq}C}}$$

From Table 4–2 we identify $5/RC \cdot 1/s(s + 1/R_{eq}C)$ as [constant/$s(s +$ constant)], which is Eq. (5). And $v_o(0^+)/[s + (1/R_{eq}C)]$, when generalized, is constant/ $(s +$ constant), or Eq. (4) of Table 4–2. Then

$$v_o(t) = -\left[\frac{5}{RC}(R_{eq}C)(1 - e^{-t/R_{eq}C})u(t)\right] + v_o(0^+)e^{-t/R_{eq}C}u(t)$$

$$= \left[-\frac{R_{eq}5}{R}(1 - e^{-t/R_{eq}C}) + v_o(0^+)e^{-t/R_{eq}C}\right]u(t)$$

Now

$$\frac{R_{eq}}{R} = \frac{RR_L}{(R + R_L)R} = \frac{R_L}{R + R_L}$$

so

$$v_o(t) = \left[-\frac{5R_L}{R + R_L}(1 - e^{-t/R_{eq}C}) + v_o(0^+)e^{-t/R_{eq}C}\right]u(t)$$

$$(5\text{-}6)$$

Notice the negative sign, which indicates $v_o(t)$ is actually of opposite polarity than we assumed. Substituting the numerical value in for R, R_L, and C,

$$v_o(t) = [-3.13(1 - e^{-t/0.375 \times 10^{-3}})$$
$$+ v_o(0^+)e^{-t/0.375 \times 10^{-3}}]u(t) \text{ V} \qquad (5\text{-}7)$$

Notice that numerical substitution was held off until last in Ex. 5–2. This was done so as to keep errors to a minimum. That is, the algebraic expression of Eq. (5–6) allows one to verify its correctness by checking its units. As an illustration we will check the units of Eq. (5–6). Since v_o has units of volts then the right-hand side must likewise have volts as its units. Look at the term $5R_L/(R + R_L)(1 - e^{-t \, R_{eq}C})$ first. Now $(1 - e^{-t/R_{eq}C})$ is unitless, hence $5R_L/(R + R_L)$ must be volts. Well, $5R_L/(R + R_L) =$ volts·ohms/ohms = volts, which is correct. We also know that e's power must be unitless. Then $t/R_{eq}C =$ unitless, which is true since $t =$ time and

$R_{eq}C = $ time. Consider the term $v_o(0^+)e^{-t/R_{eq}C}$ next. Now $v_o(0^+)$ has units of volts and $e^{-t/R_{eq}C}$ is unitless, therefore $v_o(0^+)e^{-t/R_{eq}C} = $ volts. The units of Eq. (5–6) have been verified.

Now let us suppose that we made numerical substitution very early in the problem and Eq. (5–7) was our solution. It would be very difficult to verify the correctness of Eq. (5–7) since we are unable to check its units, that is, what are the units of 3.13? In summary, it is usually a good idea to work with algebra until the last step.

5–3 Determining Initial Conditions

In Eqs. (5–5) and (5–7) we have the initial conditions $e_{in}(0^+)$ and $v_o(0^+)$ for which we would like to determine numerical values. To determine initial values for any circuit a relatively simple analysis is performed. We essentially analyze the circuit at $t = t_0^-$, where t_0 is the zero reference ($t_0 \equiv 0$ usually) and determine the values of currents and/or voltages of interest at that time for by knowing the values at $t = t_0^-$ the values at $t = t_0^+$ can be determined.

From elementary circuit theory we know that capacitors act as effective short circuits to any change in voltage across them, that is, capacitors resist any change in their potential. Then if we have a capacitor which has E_1 volts across it and then E_2 volts, where $E_2 > E_1$ is applied the capacitor appears as a short circuit to $E_2 - E_1$ volts since that is the amount of potential change.

Also from elementary circuit theory we know that inductors resist any change in the current flowing through them. Under this condition inductors will appear as open circuits to any current different than that already flowing through it. Thus, if I_1 amps is established as the current flow and then suddenly it is attempted to increase the current to I_2, $I_2 > I_1$, then the inductor appears as an open circuit to $I_2 - I_1$ amps.

We will now consider some examples to demonstrate these points.

Example 5–3 For the circuit and driving force shown in Fig. 5–6 find the current i at $t = t_0^-$ and $t = t_0^+$, which is written as $i(t_0^-)$ and $i(t_0^+)$ respectively. Solve the problem using elementary circuit theory.

Solution We know that for $t < t_0$ the capacitor will charge to E_1 volts, hence for $t = t_0^-$ the circuit appears as in Fig. 5–7. To find $i(t_0^-)$ we write a loop equation and solve for $i(t_0^-)$. Thus,

$$E_1 - E_1 - Ri(t_0^-) = 0$$

so
$$i(t_0^-) = 0$$

Since capacitors resist change in potential at $t = t_0^+$ the capacitor will still be charged to E_1 volts (remember

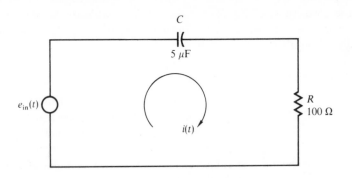

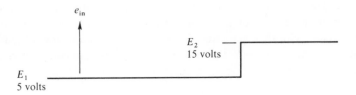

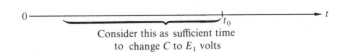

Consider this as sufficient time
to change C to E_1 volts

FIGURE 5–6

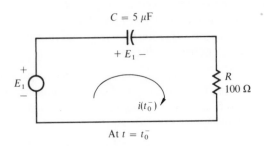

At $t = t_0^-$

FIGURE 5–7

$t_0^+ \cong t_0^-$) but now $e_{in}(t_0^+) = E_2$ volts. Then the circuit appears as shown in Fig. 5–8 for $t = t_0^+$. Again, writing a loop equation and solving $i(t_0^+)$,

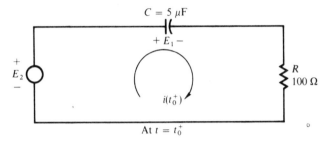

At $t = t_0^+$

FIGURE 5–8

$$E_2 - E_1 - Ri(t_0^+) = 0$$

or

$$i(t_0^+) = \frac{E_2 - E_1}{R} = \frac{15 - 5}{100} = 0.1 \text{ A}$$

The most important point to this example is to realize that at the time $t = t_0^+$ the voltage source $e_{in}(t)$ increased from E_1 to E_2 volts, and that the capacitor was an effective short circuit to the *change in potential*. Then for this point in time the equivalent circuit appears as shown in Fig. 5–9. To verify this circuit solve for $i(t_0^+)$ from it.

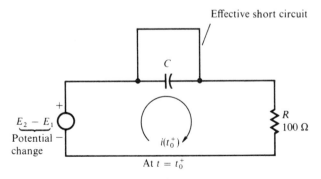

At $t = t_0^+$

FIGURE 5–9

Example 5–4   Find the voltages $v_o(t_0^-)$ and $v_o(t_0^+)$ for the circuit and driving force shown in Fig. 5–10. Use elementary circuit techniques.

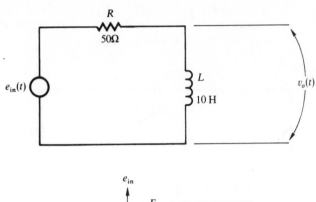

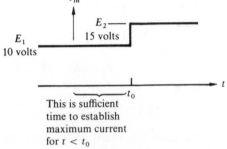

FIGURE 5–10

Solution   At $t = t_0^-$ the equivalent circuit is as shown in Fig. 5–11.

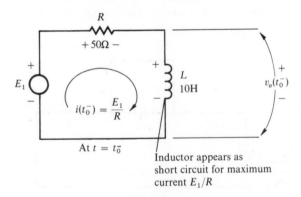

FIGURE 5–11

To find $v_o(t_0^-)$ we will write a loop equation and solve for $v_o(t_0^-)$. Hence,

$$E_1 - Ri(t_0^-) - v_0(t_0^-) = E_1 - R\left(\frac{E_1}{R}\right) - v_o(t_0^-) = 0$$

or

$$v_o(t_0^-) = 0$$

For $t = t_0^+$ we know $i(t_0^-) \cong i(t_0^+) = E_1/R$ since the current through the inductor is maintained. And at

$$t = t_0^+ \qquad e_{in}(t_0^+) = E_2$$

thus the circuit for $t = t_0^+$ is as shown in Fig. 5–12. To solve for $v_o(t_0^+)$ we will write a loop equation. Hence,

$$E_2 - Ri(t_0^+) - v_o(t_0^+) = 0$$

or

$$v_o(t_0^+) = E_2 - Ri(t_0^+) = E_2 - R\left(\frac{E_1}{R}\right) = E_2 - E_1$$

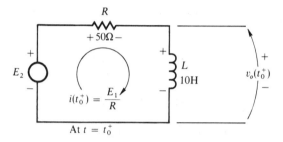

FIGURE 5–12

An equivalent circuit for $t = t_0^+$ is as shown in Fig. 5–13. Notice that the inductor is an effective open circuit to the *change in potential*. To verify this circuit solve for $v_o(t_0^+)$ from it.

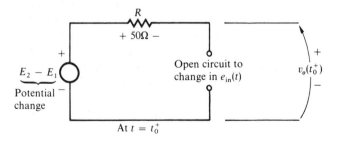

FIGURE 5–13

Example 5–5   From e_{in} given and the circuit shown in Fig. 5–14 find the initial conditions $v_1(0^+)$, $v_2(0^+)$, $v_3(0^+)$, and $v_4(0^+)$.

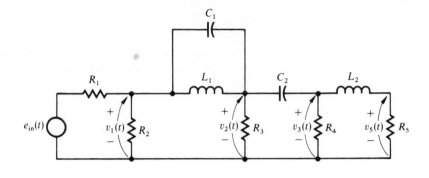

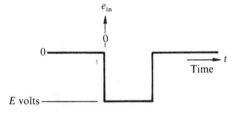

Note: Node voltage polarities are assumed

FIGURE 5–14

Solution   Before determining the initial condition at $t = 0^+(t_0 \equiv 0)$ we must first determine the currents and voltages at $t = 0^-$. For $t = 0^-$ the circuit has no driving force $[e_{in}(0^-) = 0]$, therefore no currents or potentials exist in the circuit. At $t = 0^+$ the driving force $e_{in}(0^+)$ equals $-E$ volts, which will attempt to change the potentials across all capacitors and the currents in all inductors. Thus every capacitor becomes an effective short circuit and each inductor an effective open circuit. Then the equivalent circuit at $t = 0^+$ is shown in Fig. 5–15.

As shown in the equivalent circuit for $t = 0^+$ we see $v_1(0^+) = v_2(0^+) = v_3(0^+)$ and $v_4(0^+) = 0$. We may easily determine $v_1(0^+)$ using elementary circuit analysis. Hence, defining $1/R_{eq} = 1/R_2 + 1/R_3 + 1/R_4$ then

$$v_1(0^+) = -\frac{R_{eq}E}{R_1 + R_{eq}} = v_2(0^+) = v_3(0^+)$$

Now that we have seen some examples in determining initial conditions we will return to finding $e_{in}(0^+)$ and $v_o(0^+)$ of Eqs. (5–5) and (5–7). From Ex. 5–1 we observe that $e_{in}(0^+) = E$ volts, and to determine $v_o(0^+)$ we must

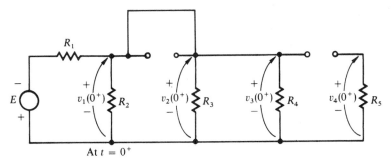

At $t = 0^+$

FIGURE 5–15

examine the circuit at $t = 0^+$. To reiterate from elementary circuit theory we know that a capacitor behaves as a short circuit when a change in voltage is applied (at $t = 0^+$). Making the capacitor a short circuit at $t = 0^+$ says $e_{in}(0^+) = v_o(0^+)$. Again, from the illustration of e_{in} we found $e_{in}(0^+) = E$, therefore, $v_o(0^+) = E$. Then $e_{in}(0^+) - v_o(0^+) = E - E = 0$, so Eq. (5–5) becomes

$$v_o(t) = Ee^{-t/RC}u(t) \tag{5–8}$$

This result can be verified by most elementary circuit books covering dc charging circuits.

Before continuing let us return to the quantity $e_{in}(0^+) - v_o(0^+)$ and attempt to determine what it describes. Writing a loop equation for the circuit yields

$$v_o(t) + (\text{voltage across } C) - e_{in}(t) = 0$$

therefore (voltage across C) $\equiv v_C(t) = e_{in}(t) - v_o(t)$. Evaluating this equation at $t = 0^+$ we have

$$v_C(0^+) = e_{in}(0^+) - v_0(0^+)$$

Hence, the quantity $e_{in}(0^+) - v_o(0^+)$ is the initial voltage across the capacitor C.

Now let us find the initial condition for Ex. 5–2 as expressed in Eq. (5–7). As we stated earlier a capacitor appears as a short circuit to any attempted voltage change, hence when the -5 volts is first applied to the circuit (at $t = 0^+$) its effect will be short circuited. And since the capacitor had zero charge prior to -5 volts being applied ($t < 0$) then $v_o(0^+) = 0$ volts. Be sure it is understood that we are making this analysis for a specific time of $t = 0^+$. As a result of $v_o(0^+) = 0$, Eq. (5–7) appears as

$$v_o(t) = -3.13(1 - e^{-t/0.375 \times 10^{-3}})u(t) \text{ V} \tag{5–9}$$

For the next example we will consider a circuit where the conditions for $t = t_0^-$ are not zero.

Example 5–6   (a) For the circuit in Fig. 5–16 determine v_0 for $t > 1$ s if the switch is to remain in position 1 for one second and then be switched to position 2. The capacitor C has zero charge for $t < 0$.

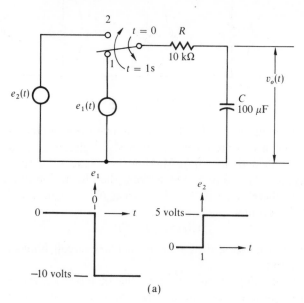

(a)

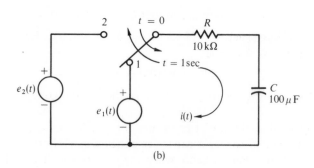

(b)

FIGURE 5–16

(b) For the circuit and conditions of part (a) determine the equation for current flowing through the capacitor C.

Solution for (a)

Step 1:   We will be using nodal analysis. The assumed polarities are as shown in Fig. 5–17.

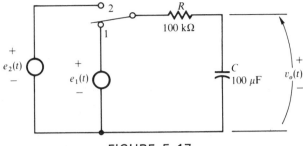

FIGURE 5–17

Step 2: We will have two time ranges to consider: for $0 < t < 1$ s, which is for when the switch is in position 1, and for $t > 1$ s, which is for when the switch is in position 2. Then we will analyze the circuit for each of those time ranges.

For $0 < t < 1$ s

$$\frac{e_1(t) - v_o(t)}{R} = C\frac{dv_o(t)}{dt}$$

$$e_1(t) = -10u(t) \text{ V}$$

For $t > 1$ s

$$\frac{e_2(t) - v_o(t)}{R} = C\frac{dv_o(t)}{dt}$$

$$e_2(t) = 5u(t) \text{ V}$$

Note: We now define $t = 1$ s as the zero reference for this switch position ($t_0 \equiv 0$).

Step 3:

For $0 < t < 1$ s

$$\frac{E_1(s) - V_o(s)}{R} = C[sV_o(s) - v_o(0^+)]$$

$$E_1(s) = -\frac{10}{s}$$

For $t > 1$ s Recall $t = 1$ s has been defined as zero.

$$\frac{E_2(s) - V_o(s)}{R} = C[sV_o(s) - v_o(0^+)]$$

$$E_2(s) = \frac{5}{s}$$

Step 4:

For $0 < t < 1$ s

$$V_o(s) = \frac{E_1(s)}{R\left(Cs + \dfrac{1}{R}\right)} + \frac{Cv_o(0^+)}{\left(Cs + \dfrac{1}{R}\right)}$$

$$= -\frac{10}{Rs\left(Cs + \dfrac{1}{R}\right)} + \frac{Cv_o(0^+)}{\left(Cs + \dfrac{1}{R}\right)}$$

For $t > 1$ s

$$V_o(s) = \frac{E_2(s)}{R\left(Cs + \dfrac{1}{R}\right)} + \frac{Cv_o(0^+)}{\left(Cs + \dfrac{1}{R}\right)}$$

$$= \frac{5}{Rs\left(Cs + \dfrac{1}{R}\right)} + \frac{Cv_o(0^+)}{\left(Cs + \dfrac{1}{R}\right)}$$

Remember, for this range $t = 0^+$ is the same point in time as 1^+ s for the range $0 < t < 1$ s.

Step 5:

For $0 < t < 1$ s

$$V_o(s) = -\frac{10}{Rs\left(Cs + \dfrac{1}{R}\right)} + \frac{Cv_o(0^+)}{\left(Cs + \dfrac{1}{R}\right)}$$

$$= -\frac{10}{RCs\left(s + \dfrac{1}{RC}\right)} + \frac{v_o(0^+)}{s + \dfrac{1}{RC}}$$

Then

$$v_o(t) = -10(1 - e^{-t/RC})u(t) + v_o(0^+)e^{-t/RC}u(t)$$
$$= -10(1 - e^{-t/RC})u(t) \text{ since } v_o(0^+) = 0$$

For $t > 1$ s

For the range $t > 1$ s we will need to find $v_o(t = 1)$ using $v_o(t)$ for $0 < t < 1$ s, since these are the initial conditions for the range $t > 1$ s. In other words, when the switch is changed from position 1 at $t = 1$ s the capacitor C will have a voltage across it equal to $v_o(1 \text{ s})$, so for $t > 1$ s $v_o(0^+) = v_o(1^+)$ using $v_o = -10(1 - e^{-t/RC})$. If the 0^+ is confusing then one could write $v_o(0^+) = v_o(1^+)$. Then for $t > 1$ s

$$V_o(s) \frac{5}{Rs\left(Cs + \dfrac{1}{R}\right)} + \frac{Cv_o(1^+)}{\left(Cs + \dfrac{1}{R}\right)}$$

To continue we must find $v_o(1^+)$, which is

$$v_o(1^+) = -10(1 - e^{-t/RC})\Big|_{t=1\ \text{s}} = -10(1 - e^{-1/1})$$
$$= -10(1 - 0.37)$$

or

$$v_o(1^+) = -6.3\ \text{V}$$

So

$$V_o(s) = \frac{5}{RC_s\left(s + \dfrac{1}{RC}\right)} - \frac{6.3}{s + \dfrac{1}{RC}}$$

therefore

$$v_o(t) = 5(1 - e^{-t/RC})u(t) - 6.3e^{-t/RC}u(t)$$
$$= (5 - 11.3e^{-t/RC})u(t)$$

where $t = 1$ s is the zero reference. In conclusion then:
For $0 < t < 1$ s

$$v_o(t) = -10(1 - e^{-t}) \tag{5-10}$$

and

For $t > 1$ s

$$v_o(t) = 5 - 11.3e^{-t} \tag{5-11}$$

One might have noticed we could have arrived at the same solution much more easily by considering the circuit to be as shown in Fig. 5–18 and then expressing e^{in} as the combination of e_1 and e_2. The method is shown in Fig. 5–18.

Step 1:   As before, the nodal voltage will be assumed to be the same polarity.

Step 2:

$$\frac{e_{\text{in}}(t) - v_o(t)}{R} = C\frac{dv_o(t)}{dt}$$

$$e_{\text{in}}(t) = -10u(t) + 15u(t - 1)$$

Step 3:

$$\frac{E_{\text{in}}(s) - V_o(s)}{R} = C[sV_o(s) - v_o(0^+)]$$

$$E_{\text{in}}(s) = -\frac{10}{s} + \frac{15}{s}e^{-s} = \frac{1}{s}(-10 + 15e^{-s})$$

Step 4:

$$V_o(s) = \frac{E_{\text{in}}(s)}{R\left(Cs + \dfrac{1}{R}\right)}, \quad \text{since } v_o(0^+) = 0.$$

$$V_o(s) = \frac{(-10 + 15e^{-s})}{Rs\left(Cs + \dfrac{1}{R}\right)}$$

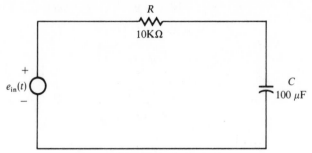

Note: $e_{in}(t)$'s polarity is assumed

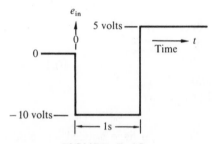

FIGURE 5–18

Step 5:

$$V_o(s) = -\frac{10}{RCs\left(s + \dfrac{1}{RC}\right)} + \frac{15e^{-s}}{RCs\left(s + \dfrac{1}{RC}\right)}$$

$$= -\frac{\text{constant}}{s(s + \text{constant})} + \frac{\text{constant} \cdot e^{-s}}{s(s + \text{constant})}$$

So

$$v_o(t) = -10(1 - e^{-t/RC})u(t) + 15[1 - e^{-(t-1)/RC}]u(t - 1)$$

or

$$v_o(t) = -10(1 - e^{-t})u(t) + 15[1 - e^{-(t-1)}]u(t - 1)$$
$$(5\text{–}12)$$

    Let us compare Eqs. (5–10) and (5–11) with Eq. (5–12) to verify the validity of those equations. For Eq. (5–12) consider the range of Eq. (5–10), that is, $0 < t < 1$ s. During this range $u(t) = 1$ and $u(t - 1) = 0$, hence Eq. (5–12) becomes $v_o(t) = -10(1 - e^{-t})$, which agrees with Eq. (5–10). And for $t > 1$ s $u(t) = u(t - 1) = 1$ so Eq. (5–12) becomes

$$v_o(t) = -10(1 - e^{-t}) + 15[1 - e^{-(t-1)}]$$
$$= 5 + 10e^{-t} - 15e^{-(t-1)}$$

Now $e^{-(t-1)} = e^1 e^{-t} = 2.7 \, e^{-t}$, therefore

$$v_o(t) = 5 + 10e^{-t} - 15(2.7)e^{-t} = 5 - 30.4e^{-t}$$
$$\text{for } t > 1 \text{ s.} \qquad \textbf{(5-13)}$$

At first glance it appears Eq. (5–11) and Eq. (5–13) disagree. The reason for the apparent disagreement is the difference in the time reference. When we speak of $t = 0$ for Eq. (5–11) we are speaking of $t = 1$ s for Eq. (5–13). Then to bring Eq. (5–11) to the same time reference as Eq. (5–13) we must subtract 1 s from the time of Eq. (5–11) [Eq. (5–11) is 1 s ahead of Eq. (5–13)], or substitute $t - 1$ for the t of Eq. (5–11). Then

$$v_o(t) = 5 - 11.3e^{-(t-1)} = 5 - 11.3(2.7)e^{-t}$$
$$= 5 - 30.4e^{-t}$$

which agrees with Eq. (5–13).

Let us also verify Eq. (5–13) by actually evaluating $v_o(t)$ at $t = 1$ s. Thus

$$v_o(1 \text{ s}) = 5 - 30.4e^{-1} = 5 - 30.4(0.37) \, .$$
$$= 5 - 11.3 = -6.3 \text{ V}$$

which agrees with the $v_o(0^+)$ that was calculated using Eq. (5–10) evaluated at $t = 1$ s.

The reader should review this problem to make certain he fully understands both methods for finding the solution. He should also understand how each method is in agreement with the other.

Solution for (b)

We must first determine the equation for i when the switch is in position 1 since it is this equation which will determine the initial conditions when the switch is thrown in position 2.

Switch in position 1 ($0 < t < 1$ s)

$$e_1(t) - Ri(t) - \frac{1}{C} \int i(t) \, dt = 0$$

or

$$e_1(t) = Ri(t) + \frac{1}{C} \int i(t) \, dt$$

where

$$e_1 = -10u(t) \text{ V}$$

Taking the Laplace

$$E_1(s) = RI(s) + \frac{1}{C}\left[\frac{I(s)}{s} + \frac{i^{(-1)}(0^+)}{s}\right]$$

where $i^{(-1)}(0^+)$ is a constant

$$E_1 = -\frac{10}{s}$$

So, we have

$$E_1(s) - \frac{i^{(-1)}(0^+)}{Cs} = \left(R + \frac{1}{Cs}\right)I(s)$$

Solving for $I(s)$

$$I(s) = \frac{E_1(s)}{R + \frac{1}{Cs}} - \frac{i^{(-1)}(0^+)}{Cs\left(R + \frac{1}{Cs}\right)}$$

Substituting $E_1(s) = -10/s$ we have

$$I(s) = -\frac{10}{s\left(R + \frac{1}{Cs}\right)} - \frac{i^{(-1)}(0^+)}{Cs\left(R + \frac{1}{Cs}\right)}$$

$$= -\frac{10}{s\left(\frac{RCs + 1}{Cs}\right)} - \frac{i^{(-1)}(0^+)}{Cs\left(\frac{RCs + 1}{Cs}\right)}$$

$$= -\frac{10}{R}\frac{1}{s + \frac{1}{RC}} - \frac{i^{(-1)}(0^+)}{RC}\frac{1}{s + \frac{1}{RC}}$$

Hence,

$$i = -\frac{10}{R}e^{-t/RC}u(t) - \frac{i^{(-1)}(0^+)}{RC}e^{-t/RC}u(t)$$

where the negative sign states the current flows in the opposite direction shown. From section 5–3 we see the initial conditions require that the capacitor C be short circuited at $t = 0^+$, hence no current will flow through C at $t = 0^+$. Thus $i(0^+) = 0$ and as a result charge will not accumulate on C, or $i^{(-1)}(0^+) = 0$ [recall $i^{(-1)}(t) =$ charge]. Then

$$i = -\frac{10}{R}e^{-t/RC}u(t) = -1 \times 10^{-3}e^{-t}u(t) = -e^{-t}u(t) \text{ mA}$$

Since we must determine $i^{(-1)}(0^+)$ for the initial condition when the switch is put into position 2 let us determine the equation $i^{(-1)}(t)$, which is charge, and then evaluate it at $t = 1$ s since $t = 1^+$ s in position 1 is $t = 0^+$ in position 2.

$$i^{(-1)} = q = -10^{-3} \int_0^t e^{-t} \, dt = -(1 - e^{-t}) \, \text{mC}$$

Evaluating $i^{(-1)}$ at $t = 1$ s, which is the charge accumulated on the capacitor C over the one-second interval,

$$i^{(-1)}(t = 1) = q(t = 1^+) = -(1 - e^{-1}) \times 10^{-3}$$
$$= -(1 - 0.37) \times 10^{-3} = -0.63 \, \text{mC}$$

or

$$i^{(-1)}_{\text{position 1}}(t = 1^+) \equiv i^{(-1)}_{\text{position 2}}(0^+)$$

We are now ready to determine i for switch position 2.

Switch in position 2 ($t > 1$ s)

$$e_2(t) = Ri(t) + \frac{1}{C} \int i(t) \, dt$$

$$e_2 = 5u(t) \, \text{V}$$

So

$$E_2(s) = RI(s) + \frac{1}{C}\left[\frac{I(s)}{s} + \frac{i^{(1)}(0^+)}{s}\right]$$

$$I(s) = \frac{E_2(s)}{R + \dfrac{1}{Cs}} - \frac{i^{(-1)}(0^+)}{Cs\left(R + \dfrac{1}{Cs}\right)}$$

$$= \frac{5}{s\left(\dfrac{RC + 1}{Cs}\right)} - \frac{i^{(-1)}(0^+)}{Cs\left(\dfrac{RCs + 1}{Cs}\right)}$$

$$= \frac{5}{R}\frac{1}{s + \dfrac{1}{RC}} - \frac{i^{(-1)}(0^+)}{RC\left(s + \dfrac{1}{RC}\right)}$$

$$= \frac{0.5 \times 10^{-3}}{s + 1} + \frac{0.67 \times 10^{-3}}{s + 1} = \frac{1.17 \times 10^{-3}}{s + 1}$$

Therefore

$$i = 1.17 \times 10^{-3}e^{-t}u(t) = 1.17e^{-t} \, \text{mA}$$

Notice the initial condition $i^{(-1)}(0^+)$ for position 2 aided the current flow i. This is true due to the negative flow of i for position 1.

As another example which requires the determination of initial conditions we will consider an *LRC* circuit.

Example 5–6(A) Given the circuit of the following figure determine the equation describing the voltage v_o as a function of time t

with the switch in position 2, that is, determine $v_o(t)$. The switch is to be in position 1 for t_2 seconds and at that time be switched to position 2.

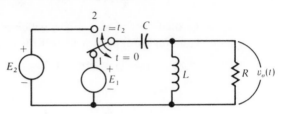

Solution

We must determine the equation for v_o valid for $0 < t \leq t_2$ since we must determine $v_o(0^+)$ and $v_o^{(-1)}(0^+)$ for position 2, which is $v_0(t = t_2)$ and $v_o^{(-1)}(t = t_2)$ of position 1.

To simplify matters let us imagine a single voltage source defined as e which has a value of E_1 for $0 \leq t \leq t_2$ and E_2 for $t > t_2$. Hence, writing a nodal equation we have

$$C \frac{d}{dt}[e(t) - v_o(t)] - \frac{1}{L} \int v_o(t)\, dt - \frac{v_o(t)}{R} = 0$$

Then

$$C[sE(s) - e(0^+) - sV_o(s) + v_o(0^+)]$$
$$- \frac{1}{L}\left[\frac{V_o(s)}{s} + \frac{v^{(-1)}(0^+)}{s}\right] - \frac{V_o(s)}{R} = 0$$

$$CsE(s) - C[e(0^+) - v_o(0^+)] - \frac{v_o^{(-1)}(0^+)}{Ls}$$

$$= \left(Cs + \frac{1}{Ls} + \frac{1}{R}\right)V_o(s)$$

$$= \left(\frac{LCRs^2 + R + Ls}{LRs}\right)V_o(s)$$

$$= \frac{C\left(s^2 + \frac{1}{RC}s + \frac{1}{LC}\right)}{s}V_o(s)$$

Hence,

$$V_o(s) = \frac{s}{s^2 + \frac{1}{RC}s + \frac{1}{LC}}\left\{sE(s) - [e(0^+) - v_o(0^+)]\right.$$

$$\left. - \frac{v_o^{(-1)}(0^+)}{LCs}\right\}$$

It is this equation which we will refer to as our general

equation since it is valid for all cases, that is position 1 or 2.

To determine v_o for $0 \leq t \leq t_2$, or position 1, let us realize that the quantity $v^{(-1)}(0^+)/L$ is the initial current flow in L at $t = 0^+$ (this will be shown later); then our general equation may be written as

$$V_o(s) = \frac{s}{s^2 + \frac{1}{RC}s + \frac{1}{LC}}\left\{sE(s) - [e(0^+) - v_o(0^+)]\right.$$
$$\left. - \frac{i_L(0^+)}{Cs}\right\}$$

Since at $t = 0$ the equivalent circuit of the above figure is that as shown below. From this figure we see that v_o is

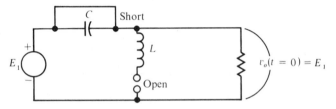

equal to E_1 due to the effective short circuit of C, hence $e(0^+) = E_1 = v_o(0^+)$. And due to the effective open circuit of L the initial current is zero, or $i_L(0^+) = 0$. Hence,

$$V_o(s) = \frac{s^2E(s)}{s^2 + \frac{1}{RC}s + \frac{1}{LC}}$$

Realize that $e(0^+) - v_o(0^+)$ is the initial voltage across the capacitor C, or $v_C(0^+)$. Now since for position 1 we may write $e = E_1u(t)$ then $E(s) = E_1/s$. So

$$V_o(s) = \frac{sE_1}{s^2 + \frac{1}{RC}s + \frac{1}{LC}}$$

We may now determine an explicit equation for v_o by determining $\mathcal{L}^{-1}[v_o(t)]$. To begin we must determine if $\zeta < 1, \zeta > 1, \zeta = 0$ or $\zeta = 1$ so that we will know which equation of Table 4–2 to apply. Since this is an algebraic approach (no values given) let us assume $\zeta < 1$, which results in Eq. (9) of Table 4–2 being of interest. Thus

$2\zeta\omega_n = 1/RC$ and $\omega_n^2 = 1/LC$ so that

$$\omega_n = \frac{1}{\sqrt{LC}} \quad \text{and} \quad \zeta = \frac{1}{2\omega_n RC} = \frac{\sqrt{LC}}{2RC} = \frac{1}{2R}\sqrt{\frac{L}{C}}$$

Now, once values are given for R, L, and C then ω_n and ζ can be calculated.

Due to the s in the numerator of $V_o(s)$ we will use Eq. (15) of Table 4–2. Thus from Eq. (15) we see that for $K = 1$ we have

$$sF(s) = \mathcal{L}\left[\frac{df(t)}{dt} \cdot u(t)\right] + f(0^+)$$

or

$$\mathcal{L}[sF(s)] = \frac{df(t)}{dt}u(t) + \mathcal{L}^{-1}[f(0^+)]$$

We now define

$$F(s) \equiv \frac{E_1}{s^2 + \dfrac{1}{RC}s + \dfrac{1}{LC}} = \frac{E_1}{s^2 + 2\zeta\omega_n s + \omega_n^2}$$

where we have already determined $\omega_n = 1/LC$ etc. Hence

$$v_o = \mathcal{L}^{-1}[V_o(s)] = \mathcal{L}^{-1}\left[\frac{sE_1}{s^2 + 2\zeta\omega_n s + \omega_n^2}\right] = \mathcal{L}^{-1}[sF(s)]$$

$$= \frac{df(t)}{dt}u(t) + \mathcal{L}^{-1}[f(0^+)]$$

where

$$F(s) = \frac{E_1}{s^2 + 2\zeta\omega_n s + \omega_n^2}$$

Out of all this we can simply state

$$v_o = \frac{df(t)}{dt}u(t) + \mathcal{L}^{-1}[f(0^+)]$$

where

$$F(s) = \frac{E_1}{s^2 + 2\zeta\omega_n s + \omega_n^2}$$

It is this equation from which we shall find our solution.

Since

$$F(s) = \frac{E_1}{s^2 + 2\zeta\omega_n s + \omega_n^2}$$

then

$$f = \frac{E_1}{\omega_n\sqrt{1 - \zeta^2}} e^{-\zeta\omega_n t} \sin \omega_n\sqrt{1 - \zeta^2}\, tu(t)$$

So

$$\frac{df(t)}{dt} = \frac{E_1}{\omega_n\sqrt{1-\zeta^2}}[\omega_n\sqrt{1-\zeta^2}\,e^{-\zeta\omega_n t}\cos\omega_n\sqrt{1-\zeta^2}\,t$$
$$-\zeta\omega_n e^{-\zeta\omega_n t}\sin\omega_n\sqrt{1-\zeta^2}\,t]$$

for $t > 0$ since

$$\frac{du(t)}{dt} = \delta(t) \quad \text{and} \quad \delta(t > 0) = 0$$

Collecting terms

$$\frac{df}{dt} = E_1 e^{-\zeta\omega_n t}\left(\cos\omega_n\sqrt{1-\zeta^2}\,t\right.$$
$$\left.-\frac{\zeta}{\sqrt{1-\zeta^2}}\sin\omega_n\sqrt{1-\zeta^2}\,t\right)$$

for $t > 0$.

Now the term $\mathcal{L}^{-1}[f(0^+)] = f(0^+)\delta(t) = 0$ since for our interest $t > 0$. Then

$$v_o = E_1 e^{-\zeta\omega_n t}\left(\cos\omega_n\sqrt{1-\zeta^2}\,t\right.$$
$$\left.-\frac{\zeta}{\sqrt{1-\zeta^2}}\sin\omega_n\sqrt{1-\zeta^2}\,t\right)u(t)$$

where $u(t)$ tells us our equation is for $t > 0$.

Just to check our equation let $t = 0^+$ which yields

$$v_o(t = 0^+) = E_1 e^0\left(\cos 0 - \frac{\zeta}{\sqrt{1-\zeta^2}}\sin 0\right) = E_1$$

which agrees with the figure on p. 263. And for $t = \infty$ (if we left the switch in position 1 for a very long time) then

$$v_o(t = \infty) = E_1 e^{-\infty}\left(\cos\infty - \frac{\zeta}{\sqrt{1-\zeta^2}}\sin\infty\right) = 0$$

since $e^{-\infty} = 0$ and $\sin\infty$ and $\cos\infty$ at most equal ± 1. From the figure on p. 262 we see this to be the case since C looks like an open circuit for dc voltages for $t \to \infty$, hence our equation is verified.

We now have an equation to determine the initial condition for position 2. For position 2 our general equation derived for position 1 is valid but now $e = E_2$ and $v_o(0^+)$ and $v_o^{(-1)}(0^+)$ are to be determined from v_o just derived. Thus

$$v_o(0^+) = \underset{\text{For position 1}}{v_o(t = t_2)} = E_1 e^{-\zeta\omega_n t_1}\left(\cos\omega_n\sqrt{1-\zeta^2}\,t_1\right.$$
$$\left.-\frac{\zeta}{\sqrt{1-\zeta^2}}\sin\omega_n\sqrt{1-\zeta^2}\,t_1\right)$$

Since this is a specific value let us define it as E; therefore

$$v_o(0^+) = E$$

Again we must realize that $t = t_2$ for position 1 is $t = 0$ for position 2. Also let us evaluate $v_o^{(-1)}(0^+)$ for position 2. Now,

$$v_o^{(-1)}(t) = \int_0^t v_o(t)\, dt = E_1\left[\int_0^t e^{-\zeta\omega_n t} \cos \omega_n\sqrt{1-\zeta^2}\,t\, dt \right.$$
$$\left. - \frac{\zeta}{\sqrt{1-\zeta^2}} \int_0^t e^{-\zeta\omega_n t} \sin \omega_n\sqrt{1-\zeta^2}\,t\, dt \right]$$

Since

$$\int e^{ax} \sin px\, dx = \frac{e^{ax}(a \sin px - p \cos px)}{a^2 + p^2}$$

and

$$\int e^{ax} \cos px\, dx = \frac{e^{ax}(a \cos px + p \sin px)}{a^2 + p^2}$$

then

$$v_o^{(-1)}(t) = \frac{\omega_n E_1 e^{-\zeta\omega_n t}}{(-\zeta\omega_n)^2 + (\omega_n\sqrt{1-\zeta^2})^2}$$
$$\times [(\sqrt{1-\zeta^2} + \zeta) \sin \omega_n\sqrt{1-\zeta^2}\,t$$
$$- (\sqrt{1-\zeta^2} - \zeta) \cos \omega_n\sqrt{1-\zeta^2}\,t]\Big|_{t=0}^{t=t}$$

$$v_o^{(-1)}(t) = E_1[(\sqrt{1-\zeta^2} + \zeta) \sin \omega_n\sqrt{1-\zeta^2}\,t$$
$$- (\sqrt{1-\zeta^2} - \zeta) \cos \omega_n\sqrt{1-\zeta^2}\,t$$
$$+ (\sqrt{1-\zeta^2} - \zeta)]$$

Evaluating $v_o^{(-1)}$ at $t = t_2$ we have

$$v_o^{(-1)}(t = t_2) \equiv v_o^{(-1)}(0^+)$$
$$= E_1[(\sqrt{1-\zeta^2} + \zeta) \sin \omega_n\sqrt{1-\zeta^2}\,t_2$$
$$- (\sqrt{1-\zeta^2} - \zeta) \cos \omega_n\sqrt{1-\zeta^2}\,t_2$$
$$+ (\sqrt{1-\zeta^2} - \zeta)]$$

which is some constant we shall define as K_1.

Thus our general equation for $V_o(s)$ may specifically be written as

$$V_o(s) = \frac{s}{s^2 + \frac{1}{RC}s + \frac{1}{LC}}\left\{E_2 - [E_2 - E] - \frac{K}{LCs}\right\}$$

since $e = E_2 u(t)$ and $e(0^+) = E_2$. Then

$$V_o(s) = \frac{sE}{s^2 + \frac{1}{RC}s + \frac{1}{LC}} - \frac{K_1}{LC\left(s^2 + \frac{1}{RC}s + \frac{1}{LC}\right)}$$

From our previous work we see that

$$\mathcal{L}^{-1}\left[\frac{sE}{s^2 + \frac{1}{RC}s + \frac{1}{LC}}\right] = Ee^{-\zeta\omega_n t}\left(\cos \omega_n\sqrt{1 - \zeta^2}t\right.$$

$$\left. - \frac{\zeta}{\sqrt{1 - \zeta^2}}\sin \omega_n\sqrt{1 - \zeta^2}t\right)u(t)$$

And from Eq. (9) of Table 4–2 we see that

$$\mathcal{L}^{-1}\left[\frac{K_1}{LC\left(s^2 + \frac{1}{RC}s + \frac{1}{LC}\right)}\right]$$

$$= \frac{K_1 e^{-\zeta\omega_n t}}{LC\omega_n\sqrt{1 - \zeta^2}}\sin \omega_n\sqrt{1 - \zeta^2}\,tu(t)$$

Hence

$$v_o = Ee^{-\zeta\omega_n t}\left[\left(\cos \omega_n\sqrt{1 - \zeta^2}t\right.\right.$$

$$\left. - \frac{\zeta}{\sqrt{1 - \zeta^2}}\sin \omega_n\sqrt{1 - \zeta^2}t\right)$$

$$\left. - \frac{K_1}{LC\omega_n\sqrt{1 - \zeta^2}}\sin \omega_n\sqrt{1 - \zeta^2}\right]u(t)$$

which is our solution (recall ζ, E, K, and ω_n may be evaluated once values for the circuit parameters are given).

For our next example we shall again consider initial conditions when waveforms are used rather than switches. Notice how much more simple the analysis becomes.

Example 5–6(B) For the circuit of the following figure determine the equation for v_o if e is as illustrated.

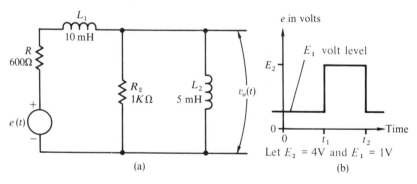

(a)   (b)

Solution   Writing the differential equations we have

$$\frac{e(t) - v_1(t)}{R_1} + \frac{1}{L_1}\int [v_o(t) - v_1(t)]\,dt = 0$$

where v_1 is the nodal voltage at the junction of R_1 and L_1.

$$\frac{1}{L_1}\int [v_1(t) - v_o(t)]\,dt - \frac{v_o(t)}{R_2} - \frac{1}{L_2}\int v_o(t)\,dt = 0$$

Taking the Laplace transform

$$\frac{E(s) - V_1(s)}{R_1} + \frac{1}{L_1}\left[\frac{V_o(s)}{s} + \frac{v_o^{(-1)}(0^+)}{s} - \frac{V_1(s)}{s}\right.$$
$$\left. - \frac{v_1^{(-1)}(0^+)}{s}\right] = 0$$

$$\frac{1}{L_1}\left[\frac{V_1(s)}{s} + \frac{v_1^{(-1)}(0^+)}{s} - \frac{V_o(s)}{s} - \frac{v_o^{(-1)}(0^+)}{s}\right] - \frac{V_o(s)}{R_2}$$
$$- \frac{1}{L_2}[V_o(s) + v_o^{(-1)}(0^+)] = 0$$

Putting the equations in determinate form

$$\frac{E(s)}{R_1} + \frac{1}{L_1 s}[v_o^{(-1)}(0^+) - v_1^{(-1)}(0^+)]$$
$$= \left(\frac{1}{R_1} + \frac{1}{L_1 s}\right)V_1(s) - \frac{1}{L_1 s}V_o(s)$$

and

$$\frac{1}{L_1 s}[v_1^{(-1)}(0^+) - v_o^{(-1)}(0^+)] - \frac{v_o^{(-1)}(0^+)}{L_2}$$
$$= -\frac{1}{L_1 s}V_1(s) + \left(\frac{1}{L_1 s} + \frac{1}{L_2 s} + \frac{1}{R_2}\right)V_o(s)$$

Let us now evaluate the initial conditions $v_o^{(-1)}(0^+)$ and $v_1^{(-1)}(0^+)$. It shall be shown later that the quantity $v_o^{(-1)}(0^+)/L$ has the units of current, hence

$$\frac{1}{L_1}[v_o^{(-1)}(0^+) - v_1^{(-1)}(0^+)] = i_{L_1}(0^+)$$

which is the value of the initial current flow in inductor L_1. Likewise $(1/L_2)v_o^{(-1)}(0^+) = i_{L_2}(0^+)$ which is the initial current flow in inductor L_2. Notice in each case it is the product of the integral of the voltage across the inductor and the reciprocal value of inductance which determines the magnitude of current flow. Hence, we may rewrite our equations:

$$\frac{E(s)}{R_1} + \frac{1}{s}i_{L_1}(0^+) = \left(\frac{1}{R_1} + \frac{1}{L_1 s}\right)V_1(s) - \frac{1}{L_1 s}V_o(s)$$

$$- \frac{1}{s}i_{L_1}(0^+) + \frac{1}{s}i_{L_2}(0^+)$$
$$= -\frac{1}{L_1 s}V_1(s) + \left(\frac{1}{L_{eq} s} + \frac{1}{R_2}\right)V_o(s)$$

where $L_{eq} = \dfrac{L_1 L_2}{L_1 + L_2}$

We were able to establish directions (signs) for $i_{L_1}(0^+)$ and $i_{L_2}(0^+)$ by recalling we chose all currents to entering node one; therefore we wrote the current through L_1 as

$$\frac{1}{L_1} \int [v_o(t) - v_1(t)] \, dt = \frac{1}{L_1}[v_o^{(-1)}(t) - v_1^{(-1)}(t)]$$

Then $[v_o(t) - v_1(t)]$ is the positive polarity, or

$$i_{L_1}(0^+) = \frac{1}{L_1}[v_o^{(-1)}(0^+) - v_1^{(-1)}(0^+)]$$

and

$$\frac{1}{L_1}[v_1^{(-1)}(0^+) - v_o^{(-1)}(0^+)] = -i_{L_1}(0^+)$$

Likewise we chose

$$\frac{1}{L_2} \int [0 - v_0(t)] \, dt = -\frac{1}{L_2} \int v_o(t) \, dt = -\frac{v_o^{(-1)}(t)}{L_2}$$

to be the positive direction for i_{L_2}, hence

$$i_{L_2}^{(-1)}(0^+) = -\frac{v_o^{(-1)}(0^+)}{L_2}$$

Using the methods of section 5–3 we see that $i_{L_1}(0^+) = 0$ and $i_{L_2}(0^+) = 0$ for L_1 and L_2 open circuited at $t = 0^+$. Then

$$\frac{E(s)}{R_1} = \left(\frac{1}{R_1} + \frac{1}{L_1 s}\right) V_1(s) - \frac{1}{L_1 s} V_o(s)$$

$$0 = -\frac{1}{L_1 s} V_1(s) + \left(\frac{1}{L_{eq} s} + \frac{1}{R_2}\right) V_o(s)$$

Solving for $V_o(s)$ using determinants

$$\Delta = \begin{vmatrix} \left(R_1 + \dfrac{1}{L_1 s}\right) & -\dfrac{1}{L_1 s} \\[2ex] -\dfrac{1}{L_1 s} & \left(\dfrac{1}{L_{eq} s} + \dfrac{1}{R_2}\right) \end{vmatrix}$$

$$= \left(\frac{1}{R_1} + \frac{1}{L_1 s}\right)\left(\frac{1}{L_{eq} s} + \frac{1}{R_2}\right) - \left(\frac{1}{L_1 s}\right)^2$$

$$= \left(\frac{1}{R_1 L_{eq}} + \frac{1}{R_1 L_1}\right)\frac{1}{s} + \left(\frac{1}{L_1 L_{eq}} - \frac{1}{L_1^2}\right)\frac{1}{s^2} + \frac{1}{R_1 R_2}$$

$$= \frac{L_1 + 2L_2}{R_1 L_1 L_2 s} + \frac{1}{L_1 L_2 s^2} + \frac{1}{R_1 R_2}$$

Putting Δ into better form by knowing it will be in the denominator we want the form $K(s^2 + as + b)$. Let us begin by putting everything under common denominator $R_1 R_2 L_1 L_2 s^2$. Thus

$$\Delta = \frac{(L_1 + 2L_2)R_2 s + R_1 R_2 + L_1 L_2 s^2}{R_1 R_2 L_1 L_2 s^2}$$

Forcing the coefficient of s^2 (the highest power of s) to be unity

$$\Delta = \frac{s^2 + \dfrac{R_2}{L_1 L_2}(L_1 + 2L_2)s + \dfrac{R_1 R_2}{L_1 L_2}}{R_1 R_2 s^2}$$

which is what we sought.

Solving for $V_o(s)$ we have

$$\Delta V_o(s) = \begin{vmatrix} \left(\dfrac{1}{R_1} + \dfrac{1}{L_1 s}\right) & \dfrac{E(s)}{R_1} \\[2mm] -\dfrac{1}{L_1 s} & 0 \end{vmatrix} = \frac{E(s)}{R_1 L_1 s}$$

or

$$V_o(s) = \frac{E(s)}{\Delta R_1 L_1 s} = \frac{\left(\dfrac{R_2}{L_1}\right) s E(s)}{s^2 + \dfrac{R_2(L_1 + 2L_2)}{L_1 L_2}s + \dfrac{R_1 R_2}{L_1 L_2}}$$

To determine v_o we must determine the input voltage $E(s)$. Now, from the figure on p. 267 we may write

$$e = 1u(t) + E[u(t - t_1) - u(t - t_2)]$$

where $E \equiv E_2 - E_1$

$$E(s) = \frac{1}{s} + \frac{E}{s}(e^{-t_1 s} - e^{-t_2 s})$$

Therefore

$$V_o(s) = \frac{\left(\dfrac{R_2}{L_1}\right)[1 + E(e^{-t_1 s} - e^{-t_2 s})]}{s^2 + \dfrac{R_2(L_1 + 2L_2)}{L_1 L_2}s + \dfrac{R_1 R_2}{L_1 L_2}}$$

In order to find $\mathcal{L}^{-1}$ we must find which equation of Table 4–2 to apply. Knowing $V_o(s)$ can be written as

$$V_o(s) = \frac{\left(\dfrac{R_2}{L_1}\right)}{s^2 + \dfrac{R_2(L_1 + 2L_2)}{L_1 L_2}s + \dfrac{R_1 R_2}{L_1 L_2}}$$

$$+ \frac{\left(\dfrac{R_2}{L_1}\right)Ee^{-t_1 s}}{s^2 + \dfrac{R_2(L_1 + 2L_2)}{L_1 L_2}s + \dfrac{R_1 R_2}{L_1 L_2}}$$

$$- \frac{\left(\dfrac{R_2}{L_1}\right)Ee^{-t_2 s}}{s^2 + \dfrac{R_2(L_1 + 2L_2)}{L_1 L_2}s + \dfrac{R_1 R_2}{L_1 L_2}}$$

Also realizing that the terms e^{-t_1s} and e^{-t_2s} are merely displacements in time (see Eq. 21 of Table 4–2) then we are simply finding

$$\mathcal{L}^{-1}\left[\frac{K}{s^2 + \dfrac{R_2(L_1 + 2L_2)}{L_1L_2}s + \dfrac{R_1R_2}{L_1L_2}}\right]$$

$$= \mathcal{L}^{-1}\left[\frac{K}{s^2 + \text{constant}\cdot s + \text{constant}}\right]$$

which is identified with Eq. (9) of Table 4–2. Thus we must determine the value of ζ to see if Eq. (6), (7), (9), or (10) of Table 4–2 applies. From Eq. (9) we see

$$2\zeta\omega_n = \frac{R_2(L_1 + 2L_2)}{L_1L_2} \quad \text{and} \quad \omega_n^2 = \frac{R_1R_2}{L_1L_2} \quad \text{so}$$

$$\zeta = \frac{R_2(L_1 + 2L_2)}{2\omega_nL_1L_2}$$

Now

$$\omega_n = \sqrt{\frac{R_1R_2}{L_1L_2}} = \sqrt{\frac{600 \times 10^3}{50 \times 10^{-6}}} = 110 \times 10^3$$

so

$$\zeta = \frac{10^3(20 \times 10^{-3})}{220 \times 10^3(50 \times 10^{-6})} = 1.8$$

Since $\zeta > 1$ we use Eq. (10) of Table 4–2. This requires factoring so that

$$s^2 + \frac{R_2(L_1 + 2L_2)}{L_1L_2}s + \frac{R_1R_2}{L_1L_2}$$

may be written as $(s + \alpha)(s + \beta)$. Now

$$s^2 + \frac{R_2(L_1 + 2L_2)}{L_1L_2}s + \frac{R_1R_2}{L_1L_2}$$

$$= s^2 + 400 \times 10^3s + 12 \times 10^9$$

Factoring

$$s_{1,2} = -200 \times 10^3 \pm \frac{1}{2}\sqrt{16 \times 10^{10} - 4.8 \times 10^{10}}$$

$$= \left(-2 \pm \frac{3.34}{2}\right) \times 10^5$$

$s_1 = -3.68 \times 10^5$ and $s_2 = -0.32 \times 10^5$, hence

$$V_o(s) = \frac{\left(\dfrac{R_2}{L_1}\right)[1 + E(e^{-t_1s} - e^{-t_2s})]}{(s + 3.68 \times 10^5)(s + 0.32 \times 10^5)}$$

First finding

$$\mathcal{L}^{-1}\left[\frac{1}{(s + 3.68 \times 10^5)(s + 0.32 \times 10^5)}\right]$$

$$= \frac{1}{3.68 \times 10^5 - 0.32 \times 10^5}(e^{-0.32 \times 10^5 t} - e^{-3.68 \times 10^5 t})u(t)$$

by letting β and α of Eq. (10) be equal to $\beta = 3.68 \times 10^5$ and $\alpha = 0.32 \times 10^5$. Thus

$$v_o = \frac{\left(\dfrac{R_2}{L_1}\right)}{3.36 \times 10^5}(e^{-0.32 \times 10^5 t} - e^{-3.68 \times 10^5 t})u(t)$$

$$+ \frac{\left(\dfrac{R_2}{L_1}\right)E}{3.36 \times 10^5}(e^{-0.32 \times 10^5 (t-t_1)} - e^{-3.68 \times 10^5 (t-t_1)})u(t - t_1)$$

$$- \frac{\left(\dfrac{R_2}{L_1}\right)E}{3.36 \times 10^5}(e^{-0.32 \times 10^5 (t-t_2)} - e^{-3.68 \times 10^5 (t-t_2)})u(t - t_2)$$

So

$$v_o = 1.79[(e^{-0.32 \times 10^5 t} - e^{-3.68 \times 10^5 t})u(t)$$
$$+ (e^{-0.32 \times 10^5 (t-t_1)} - e^{-3.68 \times 10^5 (t-t_1)}u(t - t_1)$$
$$- (e^{-0.32 \times 10^5 (t-t_2)} - e^{-3.68 \times 10^5 (t-t_2)}u(t - t_2)]\ V$$

As practice it is suggested the reader work this problem again using a switch and two dc voltage sources to generate e. This will allow the reader to determine the initial conditions for $t = 0$, $t = t_1$, and $t = t_2$. The same results we just obtained should be derived.

5–4 Graphical Interpretation of Solutions

As another example of time reference and initial conditions we will consider a pulse being applied to Ex. 5–1. We will also sketch the results so as to begin to get a physical interpretation of our solutions.

Example 5–7   Suppose that for Ex. 5–1 we were given e_{in} as shown in Fig. 5–19 and asked to find v_o.
    We know from Ex. 5–1, Eq. (5–3), that

$$V_o(s) = \frac{sE_{in}(s) - [e_{in}(0^+) - v_o(0^+)]}{s + \dfrac{1}{RC}}$$

From this equation we see that we must determine $E_{in}(s)$ in explicit form in order that $V_o(s)$ be an explicit equation. Writing an equation for $e_{in}(t)$ we have

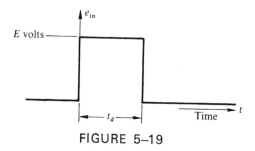

FIGURE 5–19

$$e_{in}(t) = Eu(t) - Eu(t - t_d)$$

where the start of the pulse is *defined* as being the zero time reference. Thus

$$E_{in}(s) = \frac{E}{s} - \frac{E}{s}e^{-t_d s} = \frac{E}{s}(1 - e^{-t_d s})$$

so

$$V_o(s) = \frac{E(1 - e^{-t_d s}) - [e_{in}(0^+) - v_o(0^+)]}{s + \dfrac{1}{RC}}$$

In order to find v_o we may wish to write $V_o(s)$ a little differently. The main alteration is to isolate the term which is a product of $e^{-t_d s}$ since in Table 4–2 we have the transform pair $\mathcal{L}[f(t - a)u(t - a)] = e^{-as}F(s)$. Then

$$V_o(s) = \frac{E - [e_{in}(0^+) - v_o(0^+)]}{s + \dfrac{1}{RC}} - \frac{E}{s + \dfrac{1}{RC}}e^{-t_d s}$$

Generalizing $V_o(s)$ we have

$$V_o(s) = \frac{\text{constant}}{s + \text{constant}} - \frac{\text{constant}}{s + \text{constant}}e^{-\text{constant}\cdot s}$$

Searching Table 4–2 we find Eq. (4) matches

$$\frac{E - [e_{in}(0^+) - v_o(0^+)]}{s + \dfrac{1}{RC}}$$

and Eq. (21) applies to $E/(s + 1/RC)e^{-t_d s}$, if we let $KF(s)$ shown in Eq. (21) be defined as $E/(s + 1/RC)$. Thus

$$\mathcal{L}^{-1}\left\{\frac{E - [e_{in}(0^+) - v_o(0^+)]}{s + \dfrac{1}{RC}}\right\}$$

$$= \{E - [e_{in}(0^+) - v_o(0^+)]\}e^{-t/RC}u(t)$$

from Eq. (4) of Table 4–2. And

$$\mathcal{L}^{-1}\left[\frac{E}{s + \dfrac{1}{RC}}e^{-t_d s}\right] = Ee^{-(t-t_d)/RC}u(t - t_d)$$

using Eq. (21) and Eq. (4) of Table 4–2. Therefore,

$$v_o(t) = \{E - [e_{\text{in}}(0^+) - v_o(0^+)]\}e^{-t/RC}u(t)$$
$$- Ee^{-(t-t_d)/RC}u(t - t_d)$$

Using the same reasoning as for Ex. 5–1 the voltage $e_{\text{in}}(0^+) - v_o(0^+) = 0$. Then $v_o(t)$ may be written as

$$v_o(t) = Ee^{-t/RC}u(t) - Ee^{-(t-t_d)/RC}u(t - t_d)$$
$$= [u(t) - e^{-t_d/RC}u(t - t_d)]Ee^{-t/RC} \qquad \text{(5–14)}$$

Now let us graph v_o as mathematically represented in Eq. (5–14). Because of the presence of $u(t)$ and $u(t - t_d)$ we may divide v_o into ranges. The ranges will be $t < 0$, $0 < t < t_d$, and $t > t_d$ based upon when $u(t)$ and $u(t - t_d)$ are equal to 1.

For the range $t < 0$

$v_o(t) = 0$ since $u(t) = u(t - t_d) = 0$

For the range $0 < t < t_d$

$v_o(t) = Ee^{-t/RC}$ since $u(t) = 1$ and $u(t - t_d) = 0$

For the range $t > t_d$

$v_o(t) = (1 - e^{t_d/RC})Ee^{-t/RC}$ since $u(t) = u(t - t_d) = 1$

To actually graph this function v_o we would have to know the numerical value of the RC time constant. However, we will sketch $v_o(t)$ for two very general cases: one for a "fast" RC time constant, which means $RC \ll t_d$ (read RC is much much less than t_d). The second case will be for a "slow" RC time constant, that is, $RC \gg t_d$.

For $RC \ll t_d$

Range 1:
$v_o(t) = 0$ for $t < 0$. This curve is obvious.

Range 2:
$v_o(t) = Ee^{-t/RC}$ for $0 < t < t_d$. Since we know the basic curve of $Ee^{-t/RC}$ (see Fig. 4–4) we will determine some points which will allow us to scale this curve. We will find two end-point values for v_o: one at $t = 0^+$ and the other

at $t = t_d$. Evaluating these points, we have

$$v_o(t = 0^+) = v_o(0^+) = Ee^{-0/RC} = E$$

and

$$v_o(t_d) = Ee^{-t_d/RC}$$

To find the point $Ee^{-t_d/RC}$ we will look at the relative magnitude of the circuit's time constant RC as compared to t_d. Now $RC \ll t_d$, from which we can determine $1 \ll (t_d/RC)$ by algebraic manipulation. $1 \ll (t_d/RC)$ states that t_d/RC is much, much larger than one. So using one as a reference $v_o(t_d) = Ee^{-\text{large number}}$, where *large number* $\gg 1$. To get a feel for what magnitude we mean by "large number" let us find some values for $e^{-\text{large number}}$. Letting *large number* = 2, 3, 4, and 5: $e^{-2} = 0.135$, $e^{-3} = 0.050$, $e^{-4} = 0.018$, and $e^{-5} = 0.0067$ for slide-rule accuracy. It appears that for *large number* $\gg 3$ then $e^{-\text{large number}}$ is relatively small in magnitude. The point being that *large number* does not have to be particularly of great magnitude to cause $e^{-\text{large number}}$ to be very small in magnitude. Then

$$v_o(t_d) = Ee^{-t_d/RC} = Ee^{-\text{large number}} \cong 0$$

Range 3:

$v_o(t) = (1 - e^{-t_d/RC})Ee^{-t/RC}$ for $t > t_d$. In viewing this equation we can see that we are dealing with the same general curve as for range 2. This can be seen by recognizing that the quantity $(1 - e^{t_d/RC})$ is a constant, hence $(1 - e^{t_d/RC})Ee^{-t/RC} = \text{constant} \cdot e^{-t/RC}$. To find the points which will indicate where this curve should be sketched on the graph let us determine $v_o(t_d)$ and $v_o(t_d + 5RC)$, where $t_d + 5RC$ is five RC time constants after $t = t_d$. Evaluating the point $t = t_d$ first we have

$$v_o(t_d) = (1 - e^{t_d/RC})Ee^{-t_d/RC} = (e^{-t_d/RC} - 1)E$$
$$\cong -E$$

since $e^{-t_d/RC} \ll 1$. And for $t = t_d + 5RC$ we have

$$v_o(t_d + 5RC) = (1 - e^{t_d/RC})Ee^{-(t_d + 5RC)/RC}$$
$$= (e^{-t_d/RC} - 1)Ee^{-5} \cong -Ee^{-5}$$

As we saw before $e^{-5} = 0.0067$, therefore

$$v_o(t_d + 5RC) \cong -Ee^{-5} \cong 0$$

Then for our three ranges we have: Range 1, which

covers $t < 0$ and follows the curve $v_o(t) = 0$; Range 2, which ranges for $0 < t < t_d$ and follows the curve

$$v_o(t) = Ee^{-t/RC}$$

(two end points were determined from this equation and these were $v_o(0^+) = E$ and $v_o(t_d) \cong 0$; Range 3, which covers $t > t_d$ and follows the curve

$$v_o(t) = (1 - e^{t_d/RC})Ee^{-t/RC}$$

End points $v_o(t_d) \cong -E$ and $v_o(t_d + 5RC) \cong 0$ were determined. Graphing these ranges results in Fig. 5–20.

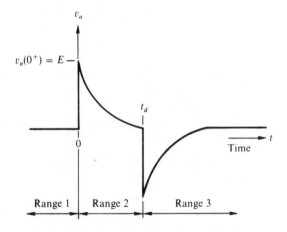

Graph of $v_o(t) = [u(t) - e^{t_d/RC}u(t - t_d)]Ee^{-t/RC}$ for $RC \ll t_d$

FIGURE 5–20

From Fig. 5–20 we see our circuit is a differentiator for $RC \ll t_d$.

Let us now graph Eq. (5–14) for the condition $RC \gg t_d$. Proceeding as before

For $RC \gg t_d$

Range 1: $v_o(t) = 0$ for $t < 0$.

Range 2: $v_o(t) = Ee^{-t/RC}$ for $0 < t < t_d$. Finding the two end points $t = 0^+$ and $t = t_d$,

$$v_o(0^+) = E$$

and

$$v_o(t_d) = Ee^{-t_d/RC} = Ee^{-\text{small number}} \cong E$$

since $e^{-\text{small number}} \cong 1$.

Range 3: $v_o(t) = (1 - e^{t_d/RC})Ee^{-t/RC}$ for $t > t_d$. For the end points $t = t_d$ and $t = t_d + 5RC$ we have

$$v_o(t_d) = (1 - e^{t_d/RC})Ee^{-t_d/RC} = (e^{-t_d/RC} - 1)E \cong 0$$

And

$$v_o(t_d + 5RC) = (1 - e^{t_d/RC})Ee^{-(t_d + 5RC)/RC}$$
$$= (e^{-t_d/RC} - 1)Ee^{-5} \cong (e^{-t_d/RC} - 1)0.0067E$$
$$\cong 0$$

since $e^{-t_d/RC} \cong 1$, which is the same value as $v_o(t_d)$.

The graph of the ranges comprising v_o is shown in Fig. 5–21.

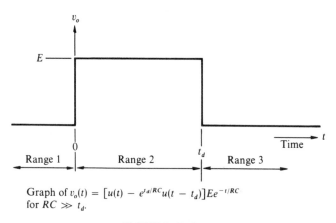

Graph of $v_o(t) = [u(t) - e^{t_d/RC}u(t - t_d)]Ee^{-t/RC}$ for $RC \gg t_d$.

FIGURE 5–21

From Fig. 5–21 we see that the input waveform e_{in} is not altered for $RC \gg t_d$. Hence, if waveform fidelity is desired then the RC time constant must be large with respect to the pulse duration t_d. It should be remembered that Fig. 5–21 is not an exact graph of v_o.

5–5   Discussion on General Equations Describing a Circuit

In our examples we were usually given the waveforms of the driving force e_{in} and as a result the shape and polarity of e_{in} were known. In many circuit analysis problems the exact waveform for e_{in} is not known or may be different from time to time. Under these conditions the implicit equations we derive relating the output and driving force must be considered a general relationship. For instance, we could consider the driving force e_{in}

of Ex. 5–1 to be general; therefore Eq. (5–3) is a general equation which is descriptive of $V_o(s)$ for *any* $E_{in}(s)$. That is, it describes the effects of the circuit on $E_{in}(s)$ to produce $V_o(s)$. To demonstrate let's consider the circuit of Ex. 5–1 for some e_{in} which is different from that shown for Ex. 5–1.

Example 5–8   Write an equation for v_o of Ex. 5–1 when e_{in} is as illustrated in Fig. 5–22.

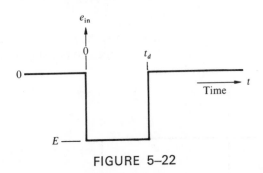

FIGURE 5–22

Solution   From Eq. (5–3) we see that

$$V_o(s) = \frac{sE_{in}(s)}{s + \dfrac{1}{RC}} - \frac{e_{in}(0^+) - v_o(0^+)}{s + \dfrac{1}{RC}}$$

From the circuit and e_{in} we can determine that $e_{in}(0^+) - v_o(0^+) = 0$.

Thus

$$V_o(s) = \frac{sE_{in}(s)}{s + \dfrac{1}{RC}} \tag{5–15}$$

which is a general equation for $V_o(s)$. To determine $E_{in}(s)$ we first write an equation for e_{in}, which is,

$$e_{in}(t) = -[u(t) - u(t - t_d)]E$$

Taking the Laplace transform of e_{in},

$$E_{in}(s) = -\frac{E}{s}(1 - e^{-t_d s})$$

Substituting $E_{in}(s)$ into Eq. (5–15) for $E_{in}(s)$ we have

$$V_o(s) = -\frac{E(1 - e^{-t_d s})}{s + \dfrac{1}{RC}} = -\frac{E}{s + \dfrac{1}{RC}} + \frac{Ee^{-t_d s}}{s + \dfrac{1}{RC}}$$

Thus

$$v_o(t) = -[u(t) - e^{t_d/RC}u(t - t_d)]Ee^{-t/RC} \quad \textbf{(5-16)}$$

which is the negative of Eq. (5–14). Then the graph of Eq. (5–14) would be the negative of Fig. 5–20, or Fig. 5–21 depending on the RC time-constant magnitude.

It is hoped that Ex. 5–8 not only demonstrates what we mean by general equation but also demonstrates again that unknown voltage polarities, whether sources or nodals, may be assumed. For once the true polarities, or directions, of the driving sources are known and are substituted in the general equation, the mathematics will correctly determine the polarities, or directions, of the unknowns for which we are solving. We will again demonstrate this in our next example.

In our next example we will utilize all the concepts previously discussed; however, to give some variation in analysis we shall solve for a current, which means we will use loop analysis.

Example 5–9   Given the circuit in Fig. 5–23 solve for the current through inductor L. The voltage generator e_{in} has the waveform shown in Fig. 5–23.

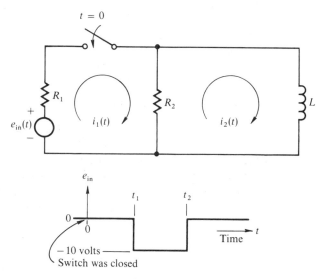

FIGURE 5–23

Solution   The voltage polarity for e_{in} and the loop current directions shown are assumed. Writing our loop equations for

$t > 0$,

$$e_{in}(t) - R_1 i_1(t) - R_2 i_1(t) + R_2 i_2(t) = 0$$

and

$$-R_2 i_2(t) + R_2 i_1(t) - L\frac{di_2(t)}{dt} = 0$$

Taking the Laplace transform

$$E_{in}(s) - R_1 I_1(s) - R_2 I_1(s) + R_2 I_2(s) = 0$$
$$-R_2 I_2(s) + R_2 I_1(s) - L[sI_2(s) - i_2(0^+)] = 0$$

Solving for the current through L, which is $I_2(s)$:

$$E_{in}(s) = (R_1 + R_2)I_1(s) - R_2 I_2(s)$$
$$Li_2(0^+) = -R_2 I_1(s) + (R_2 + Ls)I_2(s)$$

Using determinants,

$$\Delta = \begin{vmatrix} (R_1 + R_2) & -R_2 \\ -R_2 & (R_2 + Ls) \end{vmatrix}$$
$$= (R_1 + R_2)(R_2 + Ls) - R_2^2$$
$$= R_1 R_2 + (R_1 + R_2)Ls$$

And

$$\Delta I_2(s) = \begin{vmatrix} (R_1 + R_2) & E_{in}(s) \\ -R_2 & Li_2(0^+) \end{vmatrix}$$
$$= (R_1 + R_2)Li_2(0^+) + R_2 E_{in}(s)$$

Therefore,

$$I_2(s) = \frac{R_2 E_{in}(s) + (R_1 + R_2)Li_2(0^+)}{R_1 R_2 + (R_1 + R_2)Ls}$$

Isolating the term containing $E_{in}(s)$ from the other terms

$$I_2(s) = \frac{R_2 E_{in}(s)}{R_1 R_2 + (R_1 + R_2)Ls} + \frac{(R_1 + R_2)Li_2(0^+)}{R_1 R_2 + (R_1 + R_2)Ls}$$

which is a general equation for $I_2(s)$.

Even though we do not know $E_{in}(s)$ explicitly, as yet, we still can put $I_2(s)$ in as convenient a form as possible in preparation for finding $i_2(t)$. Using the procedures of section 4–16 as a guide we will force the coefficient of s to unity. Hence

$$I_2(s) = \frac{R_2}{(R_1 + R_2)L}\left[\frac{E_{in}(s)}{s + \dfrac{R_1 R_2}{(R_1 + R_2)L}}\right] + \frac{i_2(0^+)}{s + \dfrac{R_1 R_2}{(R_1 + R_2)L}}$$

$$= \frac{R_{eq}}{R_1 L}\frac{E_{in}(s)}{s + \dfrac{R_{eq}}{L}} + \frac{i_2(0^+)}{s + \dfrac{R_{eq}}{L}} \tag{5–17}$$

recognizing

$$R_{eq} = \frac{R_1 R_2}{R_1 + R_2}$$

This is as far as we can go until we determine an explicit equation for $E_{in}(s)$.

Determining $E_{in}(s)$ from the problem we have

$$e_{in}(t) = -E[u(t - t_1) - u(t - t_2)]$$

therefore

$$E_{in}(s) = -\frac{E}{s}(e^{-t_1 s} - e^{-t_2 s})$$

Substituting this in Eq. (5–17) for $E_{in}(s)$,

$$I_2(s) = \frac{R_{eq}}{R_1 L}\left[-\frac{E(e^{-t_1 s} - e^{-t_2 s})}{s\left(s + \dfrac{R_{eq}}{L}\right)} \right] + \frac{i_2(0^+)}{s + \dfrac{R_{eq}}{L}}$$

$$= -\frac{R_{eq}E}{R_1 L}\left[\frac{e^{-t_1 s}}{s\left(s + \dfrac{R_{eq}}{L}\right)} - \frac{e^{-t_2 s}}{s\left(s + \dfrac{R_{eq}}{L}\right)} \right] + \frac{i_2(0^+)}{s + \dfrac{R_{eq}}{L}}$$

$$\tag{5-18}$$

Notice that $I_2(s)$ is negative, therefore it is in the opposite direction than we assumed.

Before actually finding the inverse Laplace transform let us use the initial and final-value theorems to see if $I_2(s)$ agrees with the circuit. This is a check to indicate if we have correctly (algebraically) solved for $I_2(s)$. Thus

$$\lim_{t \to 0^+} i_2(t) = i(0^+) = \lim_{s \to \infty} [sI(s)]$$

$$= \lim_{s \to \infty} \left\{ -\frac{R_{eq}E}{R_1 L}\left[\frac{e^{-t_1 s}}{s + \dfrac{R_{eq}}{L}} - \frac{e^{-t_2 s}}{s + \dfrac{R_{eq}}{L}} \right] \right.$$

$$\left. + \frac{si_2(0^+)}{s + \dfrac{R_{eq}}{L}} \right\}$$

$$= \lim_{s \to \infty} \left\{ -\frac{R_{eq}}{R_1 L}\left[\frac{e^{-t_1 s}}{s\left(1 + \dfrac{R_{eq}}{Ls}\right)} - \frac{e^{-t_2 s}}{s\left(1 + \dfrac{R_{eq}}{Ls}\right)} \right] \right.$$

$$\left. + \frac{i_2(0^+)}{1 + \dfrac{R_{eq}}{Ls}} \right\}$$

$$= i_2(0^+)$$

which agrees with the circuit. For the final value $i_2(\infty)$,

$$i_2(\infty) = \underset{t \to \infty}{\text{limit}}\, i_2(t) = \underset{s \to 0}{\text{limit}}\, [sI(s)]$$

$$= \underset{s \to 0}{\text{limit}}\left\{ -\frac{R_{eq}E}{R_1 L}\left[\frac{e^{-t_1 s}}{\left(s + \dfrac{R_{eq}}{L}\right)} - \frac{e^{-t_2 s}}{\left(s + \dfrac{R_{eq}}{L}\right)} \right] \right.$$

$$\left. + \frac{i_2(0^+)}{1 + \dfrac{R_{eq}}{Ls}} \right\}$$

$$= -\frac{R_{eq}E}{R_1 L}\left(\frac{L}{R_{eq}} - \frac{L}{R_{eq}} \right) = 0$$

Now $t = \infty$ is a long time after t_2, therefore $e_{in}(\infty) = 0$ volts, so $i_2(\infty)$ would be zero. Another way to verify that this is correct is to say that $e_{in}(t) = -Eu(t - t_1)$. Then the term $e^{-t_2 s}/(s + R_{eq}/L)$ would not appear in $I_2(s)$ and therefore

$$i_2(\infty) = -\frac{R_{eq}E}{R_1 L}\left(\frac{L}{R_{eq}} \right) = -\frac{E}{R_1}$$

We know that for $t = \infty$ the inductor will appear as a dc short circuit, hence the current through L would be $-E/R_1$.

We have verified that Eq. (5–18) is most probably written correctly by using the initial and final value theorems. We must now determine the value of $i_2(0^+)$. We will approach this problem as we did in earlier examples. From elementary circuit theory we know that inductors will attempt to maintain the same magnitude and direction of current flow, or, to reiterate, they resist a change in value and direction of current flow. Then if we can determine the value of $i_2(0^-)$, where 0^- means "just less than 0," we should have $i_2(0^+)$, for $i_2(0^-) \cong i_2(0^+)$. Looking at our circuit at $t = 0^-$ we have effectively the circuit shown in Fig. 5–24. Notice the voltage source e_{in} is short-circuited. This is true since for $t = 0^-$ $e_{in}(t < 0) = 0$ volts, which is a short circuit. From the circuit we can see that $i_2(0^-) = 0$, therefore $i_2(0^+) = 0$. Then Eq. (5–18) may be written as

$$I_2(s) = -\frac{R_{eq}E}{R_1 L}\left[\frac{e^{-t_1 s}}{s\left(s + \dfrac{R_{eq}}{L}\right)} - \frac{e^{-t_2 s}}{s\left(s + \dfrac{R_{eq}}{L}\right)} \right] \qquad \textbf{(5–19)}$$

We may now take the inverse Laplace transform of

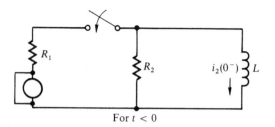

For $t < 0$

FIGURE 5-24

$I_2(s)$. Hence,

$$i_2(t) = -\frac{R_{eq}E}{R_1 L}\mathcal{L}^{-1}\left[\frac{e^{-t_1 s}}{s\left(s + \dfrac{R_{eq}}{L}\right)} - \frac{e^{-t_2 s}}{s\left(s + \dfrac{R_{eq}}{L}\right)}\right]$$

Generalizing the terms we have

$$\frac{e^{-t_1 s}}{s\left(s + \dfrac{R_{eq}}{L}\right)} = \frac{\text{constant} \cdot e^{-\text{constant} \cdot s}}{s(s + \text{constant})} \qquad (5\text{-}20\text{a})$$

and

$$\frac{e^{-t_2 s}}{s\left(s + \dfrac{R_{eq}}{L}\right)} = \frac{\text{constant} \cdot e^{-\text{constant} \cdot s}}{s(s + \text{constant})} \qquad (5\text{-}20\text{b})$$

Searching Table 4–2 we find Eq. (21) identifies with both Eqs. (5–20a) and (b), where $KF(s) = 1/[s(s + (R_{eq}/L))]$ in both cases. And to find $f(t)$ we will use Eq. (5) of Table 4–2. Then for Eqs. (5–20a) and (b) we will use Eqs. (21) and (5) of Table 4–2.

Thus

$$\mathcal{L}^{-1}\left[\frac{e^{-t_1 s}}{s\left(s + \dfrac{R_{eq}}{L}\right)}\right] = \mathcal{L}^{-1}[Ke^{-as}F(s)]$$

$$= Kf(t - a)u(t - a)$$

where

$$F(s) = \frac{1}{s\left(s + \dfrac{R_{eq}}{L}\right)}$$

therefore

$$f(t) = \frac{L}{R_{eq}}(1 - e^{-R_{eq}t})u(t)$$

And from Eq. (21)

$$f(t - a)u(t - a) = f(t - t_1(u)t - t_1)$$

$$= \frac{L}{R_{eq}}[1 - e^{(-R_{eq}/L)(t-t_1)}]u(t - t_1)$$

since $a = t_1$. Then

$$\mathcal{L}^{-1}\left[\frac{e^{-t_1 s}}{s\left(s + \dfrac{R_{eq}}{L}\right)}\right] = \frac{L}{R_{eq}}(1 - e^{(-R_{eq}/L)(t-t_1)})u(t - t_1)$$

and

$$\mathcal{L}^{-1}\left[\frac{e^{-t_2 s}}{s\left(s + \dfrac{R_{eq}}{L}\right)}\right] = \frac{L}{R_{eq}}(1 - e^{(-R_{eq}/L)(t-t_2)})u(t - t_2)$$

Combining the results we have

$$i_2(t) = -\frac{R_{eq}E}{R_1 L}\left[\frac{L}{R_{eq}}(1 - e^{(-R_{eq}/L)(t-t_1)}u(t - t_1)\right.$$

$$\left. - \frac{L}{R_{eq}}(1 - e^{(-R_{eq}/L)(t-t_2)})u(t - t_2)]\right]$$

$$= -\frac{E}{R_1}[(1 - e^{(-R_{eq}/L)(t-t_1)}u(t - t_1)]$$

$$- (1 - e^{(-R_{eq}/L)(t-t_2)}u(t - t_2) \tag{5-21}$$

To sketch Eq. (5–21) we realize that we have three ranges due to the presence of $u(t - t_1)$ and $u(t - t_2)$. These ranges are $t < t_1$, $t_1 < t < t_2$, and $t > t_2$. We will consider how $i_2(t)$ behaves in each range and then "put the pieces together." Hence,

Range 1:   For $t < t_1$

$$i_2(t) = 0$$

since $u(t - t_1) = u(t - t_2) = 0$.

Range 2:   For $t_1 < t < t_2$

$$i_2(t) = -\frac{E}{R_1}[1 - e^{(-R_{eq}/L)(t-t_1)}]$$

since $u(t - t_1) = 1$ and $u(t - t_2) = 0$. The curve for $K(1 - e^{-\alpha t})u(t)$ appears as Fig. 5–25(a).

Then

$$-\frac{E}{R_1}[1 - e^{-(R_{eq}/L)t}]u(t)$$

would appear as Fig. 5–25(b). Since we are shifted by t_1

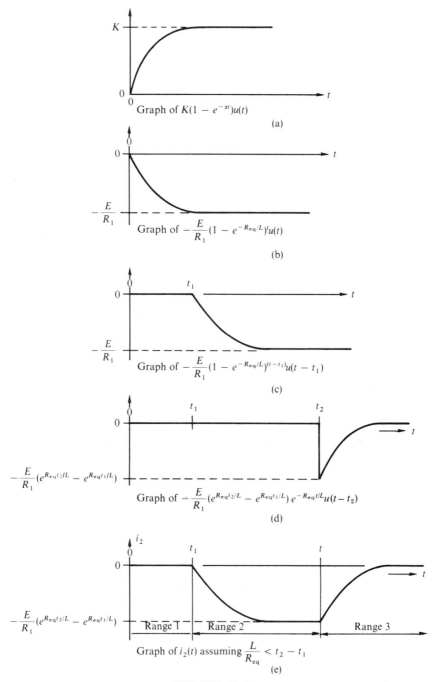

Graph of $K(1 - e^{-\alpha t})u(t)$

(a)

Graph of $-\dfrac{E}{R_1}(1 - e^{-R_{eq}/L)t}u(t)$

(b)

Graph of $-\dfrac{E}{R_1}(1 - e^{-R_{eq}/L)(t-t_1)}u(t - t_1)$

(c)

Graph of $-\dfrac{E}{R_1}(e^{R_{eq}t_2/L} - e^{R_{eq}t_1/L})e^{-R_{eq}t/L}u(t - t_2)$

(d)

Range 1   Range 2   Range 3

Graph of $i_2(t)$ assuming $\dfrac{L}{R_{eq}} < t_2 - t_1$

(e)

FIGURE 5–25

then $-E/R_1[1 - e^{-(R_{eq}/L)(t-t_1)}]u(t - t_1)$ appears as Fig. 5-25(c).

Range 3: For $t > t_2$

$$i_2(t) = -\frac{E}{R_1}[e^{-(R_{eq}/L)(t-t_2)} - e^{-(R_{eq}/L)(t-t_1)}]$$

$$= -\frac{E}{R_1}[e^{(R_{eq}/L)t_2} - e^{(R_{eq}/L)t_1}e^{-(R_{eq}/L)t}]$$

Now

$$\frac{E}{R_1}[e^{(R_{eq}/L)t_2} - e^{(R_{eq}/L)t_1}] = \text{[a constant]}$$

therefore $i_2(t) = -\text{constant} \cdot e^{-(R_{eq}/L)t}$ which follows the curve of Fig. 5-25(d). Putting the pieces together and assuming that the time constant L/R^{eq} is such as to allow maximum current to be reached in range 2, that is $L/R_{eq} \ll t_2 - t_1$, we have Fig. 5-25(e).

Example 5–10   For e_{in} and i as shown in Fig. 5-26 determine the current i_L which flows through R_L. The positive direction for i is arbitrarily defined as flowing out of its #1 terminal.

Solution   Assuming the voltage polarity for e_{in} and current direction for i we have the circuit shown in Fig. 5-27. Converting the current source to an equivalent voltage source and drawing the assumed loop currents we have the circuit shown in Fig. 5-28. Writing the differential equations,

$$e_{in}(t) - (R_1 + R_2)i_1(t) - R_2i(t)$$
$$- \frac{1}{C}\int i_1(t)\, dt + \frac{1}{C}\int i_L(t)\, dt = 0$$

and

$$-\frac{1}{C}\int i_L(t)\, dt + \frac{1}{C}\int i_1(t)\, dt - R_Li_L(t) = 0$$

Then

$$E_{in}(s) - (R_1 + R_2)I_1(s) - R_2I(s)$$
$$- \frac{1}{C}\left[\frac{I_1(s)}{s} + \frac{i_1^{(-1)}(0^+)}{s}\right] + \frac{1}{C}\left[\frac{I_L(s)}{s} + \frac{i_L(0^+)}{s}\right] = 0$$

and

$$-\frac{1}{C}\left[\frac{I_L(s)}{s} + \frac{i_L^{(-1)}(0^+)}{s}\right] + \frac{1}{C}\left[\frac{I_1(s)}{s} + \frac{i_1^{(-1)}(0^+)}{s}\right]$$
$$- R_LI_L(s) = 0$$

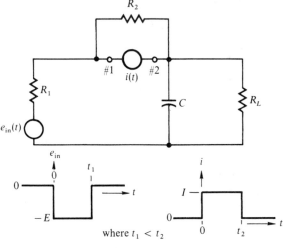

where $t_1 < t_2$

FIGURE 5–26

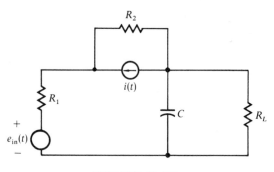

FIGURE 5–27

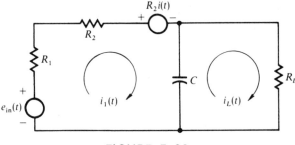

FIGURE 5–28

Now $i^{(-1)}(0^+)$ means $\int i(t)\, dt$ evaluated at $t = 0^+$. And

$$\int i(t)\, dt = \int \frac{dq}{dt}\, dt = \int dq = q(t)$$

so

$$i^{(-1)}(0^+) = q(t)\Big|_{t=0^+} = q(0^+)$$

So $i^{(-1)}(0^+)/C = q(0^+)/C = v_C(0^+) =$ initial voltage across capacitor.

Note: Recall $q_C(t) = Cv_C(t)$, therefore $v_C(t) = q_C(t)/C$. Then $i_1^{(-1)}(0^+)/C = v_{C_1}(t)$ and $i_L^{(-1)}(0^+)/C = -v_{C_L}(0^+)$. Using the techniques from before we find $v_C(0^+) = 0$, therefore

$$E_{in}(s) - (R_1 + R_2)I_1(s) - R_2I(s) - \frac{I_1(s)}{Cs} + \frac{I_L(s)}{Cs} = 0$$

and

$$-\frac{I_L(s)}{Cs} + \frac{I_1(s)}{Cs} - R_LI_L(s) = 0$$

Arranging these equations in determinate form,

$$E_{in}(s) - R_2I(s) = \left[(R_1 + R_2) + \frac{1}{Cs}\right]I_1(s) - \frac{1}{Cs}I_L(s)$$

$$0 = -\frac{1}{Cs}I_1(s) + \left(R_L + \frac{1}{Cs}\right)I_L(s)$$

from which we find

$$\Delta = \begin{vmatrix} \left[(R_1 + R_2) + \dfrac{1}{Cs}\right] & -\dfrac{1}{Cs} \\[2ex] -\dfrac{1}{Cs} & (R_L + Cs) \end{vmatrix}$$

$$= \left[(R_1 + R_2) + \frac{1}{Cs}\right]\left(R_L + \frac{1}{Cs}\right) - \left(\frac{1}{Cs}\right)^2$$

$$= R_L(R_1 + R_2) + (R_1 + R_2 + R_L)\frac{1}{Cs}$$

and

$$\Delta I_L(s) = \begin{vmatrix} \left[(R_1 + R_2) + \dfrac{1}{Cs} \right. & [E_{in}(s) - R_2I(s)] \\[2ex] -\dfrac{1}{Cs} & 0 \end{vmatrix}$$

$$= \frac{E_{in}(s) - R_2I(s)}{Cs}$$

or

$$I_L(s) = \frac{E_{in}(s) - R_2 I(s)}{Cs\left[(R_1 + R_2 + R_L)\frac{1}{Cs} + R_L(R_1 + R_2)\right]}$$

Putting $I_L(s)$ in better form we have

$$I_L(s) = \frac{E_{in}(s) - R_2 I(s)}{[(R_1 + R_2 + R_L) + R_L(R_1 + R_2)Cs]}$$

$$= \frac{E_{in}(s) - R_2 I(s)}{R_L(R_1 + R_2)C\left[s + \dfrac{R_1 + R_2 + R_L}{R_L(R_1 + R_2)C}\right]}$$

Now

$$\frac{R_1 + R_2 + R_L}{R_L(R_1 + R_2)} = \frac{1}{R_{eq}}$$

so

$$I_L(s) = \frac{E_{in}(s) - R_2 I(s)}{R_L(R_1 + R_2)C\left(s + \dfrac{1}{R_{eq}C}\right)}$$

$$= \frac{E_{in}(s)}{R_L(R_1 + R_2)C\left(s + \dfrac{1}{R_{eq}C}\right)}$$

$$- \frac{R_2 I(s)}{R_L(R_1 + R_2)C\left(s + \dfrac{1}{R_{eq}C}\right)} \tag{5-22}$$

Writing the expressions for e_{in} and i we have

$$e_{in}(t) = -Eu(t) + Eu(t - t_1)\ \text{V}$$

and

$$i(t) = Iu(t) - Iu(t - t_2)\ \text{A}$$

Thus

$$E_{in}(s) = -\frac{E}{s}(1 - e^{-t_1 s})$$

and

$$I(s) = \frac{I}{s}(1 - e^{-t_2 s})$$

Substituting these explicit expressions into Eq. (5–22) we then have an explicit equation for $I_L(s)$. Hence,

$$I_L(s) = -\frac{E(1 - e^{-t_1 s})}{R_L(R_1 + R_2)Cs\left(s + \dfrac{1}{R_{eq}C}\right)}$$

$$- \frac{R_2 I(1 - e^{-t_2 s})}{R_L(R_1 + R_2)Cs\left(s + \dfrac{1}{R_{eq}C}\right)} \tag{5-23}$$

To determine i_L notice each term of Eq. (5–23) is basically

$$\frac{K(1 - e^{-ks})}{s\left(s + \frac{1}{R_{eq}C}\right)} \tag{5-24}$$

Then let us define

$$K_1 \equiv \frac{E}{R_L(R_1 + R_2)C}$$

and

$$K_2 = \frac{R_2I}{R_L(R_1 + R_2)C}$$

and write

$$I_L(s) = \frac{K_1(1 - e^{-t_1s})}{s\left(s + \frac{1}{R_{eq}C}\right)} - \frac{K_2(1 - e^{-t_2s})}{s\left(s + \frac{1}{R_{eq}C}\right)} \tag{5-25}$$

Finding the inverse Laplace of Eq. (5–24) means evaluating

$$\mathcal{L}^{-1}\left[\frac{K(1 - e^{-ks})}{s\left(s + \frac{1}{R_{eq}C}\right)}\right] = \mathcal{L}^{-1}\left[\frac{K}{s\left(s + \frac{1}{R_{eq}C}\right)} - \frac{Ke^{-ks}}{s\left(s + \frac{1}{R_{eq}C}\right)}\right]$$

Well

$$\mathcal{L}^{-1}\left[\frac{K}{s\left(s + \frac{1}{R_{eq}C}\right)}\right] = KR_{eq}C(1 - e^{-t/R_{eq}C})u(t)$$

and

$$\mathcal{L}^{-1}\left[\frac{Ke^{-ks}}{s\left(s + \frac{1}{R_{eq}C}\right)}\right] = KR_{eq}C(1 - e^{-(t-k)/R_{eq}C})u(t - k)$$

Then from (5–25)

$$
\begin{aligned}
i_L(t) &= K_1 R_{eq}C[(1 - e^{-t/R_{eq}C}u(t) \\
&\quad - (1 - e^{-(t-t_1)/R_{eq}C})u(t - t_1)] \\
&\quad - K_2 R_{eq}C[(1 - e^{-t/R_{eq}C})u(t) \\
&\quad - (1 - e^{-(t-t_2)/R_{eq}C})u(t - t_2)] \\
&= R_{eq}C[(K_1 - K_2)(1 - e^{-t/R_{eq}C})u(t) \\
&\quad - K_1(1 - e^{-(t-t_1)/R_{eq}C})u(t - t_1) \\
&\quad + K_2(1 - e^{-(t-t_2)/R_{eq}C})u(t - t_2)]
\end{aligned}
$$

where

$$K_1 = \frac{E}{R_L(R_1 + R_2)C}$$

and

$$K_2 = \frac{R_2 I}{R_L(R_1 + R_2)C}$$

So factoring $1/R_L(R_1 + R_2)C$ we have

$$i_L(t) = \frac{1}{R_1 + R_2 + R_L}[(E - R_2 I)(1 - e^{-t/R_{eq}C})u(t)$$
$$- E(1 - e^{-(t-t_1)/R_{eq}C})u(t - t_1)$$
$$+ R_2 I(1 - e^{-(t-t_2)/R_{eq}C})u(t - t_2)] \qquad (5\text{-}26)$$

To sketch $i_L(t)$ we would proceed as before. That is,

For $0 < t < t_1$: $u(t) = 1$ and $u(t - t_1) = u(t - t_2) = 0$

$$i_L(t) = \frac{E - R_2 I}{R_1 + R_2 + R_L}(1 - e^{-t/R_{eq}C})$$

For $t_1 < t < t_2$: $u(t) = u(t - t_1) = 1$ and $u(t - t_2) = 0$

$$i_L(t) = \frac{1}{R_1 + R_2 + R_L}[(E - R_2 I)(1 - e^{-t/R_{eq}C})$$
$$- E(1 - e^{-(t-t_1)/R_{eq}C})]$$
$$= \frac{1}{R_1 + R_2 + R_L}[(R_2 I - E)e^{-t/R_{eq}C}$$
$$- R_2 I + E e^{-(t-t_1)/R_{eq}C}]$$
$$= \frac{1}{R_1 + R_2 + R_L}[(R_2 I + E e^{t_1/R_{eq}C} - E) - R_2 I]$$

which looks like

$$i_L(t) = \text{constant} \cdot e^{-t/_{eq}C} - \text{constant}$$
$$= -(\text{constant} - \text{constant} \cdot e^{-t/R_{eq}C})$$

For $t > t_2$: All unit steps $= 1$

$$i_L(t) = \frac{1}{R_1 + R_2 + R_L}[(R_2 I + E e^{t_1/R_{eq}C} - E)]e^{-t/R_{eq}C}$$
$$- R_2 I + R_2 I(1 - e^{-(t-t_2)/R_{eq}C})$$
$$= \frac{1}{R_1 + R_2 + R_L}[(1 - e^{t_2 R_{eq}C})R_2 I$$
$$- (1 - e^{t_1/R_{eq}C})E]e^{-t/R_{eq}C}$$

which is $i_L(t) = \pm\text{constant} \cdot e^{-t/R_{eq}C}$. Since we are working with algebraic quantities we can only sketch probable curves for $i_L(t)$. These curves are shown in Fig. 5–29.

5–6 Development of Universal Curves for Quadratic Equations and Their Uses

From the examples already worked it becomes obvious that we need some relatively quick method to determine points for our solutions to be

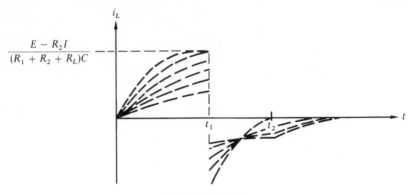

FIGURE 5–29

graphed. In the example coming up we will construct just such a means. This example will be approached so that it will not only again show the need for this method but will also justify this particular method.

Example 5–11   Given the circuit of Fig. 5–30(a): (a) determine the general expression for $V_o(s)$; (b) for the input voltage e_{in}, illustrated in Fig. 5–30(c), determine v_o. Let $R = 1\ k\Omega$, $C = 6\ pF\ (p = 10^{-12})$ and $L = 1\ \mu H$; (c) repeat part (b) for $R = 1\ k\Omega$, $C = 0.01\ pF$, and $L = 1\ \mu H$.

Solution   (a) We shall write a nodal equation at the node of v_o. The assumed polarities are those shown in Fig. 5–30(b). The nodal equation is

$$\frac{e_{in}(t) - v_o(t)}{R} - C\frac{dv_o(t)}{dt} - \frac{1}{L}\int v_o(t)\, dt = 0 \qquad (5\text{--}27)$$

Taking the Laplace of Eqs. (5–27) and then solving for $V_o(s)$ we have

$$\frac{E_{in}(s) - V_o(s)}{R} - C[sV_o(s) - v_o(0^+)] - \frac{1}{L}\left[\frac{V_o(s)}{s}\right.$$

$$\left. + \frac{v_n^{(-1)}(0^+)}{s}\right] = 0$$

$$\frac{E_{in}(s)}{R} + Cv_o(0^+) - \frac{1}{Ls}v_o^{(-1)}(0^+) = \left(\frac{1}{R} + Cs + \frac{1}{Ls}\right)V_o(s)$$

therefore,

$$V_o(s) = \left[\frac{E_{in}(s)}{R} + Cv_o(0^+) - \frac{1}{Ls}v_o^{(-1)}(0^+)\right]\frac{1}{\left(\frac{1}{R} + Cs + \frac{1}{Ls}\right)}$$

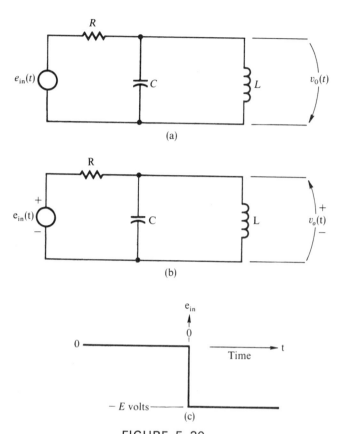

FIGURE 5–30

We could write $V_o(s)$ as

$$V_o(s) = \frac{E_{in}(s)}{R\left(\dfrac{1}{R} + Cs + \dfrac{1}{Ls}\right)} + \frac{Cv_o(0^+)}{\dfrac{1}{R} + Cs + \dfrac{1}{Ls}}$$
$$- \frac{v_o^{(-1)}(0^+)}{Ls\left(\dfrac{1}{R} + Cs + \dfrac{1}{Ls}\right)} \qquad (5\text{–}28)$$

which is slightly better form.

(b) For part (b) we are given the waveform e_{in} and therefore we can write an explicit equation for $E_{in}(s)$, which will allow $V_o(s)$ of Eq. (5–28) to be expressed explicitly. Thus, writing an equation for the driving force e_{in}

$$e_{in}(t) = -Eu(t)$$

Then

$$E_{\text{in}}(s) = -\frac{E}{s}$$

and therefore

$$V_o(s) = -\frac{E}{Rs\left(\dfrac{1}{R} + Cs + \dfrac{1}{Ls}\right)} + \frac{Cv_o(0^+)}{\dfrac{1}{R} + Cs + \dfrac{1}{Ls}}$$

$$\frac{v_o^{(-1)}(0^+)}{Ls\left(\dfrac{1}{R} + Cs + \dfrac{1}{Ls}\right)} \qquad (5\text{–}29)$$

Since we now know explicitly how e_{in} appears we may now determine the initial conditions. Again from elementary circuit theory we know that capacitors appear as short circuits to any change in voltage across them. Hence, defining v_C as the voltage across a capacitor we can state $v_C(0^-) \cong v_C(0^+)$. Also since inductors resist any change in current flow then $i_L(0^-) \cong i_L(0^+)$, where i_L defines the current flowing through the inductor. We will analyze our circuit at $t = 0^-$ and determine $v_C(0^-)$ and $i_L(0^-)$ since $v_C(0^-) \cong v_C(0^+) = v_o(0^+)$ and

$$i_L(0^-) \cong i_L(0^+) = \frac{v_o^{(-1)}(0^+)}{L}$$

It might be well at this time to interpret and demonstrate that $v^{(-1)}(0^+)/L$ is the initial value of current for the inductor L. We know

$$v_L(t) = \text{voltage across } L = v_o(t) = L\frac{di_L(t)}{dt}$$

Then

$$di_L = \frac{1}{L}v_o(t)\,dt$$

from which

$$\int di_L = \frac{1}{L}\int v_o(t)\,dt$$

Now

$$\int di_L = i_L(t)$$

and

$$\int v_o(t)\,dt = v_o^{(-1)}(t)$$

So

$$i_L(t) = \frac{v^{(-1)}(t)}{L}$$

or

$$i_L(0^+) = \frac{v^{(-1)}(0^+)}{L}$$

Then Eq. (5–28) can be written as

$$V_o(s) = -\frac{E}{Rs\left(\dfrac{1}{R} + Cs + \dfrac{1}{Ls}\right)} + \frac{Cv(0^+)}{\dfrac{1}{R} + Cs + \dfrac{1}{Ls}}$$
$$-\frac{i_L(0^+)}{s\left(\dfrac{1}{R} + Cs + \dfrac{1}{Ls}\right)} \qquad \text{(5–30)}$$

To continue with determining the initial conditions at $t = 0^-$. The equivalent circuit at $t = 0^-$ is as shown in Fig. 5–31. Again the voltage source $e_{in}(t)$ appears as a

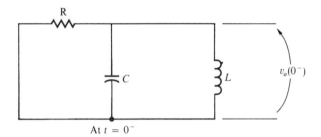

At $t = 0^-$

FIGURE 5–31

short circuit since $e_{in}(0^-) = 0$. As we see from this circuit there is no driving force, hence no voltage drops or current flows; therefore $i_L(0^-) = 0$ and $v_o(0^-) = 0$.

Since the initial conditions are zero Eq. (5–30) may be rewritten as

$$V_o(s) = -\frac{E}{Rs\left(\dfrac{1}{R} + Cs + \dfrac{1}{Ls}\right)} \qquad \text{(5–31)}$$

To find v_o from Eq. (5–31), using the procedures established in section 4–16, we must first determine the highest power of s so that we can force its coefficient to unity. In order to do this we will first put the term $1/R + Cs +$

$1/Ls$ under common denominator. Hence,

$$\frac{1}{R} + Cs + \frac{1}{Ls} = \frac{Ls + RLCs^2 + R}{RLs}$$

Forcing s^2 to have a coefficient of unity we have,

$$\frac{RLCs^2 + Ls + R}{RLs} = \frac{C\left(s^2 + \frac{1}{RC}s + \frac{1}{LC}\right)}{s}$$

Equation (5–31) can now be written as

$$V_o(s) = -\frac{E}{RC\left(s^2 + \frac{1}{RC}s + \frac{1}{LC}\right)}$$

We next generalize this equation,

$$V_o(s) = -\frac{\dfrac{E}{RC}}{s^2 + \dfrac{1}{RC}s + \dfrac{1}{LC}}$$

$$= -\frac{\text{constant}}{s^2 + \text{constant} \cdot s + \text{constant}} \qquad (5\text{-}32)$$

From Table 4–2 we find that Eq. (9) identifies Eq. (5–32) as a quadratic, which means we must determine ζ in order to know whether Eq. (6), (7), (9), or (10) applies. Solving for ζ by equating denominators and then solving like coefficients we have,

$$s^2 + \frac{1}{RC}s + \frac{1}{LC} = s^2 + 2\zeta\omega_n s + \omega_n^2$$

from which we find

$$2\zeta\omega_n = \frac{1}{RC} \quad \text{and} \quad \omega_n^2 = \frac{1}{LC}$$

So $\omega_n = 1/\sqrt{LC}$ (interested only in positive values), and

$$\zeta = \frac{1}{2\omega_n RC} = \frac{\sqrt{LC}}{2RC} = \frac{1}{2R}\sqrt{\frac{L}{C}}$$

Substituting the values for R, L, and C we find

$$\zeta = \frac{1}{2 \times 10^3}\sqrt{\frac{1 \times 10^{-6}}{6 \times 10^{-12}}} = \frac{\sqrt{0.167}}{2} < 1$$

Since ζ has a value less than one, Eq. (9) of Table 4–2 applies.

Therefore,

$$v_o(t) = -\mathcal{L}^{-1}\left[\frac{E}{RC\left(s^2 + \frac{1}{RC}s + \frac{1}{LC}\right)}\right]$$

$$= -\frac{E}{RC\left[\frac{1}{\sqrt{LC}}\sqrt{1 - \left(\frac{1}{2R}\sqrt{\frac{L}{C}}\right)^2}\right]}e^{-t/2RC}$$

$$\sin\left[\frac{\sqrt{1 - \left(\frac{1}{2R}\sqrt{\frac{L}{C}}\right)^2}}{\sqrt{LC}}\right]tu(t)$$

$$= -\frac{2\sqrt{L}\,E}{\sqrt{4R^2C - L}}e^{-t/2RC}\sin\frac{\sqrt{4R^2C - L}}{2RC\sqrt{L}}tu(t)$$

$$(5\text{-}33)$$

Then

$$v_o(t) = -\frac{2 \times 10^{-3}E}{\sqrt{24 \times 10^{-6} - 10^{-6}}}e^{-t/12 \times 10^{-9}}$$

$$\sin\frac{\sqrt{23} \times 10^{-3}}{12 \times 10^{-12}}tu(t)$$

$$= -0.416Ee^{-t/12 \times 10^{-9}}\sin 0.4 \times 10^9 tu(t) \quad (5\text{-}34)$$

To aid us in graphing Eq. (5-34) we will interrupt our analysis to develop a family of curves which have the same graphical form as Eq. (5-34).

Consider the general equation

$$f(t) = \frac{K}{\omega_n\sqrt{1 - \zeta^2}}e^{-\zeta\omega_n t}\sin\omega_n\sqrt{1 - \zeta^2}t \quad (5\text{-}35)$$

which is Eq. (9) of Table 4–2. If we plotted a family of curves for various values of ζ from Eq. (5-35) this would graphically demonstrate how $f(t)$ behaves as a function of ζ. And if we normalize Eq. (5-35) and then plot this family of curves we would have a set of "universal curves" which could be used to plot other curves, as we shall demonstrate. The development of these universal curves and their application is the topic to be considered now.

A rough sketch of Eq. (5-35) would appear as Fig. 5-32(a). As one can see Fig. 5-32(a) is composed of the sinewave, $\sin\omega_n\sqrt{1 - \zeta^2}t$, being forced to zero, or "damped out", by $e^{-\zeta\omega_n t}$. Then we are dealing with a damped-out oscillation that has a frequency of $\omega_n\sqrt{1 - \zeta^2}$ rad/s.

It is now that we might wish to examine the reasons for the nomenclature used in Eq. (5-35). From elementary circuit theory we know that circuits which contain inductance and capacitance have a natural resonant

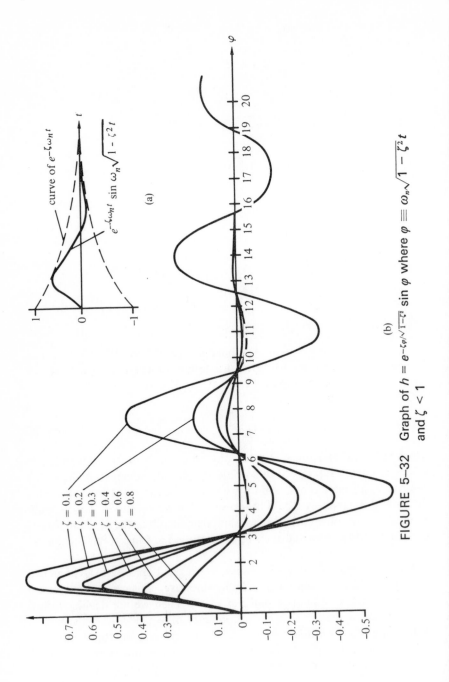

FIGURE 5–32   Graph of $h = e^{-\zeta\varphi/\sqrt{1-\zeta^2}} \sin \varphi$ where $\varphi \equiv \omega_n\sqrt{1-\zeta^2}\, t$ and $\zeta < 1$

$\zeta = 0.1$
$\zeta = 0.2$
$\zeta = 0.3$
$\zeta = 0.4$
$\zeta = 0.6$
$\zeta = 0.8$

(a)

curve of $e^{-\zeta\omega_n t}$

$e^{-\zeta\omega_n t} \sin \omega_n\sqrt{1 - \zeta^2}\, t$

(b)

frequency, where the natural resonant frequency is that frequency at which the circuit would self-sustain an oscillation of energy between the inductance and capacitance if no damping (resistance) were present. We designate the symbol for natural resonant frequency as ω_n. In Ex. 5–11 we found $\omega_n = 1/\sqrt{LC}$, which is the natural resonant frequency of that circuit, and this agrees with elementary circuit theory. From the quantity $\omega_n\sqrt{1 - \zeta^2}$ we see that when ζ is present the natural resonant frequency ω_n is altered by the factor $\sqrt{1 - \zeta^2}$. To represent this modification of the natural resonant frequency, which occurs when ζ is present, we use the symbol ω_d, and term it the damped resonant frequency. Then $\omega_d = \omega_n\sqrt{1 - \zeta^2}$, or $\sin \omega_n\sqrt{1 - \zeta^2}t = \sin \omega_d t$. As we previously stated the sinewave is being damped out by $e^{-\zeta\omega_n t}$, then $\zeta\omega_n$ determines how fast the damping occurs. Since ω_n is already defined we will define ζ as the damping constant. Using the term ω_d we may write Eq. (5–35) as

$$f(t) = \frac{K}{\omega_d}e^{-\zeta/\sqrt{1-\zeta^2}\,\omega_d t} \sin \omega_d t \qquad (5\text{–}36)$$

To continue, rather than plotting the family of curves from Eq. (5–36) for various values of ζ we will universalize Eq. (5–36) by normalizing it and then plot from that equation. Normalizing Eq. (5–36) and defining the new unitless dependent variable as h we have,

$$h(t) \equiv \frac{\omega_d}{K}f(t) = e^{-\zeta/\sqrt{1-\zeta^2}\,\omega_d t} \sin \omega_d t \qquad (5\text{–}37)$$

Also let us define a new independent variable φ, which will be defined as $\omega_d t$. Then

$$h(\varphi) = \frac{\omega_d}{K}f(t) = e^{-\zeta/\sqrt{1-\zeta^2}\,\varphi} \sin \varphi \qquad (5\text{–}38)$$

where $\varphi \equiv \omega_d t$.

Equation (5–38) is the equation from which we shall plot our first set of universal curves. Notice that φ is a function of t and that the period of Eq. (5–38) is found from φ. That is, $\varphi = \omega_d t$ so $\omega_d T = 2\pi$, or

$$T = \frac{2\pi}{\omega_d} = \frac{2\pi}{\omega_n\sqrt{1 - \zeta^2}} \qquad (5\text{–}39)$$

To aid in plotting Eq. (5–38) we will find the maximum and minimum points and the crossover points on the φ-axis. Between these points we can estimate the curves for the various values of ζ fairly accurately.

We shall begin by determining the maximum and minimum points. Hence, from Eq. (5–38)

$$\frac{dh}{d\varphi} = \frac{d}{d\varphi}[e^{-\zeta\varphi/\sqrt{1-\zeta^2}} \sin \varphi] = -\frac{\zeta e^{-\zeta\varphi/\sqrt{1-\zeta^2}}}{\sqrt{1 - \zeta^2}} \sin \varphi + e^{-\zeta\varphi/\sqrt{1-\zeta^2}} \cos \varphi$$

Setting $dh/d\varphi$ equal to zero and solving for the value of φ, which we shall label φ_M, at which this occurs, thus

$$\frac{dh}{d\varphi} = 0 = -\frac{\zeta e^{-\zeta\varphi_M/\sqrt{1-\zeta^2}}}{\sqrt{1-\zeta^2}} \sin \varphi_M + e^{-\zeta\varphi_M/\sqrt{1-\zeta^2}} \cos \varphi_M$$

or

$$\frac{\zeta}{\sqrt{1-\zeta^2}} \sin \varphi_M = \cos \varphi_M$$

Then solving for φ_M we have

$$\frac{\sin \varphi_M}{\cos \varphi_M} = \frac{\sqrt{1-\zeta^2}}{\zeta} = \tan \varphi_M$$

so

$$\varphi_M = \tan^{-1}\frac{\sqrt{1-\zeta^2}}{\zeta} \tag{5-40}$$

This is our equation for determining the value of φ for the maximum or minimum value of h. Since we are dealing with periodic angles we know that φ_M is periodic, hence we can state that the maximum and minimum positions of φ can be determined by the equation

$$\varphi_N = \varphi_M + (N-1)\pi, \quad \text{where } N = 1, 2, 3, \ldots \tag{5-41}$$

Since φ_N locates the position of the maximum or minimum value of h then we must substitute φ_N for φ in Eq. (5–38) to evaluate the magnitude of h at φ_N. Hence

$$h_N = h(\varphi = \varphi_N) = e^{-\zeta\varphi_N/\sqrt{1-\zeta^2}} \sin \varphi_N$$

Now $\sin \varphi_N$ has the same magnitude as $\sin \varphi_M$ but possibly a different sign. Hence, it can be shown that the equation for h_N can be written as

$$h_N = (-1)^{N+1}e^{-\zeta\varphi_N/\sqrt{1-\zeta^2}} \sin \varphi_M \tag{5-42}$$

To determine the crossover points we simply realize that for values of φ equal to $0, \pi, 2\pi, 3\pi, 4\pi, \ldots k\pi$, where $k = 0, 1, 2, 3 \ldots$, the value of $\sin \varphi$ is zero. Hence, the values of φ_C, the crossover points, are

$$\varphi_C = k\pi, \quad \text{where } k = 0, 1, 2, 3 \ldots$$

We shall next apply Eqs. (5–40), (5–41), and (5–42) to obtain points for plotting the family of curves for various values of ζ.

> *Sample Calculations:* To determine the first point ($N = 1$) of φ we evaluate Eq. (5–40) for each value of ζ and then apply Eq. (5–41). Thus
>
> For $\zeta = 0.1$
>
> $$\varphi_M = \tan^{-1}\frac{\sqrt{1 - (0.1)^2}}{0.1} \simeq \tan^{-1} 10 = 84.3° = 1.47 \text{ rad}$$

For $\zeta = 0.2$

$$\varphi_M = \tan^{-1} \frac{\sqrt{0.96}}{0.2} \simeq \tan^{-1} \frac{0.98}{0.2} = \tan^{-1} 4.9 = 78.5°$$
$$= 1.37 \text{ rad}$$

For $\zeta = 0.3$

$$\varphi_N = \tan^{-1} 3.2 = 72.5° = 1.26 \text{ rad}$$

For $\zeta = 0.4$

$$\varphi_M = \tan^{-1} 2.3 = 66.5° = 1.16 \text{ rad}$$

For $\zeta = 0.6$

$$\varphi_M = \tan^{-1} 1.33 = 53° = 0.93 \text{ rad}$$

For $\zeta = 0.8$

$$\varphi_M = \tan^{-1} 0.75 = 37° = 0.65 \text{ rad}$$

Next we apply Eq. (5–42), hence

For $\zeta = 0.1$

$$h_1 = (-1)^{1+1} e^{-0.1(1.47)/\sqrt{1-(0.1)^2}} \sin 84.3° \simeq e^{-0.147}$$
$$= 0.864$$

For $\zeta = 0.2$

$$h_1 = (-1)^{1+1} e^{-1.37/4.9} \sin 78.5° = 0.74$$

For $\zeta = 0.3$

$$h_1 = e^{-1.26/3.2} \sin 72.5 = 0.64$$

and so on. To determine the next collection of points we let $N = 2$ and evaluate Eqs. (5–41) and (5–42). Hence

For $\zeta = 0.1$

$$\varphi_2 = \varphi_M + \pi = 1.47 + 3.14 = 4.61 \text{ rad}$$
$$h_2 = (-1)^{2+1} e^{-0.1(4.61)/\sqrt{1-(0.1)^2}} \sin 84.3° = -0.63$$

For $\zeta = 0.2$

$$\varphi_2 = 1.37 + 3.14 = 4.51 \text{ rad}$$
$$h_2 = -e^{-4.51/4.9} \sin 78.5° = -0.39$$

The remainder of the points and those already calculated are shown in Table 5–1 and are plotted in Fig. 5–32(b). The crossover points are not calculated here since they are obvious from φ_c.

TABLE 5–1   Points for Plotting Fig. 5–32(b)

N	$\zeta = 0.1$		$\zeta = 0.2$		$\zeta = 0.3$		$\zeta = 0.4$		$\zeta = 0.6$		$\zeta = 0.8$	
	φ_N	h_N	φ_N	h_N	φ_N	h_N	φ_N	h_N	φ_N	h_N	φ_N	h_N
1	1.47	0.86	1.37	0.74	1.26	0.64	1.16	0.56	0.93	0.40	0.65	0.25
2	4.61	−0.63	4.51	−0.39	4.40	−0.24	4.30	−0.14	4.07	−0.04	3.79	$\cong 0$
3	7.75	0.45	7.65	0.18	7.54	0.08	Approximately zero for h		Approximately zero for h			
4	10.89	−0.34	10.68	0.04	Approximately zero for h							
5	13.99	0.25	Approximately zero for h									
6	17.17	−0.16	$''$									
7	20.37	0.13	$''$									

302

Now that we have the universal curves of Fig. 5–32(b) we will demonstrate their use as an aid to plotting other curves. The manner in which we will use any universal curve (more are to come) is as a multiplier. That is, suppose we wish to plot

$$y(t) = 1.07 \times 10^{-3}e^{-348t} \sin 940t \qquad \text{for } t > 0$$

Comparing this equation with Eq. (5–38) we recognize that by defining $348t \equiv \zeta\varphi/\sqrt{1 - \zeta^2}$ and $940t \equiv \varphi$ we may state $h(\varphi) = e^{-348t} \sin 940t$, hence, $y(t) = 1.07 \times 10^{-3}h(\varphi)$. As can be seen the universal curve $h(\varphi)$ is used as a multiplier. In essence we are plotting the universal curve and using the magnitude 1.07×10^{-3} as a scale factor.

To plot the universal curve for a specific ζ we will pick points of interest from Fig. 5–32(b) for that value of ζ. The points of interest are those points which we feel are necessary in order to make an accurate plot. Then we will possibly want points on the curve at: rapid changes in the dependent variable, maximum and minimum points, changes in driving forces, etc.

To demonstrate let us return to Eq. (5–34) and plot that equation using the universal curves of Fig. 5–32(b) as an aid. Rewriting Eq. (5–34) for convenience:

$$v_o(t) = -0.416Ee^{-t/12 \times 10^{-9}} \sin 0.4 \times 10^9 tu(t) \qquad (5\text{–}34)$$

From Eq. (5–38) we see that by defining $\zeta\varphi/\sqrt{1 - \zeta^2} = t/12 \times 10^{-9}$ and $\varphi = 0.4 \times 10^9 t$ we may write Eq. (5–34) as $v_o(t) = -0.416Eh(\varphi)$, where $\varphi = \varphi(t)$. In order to use Fig. 5–32(b) we must know which curve to use, which means determining the value of ζ. From the preceding

$$\frac{\zeta\varphi}{\sqrt{1 - \zeta^2}} = \frac{\zeta(0.4 \times 10^9 t)}{\sqrt{1 - \zeta^2}} = \frac{t}{12 \times 10^{-9}}$$

since $\varphi = 0.4 \times 10^9 t$, thus

$$\frac{0.4 \times 10^9 \zeta}{\sqrt{1 - \zeta^2}} = \frac{1}{12 \times 10^{-9}}$$

Squaring both sides of the equation

$$\frac{0.16 \times 10^{18}\zeta^2}{1 - \zeta^2} = \frac{1}{144 \times 10^{-18}}$$

Solving for ζ^2

$$144 \times 10^{-18}(0.16 \times 10^{18})\zeta^2 = 1 - \zeta^2$$

or $25\zeta^2 = 1$ so $\zeta = \frac{1}{5}$ (interested only in positive values) $= 0.20$. Then the curve for $\zeta = 0.2$ of Fig. 5–32(b) is of concern to us.

The points of interest would probably be the maximum and minimum points and the points where $h(\varphi)$ cross over from positive to negative values and vice versa, that is, where $h(\varphi) = 0$. From Fig. 5–32(b) these were determined and recorded in Table 5–2.

TABLE 5–2 For $\zeta = 0.2$

φ	$h(\varphi)$
1.37	0.74
3.14	0.00
4.51	−0.39
6.28	0.00
7.65	0.18
9.52	0.00
10.68	−0.04
12.52	0.00

We must now interpret these points in terms of t and v_o rather than φ and h. Recall we defined that $\varphi = 0.4 \times 10^9 t$, hence the points for φ in Table 5–2 can easily be converted to t. Also we know that $v_o(t) = -0.416Eh(\varphi)$, so the points of Table 5–2 for $h(\varphi)$ can be used. As sample calculations:

For $\varphi = \varphi_1 = 1.37$ and $h(\varphi = \varphi_1) = 0.74$

$t = \varphi/0.4 \times 10^9$ from our definition of $\varphi = 0.4 \times 10^9 t$, hence

$$t_1 = \frac{\varphi_1}{0.4 \times 10^9} = \frac{1.37}{0.4 \times 10^9} = 3.43 \times 10^{-9}\,\text{s} = 3.43\,\text{ns}$$

and

$$v_{o_1} = v_o(t = t_1) = -0.416Eh(\varphi = \varphi_1) = -0.416E(0.74)$$
$$= -0.30E\,\text{V (For plotting purposes we round off.)}$$

For $\varphi = \varphi_2 = 4.51$ and $h(\varphi = \varphi_2) = -0.39$

$$t_2 = \frac{\varphi_2}{0.4 \times 10^9} = \frac{4.51}{0.4 \times 10^9} = 11.30\,\text{ns}$$

and

$$v_{o_2}(t = t_2) = -0.416Eh_2 = -0.416(-0.39) = 0.17E\,\text{V}$$

The remaining points are given in Table 5–3.

Plotting the points in Table 5–3 yields the graph shown in Fig. 5–33. If a more accurate plot is desired then more points should be plotted using Fig. 5–32(b) as an aid.

Let us verify the resultant graph of Fig. 5–33 by actual numerical calculation of Eq. (5–34). Evaluating Eq. (5–34) at $t = 6$ ns we have

TABLE 5–3 For $\xi = 0.2$

φ	$h(\varphi)$	t in ns	v_o in volts
0.00	0.00	0.00	0.00
1.37	0.74	3.43	$-0.30E$
3.14	0.00	7.86	0.00
4.52	-0.39	11.72	$0.17E$
6.28	0.00	15.74	0.00
7.65	0.18	19.10	$-0.08E$
9.52	0.00	23.80	0.00
10.68	-0.04	26.70	$0.02E$ (approx.)
12.52	0.00	31.40	0.00

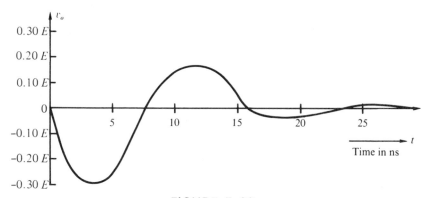

FIGURE 5–33

$$v_o(t = 6 \times 10^{-9}) = -0.416Ee^{-6\times10^{-9}/12\times10^{-9}} \sin 0.4 \times 10^9(6 \times 10^{-9})$$
$$= -0.416E \sin 2.4 = -0.252E \sin 2.4$$

We realize that $\sin 2.4 = \sin 137°$ since 2.4 radians $= 137°$ then

$$v_o(6 \text{ ns}) = -0.252E(0.68) = -0.169E$$

From our graph we see $v_o(6 \text{ ns}) = -0.17E$, hence for all practical purposes they agree. As another check let us evaluate Eq. (5–34) at $t = 20$ ns. Thus

$$v_o(20 \text{ ns}) = -0.416Ee^{-20\times10^{-9}/12\times10^{-9}} \sin 0.4 \times 10^9(20 \times 10^{-9})$$
$$= -0.416Ee^{-1.66} \sin 8.0 = -0.079E \sin 458°$$
$$= -0.079E(0.987) = -0.078E$$

From our graph $v_o(20 \text{ ns}) = -0.08E$, which agrees with the calculated value. This verifies our results of part (b).

(c) To find a solution for part (c) of example 5–11 we return to Eq. (5–32) and as before determine the magnitude of ζ so that we will know which quadratic equation of Table 4–2 to apply. Now we already found that algebraically $\zeta = (1/2R)/(\sqrt{L/C})$, so for this case

$$\zeta = \frac{10^{-3}}{2}\sqrt{\frac{10^{-6}}{10^{-14}}} = 5, \quad \text{or} \quad \zeta > 1$$

Since $\zeta > 1$ we shall use Eq. (10) of Table 4–2, which indicates we must construct another universal curve derived from Eq. (10). From Eq. (10) of Table 4–2 we are plotting

$$f(t) = \frac{K}{\beta - \alpha}(e^{-\alpha t} - e^{-\beta t})$$

where

$$s^2 + 2\zeta\omega_n s + \omega_n^2 = (s + \alpha)(s + \beta) \qquad \textbf{(5-43)}$$

Then let us interrupt this example to develop this universal curve.

We shall begin to develop this next universal curve by determining α and β from the quadratic equation $s^2 + 2\zeta\omega_n s + \omega_n^2$. The roots of the quadratic, s_1 and s_2, are

$$s_{1,2} = -\zeta\omega_n \pm \frac{1}{2}\sqrt{4\zeta^2\omega_n^2 - 4\omega_n^2} = -\zeta\omega_n \pm \omega_n\sqrt{\zeta^2 - 1} \qquad \textbf{(5-44)}$$

Now, for a root we know that we may write $(s + \alpha)\big|_{s=s_1} = 0$ and $(s + \beta)\big|_{s=s_2} = 0$ or $(s + \alpha)\big|_{s=s_2} = 0$ and $(s + \beta)\big|_{s=s_1} = 0$. Then it is somewhat arbitrary whether we state that $(s_1 + \alpha)(s_2 + \beta) = 0$, or $(s_2 + \alpha)(s_1 + \beta) = 0$; that is, it is all by definition. There is a "best way" to base our definition of our roots and that is to let Eq. (5–43) make the decision. From Eq. (5–43) we see that if $\alpha > \beta$ then Eq. (5–43) is the negative of that shown, so let us require $\beta > \alpha$ to keep Eq. (5–34) positive. Then let us define $(s + \alpha)\big|_{s=s_1} = 0$ and $(s + \beta)\big|_{s=s_2} = 0$ and then determine the proper roots s_1 and s_2. Hence, $(s + \alpha)\big|_{s=s_1} = s_1 + \alpha = 0$, so $\alpha = -s_1$ and $(s + \beta)\big|_{s=s_2} = s_2 + \beta = 0$ so $\beta = -s_2$. Determining s_1 and s_2 we refer back to Eq. (5–44) and see that in order that $\beta > \alpha$ we must define $s_1 = -\zeta\omega_n + \omega_n\sqrt{\zeta^2 - 1}$ and $s_2 = -\zeta\omega_n - \omega_n\sqrt{\zeta^2 - 1}$ for then $\alpha = -s_1 = \zeta\omega_n - \omega_n\sqrt{\zeta^2 - 1}$ and $\beta = -s_2 = \zeta\omega_n + \omega_n\sqrt{\zeta^2 - 1}$.

Substituting the algebraic values for and into Eq. (4-43) we have

$$f(t) = \frac{K}{2\omega_n\sqrt{\zeta^2 - 1}}[e^{-(\zeta\omega_n - \omega_n\sqrt{\zeta^2-1})t} - e^{-(\zeta\omega_n + \omega_n\sqrt{\zeta^2-1})t}]u(t)$$

$$= \frac{K}{2\omega_n\sqrt{\zeta^2 - 1}}e^{-\zeta\omega_n t}(e^{\omega_n\sqrt{\zeta^2-1}t} - e^{-\omega_n\sqrt{\zeta^2-1}t})u(t) \qquad (5\text{-}45)$$

To universalize Eq. (5-45) we shall normalize it and define a new dependent variable g. That is

$$g(t) \equiv \frac{2\omega_n\sqrt{\zeta^2 - 1}}{K}f(t) = e^{-\zeta\omega_n t}(e^{\omega_n\sqrt{\zeta^2-1}t} - e^{-\omega_n\sqrt{\zeta^2-1}t})u(t) \qquad (5\text{-}46)$$

Let us also define a new dependent variable x such that

$$x \equiv \omega_n\sqrt{\zeta^2 - 1}t$$

Now from Eq. (5-46),

$$g(x) = \frac{2\omega_n\sqrt{\zeta^2 - 1}}{K}f(t) = e^{-(\zeta/\sqrt{\zeta^2-1})x}(e^x - e^{-x})u(x)$$

$$= [e^{[1-(\zeta/\sqrt{\zeta^2-1})]x} - e^{-[1+(\zeta/\sqrt{\zeta^2-1})]x}]u(x)$$

$$= [e^{-[(\zeta/\sqrt{\zeta^2-1})-1]x} - e^{-[(\zeta/\sqrt{\zeta^2-1})+1]x}]u(x) \qquad (5\text{-}47)$$

since $t = x/\omega_n\sqrt{\zeta^2 - 1}$.

It is Eq. (5-47) that we shall plot as our universal curve representing Eq. (10) of Table 4-2.

To gather points let us find the maximum and minimum points using Maxima and Minima criteria. To apply Maxima and Minima we will follow these criteria: the curve of some general equation $f(t)$ is at a maximum if $f'(t_0) = 0$, where the prime here indicates d/dt, and $f'(t)$ changes from a positive value to a negative value as t increases about the point t_0. The curve of $f(t)$ is at a minimum if $f'(t_0) = 0$ and $f'(t)$ changes from a negative value to a positive value about the point t_0. Taking the derivative of Eq. (5-46),

$$\frac{dg(x)}{dx} = g'(x) = -\left(\frac{\zeta}{\sqrt{\zeta^2 - 1}} - 1\right)e^{-[(\zeta/\sqrt{\zeta^2-1})-1]x}$$

$$+ \left(\frac{\zeta}{\sqrt{\zeta^2 - 1}} + 1\right)e^{-[(\zeta/\sqrt{\zeta^2-1})+1]x}, \quad \text{for } x > 0 \qquad (5\text{-}48)$$

To determine at what value of x, say x_0, this maximum or minimum occurs we set $g'(x_0)$ equal to zero, then solve for x_0. Hence,

$$g'(x_0) = 0 = -\left(\frac{\zeta}{\sqrt{\zeta^2 - 1}} - 1\right)e^{-[(\zeta/\sqrt{\zeta^2-1})-1]x_0}$$

$$+ \left(\frac{\zeta}{\sqrt{\zeta^2 - 1}} + 1\right)e^{-[(\zeta/\sqrt{\zeta^2-1})+1]x_0} \qquad (5\text{-}49)$$

or

$$-\left(\frac{\zeta}{\sqrt{\zeta^2-1}}-1\right)e^{-[(\zeta/\sqrt{\zeta^2-1})-1]x_0} = -\left(\frac{\zeta}{\sqrt{\zeta^2-1}}+1\right)e^{-[(\zeta/\sqrt{\zeta^2-1})+1]x_0}$$

$$\left(\frac{\zeta}{\sqrt{\zeta^2-1}}-1\right)e^{x_0} = \left(\frac{\zeta}{\sqrt{\zeta^2-1}}+1\right)e^{-x_0}$$

from which we find

$$e^{2x_0} = \frac{\left(\dfrac{\zeta}{\sqrt{\zeta^2-1}}+1\right)}{\left(\dfrac{\zeta}{\sqrt{\zeta^2-1}}-1\right)} = \frac{\zeta+\sqrt{\zeta^2-1}}{\zeta-\sqrt{\zeta^2-1}}$$

Solving for x_0

$$2x_0 = \ln\frac{\zeta+\sqrt{\zeta^2-1}}{\zeta-\sqrt{\zeta^2-1}}$$

therefore

$$x_0 = \frac{1}{2}\ln\frac{\zeta+\sqrt{\zeta^2-1}}{\zeta-\sqrt{\zeta^2-1}} \tag{5-50}$$

We must now investigate Eq. (5–48) and see if x_0 occurs at a maximum or minimum. Hence, from Eq. (5–48)

$$g'(x_0) = 0 = -\left(\frac{\zeta}{\sqrt{\zeta^2-1}}-1\right)e^{-[(\zeta/\sqrt{\zeta^2-1})-1]x_0}$$
$$+\left(\frac{\zeta}{\sqrt{\zeta^2-1}}+1\right)e^{-[(\zeta/\sqrt{\zeta^2-1})+1]x_0} \tag{5-51}$$

Defining $K_1 \equiv -[(\zeta/(\sqrt{\zeta^2-1}))-1]$ and $K_2 \equiv [(\zeta/\sqrt{\zeta^2-1})+1]$

$$g'(x_0) = K_1 e^{K_1 x_0} + K_2 e^{-K_2 x_0}$$

Then

$$\frac{K_1}{K_2} = -\frac{e^{-K_2 x_0}}{e^{K_1 x_0}} = -e^{-(K_1+K_2)x_0}$$

or

$$K_1 = -K_2 e^{-(K_1+K_2)x_0}$$

Substituting this into Eq. (5–48) using our definition of K_1 and K_2 then

$$g'(x) = K_1 e^{K_1 x} + K_2 e^{-K_2 x} = -K_2 e^{-(K_1+K_2)x_0} \cdot e^{K_1 x} + K_2 e^{-K_2 x}$$
$$= -K_2 e^{[(x-x_0)K_1-K_2 x_0]} + K_2 e^{-K_2 x} \tag{5-52}$$

We can easily verify the validity of Eq. (5–52) by evaluating it at $x = x_0$ since we know $g'(x_0) = 0$. Now if x_0 occurs at a maximum $g'(x_0^-) > 0$ and $g'(x_0^+) < 0$ as stated by our criteria. Notice we are just evaluating the slope of $g(x)$ about the point x_0. From Eq. (5–52) for $x = x_0^-$ we have

$$g'(x_0^-) = -K_2 e^{[(x_0^--x_0)K_1-K_2 x_0]} + K_2 e^{-K_2 x_0^-}$$
$$= -K_2 e^{-K_2 x_0^-} + K_2 e^{-K_2 x_0^-} > 0$$

since $e^{-K_2^+ x_0^-} < e^{-K_2 x_0^-}$. And

$$g'(x_0^+) = -K_2 e^{[(x_0^+ - x_0)K_1 - K_2 x_0]} + K_2 e^{-K_2 x_0^+}$$
$$= -K_2 e^{-K_2^- x_0^+} + K_2 e^{-K_2 x_0^+} < 0$$

since $e^{-K_2^- x_0^+} < e^{-K_2 x_0^+}$

Then $g(x)$ is a maximum at $x = x_0$, so

$$g_{max} = g(x_0) = e^{-(\zeta/\sqrt{\zeta^2 - 1})x_0}(e^{x_0} - e^{-x_0}) \tag{5-53}$$

as seen from Eq. (5–47).

We are now able to determine the point on x at which the maximum value of $g(x)$ occurs and also its magnitude at that point. We will also need some additional points to plot Eq. (5–47) so let us choose to determine the magnitude of $g(x)$ at x equal to: 0.5, 1.0, 5.0, 10.0, and 20.0.

Sample Calculations for $\zeta > 1$
For $\zeta = 2$:

$$x_0 = \frac{1}{2}\ln\frac{\sqrt{4-1}+2}{2-\sqrt{4-1}} = \frac{1}{2}\ln 13.81 = 1.31$$

as calculated from Eq. (5–51). And from Eqs. (5–47) and (5–53),

$$g_{max} = g(1.31) = e^{-(2/1.73)(1.31)}(e^{1.31} - e^{-1.31}) = 0.755$$
$$g(0.5) = e^{-1.16(0.5)}(e^{0.5} - e^{-0.5}) = 0.582$$
$$g(1.0) = e^{-1.16}(e^{1.0} - e^{-1.0}) = 0.740$$
$$g(5.0) = e^{-1.16(5.0)}(e^{5.0} - e^{-5.0}) \cong e^{-1.16(5.0)} \cdot e^{5.0}$$
$$= e^{-0.16(5.0)} = 0.450$$

Since $e^{-x} \ll e^x$ for $x \geq 5$ we may approximate Eq. (5–47) as

$$g(x) \cong e^{-[(\zeta/\sqrt{\zeta^2-1})-1]x} \qquad \text{for } e^x \gg e^{-x} \tag{5-54}$$

Thus

$$g(10) \cong e^{-(1.16-1.00)10} = e^{-1.60} = 0.200$$
$$g(20) \cong e^{-0.16(20)} = e^{-3.20} = 0.040$$

Putting these values and others in table form we have Table 5–4. These points are plotted in Fig. 5–34(a).

Now that we have developed the universal curve of Fig. 5–34(a) we will return to Ex. 5–11(part c).

> We have already identified $\zeta = 5$ for Eq. (5–32) and as a result have concluded we will use Eq. (10) of Table 4–2 for finding the inverse Laplace transform. Then from (5–32) and Eq. (10) we find

TABLE 5–4   (All values are rounded off to nearest hundredth)

x	$\zeta = 1.5$	$\zeta = 2$	$\zeta = 3$	$\zeta = 4$	$\zeta = 6$	$\zeta = 10$
	$x_0 = 0.96$ g_{max} $= 0.60$	$x_0 = 1.31$ g_{max} $= 0.75$	$x_0 = 1.76$ g_{max} $= 0.86$	$x_0 = 2.06$ g_{max} $= 0.90$	$x_0 = 2.39$ g_{max} $= 0.96$	$x_0 = 2.88$ g_{max} $= 0.97$
	$g(x)$	$g(x)$	$g(x)$	$g(x)$	$g(x)$	$g(x)$
0	0	0	0	0	0	0
0.50	0.53	0.58	0.61	0.62	0.63	0.63^+
1.00	0.60	0.74	0.81	0.83	0.85	0.86
5.00	0.18	0.45	0.74	0.82	0.90	0.95
10.00	0.03	0.20	0.55	0.67	0.82	0.91
20.00	0.01	0.04	0.30	0.45	0.67	0.82
50.00	$\cong 0$	$\cong 0$	0.05	0.14	0.37	0.62

$$v_o(t) = -\mathcal{L}^{-1}\left[\frac{\dfrac{E}{RC}}{s^2 + \dfrac{1}{RC}s + \dfrac{1}{LC}}\right]$$

$$= -\mathcal{L}^{-1}\left[\frac{K}{s^2 + 2\zeta\omega_n s + \omega_n^2}\right]$$

$$= -\frac{K}{\beta - \alpha}(e^{-\alpha t} - e^{-\beta t})u(t) \qquad (5\text{-}55)$$

From our work in developing the universal curve of Fig. 5–34(a) we have determined that

$$\alpha = \zeta\omega_n - \omega_n\sqrt{\zeta^2 - 1} \quad \text{and} \quad \beta = \zeta\omega_n + \omega_n\sqrt{\zeta^2 - 1}$$

where from part (b) we determined $2\zeta\omega_n = 1/RC$ and $\omega_n = 1/\sqrt{LC}$. And from Eq. (5–55) we see that $K = E/RC$, therefore Eq. (5–55) can be written as

$$v_o(t) = -\frac{\dfrac{E}{RC}}{2\omega_n\sqrt{\zeta^2 - 1}}e^{-\zeta\omega_n t}(e^{\omega_n\sqrt{\zeta^2 - 1}\,t} - e^{-\omega_n\sqrt{\zeta^2 - 1}\,t})u(t)$$

$$(5\text{-}56)$$

From Eq. (5–46) we may write Eq. (5–56) as

$$v_o(t) = -\frac{\dfrac{E}{RC}}{2\omega_n\sqrt{\zeta^2 - 1}}g(t) \qquad (5\text{-}57)$$

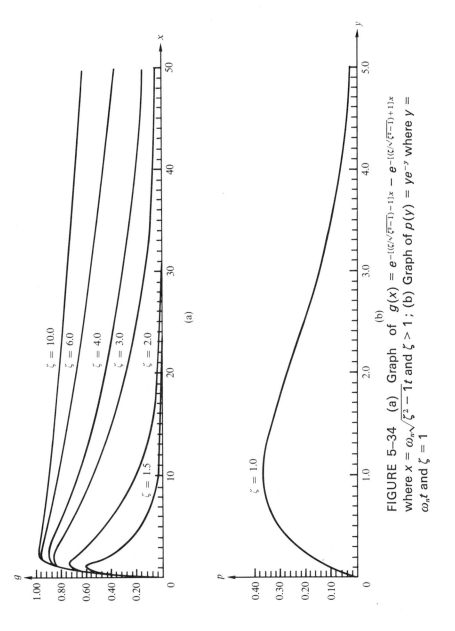

FIGURE 5-34 (a) Graph of $g(x) = e^{-[(\zeta/\sqrt{\zeta^2-1})-1]x} - e^{-[(\zeta/\sqrt{\zeta^2-1})+1]x}$ where $x = \omega_n\sqrt{\zeta^2-1}\,t$ and $\zeta > 1$; (b) Graph of $p(y) = ye^{-y}$ where $y = \omega_n t$ and $\zeta = 1$

Defining $x \equiv \omega_n\sqrt{\zeta^2 - 1}t$, from which we find $t = x/\omega_n\sqrt{\zeta^2 - 1}$, we then have $g(x)$ of Eq. (5–47) so

$$v_o(t) = -\frac{\dfrac{E}{RC}}{2\omega_n\sqrt{\xi^2 - 1}}g(x) \qquad (5\text{–}58)$$

which can be plotted from Fig. 5–34(a). Notice we have the option to write v_o of Eq. (5–58) as $v_o(t)$ or $v_o(x)$ since $x = x(t)$.

Our next step is to obtain numerical values for the constants of Eq. (5–58), hence

$$\omega_n = \frac{1}{\sqrt{LC}} = \frac{1}{\sqrt{10^{-6}(10^{-14})}} = 10^{10} \text{ rad/s}$$

$$RC = 10^3(10^{-14}) = 10^{-11} \text{ s}$$

and

$$\sqrt{\zeta^2 - 1} = \sqrt{24} = 4.9$$

So from Eq. (5–58)

$$v_o(t) = \frac{-E}{2(10^{-11})(10^{10})4.9}g(x) = -1.02Eg(x) \qquad (5\text{–}59)$$

We shall now go to Fig. 5–34(a) and pick points of interest for $\zeta = 5$ and record these in tabular form. The first obvious problem is that Fig. 5–34(a) does not have a curve for $\zeta = 5$, hence we shall approximate. On viewing Fig. 5–34(a) we see that $\zeta = 5$ is not half way between $\zeta = 4$ and $\zeta = 6$. We will approximate $\zeta = 5$ to be closer to $\zeta = 6$. It is the author's guess that our points of interest will be at: $x = 1$, 2.2 (approximate maximum x_0), 4, 5, 10, 15, 20, 25, 30, 50. Notice the points are close for $1 \leq x \leq 5$ since most of the "fast" changes occurred in that range. Table 5–5 shows the points read from Fig. 5–34(a) for $\zeta = 5$ (approximately half way between $\zeta = 4$ and $\zeta = 6$) and for the values of x indicated.

From Table 5–5, Eq. (4–59) and the equation

$$t = \frac{x}{\omega_n\sqrt{\zeta^2 - 1}} = \frac{x}{4.9 \times 10^{10}}$$
$$= 20.4x \times 10^{-12} = 20.4x\,p\text{s}$$

where $p = 10^{-12}$, we determine Table 5–6. Using Table 5–6 we plot Fig. 5–35.

We will now verify Fig. 5–35 by calculating various points for v_o using Eq. (5–56). Hence,

TABLE 5-5   For $\zeta = 5$

x	$g(x)$
0	0
1.0	0.88
2.2	0.92
4.0	0.90
5.0	0.87
10.0	0.73
15.0	0.64
20.0	0.58
25.0	0.56
30.0	0.47
50.0	0.30

TABLE 5-6:   For $\zeta = 5$ (values are rounded off)

x	$g(x)$	$t = 20.4x \times 10^{-12}$ t in ps	$v_o(t) = -1.02Eg(x)$ v_o in volts
0.0	0.00	00.0	-0.00
1.0	0.88	20.4	$-0.90E$
2.2	0.92	44.8	$-0.94E$
4.0	0.90	81.6	$-0.92E$
5.0	0.87	102.0	$-0.89E$
10.0	0.73	204.0	$-0.74E$
15.0	0.64	306.0	$-0.65E$
20.0	0.58	408.0	$-0.59E$
25.0	0.56	510.0	$-0.57E$
30.0	0.47	612.0	$-0.48E$
50.0	0.30	1020.0	$-0.31E$

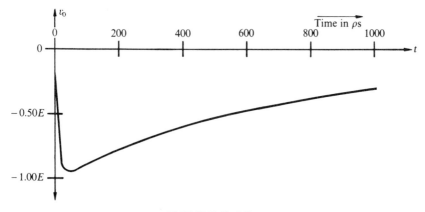

FIGURE 5-35

$$v_o(t) = -1.02Ee^{-t/20 \times 10^{-12}}(e^{0.049 \times 10^{-12}t} - e^{-0.049 \times 10^{-12}t})u(t)$$

$$(5-60)$$

Evaluating Eq. (5–60) at $t = 44.8$ ps we have

$$v_o(44.8 \times 10^{-12})$$
$$= -1.02Ee^{-44.8/20}[e^{0.049(44.8)} - e^{-0.049(44.8)}]$$
$$= -1.02Ee^{-2.24}(e^{2.20} - e^{-2.20})$$
$$= -1.02E(0.106)(9.40 - 0.11) = -0.90E$$

which agrees with Fig. 5–35. For a second point we will choose $t = 510$ ps. Then at $t = 510$ ps

$$v_o(510 \ ps) = -1.02Ee^{-510/20}(e^{25.0} - e^{-25.0})$$
$$\cong -1.02e^{-0.5}$$
$$= -1.02(0.606)E = -0.62E$$

Our graph and Table 5–6 say that $v_o(510 \ ps) \cong -0.57E$, but for all practical purposes these values agree. We shall consider Fig. 5–35 as verified.

Let us look at Ex. 5–11(c) as if we were given the equation

$$v_o(t) = -1.02E(e^{-0.10 \times 10^{10}t} - e^{-9.9 \times 10^{10}t})u(t) \qquad (5-61)$$

and asked to graph it using a universal curve. Our first objective would be to identify which universal curve to use, Fig. 5–32(b) or Fig. 5–34(a). After that we must find which ζ curve applies. To determine which universal curve applies we compare Eq. (5–61) with Eqs. (5–35) and (5–45). We see that Eqs. (5–45) and (5–61) are the same form, hence we use Fig. 5–34(a). Thus we may equate Eqs. (5–45) and (5–61),

$$v_o(t) = -1.02E(e^{-0.10 \times 10^{10}t} - e^{-9.9 \times 10^{10}t})u(t)$$

$$= \frac{K}{2\omega_n\sqrt{\zeta^2 - 1}}[e^{-(\zeta\omega_n - \omega_n\sqrt{\zeta^2 - 1})t} - e^{-(\zeta\omega_n + \omega_n\sqrt{\zeta^2 - 1})t}]u(t) \qquad (5-62)$$

It is from Eq. (5–62) we shall determine the value of ζ. We can do this by equating powers of e. We know that $(\zeta\omega_n - \omega_n\sqrt{\zeta^2 - 1})$ is the smallest magnitude, therefore

$$0.10 \times 10^{10} = \zeta\omega_n - \omega_n\sqrt{\zeta^2 - 1}$$

which also means $9.9 \times 10^{10} = \zeta\omega_n + \omega_n\sqrt{\zeta^2 - 1}$. Thus

$$\omega_n(\zeta - \sqrt{\zeta^2 - 1}) = 0.10 \times 10^{10} = 10^9$$

or

$$\omega_n = \frac{10^9}{\zeta - \sqrt{\zeta^2 - 1}}$$

So

$$9.9 \times 10^{10} = \frac{\zeta \times 10^9}{\zeta - \sqrt{\zeta^2 - 1}} + \frac{\sqrt{\zeta^2 - 1} \times 10^9}{\zeta - \sqrt{\zeta^2 - 1}}$$

or

$$99 = \frac{\zeta + \sqrt{\zeta^2 - 1}}{\zeta - \sqrt{\zeta^2 - 1}}$$

Solving for ζ,

$$99(\zeta - \sqrt{\zeta^2 - 1}) = \zeta + \sqrt{\zeta^2 - 1}$$
$$98\zeta = 100\sqrt{\zeta^2 - 1}$$
$$\zeta = 1.02\sqrt{\zeta^2 - 1}$$

Squaring both sides

$$\zeta^2 = 1.04(\zeta^2 - 1), \quad \text{so} \quad 0.04\zeta^2 = 1$$

and $\zeta^2 = 1/0.04 = 25$, therefore $\zeta = 5$, which agrees with what we found in Ex. 5–11(c). To plot Eq. (5–62) is a repeat of Ex. 5–11(c); that is, Eq. (5–62) could be written as $v_o(t) = -1.02Eg(x)$, where

$$x = \omega_n\sqrt{\zeta^2 - 1}t = \frac{\sqrt{\zeta^2 - 1} \times 10^9 t}{\zeta - \sqrt{\zeta^2 - 1}}$$

To complete the universal curves for a quadratic of the form for Eq. (9) in Table 4–2 we will need to graph a universal curve for Eq. (6) of Table 4–2, that is, for $\zeta = 1$. Equation (6) of Table 4–2 takes the form of

$$f(t) = \frac{K}{(2 - 1)!}te^{-\alpha t}u(t) \qquad (5\text{–}63)$$

since $n = 2$ for $\zeta = 1$. Now, from $\alpha = \zeta\omega_n - \omega_n\sqrt{\zeta^2 - 1}$ and $\beta = \zeta\omega_n + \omega_n\sqrt{\zeta^2 - 1}$, determined in Ex. 5–11(c), we know that for $\zeta = 1$ that $\alpha = \beta = \omega_n$. Then Eq. (5–63) becomes

$$f(t) = Kte^{-\omega_n t}u(t) \qquad (5\text{–}64)$$

If we were to plot Eq. (5–64) on the same graph as Eq. (5–47) we would have to keep the same scale on the horizontal axis. From Eq. (5–47) we know that $t = x/\omega_n\sqrt{\zeta^2 - 1}$, which for $\zeta = 1$ is undefined. Hence, we cannot graph Eq. (5–63) on the same graph as Eq. (5–47). We will make a separate graph for Eq. (5–63). Before graphing Eq. (5–63) let us make it universal by defining

$$y \equiv \omega_n t \qquad (5\text{–}65)$$

and also normalizing. Thus $f(t) = K(y/\omega_n)e^{-y}u(y)$, or defining p as $(\omega_n/K)f(t)$,

$$p(y) \equiv \frac{\omega_n}{K}f(t) = ye^{-y}u(y) \qquad (5\text{–}66)$$

where $y = y(t)$.

Finding the maximum or minimum point,

$$\frac{dp(y)}{dy} = \frac{d}{dy} y e^{-y}$$

for $y > 0$, or

$$p'(y) = e^{-y} - y e^{-y}$$

Solving for when $p' = 0$, which we will call y_0,

$$p'(y_0) = e^{-y_0} - y_0 e^{-y_0} = 0$$

or

$$1 - y_0 = 0$$

so

$$y_0 = 1 \qquad\qquad (5\text{-}67)$$

Other points are calculated as follows.

Sample calculations for $\zeta = 1$

$$p_{max} = p(y_0) = e^{-1} = 0.37$$
$$p(0.5) = 0.5 e^{-0.5} = 0.5(0.606) = 0.303$$
$$p(1.5) = 1.5 e^{-1.5} = 1.5(0.222) = 0.333$$
$$p(2.0) = 2.0 e^{-2.0} = 2.0(0.136) = 0.272$$
$$p(3.0) = 3.0 e^{-3.0} = 3.0(0.050) = 0.150$$
$$p(4.0) = 4.0 e^{-4.0} = 0.072$$

These points are plotted in Fig. 5–34(b).

We now have Figs. 5–32(b), 5–34(a) and (b) to aid us in plotting equations of the forms resulting from Eqs. (6), (9), and (10) of Table 4–2. We must remember that when using Figs. 5–32(b), 5–34(a) and (b) we *must* put the equation we wish to plot in the form which corresponds to the figure we are using. And to determine which is the proper curve of the figure to use the value of ζ must be known.

Also keep in mind that there are many values of ζ not represented in those figures mentioned here; however, there is a sufficient number that one could estimate any value of ζ and be correct from a practical consideration. It might be well to show that $\zeta = 10$ and $\zeta = 100$ are very close. For $\zeta = 100$

$$g(x) \cong e^{-x}(e^x - e^{-x}) = 1 - e^{-2x}$$

For various values of x we have

$$g(3) \cong 1 - e^{-6} = 1 - 0.0025 \cong 1.0$$
$$g(5) \cong 1 - e^{-10} \cong 1$$

As one can see as ζ increases beyond 10 then g approaches a magnitude of unity, which is not too different in value from $\zeta = 10$.

We will consider another example which results in a quadratic solution. This will allow us to use either Fig. 5–32, 5–34(a), or 5–34(b), depending on the value of ζ.

Example 5–12   Given the circuit in Fig. 5–36 determine the current flowing through R_L and sketch its waveform.

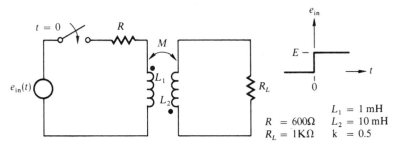

$L_1 = 1\,\text{mH}$
$R = 600\,\Omega$ $L_2 = 10\,\text{mH}$
$R_L = 1\,\text{K}\Omega$ $k = 0.5$

FIGURE 5–36

Solution   Since we are seeking the solution to a current we will use loop analysis. We will begin by assuming a voltage polarity for e_{in} and the loop current directions. Also, the self-induced and mutually induced voltages must be determined. The circuit for these considerations appears in Fig. 5–37.

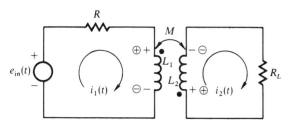

FIGURE 5–37

Writing the two loop equations,

$$e_{\text{in}}(t) - Ri_1(t) - L_1\frac{di_1(t)}{dt} - M\frac{di_2(t)}{dt} = 0$$

and

$$-L_2\frac{di_2(t)}{dt} - M\frac{di_1(t)}{dt} - R_L i_2(t) = 0$$

Taking the Laplace transform

$$E_{in}(s) - RI_1(s) - L_1[sI_1(s) - i_1(0^+)]$$
$$- M[sI_L(s) - i_L(0^+)] = 0$$

and

$$-L_2[sI_L(s) - i_L(0^+)] - M[sI_1(s) - i_1(0^+)] - R_L I_L(s) = 0$$

Collecting terms, where knowns are on one side of the equation and unknowns (loop currents) on the other,

$$E_{in}(s) + L_1 i_1(0^+) + M i_L(0^+)$$
$$= (R + L_1 s)I_1(s) + MsI_L(s) \qquad \textbf{(5–68a)}$$

$$L_2 i_L(0^+) + M i_1(0^+)$$
$$= MsI_1(s) + (R_L + L_2 s)I_L(s) \qquad \textbf{(5–68b)}$$

Using determinants we solve for $I_L(s)$,

$$\Delta = \begin{vmatrix} (R + L_1 s) & Ms \\ Ms & (R_L + L_2 s) \end{vmatrix}$$
$$= (R + L_1 s)(R_L + L_2 s) - (Ms)^2$$
$$= (L_1 L_2 - M^2)s^2 + (RL_2 + R_L L_1)s + RR_L$$

and

$$\Delta I_L(s) = \begin{vmatrix} (R + L_1 s) & [E_{in}(s) + L_1 i_1(0^+) + M i_L(0^+)] \\ Ms & [L_2 i_L(0^+) + M i_1(0^+)] \end{vmatrix}$$
$$= (R + L_1 s)[L_2 i_L(0^+) + M i_1(0^+)]$$
$$- Ms[E_{in}(s) + L_1 i_1(0^+) + M i_L(0^+)]$$

therefore

$$I_L(s) =$$
$$\frac{(R + L_1 s)[L_2 i_L(0^+) + M i_1(0^+)] - Ms[E_{in}(s) + L_1 i_1(0^+) + M i_L(0^+)]}{(L_1 L_2 - M^2)s^2 + (RL_2 + R_L L_1)s + RR_L}$$
$$\textbf{(5–69)}$$

which is a solution.

Equation (5–69) could appear simpler by defining the quantities

$$L_2 i_L(0^+) + M i_1(0^+) = \text{constant} \equiv V_1 \qquad \textbf{(5–70a)}$$

and

$$L_1 i_1(0^+) + M i_L(0^+) = \text{constant} \equiv V_2 \qquad \textbf{(5–70b)}$$

then Eq. (5–69) would appear as

$$I_L(s) = \frac{(R + L_1 s)V_1 - Ms[E_{in}(s) + V_2]}{(L_1 L_2 - M^2)s^2 + (RL_2 + R_L L_1)s + RR_L}$$
$$\textbf{(5–71)}$$

The point being made from Eqs. (5–70a) and (b) is that one can use *his* own definitions of quantities to simplify.

In preparation for finding the inverse Laplace transform we must: (1) determine the initial conditions; (2) force the highest power of s to have a coefficient of unity for Eq. (5–71); (3) determine the explicit equation for $E_{in}(s)$; (4) determine the magnitude of ζ.

From the circuit and e_{in} we can easily determine that all initial conditions are zero. Then $V_1 = V_2 = 0$ and Eq. (5–71) becomes

$$I_L(s) = -\frac{MsE_{in}(s)}{(L_1L_2 - M^2)s^2 + (RL_2 + R_LL_1)s + RR_L}$$

Forcing the highest power of s to unity we have

$$I_L(s) = -\frac{M}{L_1L_2 - M^2} \frac{sE_{in}(s)}{s^2 + \dfrac{RL_2 + R_LL_1}{L_1L_2 - M^2}s + \dfrac{RR_L}{L_1L_2 - M^2}}$$

$$\text{(5–72)}$$

From the waveform of e_{in} we know that $e_{in}(t) = Eu(t)$. Then $E_{in}(s) = E/s$. Substituting this in Eq. (5–72) we have

$$I_L(s) = -\frac{ME}{L_1L_2 - M^2} \frac{1}{s^2 + \dfrac{RL_2 + R_LL_1}{L_1L_2 - M^2}s + \dfrac{RR_L}{L_1L_2 - M^2}}$$

$$\text{(5–73)}$$

To determine ζ we equate like coefficients of Eq. (5–73) and Eq. (9) of Table 4–2. Hence, $(RL_2 + R_LL_1)/(L_1L_2 - M^2) = 2\omega_n\zeta$ for s and $RR_L/(L_1L_2 - M^2) = \omega_n^2$ for s^0. Thus

$$\zeta = \frac{1}{2\omega_n}\frac{RL_2 + R_LL_1}{L_1L_2 - M^2}$$

$$= \frac{1}{2\sqrt{\dfrac{RR_L}{L_1L_2 - M^2}}}\frac{RL_2 - R_LL_1}{L_1L_2 - M^2}$$

$$= \frac{(RL_2 + R_LL_1)}{2\sqrt{RR_L(L_1L_2 - M^2)}}$$

Now

$$k = \frac{M}{\sqrt{L_1L_2}}$$

so

$$\zeta = \frac{RL_2 + R_LL_1}{2\sqrt{RR_LL_1L_2(1 - k^2)}} \qquad \text{(5–74)}$$

Substituting values into Eq. (5–74)

$$\zeta = \frac{600(10 \times 10^{-3}) + 10^3(10^{-3})}{2\sqrt{600 \times 10^3(10 \times 10^{-6})(1 - 0.25)}} = 1.65$$

Since $\zeta > 1$ we must use Eq. (10) of Table 4–2.

Before we can use Eq. (10) we must factor the denominator of Eq. (5–73) so that it appears in the same form as Eq. (10). There are several ways to do this, of which

$$s_{1,2} = -\frac{RL_2 + R_L L_1}{2(L_1 L_2 - M^2)}$$
$$\pm \frac{1}{2}\sqrt{\left(\frac{RL_2 + R_L L_1}{L_1 L_2 - M^2}\right)^2 - \frac{4RR_L}{L_1 L_2 - M^2}}$$

$s_1 = \alpha$ and $s_2 = -\beta$ is the most obvious. However, a less bulky method would be as we handled Eq. (5–43). From the works of Eq. (5–43) we have Eq. (5–44), or

$$\alpha = \zeta\omega_n - \omega_n\sqrt{\zeta^2 - 1} = \omega_n(\zeta - \sqrt{\zeta^2 - 1})$$

and

$$\beta = \zeta\omega_n + \omega_n\sqrt{\zeta^2 - 1} = \omega_n(\zeta + \sqrt{\zeta^2 - 1})$$

where Eq. (5–74) describes ζ. We found ω_n to be

$$\omega_n = \sqrt{\frac{RR_L}{L_1 L_2 - M^2}} = \sqrt{\frac{RR_L}{L_1 L_2(1 - k^2)}}$$

The value of ω_n is

$$\omega_n = \sqrt{\frac{600 \times 10^3}{7.5 \times 10^{-6}}} = 2.83 \times 10^5 = 0.283 \times 10^6 \text{ rad/s}$$

So

$$\alpha = 0.283 \times 10^6(1.65 - \sqrt{2.72 - 1}) = 0.100 \times 10^6$$

and

$$\beta = 0.283 \times 10^6(1.65 + \sqrt{2.72 - 1}) = 0.837 \times 10^6$$

Therefore

$$I_L(s) = -\frac{k\sqrt{L_1 L_2}E}{L_1 L_2(1 - k^2)}$$
$$\times \frac{1}{(s + 0.100 \times 10^6)(s + 0.837 \times 10^6)}$$

or

$$I_L(s) = -0.211$$
$$\times 10^3 E \frac{1}{(s + 0.100 \times 10^6)(s + 0.837 \times 10^6)}$$

$$(5\text{–}75)$$

Thus

$$i_L(t) = -0.211$$
$$\times 10^3 E\left[\frac{10^{-6}}{0.837-0.100}(e^{-0.100\times10^6 t}-e^{-0.837\times10^6 t})\right]u(t)$$

or

$$i_L(t) = -0.287E \times 10^{-3}(e^{-0.100\times10^6 t} - e^{-0.837\times10^6 t})u(t)$$

$$(5\text{-}76)$$

Notice that we retained the negative sign of Eq. (5–76) by choosing $\beta > \alpha$. (We stated the reason for $\beta > \alpha$ in Ex. 5–11.) This means of course i_L is in the opposite direction than what we assumed. If we would have chosen to write Eq. (5–76) as

$$i_L(t) = 0.287E \times 10^{-3}(e^{-0.837\times10^6 t} - e^{-0.100\times10^6 t})u(t)$$

$$(5\text{-}77)$$

by letting $\alpha > \beta$, then the absence of the negative sign would at first glance lead us to believe we assumed i_L in the correct direction. However, a closer examination of Eq. (5–77) would show i_L is still negative since $e^{-0.100\times10^6 t} > e^{-0.837\times10^6 t}$, but we do not wish to have to make this detailed an observation if possible. In summary, then, keep the negative sign in plain view so that it is obvious at a glance that the flow of i_L is the reverse shown and this is done by compliance with keeping $\beta > \alpha$.

To plot Eq. (5–76) we recognize Eq. (5–47) expresses the universal curve we are to use, hence we make the necessary substitution $g(x) = e^{-0.100\times10^6} - e^{-0.837\times10^6 t}$, where $t = x/\omega_n\sqrt{\zeta^2 - 1} = 2.70x \times 10^{-6} = 2.70x \ \mu s$, into Eq. (5–76). Then Eq. (5–76) can be written as

$$i_L(t) = -0.287 \times 10^{-3}Eg(x) \qquad (5\text{-}78)$$

From Fig. 5–34(a), for $\zeta = 1.65$ (we will approximate ζ), we will pick those points which appear to be the "best" points. Again, by "best" points we mean those points which will best assist in plotting our curve. Picking the points at $x = 1, 3, 5,$ and 10 we have Table 5–7. Plotting the points of Table 5–7 we have Fig. 5–38.

From Fig. 5–38 we see that a dc potential cannot sustain a current which is an induced current.

Let us now suppose that we were given Eq. (5–77) and asked to plot it. As we stated in Ex. 5–11(c), when given

TABLE 5-7   For $\zeta = 1.65$

x	$g(x)$	$t = 2.70x\ \mu s$ t in μs	$i_L(t) = -0.287 \times 10^{-3}E$ i_L in mA
0	0	0.00	0.00
1	0.68	2.70	$-0.20E$
3	0.45	8.10	$-0.13E$
5	0.30	.13.50	$-0.09E$
10	0.15	27.00	$-0.04E$

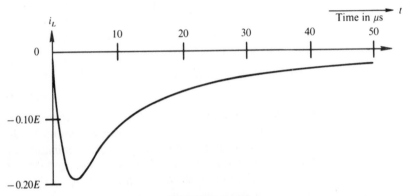

FIGURE 5-38

this type of problem our first objective would be to identify which universal curve to use and secondly we would determine the value of ζ. From the form of Eq. (5–77) we identify it as that of Eq. (5–47), therefore Fig. 5–34(a) is used. To determine ζ we will equate powers of e using Eq. (5–46). Hence

$$g(t) = e^{-(\zeta\omega_n - \omega_n\sqrt{\zeta^2-1})t} - e^{-(\zeta\omega_n + \omega_n\sqrt{\zeta^2-1})t}$$
$$= -(e^{-0.837\times10^6 t} - e^{-0.100\times10^6 t}) \qquad \textbf{(5-79)}$$

Now since $(\zeta\omega_n + \omega_n\sqrt{\zeta^2-1}) > (\zeta\omega_n - \omega_n\sqrt{\zeta^2-1})$ we find by equating powers of e,

$$0.837 \times 10^6 = \zeta\omega_n + \omega_n\sqrt{\zeta^2 - 1} = \omega_n(\zeta + \sqrt{\zeta^2 - 1})$$

and

$$0.100 \times 10^6 = \omega_n(\zeta - \sqrt{\zeta^2 - 1})$$

From this we find $\omega_n = (0.837 \times 10^6)/(\zeta + \sqrt{\zeta^2 - 1})$ so

$$0.100 \times 10^6 = \frac{0.837 \times 10^6(\zeta - \sqrt{\zeta^2 - 1})}{\zeta + \sqrt{\zeta^2 - 1}}$$

or

$$0.100 \times 10^6(\zeta + \sqrt{\zeta^2 - 1}) = 0.837 \times 10^6(\zeta - \sqrt{\zeta^2 - 1})$$

Thus

$$0.937\sqrt{\zeta^2 - 1} = 0.737\zeta$$

or

$$\zeta = 1.27\sqrt{\zeta^2 - 1}$$

Squaring both sides

$$\zeta^2 = 1.62(\zeta^2 - 1)$$

from which we find

$$\zeta^2 = \frac{1.62}{0.62} = 2.60$$

therefore

$$\zeta = 1.61$$

Before we calculated $\zeta = 1.65$, but for all practical purposes $\zeta = 1.65 \cong 1.61$.

Then we will use Fig. 5–34(a) with $\zeta \cong 1.65$ and Eq. (5–79) to plot Eq. (5–77). Hence

$$i_L(t) = 0.287E \times 10^{-3}[-g(t)]$$

or

$$i_L(t) = -0.287E \times 10^{-3}g(x)$$

where $x = \omega_n\sqrt{\zeta^2 - 1}t$, which is Eq. (5–78).

For the next example let us consider a single pulse being applied to the circuit of Ex. 5–12.

Example 5–13   For the circuit of Ex. 5–12 apply e_{in} as shown in Fig. 5–39 and determine i_L. Also graph your results. (a) For

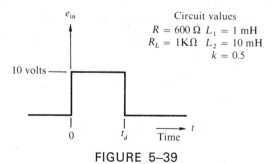

Circuit values
$R = 600\ \Omega \quad L_1 = 1\ \text{mH}$
$R_L = 1\text{K}\Omega \quad L_2 = 10\ \text{mH}$
$k = 0.5$

FIGURE 5–39

the first consideration let $t_d = 100$ μs. (b) For a second consideration let $t_d = 20$ μs.

Solution

Since e_{in} is to have two different pulse duration values let us write a general algebraic equation for e_{in}. Then we may substitute the appropriate value for t_d when needed. Hence,

$$e_{in}(t) = 10u(t) - 10u(t - t_d)$$

so

$$E_{in}(s) = \frac{10}{s}(1 - e^{-t_d s})$$

One will quickly notice we have already done a great deal of the work for this example in Ex. 5–12. Our work to follow will be general, for the solution of i_L, by retaining t_d. Once i_L is found we will become specific by substituting $t_d = 100$ μs for part (a) and $t_d = 20$ μs for part (b). From Eq. (5–72)

$$I_L(s) = -\frac{M}{L_1 L_2 - M^2} \frac{s E_{in}(s)}{s^2 + \dfrac{RL_2 + R_L L_1}{L_1 L_2 - M^2} s + \dfrac{RR_L}{L_1 L_2 - M^2}}$$

$$(5\text{–}72)$$

or, for this example,

$$I_L(s) = -\frac{M}{L_1 L_2 - M^2} \frac{10(1 - e^{-t_d s})}{s^2 + \dfrac{RL_2 + R_L L_1}{L_1 L_2 - M^2} s + \dfrac{RR_L}{L_1 L_2 - M^2}}$$

$$(5\text{–}80)$$

Substituting the numerical values for the components and factoring we have

$$I_L(s) = -2.11 \times 10^3 \frac{1 - e^{-t_d s}}{(s + 0.100 \times 10^6)(s + 0.837 \times 10^6)}$$

$$(5\text{–}81)$$

as determined from Eq. (5–75). Notice that the E of Eq. (5–75) for this example is equal to 10.

To find the inverse Laplace transform of Eq. (5–81) we refer to our work of Ex. 5–12. That is, compare Eq. (5–81) with Eq. (5–75) and it is clear that they are the same except for the $e^{-t_d s}$ term. Let us isolate that term by writing Eq. (5–81) as

$$I_L(s) = -2.11 \times 10^3 \left[\frac{1}{(s + 0.100 \times 10^6)(s + 0.837 \times 10^6)} \right. $$
$$\left. - \frac{e^{-t_d s}}{(s + 0.100 \times 10^6)(s + 0.837 \times 10^6)} \right] \quad (5\text{–}82)$$

The term containing $e^{-t_d s}$ clearly identifies itself with Eq. (21) of Table 4–2. Then from Eqs. (5–75), (5–76), and (21) of Table 4–2 i_L, found from Eq. (5–82), is

$$i_L(t) = -2.11 \times 10^3 \left\{ \frac{10^{-6}}{0.737} (e^{-0.100 \times 10^6 t} - e^{-0.837 \times 10^6 t}) u(t) \right.$$
$$\left. - \frac{10^{-6}}{0.737} (e^{-0.100 \times 10^6 (t-t_d)} - e^{-0.837 \times 10^6 (t-t_d)}) u(t - t_d) \right\}$$

or

$$i_L(t) = -2.87 \times 10^{-3} \{ (e^{-0.100 \times 10^6 t} - e^{-0.837 \times 10^6 t}) u(t)$$
$$- (e^{-0.100 \times 10^6 (t-t_d)} - e^{-0.837 \times 10^6 (t-t_d)}) u(t - t_d) \}$$

$$\tag{5–83}$$

Equation (5–83) is the mathematical expression of i_L for any pulse duration of value t_d.

To graph Eq. (5–83) we will consider the various ranges of t resulting because of the presence of $u(t)$ and $u(t - t_d)$. Hence,

For $t < 0$: $u(t) = u(t - t_d) = 0$, hence

$$i_L(t) = 0 \tag{5–84}$$

For $0 < t < t_d$: $u(t) = 1$ and $u(t - t_d) = 0$, so

$$i_L(t) = -2.87 \times 10^{-3} (e^{-0.100 \times 10^6 t} - e^{-0.837 \times 10^6 t}) \tag{5–85}$$

For $t > t_d$: $u(t) = u(t - t_d) = 1$

$$i_L(t) = -2.87 \times 10^{-3} [(e^{-0.100 \times 10^6 t} - e^{-0.837 \times 10^6 t})$$
$$- (e^{-0.100 \times 10^6 (t-t_d)} - e^{-0.837 \times 10^6 (t-t_d)})] \tag{5–86}$$

Equations (5–84), (5–85), and (5–86) fully describe i_L for all time for some general pulse duration t_d. Then our next step is to become specific.

(a) For $t_d = 100$ μs we have:

For $t < 0$

$$i_L(t) = 0$$

from Eq. (5–84).

For $0 < t < t_d = 100$ μs

$$i_L(t) = -2.87 \times 10^{-3} (e^{-0.100 \times 10^6 t} - e^{-0.837 \times 10^6 t})$$

from Eq. (5–85).

For $t > t_d = 100$ μs

$$i_L(t) = -2.87 \times 10^{-3} [(e^{-0.100 \times 10^6 t} - e^{-0.837 \times 10^6 t})$$
$$- (e^{-0.100 \times 10^6 (t - 100 \times 10^{-6})} - e^{-0.837 \times 10^6 (t - 100 \times 10^{-6})})]$$

$$\tag{5–87}$$

In viewing i_L for the various ranges of time we see that for $t < t_d = 100 \ \mu$s this problem is a repeat of Ex. 5–12; that is, for $0 < t < t_d = 100 \ \mu$s compare i_L with Eq. (5–77). Then Eq. (5–78) is also valid for this example if $E = 10$, so:

For $0 < t < t_d = 100 \ \mu$s

$$i_L(t) = -2.87 \times 10^{-3} g(x) \qquad \textbf{(5–88)}$$

where $x = \omega_n \sqrt{\zeta^2 - 1} \ t$, or $t = 2.70x \ \mu$s. Also then Table 5–7 is valid for this range except we will want to carry t out to $100 \ \mu$s and let $E = 10$. To carry t out to $100 \ \mu$s means going out to an x value of

$$x_d = \frac{t_d}{2.70 \times 10^{-6}} = \frac{100 \times 10^{-6}}{2.70 \times 10^{-6}} = 37$$

Our extended values of x for Table 5–7 appear in Table 5–8.

TABLE 5–8   For $0 < t < t_d = 100 \ \mu$s

x	$g(x)$	$t = 2.70x \times 10^{-6}$ t in μs	$i_L(t) = -2.87 \times 10^{-3} g(x)$ i_L in mA
0	0.00	0.00	0.00
1	0.68	2.70	−2.00
3	0.45	8.10	−1.29
5	0.30	13.50	−0.86
10	0.15	27.00	−0.43
20	0.00+	54.00	−0.00+
37	0.00	100.00	0.00

Note: 0.00+ means just slightly larger than zero, but not enough to measure.

And for $t > t_d = 100 \ \mu$s we see that Eq. (5–87) may be expressed as

$$i_L(t) = -2.87 \times 10^{-3} [g(x) - (e^{-0.100 \times 10^6 (t - 100 \times 10^{-6})}$$
$$- e^{-0.837 \times 10^6 (t - 100 \times 10^{-6})})] \qquad \textbf{(5–89)}$$

The term $-2.87 \times 10^{-3} g(x)$, which appears in Eq. (5–89), is the same as Eq. (5–88). Now Eq. (5–88) describes the current established for $0 < t < t_d = 100 \ \mu$s; hence, for it to appear in the range $t > t_d = 100 \ \mu$s means it represents the influence of the range $0 < t < t_d = 100 \ \mu$s on the range $t > t_d = 100 \ \mu$s. In other words, the current established when the driving force $e_{in}(0 < t < 100 \ \mu s) = 10$ V will show its influence on the current when $e_{in}(t > 100 \ \mu s) = 0$. To determine this influence refer to Table 5-8 where we see that for $t > 100 \ \mu s \ g(x) = 0$. Then for this particular case [for part (b) this will not be true] $g(x)$ of Eq. (5–89) may be equated to zero. Remember Eq. (5–89) is valid *only* for $t > 100 \ \mu s$. Writing Eq. (5–89) under this circumstance we have

$$i_L(t) = 2.87 \times 10^{-3}(e^{-0.100 \times 10^6(t - 100 \times 10^{-6})}$$
$$- e^{-0.837 \times 10^6(t - 100 \times 10^{-6})}) \qquad \textbf{(5–90)}$$

At first glance of Eq. (5–90) we might believe the construction of another universal curve is in order. This new universal curve would be the graphical display of the shifted function

$$e^{-\alpha(t - t_d)} - e^{-\beta(t - t_d)} \qquad \textbf{(5–91)}$$

which is of the same form as Eq. (5–90). Fortunately, however, this is not necessary.

Since our independent variable t is relative we can adjust its reference to suit our needs. That is, let us define a new variable, t', which is to have its zero reference at $t = t_d$; then as a function of t we express t' as

$$t' = t - t_d \qquad \textbf{(5–92)}$$

Substituting Eq. (5–92) into Eq. (5–91) we have

$$e^{-\alpha(t - t_d)} - e^{-\beta(t - t_d)} = e^{-\alpha t'} - e^{-\beta t'} \text{ for } t' = t - t_d \qquad \textbf{(5–93)}$$

Notice another way we could have arrived at the definition of t' is simply to define it equal to the shifted portion $(t - t_d)$ of the power of e. This method recognizes the quantity $(t - t_d)$ as being that which makes Eq. (5–91) different from the form $e^{-\alpha t} - e^{-\beta t}$, from which Fig. 5-34(a) was plotted. To make Eq. (5–91) appear in the same form as $e^{-\alpha t} - e^{-\beta t}$, but as a function of t' rather than t, we define $t - t_d$ as t'. Then

$$e^{-\alpha(t - t_d)} - e^{-\beta(t - t_d)} = e^{-\alpha t'} - e^{-\beta t'}$$

So we now have a familiar form of $e^{-\alpha t'} - e^{-\beta t'}$ and Fig. 5-34(a) can be used simply by calling the horizontal axis x' rather than x. This is the same problem as if we wished to plot $e^{-\alpha y} - e^{-\beta y}$ using Fig. 5-34(a). Under these conditions we would change the horizontal axis of Fig. 4–34(a) from x to some new variable, say z, since x no longer applies $(x = \omega_n\sqrt{\zeta^2 - 1}t)$. So for a horizontal axis of z we would have the relationship $z = \omega_n\sqrt{\zeta^2 - 1}y$, assuming α and β have the magnitudes previously determined. Then for our definition of t' and changing the horizontal axis of Fig. 5–34(a) to, say, x', we have

$$x' = \omega_n\sqrt{\zeta^2 - 1}\,t' \quad \text{where} \quad t' = t - t_d \quad \text{(5–94)}$$

Notice this changes only the name of the horizontal axis of Fig. 5–34(a) and nothing else. To give clarity to the concepts discussed we will return to Eq. (5–90) and apply them.

To plot Eq. (5–90) using the concepts discussed let us begin by defining

$$t' = t - 100 \times 10^{-6} \quad \text{(5–95)}$$

which compares to Eq. (5–92). Then Eq. (5–90) becomes

$$i_L(t) = 2.87 \times 10^{-3}(e^{-0.100 \times 10^6 t'} - e^{-0.837 \times 10^6 t'}) \quad \text{(5–96)}$$

which compares to Eq. (5–93). Next we search the universal curves to identify which one applies, and in this case Fig. 5–34(a) does since Eq. (5–96) has the same form as

$$e^{-[(\zeta/\sqrt{\zeta^2-1})-1]x} - e^{-[(\zeta/\sqrt{\zeta^2-1})+1]x}$$

Since the independent variable x was defined in terms of t we must redefine x, that is, Eq. (5–96) is in terms of t' not t, so let us change the x to x' and then

$$x' \equiv \omega_n\sqrt{\zeta^2 - 1}\,t'$$

which is Eq. (5–94). For this case

$$t' = \frac{1}{\omega_n\sqrt{\zeta^2 - 1}}x' = 2.70x' \times 10^{-6} = 2.70x'\mu s$$

$$\text{(5–97)}$$

Then Eq. (5–96) can be written as

$$i_L(t) = 2.87 \times 10^{-3}g(x') \quad \text{(5–98)}$$

Notice we still can write $i_L(t)$ since $x' = x'(t)$ as can be seen from Eqs. (5–95) and (5–97). All that is left now is to proceed as we have before. In fact Table 5–8 will be very similar to the table we will construct for Eq. (5–98) except that x' is not bounded by an upper limit as was x. Recall we calculated that our upper limit for Table 5–8 was

$t_d = 100$ μs, which corresponded to $x(t = t_d) = x_d = 100/2.70 = 37$. However, for this range we are interested in $t > 100$ μs, so we have no upper limit except for when $g(x') \cong 0$. From Fig. 5–34(a) we see that this occurs at approximately $x' = 20$ [recall x' has replaced x in Fig. 5–34(a) for this case]. From Eqs. (5–95), (5–97), and (5–98) we may plot Eq. (5–96). This is demonstrated in the following calculations.

Sample Calculations

From Fig. 5–34(a), or Table 5–8 for $\zeta = 1.65$:

For $x' = 0$

$$g(x') = 0; \quad t' = 2.70x' \times 10^{-6} = 0.00$$

from Eq. (5–97), $t = t' + 100$ μs from Eq. (5–95), so $t = 0.00 + 100 \times 10^{-6} = 100$ μs and from Eq. (5–98) $i_L(t = 100 \ \mu\text{s}) = 2.87 \times 10^{-3}(0.00) = 0$.

For $x' = 1$

$$g(x' = 1) \doteq 0.68, \quad t' = 2.70(1) \times 10^{-6} = 2.70\mu\text{s}$$

$$t = 2.70 \times 10^{-6} + 100 \times 10^{-6} = 102.70\mu\text{s}$$

$$i_L(t = 102.70\mu\text{s}) = 2.87 \times 10^{-3}(0.68) = 2.00\text{mA}$$

For $x' = 3$

$$g(x' = 3) = 0.45, \quad t' = 8.10\mu\text{s}$$

$$t = (8.10 + 100.00) \times 10^{-6} = 108.10\mu\text{s}$$

$$i_L(t = 108.10\mu\text{s}) = 2.87 \times 10^{-3}(0.45) = 1.29\text{mA}$$

The remaining points are shown in Table 5–9.

TABLE 5–9   For $t > t_d = 100$ μs

x'	$g(x')$	$t' = 2.70x'$ $\times 10^{-6}$ t' in μs	$t = t' + 100$ $\times 10^{-6}$ t in μs	$i_L(t) = 2.87$ $\times 10^{-3}g(x')$ i_L in mA
0	0.00	0.00	100.00	0.00
1	0.68	2.70	102.70	2.00
3	0.45	8.10	108.10	1.29
5	0.30	13.50	113.50	0.86
10	0.15	27.00	127.00	0.43
20	0.00+	54.00	154.00	0.00+

From Tables 5–8 and 5–9 we have the graph of i_L as shown in Fig. 5–40(b) with e_{in} graphed in Fig. 5–40(a) for the purpose of reference.

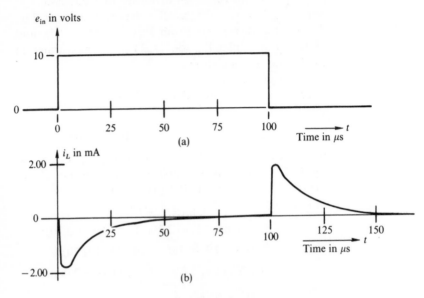

FIGURE 5–40

(b) This part is handled much the same as was part (a). Hence, referring to Eqs. (5–84), (5–85), and (5–86) we may write:

For $t < 0$

$$i_L(t) = 0$$

For $0 < t < t_d = 20 \ \mu s$

$$i_L(t) = -2.87 \times 10^{-3}(e^{-0.100 \times 10^6 t} - e^{-0.837 \times 10^6 t})$$
$$= -2.87 \times 10^{-3} g(x)$$

where

$$g(x) = e^{-0.100 \times 10^6 t} - e^{-0.837 \times 10^6}$$

For $t > t_d = 20 \ \mu s$

$$i_L(t) = -2.87 \times 10^{-3}[(e^{-0.100 \times 10^6 t} - e^{-0.837 \times 10^6 t})$$
$$-(e^{-0.100 \times 10^6 (t - 20 \times 10^{-6})} - e^{-0.837 \times 10^6 (t - 20 \times 10^{-6})}]$$
$$= -2.87 \times 10^{-3}[g(x) - (e^{-0.100 \times 10^6 (t - 20 \times 10^{-6})}$$
$$-e^{-0.837 \times 10^6 (t - 20 \times 10^{-6})})] \tag{5–99}$$

As we did in part (a) let us use Eq. (5–92) to define t', thus

$$t' = t - 20 \times 10^{-6} \qquad (5\text{-}100)$$

Substituting Eq. (5–100) into Eq. (5–99),

$$i_L(t) = -2.87 \times 10^{-3}[g(x) - (e^{-0.100 \times 10^6 t'} - e^{-0.873 \times 10^6 t'})] \qquad (5\text{-}101)$$

As in part (a) let us determine if $g(x)$ has any significance for $t > t_d$. From

$$x = \frac{t}{2.70 \times 10^{-6}}$$

we see that

$$x_d = \frac{t_d}{2.70 \times 10^{-6}} = \frac{20 \times 10^{-6}}{2.70 \times 10^{-6}} = 7.40$$

From Fig. 5–34(a) we find $g(7.40) \cong 0.20$, which means we cannot neglect $g(x)$ as we did in part (a).

To simplify Eq. (5–101) let us define

$$g(x') \equiv e^{-0.100 \times 10^6 t'} - e^{-0.837 \times 10^6 t'} \qquad (5\text{-}102)$$

where we have shown through Eq. (5–98) the justification for such a definition. It should again be noted, as in part (a), that x' is related to t' by the same equations that x is related to t, that is Eq. (5–97), or $x' = t'/2.70 \times 10^{-6}$. Then Eq. (5–101) may be written as

$$i_L(t) = -2.87 \times 10^{-3}[g(x) - g(x')] \qquad (5\text{-}103)$$

where

$$x = \frac{t}{2.70 \times 10^{-6}} = \frac{t' + t_d}{2.70 \times 10^{-6}} = x' + x_d = x' + 7.4$$

since

$$x' = \frac{t'}{2.70 \times 10^{-6}} \quad \text{and} \quad x_d = \frac{t_d}{2.70 \times 10^{-6}} = \frac{20}{2.70} = 7.4$$

We are now in a position to determine points with which to plot i_L for the various ranges of t. Consider the range $0 < t < 20\ \mu s$ first: we are plotting $i_L(t) = -2.87 \times 10^{-3}(e^{-0.100 \times 10^6 t} - e^{-0.837 \times 10^6 t})$, or $i_L(t) = -2.87 \times 10^{-3}g(x)$. Since our upper limit of t for this range is $20\ \mu s$ our upper limit of x in Fig. 5–34(a) is $x = 7.4$. Hence our table for this range will be for $0 \le x \le 7.4$. Since this is a repeat of the points in Table 5–8, except $x \le 7.4$, we shall gather our points from that table. These points are shown in Table 5–10.

TABLE 5–10   For $0 < t < t_d = 20\ \mu s$

x	$g(x)$	$t = 2.70x \times 10^{-6}$ t in μs	$i_L(t) = -2.87 \times 10^{-3}g(x)$ i_L in mA
0	0.00	0.00	0.00
1	0.68	2.70	−2.00
3	0.45	8.10	−1.29
5	0.30	13.50	−0.89
7.4	0.20	20.00	−0.57

And now to determine points for Eq. (5–103). We will first determine our points of interest for x', which will be the same as for x' in Table 5–9. These points will allow us to determine $g(x')$ from Fig. 5–34(a), or from Table 5–9, and we can calculate t' from $t' = 2.70x' \times 10^{-6}$ and x from $x = x' + x_d$. Once we know what value x corresponds to our chosen value of x' we can determine $g(x)$ from Fig. 5–34(a). We can then determine $i_L(t)$ from

$$i_L(t) = -2.87 \times 10^{-3}[g(x) - g(x')]$$

The value of t can be determined from $t = t' + t_d$. This will now be demonstrated in some calculations.

Sample Calculations

For $x' = 0$: $x = x' + x_d = 0 + 7.4 = 7.4$, and from Fig. 5–34(a) $g(x' = 0) = 0$, $t' = 2.70x' \times 10^{-6} = 0$, $t = t' + t_d = 0 + 20 \times 10^{-6} = 20\ \mu s$, $g(x = 7.4) = 0.20$ determined from Fig. 5–34(a), $i_L(t = 20\mu s) = -2.87 \times 10^{-3}[g(x) - g(x')] = -2.87 \times 10^{-3}(0.20)$ therefore,

$$i_L(t = 20\mu s) = -0.57\ \text{mA}$$

For $x' = 1$: $x = x' + x_d = 1 + 7.4 = 8.4$, $g(x' = 1) = 0.68$, $t' = 2.70x' \times 10^{-6} = 2.70\ \mu s$, $t = t' + t_d = (2.70 + 20) \times 10^{-6} = 22.70\ \mu s$, $g(x = 8.4) = 0.18$ and

$$i_L(t = 22.70\mu s) = -2.87 \times 10^{-3}[0.18 - 0.68] = 1.43\ \text{mA}$$

For $x' = 3$: $x = 3 + 7.40 = 10.40$, $g(x' = 3) = 0.45$, $t' = 8.10\ \mu s$, $t = (8.10 + 20)\ \mu s = 28.10\ \mu s$, $g(x = 10.40) = 0.10$

and

$$i_L(t = 28.10 \ \mu s) = -2.87 \times 10^{-3}(0.10 - 0.45) = 1.00 \ \text{mA}$$

These points and others of interest appear in Table 5–11.

TABLE 5–11

x'	$x = x' + 7.4$	$g(x')$	$g(x)$	$t = 2.70x'$ $\times 10^{-6}$ t' in μs	$t = t' + t_d$ t in μs	$i_L(t) = -2.87$ $\times 10^{-3}g(x)$ $- g(x)$ i_L in mA
0	7.4	0.00	0.20	0.00	20.00	−0.57
1	8.4	0.68	0.18	2.70	22.70	1.43
3	10.4	0.45	0.10	8.10	28.10	1.00
5	12.4	0.30	0.05	13.50	33.50	0.72
10	17.4	0.15	0.01	27.00	47.00	0.40
20	27.4	0.00⁺	0.00	54.00	74.00	0.00⁺

Plotting the points of Tables 5–10 and 5–11 we get the graph of Fig. 5–41(b), where e_{in} has been plotted at the top for a reference.

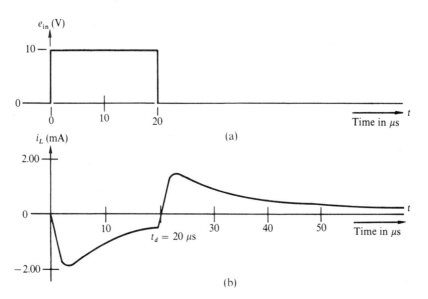

FIGURE 5–41

Let us verify the graph of Fig. 5–41(b) by substituting some value of t in Eq. (5–83). Choosing $t = 25$ μs we have

$i_L(t = 25\mu s)$

$= -2.87 \times 10^{-3}[(e^{-2.50} - e^{-20.9}) - (e^{-0.50} - e^{-4.18})]$

$= -2.87 \times 10^{-3}[(0.082 - 0^+) - (0.607 - 0.016)]$

$= -2.87 \times 10^{-3}(-0.509) = 1.45$ mA

At $t = 25$ μs the graph shows $i_L(25 \mu s)$ has a value of approximately 1.35 mA. This gives a percentage difference of $0.10 \times 100/1.45 = 6.9\%$. Considering we had to estimate ζ this is very accurate. From a practical standpoint we can say the two values agrees.

Before leaving Ex. 5–13 one should compare Fig. 5–40(b) with that of Fig. 5–41(b). Realize the difference between the two exists because of the relative magnitude of the circuit's time constant compared to the pulse duration t_d. For Fig. 5–40(b) the time constant was fast enough to allow the current to drop to zero before a change in the driving force was seen by the circuit. However, for Fig. 5–41(b) the time constant was too slow. During $0 < t < t_d$ the current was not allowed enough time to decrease to zero. Therefore, when the driving force e_{in} changed values at $t = t_d$ a current of approximately -0.57 mA was flowing in L_2. This current is very much like an initial condition for $t > t_d$. Also understand that if we applied a second pulse to the circuit conditions of Fig. 5–41(b) at $t = 50\mu s$ then we would have initial conditions of $i_L(50 \mu s) \cong 0.50$ mA.

For another graphical example let's return to the circuit of Fig. 5–30 of Ex. 5–11 using the component values of part (b) from that example. This example will also be for a slow time constant as was part (b) of Ex. 5–11.

Example 5–14   Given the circuit of Fig. 5–30 graph $v_o(t)$ for the driving force $e_{in}(t)$ as shown in Fig. 5–42. The component values are: $R = 1$ kΩ, $C = 6\rho$F, and $L = 1$ μH.

Solution   From Eq. (5–28) of Ex. 5–11 we know

$$V_o(s) = \frac{E_{in}(s)}{R\left(\dfrac{1}{R} + Cs + \dfrac{1}{Ls}\right)} = \frac{sE_{in}(s)}{RC\left(s^2 + \dfrac{1}{RC}s + \dfrac{1}{LC}\right)}$$

$$(5\text{–}104)$$

since

$$v_o(0^+) = 0$$

Now, $e_{in}(t) = 5u(t) - 5u(t - t_d)$V. It is easier to write t_d rather than 14.5×10^{-9} so $E_{in}(s) = (5/s)(1 - e^{-t_d s})$.

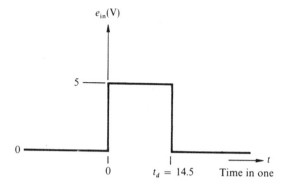

FIGURE 5-42

Substituting this value into Eq. (5-104) we have

$$V_o(s) = \frac{5(1 - e^{-t_d s})}{RC\left(s^2 + \frac{1}{RC}s + \frac{1}{LC}\right)} \qquad (5\text{-}105)$$

Next let us determine the value of ζ so that we will know which equation of Table 4-2 to use. From before

$$\zeta = \frac{1}{2R}\sqrt{\frac{L}{C}} = \frac{1}{2 \times 10^3}\sqrt{\frac{10^{-6}}{6 \times 10^{-12}}} = 0.20$$

which states Eq. (9) of Table 4-2 applies. Then

$$v_o(t) = \frac{5}{RC\omega_n\sqrt{1 - \zeta^2}}[e^{-\zeta\omega_n t}\sin\omega_n\sqrt{1 - \zeta^2}\,tu(t)$$
$$- e^{-\zeta\omega_n(t - t_d)}\sin\omega_n\sqrt{1 - \zeta^2}(t - t_d)u(t - t_d)]$$
$$(5\text{-}106)$$

Also from Ex. 5-11 we found

$$\omega_n = \frac{1}{\sqrt{LC}} = 0.406 \times 10^9$$

and

$$\omega_d = \omega_n\sqrt{1 - \zeta^2} = 0.406(0.98) \times 10^9 = 0.400 \times 10^9$$

(Notice ω_d approaches ω_n as ζ approaches zero.) Putting these values into Eq. (5-106) we have

$$v_o(t) = \frac{5}{6 \times 10^{-9}(0.40 \times 10^9)}[e^{-0.20(0.40 \times 10^9)t}\sin 0.40$$
$$\times 10^9 tu(t) - e^{-0.20(0.406 \times 10^9)(t - t_d)}\sin 0.40$$
$$\times 10^9(t - t_d)u(t - t_d)]$$

or

$$v_o(t) = 2.08[e^{-82.5 \times 10^6 t} \sin 0.40 \times 10^9 t u(t)$$
$$- e^{-82.5 \times 10^6 (t-t_d)} \sin 0.40 \times 10^9 (t - t_d) u(t - t_d)]$$
(5–107)

We are leaving the shifted quantity $t - t_d$ in algebraic form rather than $t - 14.5 \times 10^{-9}$ as a matter of convenience.

To plot Eq. (5–107) we shall proceed as we have in the past, that is, we shall determine v_o for various ranges of t. From Eq. (5–107) we see three ranges are to be considered: $0 < t$, $0 < t < t_d$, and $t > t_d$. Then

For $0 < t$
$$v_o(t) = 0$$

For $0 < t < t_d$
$$v_o(t) = 2.08 e^{-82.5 \times 10^6 t} \sin 0.40 \times 10^9 t$$

By defining $\varphi \equiv 0.40 \times 10^9 t$ we may write
$$v_o(t) = 2.08 \, h(\varphi) \tag{5–108}$$

This requires that $\zeta\varphi/\sqrt{1 - \zeta^2} = 82.5 \times 10^6 t$. To verify this we calculate $\zeta/\sqrt{1 - \zeta^2}$ for $\zeta = 0.20$ and then determine $\zeta\varphi/\sqrt{1 - \zeta^2}$, which must equal $82.5 \times 10^6 t$, where $\varphi = 0.40 \times 10^9 t$. Carrying this out we have

$$\frac{\zeta\varphi}{\sqrt{1 - \zeta^2}} = \frac{0.20\varphi}{\sqrt{0.96}} = \frac{0.20(0.40 \times 10^9 t)}{0.98} = 82 \times 10^6 t$$

which for slide-rule accuracy agrees with $82.5 \times 10^6 t$.

For $t > t_d$
$$v_o(t) = 2.08[e^{-82.5 \times 10^6 t} \sin 0.40 \times 10^9 t$$
$$- e^{-82.5 \times 10^6 t(t-t_d)} \sin 0.40 \times 10^9 (t - t_d)]$$

By defining $t' = t - t_d$ and using Eq. (5–108) we may write v_o for this range as
$$v_o(t) = 2.08[h(\varphi) - e^{-82.5 \times 10^6 t'} \sin 0.40 \times 10^9 t']$$

Now, let us call φ of Fig. 5–32(b) φ' and then define $\varphi' \equiv 0.40 \times 10^9 t'$. Under this definition v_o may be written as
$$v_o(t) = 2.08[h(\varphi) - h(\varphi')] \tag{5–109}$$

It is from Eq. (5–109) we shall plot the waveform described by Eq. (5–107).

Before determining the points of interest from Fig. 5–32(b) we need to convert our t-ranges to φ and φ' ranges. For the range of $0 < t < t_d = 14.5 \times 10^{-9}$ we have $0(0.40 \times 10^9) < 0.40 \times 10^9 t < 0.40 \times 10^9 t_d$, or $0 < \varphi < \varphi_d = 5.8$, since $\varphi = 0.40 \times 10^9 t$. For the range $t > t_d$ we have $t' + t_d > t_d$ since $t = t' + t_d$, as found from the definition $t' = t - t_d$. Then solving the inequality for t' we have $t' > 0$. So in terms of φ' the condition $t' > 0$ says $\varphi' > 0$, or, simply, we are interested in the curve $\zeta = 0.20$ so long as it has a magnitude. In summary, the t-range $0 < t < t_d = 14.5$ ηs converts to $0 < \varphi < \varphi_d = 5.8$ and the t-range $t > t_d$ converts to $\varphi' > 0$.

Choosing the points of interest from Fig. 5–32(b) over the range $0 < \varphi < 5.8$ for $\zeta = 0.20$ we have the points of Table 5–12.

TABLE 5–12   For $0 < \varphi < 5.8$ when $\zeta = 0.2$

φ	h(φ)	$t = \dfrac{\varphi}{0.40} \times 10^{-9}$ t in ns	$v_o = 2.08\text{h}(\varphi)$ v_o in volts
0.00	0.00	0.00	0.00
1.37	0.74	3.42	1.54
3.14	0.00	7.84	0.00
4.51	−0.39	11.30	−0.81
5.80	−0.18	14.50	−0.37

For the t-range of $t > t_d$ we will select points from Fig. 5–32(b) for $\varphi' > 0$. After finding the corresponding values for h(φ') we must also determine the corresponding values of φ, where $\varphi = \varphi' + \varphi_d$, which will allow us to determine h(φ). Once h(φ') and h(φ) are known, $v_o(t)$ can be determined from Eq. (5–109). That is, for $\varphi' = \pi/2$ we have h(φ') = 0.73 as determined from Fig. 5–32(b), also $\varphi = \varphi' + \varphi_d = \pi/2 + 5.80 = 7.37$ and h($\varphi = 7.37$) = 0.21, which is also determined from Fig. 5–32(b). So

$$t = t' + t_d = \frac{1}{0.40 \times 10^9}(\varphi' + \varphi_d) = \frac{7.37}{0.40} \times 10^{-9}$$

$$= 18.40 \, \eta \, \text{s}$$

and

$$v_o(t = 18.40 \, \eta \, \text{s}) = 2.08[\text{h}(\varphi) - \text{h}(\varphi')]$$
$$= 2.08(0.21 - 0.73) = -1.08 \text{ V}$$

For our next point let us choose $\varphi' = 3\pi/2$. Then $\text{h}(\varphi') = -0.40$ and $\varphi = (3\pi/2) + 5.80 = 10.50$ from which we find $\text{h}(\varphi = 10.50) = -0.09$. And for $\varphi = 10.50$ we have

$$t = \frac{10.50}{0.40} \times 10^{-9} = 26.20 \, \eta \text{s}$$

then

$$v_o(t = 26.20 \, \eta \text{s}) = 2.08[-0.09 - (-0.40)] = 2.08(0.31)$$
$$= 0.64 \text{ V}$$

These points and others are shown in Table 5–13.

TABLE 5–13   For $\varphi' > 0$ when $\zeta = 0.2$

φ'	$\text{h}(\varphi')$	$\varphi = \varphi' + \varphi_d$	$\text{h}(\varphi)$	$t = \dfrac{\varphi' + \varphi_d}{0.40}$ $\times 10^{-9}$ t in ns	$v_o(t) =$ $2.08[\text{h}(\varphi) - \text{h}(\varphi')]$ v_o in volts
0.00	0.00	$5.80 = \varphi_d$	−0.18	14.50	−0.37
1.37	0.74	7.17	0.16	17.90	−1.21
3.14	0.00	8.94	0.06	22.39	0.12
4.51	−0.39	10.31	−0.04	25.80	0.73
6.28	0.00	12.08	−0.01	30.20	−0.02
7.65	0.18	13.45	$\cong 0.00$	33.60	−0.37
9.52	0.00	15.20	0.00	38.00	0.00
10.68	−0.04	16.48	0.00	41.00	−0.08
12.52	0.00	18.40	0.00	46.20	0.00

Combining Tables 5–12 and 5–13 we get Table 5–14, which contains sufficient points necessary to plot v_o.

Plotting the points of Table 5–14 we have Fig. 5–43. Notice v_o is similar to i_L of Fig. 5–41(b) in that the circuit's time constant was too slow compared to the pulse duration t_d. These waveforms resulted due to

TABLE 5–14: For $t > 0$

t in ns	v_o in volts
0.00	0.00
3.42	1.54
7.82	0.00
11.30	−0.81
14.50	−0.37
17.90	−1.21
22.39	0.12
25.80	0.73
30.20	−0.02
33.60	−0.37
38.00	0.00
41.00	−0.08
46.20	0.00

the presence of initial conditions in the circuit when the driving force changed magnitude at $t = t_d = 14.50$ ns.

Let us verify Fig. 5–43(a) by evaluating v_o at some point for $t_d < t < 50 \, \eta$s. Choosing $t = 20 \, \eta$s we have from Eq. (5–107)

$$v_o(t = 20 \, \eta s) = 2.08[e^{-82.5(20) \times 10^{-3}} \sin 0.40(20)$$
$$- e^{-82.5(20-14.5) \times 10^{-3}} \sin 0.40(20 - 14.5)]$$
$$= 2.08[e^{-1.65} \sin 8 - e^{-0.413} \sin 2.2]$$

Converting radians to degrees, $(180°/\pi)8 = 458°$ and $(180°/\pi)2.2 = 126°$. Now

$$e^{-1.65} \sin 458° = 0.192 \sin 98° = 0.192(0.985) = 0.189$$

and

$$e^{-0.413} \sin 2.2 = 0.660 \sin 126° = 0.660(0.810) = 0.534$$

Then

$$v_o(20 \, \eta s) = 2.08(0.189 - 0.534) = -0.717 \text{ V}$$

From our graph of Fig. 5–43(b) it is estimated $v_o(20 \, \eta s) \cong -0.70$. For all practical purposes these values agree.

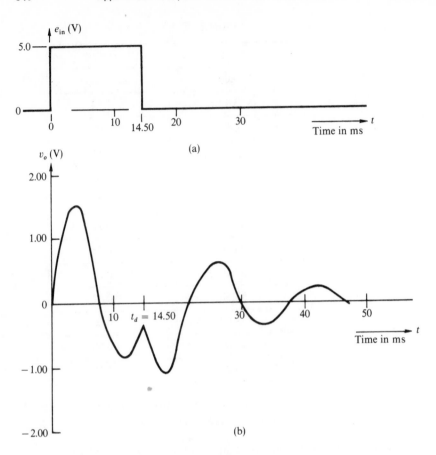

FIGURE 5–43

5–7 Circuit Analysis When the Driving Force Is Periodic

Thus far our analyses have been for dc voltages and nonperiodic driving forces. For the next example we will apply a periodic waveform to our circuit. The same general procedures will be followed in applying this waveform as were used in Ex. 5–13; that is, we will first adjust the pulse duration t_d so that the circuit's time constant is fast compared to t_d. For the second case t_d will be adjusted such that the circuit's time constant is slow [see Figs. 5–40(b) and 5–41(b)].

Example 5–15   Repeat Ex. 5–13 except have e_{in} be periodic. (a) For part (a) have $T = 300$ μs. (b) Have $T = 45$ μs. Before beginning compare the value of T for part (a) with Fig. 5–40(b) and the value of T for part (b) with Fig. 5–41(b). One should be able to see from these figures why approximately the values of 300 μs and 45 μs were chosen to demonstrate the effect of a circuit's time constant on a periodic waveform.

Solution   We will find a general solution and then substitute the specific values for parts (a) and (b). The general equation for $I_L(s)$, which is

$$I_L(s) = -\frac{M}{L_1L_2 - M^2} \frac{sE_{in}(s)}{s^2 + \frac{RL_2 + R_LL_1}{L_1L_2 - M^2}s + \frac{RR_L}{L_1L_2 - M^2}}$$

(5-72)

of Ex. 5–13, applies. Substituting the circuit component values into Eq. (5–72) we have

$$I_L(s) = -211\frac{sE_{in}(s)}{(s + 0.100 \times 10^6)(s + 0.837 \times 10^6)}$$

(5-110)

as can be verified from Eq. (5–81). We also know from Ex. 5–13 that $\zeta = 1.65$.

For the general conditions of both parts (a) and (b) described in this example e_{in} appears as shown in Fig. 5–44. Writing an equation for e_{in} we refer to Eq. (22) of Table 4–2, that is,

$$e_{in}(t) = \sum_{n=0}^{m} e_1(t - nT)u(t - nT)$$ (5-111)

Now e_1 is the first periodic period of e_{in}, which is,

$$e_{in_1}(t) = 10u(t) - 10u(t - t_d)$$ (5-112)

Then Eq. (5–111) can be written as

$$e_{in}(t) = 10\sum_{n=0}^{m}\{u(t - nT) - u[t - (t_d + nT)]\}$$

(5-113)

Equation (5–110) tells us to determine $E_{in}(s)$, so referring again to Eq. (22) of Table 4–2 we find

$$E_{in}(s) = \mathcal{L}\left[10\sum_{n=0}^{m}\{u(t) - nT) - u[t - (t_d + nT)]\}\right]$$

$$= E_{in_1}(s)\sum_{n=0}^{m}e^{-nTs}$$ (5-114)

in order to determine $E_{in_1}(s)$ we simply transform Eq. (5–112), $E_{in_1}(s) = (10/s)(1 - e^{-t_ds})$. So Eq. (5–114) is explicitly written as

$$E_{in}(s) = \frac{10}{s}(1 - e^{-t_ds})\sum_{n=0}^{m}e^{-nTs}$$ (5-115)

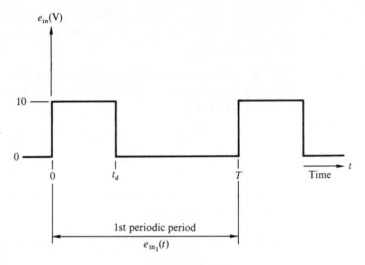

FIGURE 5–44

We are in a position now to determine the explicit equation for $I_L(s)$ by substituting Eq. (5–115) into Eq. (5–110). Hence,

$$I_L(s) = -2.11 \times 10^3 \frac{(1 - e^{-t_d s}) \sum_{n=0}^{m} e^{-nTs}}{(s + 0.100 \times 10^6)(s + 0.837 \times 10^6)}$$

$$= \frac{-2.11 \times 10^3}{(s + 0.100 \times 10^6)(s + 0.837 \times 10^6)}$$

$$\times \left[\sum_{n=0}^{m} (e^{-nTs} - e^{-(t_d + nT)s}) \right] \qquad \textbf{(5–116)}$$

Compare Eq. (5–116) with Eq. (5–81).

The manner in which we shall approach finding the inverse of Eq. (5–116) will be to first expand the series $\sum_{n=0}^{m} e^{-nTs}$ and $\sum_{n=0}^{m} e^{-(t_p + nT)s}$. This will give clarity to the problem. Thus,

$$I_L(s) = -2.11 \times 10^3 \left[\frac{1}{(s + \alpha)(s + \beta)} - \frac{e^{-t_d s}}{(s + \alpha)(s + \beta)} \right.$$

$$+ \frac{e^{-Ts}}{(s + \alpha)(s + \beta)} - \frac{e^{-(t_d + T)s}}{(s + \alpha)(s + \beta)}$$

$$+ \frac{e^{-2Ts}}{(s + \alpha)(s + \beta)} - \frac{e^{-(t_d + 2T)s}}{(s + \alpha)(s + \beta)}$$

$$\left. + \cdots + \frac{e^{-mTs}}{(s + \alpha)(s + \beta)} - \frac{e^{-(t_d + mT)s}}{(s + \alpha)(s + \beta)} \right]$$

$$\textbf{(5–117)}$$

where $\alpha = 0.100 \times 10^6$ and $\beta = 0.837 \times 10^6$.

We know that whenever e^{-as} appears in the numerator of a term this indicates the inverse Laplace of that term is shifted "a" units in the positive t-direction and also the inverse is multiplied by $u(t - a)$. As we see in Eq. (5–117) we have $e^{-t_d s}$, e^{-Ts}, $e^{-(t_d+T)s}$ etc, etc; hence we will have several shifted functions when the inverse of Eq. (5–117) is found.

Performing the inverse Laplace transform on Eq. (5–117) we have,

$$
\begin{aligned}
i_L(t) = -2.87 \times 10^{-3}\{&(e^{-\alpha t} - e^{-\beta t})u(t) \\
&- (e^{-\alpha(t-t_d)} - e^{-\beta(t-t_d)})u(t - t_d) \\
&+ (e^{-\alpha(t-T)} - e^{-\beta(t-T)})u(t - T) \\
&- (e^{-\alpha[t-(t_d+T)]} - e^{-\beta[t-(t_d+T)]})u[t - (t_d + T)] \\
&+ \cdots + (e^{-\alpha(t-mT)} - e^{-\beta(t-mT)})u(t - mT) \\
&- (e^{-\alpha[t-(t_d+mT)]} - e^{-\beta[t-(t_d+mT)]})u[t - (t_d + mT)]\}
\end{aligned}
$$

$$(5\text{–}118)$$

To graph Eq. (5–118) we will proceed as before; that is, we will consider t in ranges.

For $t < 0$: All unit step functions are zero, hence

$$i_L(t) = 0 \qquad (5\text{–}119a)$$

For $0 < t < t_d$: $u(t) = 1$, and all other unit steps $= 0$.

$$i_L(t) = -2.87 \times 10^{-3}(e^{-\alpha t} - e^{-\beta t}) \qquad (5\text{–}119b)$$

For $t_d < t < T$: $u(t) = u(t - t_d) = 1$. All other unit steps $= 0$.

$$i_L(t) = -2.87 \times 10^{-3}[(e^{-\alpha t} - e^{-\beta t}) - (e^{-\alpha(t-t_d)} - e^{-\beta(t-t_d)}]$$

$$(5\text{–}119c)$$

This completes the first period T. We will now begin on the second period.

For $T < t < T + t_d$: $u(t) = u(t - t_d) = u(t - T) = 1$. All other unit steps $= 0$.

$$
\begin{aligned}
i_L(t) = -2.87 \times 10^{-3}[&(e^{-\alpha t} - e^{-\beta t}) - (e^{-\alpha(t-t_d)} - e^{-\beta(t-t_d)}) \\
&+ (e^{-\alpha(t-T)} - e^{-\beta(t-T)})]
\end{aligned}
\qquad (5\text{–}119d)
$$

If one studies Eq. (5–119d) and Eq. (5–119c) he sees that the term $[(e^{-\alpha t} - e^{-\beta t}) - (e^{-\alpha(t-t_d)} - e^{-\beta(t-t_d)}]$ describes the influence of the current from the first period on the second period. We will see for part (a) this term approaches zero by the time $t = T$.

Even though many more ranges exist we will only consider up to the next range, which will allow us to graph two periods. The reason we are investigating only two periods is that, just maybe, two periods will be enough to determine what the waveforms from there on will be like; that is, the waveform may become periodic. If not we will return back to Eq. (5–118) to determine i_L for more ranges. For the next range,

For $\ T + t_d < t < 2T$: $\ u(t) = u(t - t_d) = u(t - T) = \overline{u[t - (t_d + T)] = 1,}$ all other unit steps $= 0$.

$$i_L(t) = -2.87 \times 10^{-3}[(e^{-\alpha t} - e^{-\beta t}) - (e^{-\alpha(t-t_d)} - e^{-\beta(t-t_d)})$$
$$+ (e^{-\alpha(t-T)} - e^{-\beta(t-T)}) - (e^{-\alpha[t-(t_d+T)]} - e^{-\beta[t-(t_d+T)]})]$$

$$\textbf{(5–119e)}$$

From our previous experience of using graphical techniques we know we will want to properly express the series of equations listed under equation number (5–119) by defining some new variables t', t'', and t''' for each range in order to handle the shifted functions. The defining of a new variable t' was the technique we used to graph Fig. 5–40(b), 5–41(b), and Fig. 5–42(c).

Equation (5–119b) can be expressed as

$$i_L(t) = -2.87 \times 10^{-3}g(x) \qquad \textbf{(5–120a)}$$

by defining

$$\alpha t \equiv \left(\frac{\zeta}{\sqrt{\zeta^2 - 1}} - 1 \right) x$$

and

$$\beta t \equiv \left(\frac{\zeta}{\sqrt{\zeta^2 - 1}} + 1 \right) x \ (\text{recall } \beta > \alpha)$$

Substituting in the values for α, β, and ζ we have

$$t = \frac{1}{\beta} \left(\frac{\zeta}{\sqrt{\zeta^2 - 1}} + 1 \right)$$

$$= \frac{1}{0.837 \times 10^6} \left(\frac{1.65}{\sqrt{(1.65)^2 - 1}} + 1 \right) x = 2.70 \times 10^{-6}x$$

which agrees with t as determined for Eq. (5–88). Also,

$$t = \frac{1}{\alpha} \left(\frac{\zeta}{\sqrt{\zeta^2 - 1}} - 1 \right) x = \frac{1}{0.100 \times 10^6}(0.26)x$$
$$\cong 2.70 \times 10^{-6}x$$

Notice that we could have used either

$$t = \frac{1}{\beta} \left(\frac{\zeta}{\sqrt{\zeta^2 - 1}} + 1 \right) x$$

or

$$t = \frac{1}{\alpha}\left(\frac{\zeta}{\sqrt{\zeta^2 - 1}} - 1\right)x$$

but calculating them both provides a double check on our math to this point.

By using our definition of αt and βt and by defining $t' \equiv t - t_d$ Eq. (5–119c) may be written as

$$i_L(t) = -2.87 \times 10^{-3}[g(x) - (e^{-\alpha t'} - e^{-\beta t})]$$

Now let us define

$$\alpha t' \equiv \left(\frac{\zeta}{\sqrt{\zeta^2 - 1}} - 1\right)x' \text{ and } \beta t' \equiv \left(\frac{\zeta}{\sqrt{\zeta^2 - 1}} + 1\right)x'$$

which gives us the relationship

$$i_L(t) = -2.87 \times 10^{-3}[g(x) - g(x')] \qquad \textbf{(5–120b)}$$

where $t = 2.70 \times 10^{-3}x'$.

For Eq. (5–119d) we will use our previous definitions and an additional one that $t'' = t - T$, which results in expressing Eq. (5–119d) as

$$i_L(t) = -2.87 \times 10^{-3}[g(x) - g(x') + g(x'')] \qquad \textbf{(5–120c)}$$

where $t'' = 2.70 \times 10^{-3}x''$. And for Eq. (5–119c) we will define another new variable t''' as $t''' \equiv t - (t_d + T)$. Hence i_L of Eq. (5–119e) may be expressed as

$$i_L(t) = -2.87 \times 10^{-3}[g(x) - g(x') + g(x'') - g(x''')]$$
$$\textbf{(5–120d)}$$

where $t''' = 2.70 \times 10^{-3}x'''$.

In order to use Eqs. (5–120) we must convert their t-range to ranges of x, x', x'', and x''' similar to what we did in Ex. 5–13. For the t-range of $0 < t < t_d$, which applies to Eq. (5–120a), we may convert to x simply by dividing by 2.70×10^{-3} since $x = t/(2.70 \times 10^{-3})$. Then dividing the inequality by 2.70×10^{-3} we have

$$\frac{0}{2.70 \times 10^{-3}} < \frac{t}{2.70 \times 10^{-3}} < \frac{t_d}{2.70 \times 10^{-3}}$$

which converts to $0 < x < x_d$ where $x_d = t_d/(2.70 \times 10^{-3})$. So Eq. (5–120a) is valid for the x-range of $0 < x < x_d$. For the t-range of $t_d < t < T$ it is a little more involved to convert. The involvement arises since for that t-range we have redefined the x-axis of Fig. 5–34(a) to x' (recall we redefined the x-axis in Ex. 5–13). Thus, we are interested in the x'-range and not the x-range. To get a clearer picture of why we want the x'-range for the t-range of $t_d < t < T$ let us examine Eq. (5–120b), which is the valid equation for this t-range. Equation (5–120b) has two terms $g(x)$ and $g(x')$. The term $g(x)$ is a "carryover" from the previous t-range $0 < t < t_d$; hence, it is, in a sense, an *historical term*. The $g(x')$ is the term which would describe i_L for this range if there were no "carryover" from the previous range, that is, if the historical term $g(x) = 0$ for $t > t_d$ or $x > x_d$. Then $g(x')$, which is the "present term" is the *dominant term* in that everything is to be referenced from it. This means that x must be referenced to x' and we will want to convert the t-range to the x'-range. To convert we begin with the t-range $t_d < t < T$. Now for this t-range we defined $t' = t - t_d$, so $t = t' + t_d$. By substituting $t = t' + t_d$ into our inequality $t_d < t < T$ we have $t_d < t' + t_d < T$. For $t_d < t' + t_d$ we see that $0 < t'$, and from $t' + t_d < T$ we find $t' < T - t_d$. Then putting this information together we have $0 < t' < T - t_d$. We also previously determined that $x' = t'/(2.70 \times 10^{-3})$, hence by dividing the inequality by 2.70×10^{-3} we have

$$\frac{0}{2.70 \times 10^{-3}} < \frac{t'}{2.70 \times 10^{-3}} < \frac{T - t_d}{2.70 \times 10^{-3}}$$

or $0 < x < x_T - x_d$ where $x_T = T/(2.70 \times 10^{-3})$. Then Eq. (5–120b) is valid for $0 < x' < x_T - x_d$.

We must also determine x in terms of x', that is $x(x')$, since $g(x)$ appears in Eq. (5–120b). From $t = t' + t_d$ we can determine $x = x' + x_d$ by dividing $t = t' + t_d$ by 2.70×10^{-3}, that is,

$$\frac{t}{2.70 \times 10^{-3}} = \frac{t' + t_d}{2.70 \times 10^{-3}} = x = x' + x_d$$

Then Eq. (5–120b) is properly defined by

$$i_L(t) = -2.87 \times 10^{-3}[g(x' + x_d) - g(x')] \quad \textbf{(5–121a)}$$

for

$$0 < x' < x_T - x_d$$

For Eq. (5–120c) we must reference our ranges to x'' since the *dominant term* (the latest term to appear) is a function of x''. The x''-range can be determined from the t-range $T < t < t_d + T$ by first substituting $t = t'' + T$, which was determined from the definition $t'' \equiv t - T$, into the inequality, thus $T < t'' + T < t_d + T$. Now for $T < t'' + T$ we find $0 < t''$ and for $t'' + T < T + t_d$ we have $t'' < t_d$. So our range of interest is $0 < t'' < t_d$ for the t''-range and $0 < x'' < x_d$ for x''-range. To determine how x behaves as a function of x'', that is determine $x(x'')$, we again make use of the definition $t'' \equiv t - T$. From this definition $t = t'' + T$, which can be converted by dividing by 2.70×10^{-3}, hence

$$\frac{t}{2.70 \times 10^{-3}} = \frac{t'' + T}{2.70 \times 10^{-3}} \quad \text{or} \quad x = x'' + x_T$$

To determine $x'(x'')$ we begin with the definitions $t'' = t - T$ and $t' = t - t_d$. Solving for $t(t'')$ we have $t = t'' + T$, which when substituted into $t' = t - t_d$ yields $t' = t'' + T - t_d$. Therefore $x' = x'' + x_T - x_d$. Equation (5–120c) may be expressed as

$$i_L(t) = -2.87 \times 10^{-3}[g(x'' + x_T) - g(x'' + x_T - x_d) + g(x'')] \qquad \textbf{(5–121b)}$$

for

$$0 < x'' < x_d$$

For our last equation our dominant term is $g(x''')$ so we must reference everything to x'''. Using the definition $t''' \equiv t - (t_d + T)$ and the t-range $T + t_d < t < 2T$ we have $T + t_d < t''' + (t_d + T) < 2T$ or $0 < t''' < T - t_d$, which is $0 < x''' < x_T - x_d$ when converted. To find $x(x''')$ we solve $t''' = t - (t_d + T)$ for t and then convert by dividing by 2.70×10^{-3}, hence $x = x''' + (x_d + T)$. For $x'(x''')$ we begin with $t' = t - t_d$, so

$$t' = t''' + (t_d + T) - t_d = t''' + T$$

Converting we have $x' = x''' + x_T$. Lastly for $x''(x''')$,

$$t'' = t - T = t''' + (t_d + T) - T = t''' + t_d$$

so

$$x'' = x''' + x_d$$

Thus Eq. (5–120d) can be expressed as

$$i_L(t) = -2.87 \times 10^{-3}[g(x''' + x_T + x_d) - g(x''' + x_T) + g(x''' + x_d) - g(x''')] \qquad \textbf{(5–121c)}$$

for $0 < x''' < x_T - x_d$

Here are the equations we will use to plot i_L.

$$i_L(t) = -2.87 \times 10^{-3} g(x) \text{ for } 0 < x < x_d, \text{ or } 0 < t < t_d$$
$$\text{(5-120a)}$$

$$i_L(t) = -2.87 \times 10^{-3}[g(x' + x_d) - g(x')]$$
$$\text{for } 0 < x' < x_T - x_d \text{ or } t_d < t < T \qquad \text{(5-121a)}$$

$$i_L(t) = -2.87 \times 10^{-3}[g(x'' + x_T)$$
$$- g(x'' + x_T - x_d) + g(x'')] \text{ for } 0 < x'' < x_d,$$
$$\text{or } T < t < T + t_d \qquad \text{(5-121b)}$$

$$i_L(t) = -2.87 \times 10^{-3}[g(x''' + x_T + x_d) - g(x''' + x_T)$$
$$+ g(x''' + x_d) - g(x''')] \text{ for } 0 < x''' < x_T - x_d$$
$$\text{or } T + t_d < t < 2T \qquad \text{(5-121c)}$$

From the general equations listed here we can plot i_L for the first two periods. To determine plots for the various gs we proceed as before in other examples. However, to make an actual plot we must become specific and assign numerical values to t_d and T.

(a) To this point we have made a general analysis; however, now we must become specific. Then for $t_d = 100$ μs and $T = 300$ μs we have

$$x_d = \frac{100 \times 10^{-6}}{2.70 \times 10^{-6}} = 37 \text{ and } x_T = \frac{300 \times 10^{-6}}{2.70 \times 10^{-6}} = 111$$

The points from Fig. 5–34(a) for the various ranges of t are given in Table 5–15.

The point $g(x = 18) = 0.00^+$ is to be interpreted as the point where g first approximates zero.

We may use the points chosen for x in Table 5–15 for the points of x' in Table 5–16 by recalling the x-axis of Fig. 5–34(a) is much like a dummy variable; hence, the

TABLE 5–15   For $0 < t < t_d = 100\mu$s or $0 < x < 37$

x	$g(x)$	$t = 2.70 \times 10^{-6}x$ t in μs	$i_L(t) = -2.87 \times 10^{-3}g(x)$ i_L in mA
0	0	0.00	0.00
1	0.68	2.10	−1.95
3	0.45	8.10	−1.29
5	0.30	13.50	−0.86
10	0.15	27.00	−0.43
18	0.00⁺	48.00	0.00⁺

TABLE 5–16   For $100\mu s = t_d < t < T = 300\mu s$ or $0 < x' < x_T - x_d = 74$

x'	$x = x' + x_d$	$g(x')$	$g(x_d + x') = g(x)$	$t = 2.70 \times 10^{-6}(x' + x_d)$ t in μs	$i_L(t) = -2.87 \times 10^{-3}[g(x_d + x') -g(x')]$ i_L in mA
0	37	0.00	0.00	100.00	0.00
1	38	0.68	0.00	102.70	1.95
3	40	0.45	0.00	108.10	1.29
5	42	0.30	0.00	113.50	0.86
10	47	0.15	0.00	127.00	0.43
18	55	0.00+	0.00	148.68	0.00

x' points of Table 5–16 are the same numerical values as x of Table 5–15. The other points resulting from x' are also shown in Table 5–16.

We have just completed the first period and from $i_L(148.68) = 0.00$ of Table 5–16 we can see that no initial conditions occur for the second period; hence, the function is periodic and is graphically the same as the first period repeated at T intervals. Referring to Eq. (22) of Table 4–2 we see that for i_L periodic,

$$i_L(t) = \sum_{n=0}^{m} i_{L_1}(t - nT)u(t - nT) \qquad (5\text{–}122)$$

where i_{L_1}, is the expression for i_L during the first period of the periodic waveform. From Eq. (5–118) for $0 < t < T$ we have

$$i_{L_1}(t) = -2.87 \times 10^{-3}[e^{-\alpha t} - e^{-\beta t})u(t)$$
$$- (e^{-\alpha(t-t_d)} - e^{-\beta(t-t_d)})u(t - t_d)]$$
$$= -2.87 \times 10^{-3}[(e^{-0.100\times10^6 t} - e^{-0.837\times10^6 t})u(t)$$
$$- (e^{-0.100\times10^6(t-t_d)} - e^{-0.837\times10^6(t-t_d)})u(t - t_d)$$
$$\qquad (5\text{–}123)$$

Substituting Eq. (5–123) into (5–122) we have

$$i_L(t) = -2.87 \times 10^{-3} \sum_{n=0}^{m} (e^{-0.100\times10^6(t-nT)}$$
$$- e^{-0.837\times10^6(t-nT)})u(t - nT) - [e^{-0.100\times10^6[t-(t_d+nT)]}$$
$$- e^{-0.837\times10^6[t-(t_d+nT)]}]u[t - (t_d + nT)]\} \qquad (5\text{–}124)$$

where $t_d = 100$ μs and $T = 300$ μs.

To graph Eq. (5–124) we merely have to plot the points from Tables 5–15 and 5–16 for the first period and then reproduce the first period since i_L is periodic starting with the first period [this will not be the case in part(b)]. This results in the graph of Fig. 5–45(b).

One should compare Fig. 5–45(b) with Fig. 5–40(b). Comparing these figures we see that they are basically the same. The difference is that one is periodic and the other is not.

(b) For this part of our example we were given $t_d = 20$ μs and $T = 45$ μs. Thus

$$x_d = \frac{20 \times 10^{-6}}{2.7 \times 10^{-6}} = 7.4 \text{ and } x_T = \frac{45 \times 10^{-6}}{2.70 \times 10^{-6}} = 16.70$$

The points from Fig. 5–34(a) for the various ranges of t are given in Tables 5–17 and 5–18, where the equations we derived in part (a) are valid for (b) by merely requiring $t_d = 20$ μs and $T = 45$ μs.

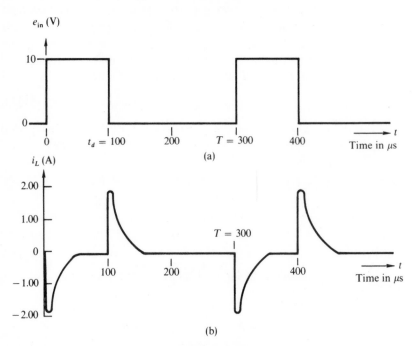

FIGURE 5–45

Notice from Table 5–17 that $i_L(t = 20 \ \mu s) = -0.52$ mA, therefore we have initial current for the next t-range.

TABLE 5–17   For $0 < t < 20 \mu s$ or $0 < x < 7.4$
to plot Eq. (5–120a)

x	$g(x)$	$t = 2.70 \times 10^{-6}x$ t in μs	$i_L(t) = -2.87 \times 10^{-3}g(x)$ i_L in mA
0	0.00	0.00	0.00
1	0.68	2.70	-1.95
3	0.45	8.10	-1.29
5	0.30	13.50	-0.86
7.4	0.18	20.00	-0.52

From Table 5–18 we see that an initial current of 0.40 mA is carried into the second period; that is, $i_L(45 \ m\mu) = 0.40$ mA. Also notice in Table 5–18 that the historical term $g(x_d + x')$, which is $g(x)$, is not contributing much at $t = 45 \ \mu s$. This means we may be able to drop it for $t > 45 \ \mu s$.

TABLE 5–18   For $20 \mu s < t < 45 \mu s$ or $0 < x' < 9.30$ to plot
Eq. (5–121a)

x'	$x = x'$ $+ x_d$	$g(x')$	$g(x' \times x_d)$ $= g(x)$	$t = 2.70$ $\times 10^{-6}(x' + x_d)$ t in μs	$i_L(t) = -2.87$ $\times 10^{-3}[g(x_d + x')$ $- g(x')]$ i_L in mA
0	7.4	0.00	0.18	20.00	-0.52
1	8.4	0.68	0.16	22.70	1.49
3	10.4	0.45	0.09	28.10	1.03
5	12.4	0.30	0.05	33.50	0.72
9.3	16.7	0.15	0.01	45.00	0.40

The next range to consider is $T < t < T + t_d$, which means Eq. (5–121b) is being plotted. Notice that the x''-range of this equation is the same as Eq. (5–120a) except that we are scaling to x'' rather than x. Then the points for x of Table 5–17 will apply for the points of x'' in Table 5–19.

Notice for the first period at the time $t = t_d = 20\ \mu s$ that $i_L(20\ \mu s) = -0.52$ mA, as shown in Table 5–18, whereas for that same relative time a period later i_L is $i_L(65\ \mu s) = -0.48$ mA, as seen from Table 5–19. Hence, the current i_L is not repeating the first period, so we cannot say that i_L is periodic as yet. Also notice from Table 5–18 we may drop $g(x)$ from any calculations henceforth since $g(x) \cong 0$ for $t > 45\ \mu s$. We will now continue to the next range for which the points of Table 5–20 were determined. Notice the points of x' in Table 5–18 apply to x''' of Table 5–20.

TABLE 5–19   For $45\mu s < t < 65\mu s$ or
$0 < x'' < 7.4$ to plot Eq. (5–121b)

x''	$x = x_T + x''$	$x' = (x_T - x_d) + x''$	$g(x'')$	$g(x_T + x'') = g(x)$	$g(x_T - x_d + x'') = g(x')$
0	16.70	9.30	0.00	0.03	0.17
1	17.70	10.30	0.68	0.01	0.10
3	19.70	12.30	0.45	0.00	0.05
5	21.70	14.30	0.30	0.00	0.02
7.4	24.70	16.70	0.18	0.00	0.01

TABLE 5–19   cont'd

x''	$t = 2.70 \times 10^{-6}$ $(x_T + x'')$ t in μs	$i_L(t) = -2.87 \times 10^{-3}$ $[g(x) - g(x') + g(x'')]$ i_L in mA
0	45.00	0.40
1	47.70	−1.80
3	53.10	−1.15
5	58.50	−0.80
7.4	65.00	−0.48

TABLE 5–20   For $65\mu s < t < 90\mu s$ or
$0 < x''' < 9.3$ to plot Eq. (5–121c)

x'''	$x' = x_T + x'''$	$x' = x_d + x'''$	$g(x''')$	$g(x'') = g(x_d + x'')$	$g(x') = g(x_T + x'')$
0	16.70	7.4	0.00	0.18	0.02
1	17.70	8.4	0.68	0.16	0.01
3	19.70	10.4	0.45	0.09	0.00
5	21.70	12.4	0.30	0.05	0.00
9.3	23.70	16.7	0.15	0.01	0.00

TABLE 5–20 cont'd

x'''	$t = 2.70 \times 10^{-6}$ $(x_d + x_T + x''')$ t in μs	$i_L(t) \cong -2.87 \times 10^{-3}$ $[-g(x') + g(x'') - g(x''')]$ i_L in mA
0	65.00	−0.48
1	67.70	1.52
3	73.10	1.03
5	78.50	0.72
9.3	90.00	0.40

When comparing Table 5–18 and Table 5–20 we see that we are beginning to repeat i_L. That is, for the same relative times the value of i_L is the same. Specifically $i_L(28.10 \ \mu s) = i_L(73.10 \ \mu s) = 1.03$ mA, $i_L(33.50 \ \mu s) = i_L(78.50 \ \mu s) = 0.72$ mA, etc. The terms $i_L(22.70 \ \mu s)$ and $i_L(67.70 \ \mu s)$ differ slightly due to graphical interpretation. The repeatiblity of Tables 5–18 and 5–20 indicates that the periodic waveform will be as Table 5–20 prescribes for the $nT + t_d < t < (n + 1)T$, where $n > 0$, portion of the periodic waveform. However, we need to verify this and also get a repeat of i_L over the range $nT < t < nT + t_d$, where $n > 1$, before we can state the waveform is periodic.

We have exhausted our equations describing the first two periods and still have not produced repeatability, therefore, we must develop some equations for $t > 2T$. From Eq. (5–118) for $2T < t < 2T + t_d$ we have

$$i_L(t) = -2.87 \times 10^{-3}[g(x) - g(x') + g(x'') - g(x''')$$
$$+ (e^{-\alpha(t-2T)} - e^{-\beta(t-2T)})]$$

Defining $t'''' \equiv t - 2T$, we have

$$i_L(t) = -2.87 \times 10^{-3}[g(x) - g(x') + g(x'') - g(x''')$$
$$+ g(x'''')] \tag{5-125}$$

where

$$x'''' = \frac{t''''}{2.70 \times 10^{-6}}$$

We may shorten Eq. (5–125) by viewing Table 5–20 and recognizing that $g(x) \cong g(x') \cong 0$ for $t > 2T = 90 \ \mu s$. Then

$$i_L(t) \cong -2.87 \times 10^{-3}[g(x'') - g(x''') + g(x)''''] \tag{5-126}$$

We must now determine $x''(x'''')$ and $x'''(x'''')$. By definition $t'''' = t - 2T$ and $t'' = t - T$, therefore $t'' = (t'''' + 2T) - T = t'''' + T$, so $x'' = x'''' + x_T$. Also by definition $t''' = t - (t_d + T)$, thus $t''' = (t'''' + 2T) - (t_d + T) = t'''' + (T - t_d)$, hence $x''' = x'''' + (x_T - x_d)$. Our range of interest for x'''' is found from $2T < t < 2T + t_d$. Substituting $t = t'''' + 2T$ in the inequality we find $0 < t'''' < t_d$ or $0 < x'''' < x_d$. Then Eq. (5–126) can be expressed as

$$i_L(t) = -2.87 \times 10^{-3}[g(x'''' + x_T) - g(x'''' + x_T - x_d)$$
$$+ g(x'''')] \tag{5-127}$$

for $0 < x'''' < x_d$. The values for Eq. (5–127) appear in Table 5–21.

From Tables 5–19 and 5–21 we see that we are now repeating for the same relative time period the pulse duration $nT < t < nT + t_d$ where $n = 0, 1, 2, 3, \ldots m$. Then everything from $t \geq T$ repeats. Thus Table 5–20 is valid for $2T + t_d < t < 3T$. Of course the gs and xs would be relabeled as one sees by comparing Tables 5–20 and 5–21. As a "for instance" x''' would be replaced by x'''''. It will be left for the reader to determine the rest of the proper labels for each column.

Since we began repeating from the second period on

TABLE 5–21   For $90\,\mu s < t < 110\,\mu s$ or
$0 < x'''' < 7.4$ to plot Eq. (5–127)

x''''	$x'' =$ $x'''' +$ x_T	$x''' =$ $x'''' +$ $(x_T - x_d)$	$g(x''')$	$g(x''')$	$g(x'')$	t in μs	$i_L(t)$ in mA
0	16.70	9.30	0.00	0.16	0.02	90.00	0.40
1	17.70	10.30	0.68	0.08	0.01	92.70	-1.75
3	19.70	12.30	0.45	0.05	0.00	98.10	-1.15
5	21.70	14.30	0.30	0.02	0.00	103.50	-0.80
7.4	24.70	16.70	0.18	0.01	0.00	115.00	-0.48

then i_{L_1} (recall for a periodic i_{L_1} is to be the first period of the *periodic* function) for this example is the second period. That is, it is the first period of periodicity. The first period appears *only* for $0 < t < T$ and at no other time. In other words it is a transient. From this point on let us call those terms which appear only once *transient terms*, and those which are repetitive we will call *steady state terms*. Then i_L is made up of its transient and steady state terms. Thus

$$i_L(t) = i_{L_{tr}}(t) + i_{L_{ss}}(t) \qquad (5\text{–}128)$$

where $i_{L_{tr}}(t)$ is the transient term and $i_{L_{ss}}(t)$ is the steady state term.

From Eq. (5–118)

$$i_{L_{tr}}(t) = -2.87 \times 10^{-3}[(e^{-\alpha t} - e^{-\beta t})u(t) \\ - (e^{-\alpha(t-t_d)} - e^{-\beta(t-t_d)})u(t - t_d)] \quad (5\text{–}129)$$

for $0 < t < T = 45\ \mu s$, $\alpha = 0.100 \times 10^6$, $\beta = 0.837 \times 10^6$, and $t_d = 20\mu s$ and also from Eq. (5–118)

$$i_{L_1}(t) = -2.87 \times 10^{-3}\{(e^{-\alpha(t-T)} - e^{-\beta(t-T)})u(t - T) \\ - (e^{-\alpha[t-(T+t_d)]} - e^{-\beta[t-(T+t_d)]})u[t - (T + t_d)]\}$$

$$(5\text{–}130)$$

Referring now to Eq. (22) of Table 4–2 and Eq. (5–130) we have for i_{ss}

$$i_{L_{ss}}(t) = \sum_{n=1}^{m} i_{L_1}(t - nT)u(t - nT) \qquad (5\text{–}131)$$

since $n = 0$ is the transient term $i_{L_{tr}}$. Then

$$i_{L_{ss}}(t) = -2.87 \times 10^{-3} \sum_{n=1}^{m} \{(e^{-\alpha(t-nT)} - e^{-\beta(t-nT)})u(t - nT)$$
$$- (e^{-\alpha[t-(nT+t_d)]} - e^{-\beta[t-(nT+t_d)]})u[t - (nT + t_d)]\}$$

(5–132)

Then Eq. (5–128) can now be written as

$$i_L(t) = -2.87 \times 10^{-3}\Big[(e^{-\alpha t} - e^{-\beta t})u(t)$$
$$- (e^{-\alpha(t-t_d)} - e^{-\beta(t-t_d)})u(t - t_d)$$
$$+ \sum_{n=1}^{m} \{(e^{-\alpha(t-nT)} - e^{-\beta(t-nT)})u(t - nT)$$
$$- (e^{-\alpha[t-(nT+ _d)]} - e^{-\beta[t-(nT+t_d)]})u[t - (nT + t_d)]\}\Big]$$

(5–133)

After seeing Eq. (5–133) in its entirety we can appreciate our graphical techniques to plot i_L. Plotting i_L from Tables 5–17, 5–18, 5–19, and 5–20 we have Fig. 5–46(b).

Be certain to see that there is a difference, even though it's a small difference, between the waveform of $i_{L_{tr}}$ and the waveform of the steady state term $i_{L_{ss}}$.

Let us pause for a moment and reflect on what we have been doing in this chapter. We began the chapter by analyzing circuits for unknown currents and voltages. The driving force was first a dc potential or dc current. For these early beginnings we made little attempt to make accurate plots of our solutions. We were satisfied with sketches, which indicated the approximate shape of our waveforms. These types of approximations are fine for initial work in design or for quick sketches when working on the "bench;" however, more accurate plots may be required in the final analysis. As we progressed our driving force waveform became more complex. To handle both our desire for accuracy and the complexity we devised graphical techniques to plot our solution. The complexity of our analysis progressed through single waveforms being applied to circuits with fast and slow time constants to periodic waveforms being applied to those type circuits.

It might be wise for us to write up a set of general procedures to be followed when using the graphical techniques we developed. These procedures will assume the equation to be plotted is in the t-plane.

Procedures for Graphical Techniques

1.   Consider the equation to be plotted in ranges of t as determined by unit step functions.

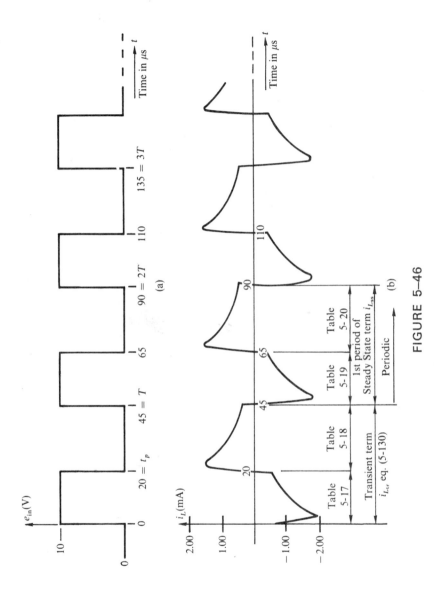

FIGURE 5-46

2.   For each range of t we must identify the equation with one, or possibly more, of our universal graphs.

3.   There is usually one form in which all the equations of the various ranges can be written, such as Eqs. (5–120c), (5–121a), (5–121b), and (5–121c) of Ex. 5–15. In order to write an equation using only one form it usually is necessary to define the time reference of that range of t to the dominant term. This means defining new variables such as t', t'', t''', etc., etc.

4.   Make a table of points for each range of t.

5.   Plot the points from the tables of procedure 3.

5–8   Development of Other Universal Curves and Their Uses

Since our graphical technique has been such a success let us now expand it to include Eqs. (4), (5), (11), and (12) of Table 4–2, which are frequently used equations. Once we have these graphs we should be able to handle just about any problems we will encounter.

Beginning with Eq. (4), let us state that

$$f(t) = Ke^{-\alpha t}u(t) = \mathcal{L}^{-1}\left[\frac{K}{s + \alpha}\right]$$

Normalizing and defining a new dependent variable q we have

$$q(t) \equiv \frac{f(t)}{K} = e^{-\alpha t} \qquad (5\text{--}134)$$

for $t > 0$. Then for our universal curve we will define $\gamma \equiv \alpha t$.

$$\gamma \equiv \alpha t \qquad (5\text{--}135)$$

and plot

$$q(\gamma) = \frac{f(t)}{K} = e^{-\gamma} \qquad (5\text{--}136)$$

where $\gamma > 0$. This graph is shown in Fig. 5–47(a).

For Eq. (5) we are considering an equation of the form

$$f(t) = \frac{K}{\alpha}(1 - e^{-\alpha t})u(t) = \mathcal{L}^{-1}\left[\frac{K}{s(s + \alpha)}\right]$$

Normalizing and defining w as the new dependent variable we have

$$w(t) \equiv \frac{\alpha f(t)}{K} = 1 - e^{-\alpha t} \quad \text{for} \quad t > 0$$

Again using $\gamma \equiv \alpha t$

$$w(\gamma) = \frac{\alpha f(t)}{K} = 1 - e^{-\gamma} \qquad (5\text{--}137)$$

for $\gamma > 0$, which is our universal curve and is plotted in Fig. 5–47(b).

In plotting the universal curves for Eqs. (11) and (12) we use some of our earlier works in developing our universal curves for Eqs. (9) and (10) of Table 4–2. Considering Eq. (11) we have an equation of the form

$$f(t) = \frac{K}{\omega_n^2}\left[1 - \frac{e^{-\zeta\omega_n t}}{\sqrt{1-\zeta^2}}\sin(\omega_n\sqrt{1-\zeta^2}\,t + \phi)\right]u(t)$$

$$= \mathcal{L}^{-1}\left[\frac{K}{s(s^2 + 2\zeta\omega_n s + \omega_n^2)}\right]$$

where $\phi = \cos^{-1}\zeta$.

Normalizing this equation and defining a new dependent variable d we have

$$d(t) \equiv \frac{\omega_n^2 f(t)}{K} = 1 - \frac{e^{-\zeta\omega_n t}}{\sqrt{1-\zeta^2}}\sin(\omega_n\sqrt{1-\zeta^2}\,t + \phi)$$

for $t > 0$. And using an already defined independent variable φ, where

$$\varphi \equiv \omega_n\sqrt{1-\zeta^2}\,t = \omega_d t \qquad (5\text{–}138)$$

$$d(\varphi) = \frac{\omega_n^2 f(t)}{K} = 1 - \left(\frac{e^{-\zeta/\sqrt{1-\zeta^2}}}{\sqrt{1-\zeta^2}}\right)\sin(\varphi + \phi) \qquad (5\text{–}139)$$

where $\phi = \cos^{-1}\zeta$. Equation (5–139) is our universal curve, which is plotted in Fig. 5–47(c).

Our last universal curve shall apply to Eq. (12) of Table 4–2. Hence, we are dealing with an equation such as

$$f(t) = \frac{K}{\alpha\beta}\left(1 - \frac{\beta}{\beta-\alpha}e^{-\alpha t} + \frac{\alpha}{\beta-\alpha}e^{-\beta t}\right)u(t) = \mathcal{L}^{-1}\left[\frac{K}{s(s+\alpha)(s+\beta)}\right]$$

$$(5\text{–}140)$$

where $\beta > \alpha$. We will stipulate $\beta > \alpha$ so that we do not become confused as to current directions or voltage polarity because of a negative sign if $\alpha > \beta$. We already discussed justification for this stipulation. We must now determine values for α and β in terms of ζ and ω_n—that is, the parameters with which we are working. We know that the denominator of Eq. (5–140) can be written as

$$s(s+\alpha)(s+\beta) = s(s^2 + 2\zeta\omega_n s + \omega_n^2)$$

Then factoring the quadratic we have $s_{1,2} = -\zeta\omega_n \pm \omega_n\sqrt{\zeta^2 - 1}$, which we have found before. Now, we have stipulated that $\beta > \alpha$ so we must choose β and α to meet that requirement. Since we may arbitrarily state that $s_1 = -\zeta\omega_n + \omega_n\sqrt{\zeta^2 - 1}$ and $s_2 = -\zeta\omega_n - \omega_n\sqrt{\zeta^2 - 1}$ then we have arbitrarily set $|s_1| < |s_2|$, or (in words) the absolute magnitude of s_1 is less than s_2. Also $(s_{1 \text{ or } 2} + \alpha) = 0$ and likewise $(s_{2 \text{ or } 1} + \beta) = 0$. Then $s_{1 \text{ or } 2} = -\alpha$ or $\alpha = -s_{1 \text{ or } 2}$ and $\beta = -s_{2 \text{ or } 1}$. Hence, we are required by the stipulation $\beta > \alpha$ to choose

$$\beta = -s_2 = \zeta\omega_n + \omega_n\sqrt{\zeta^2 - 1} \qquad \textbf{(5–141a)}$$

and

$$\alpha = -s_1 = \zeta\omega_n - \omega_n\sqrt{\zeta^2 - 1} \qquad \textbf{(5–141b)}$$

With our choice of α and β Eq. (5–140) now appears as

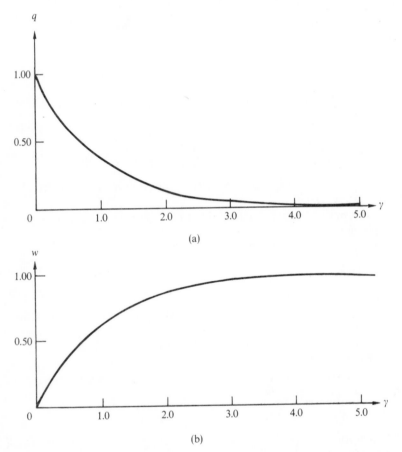

(a)

(b)

FIGURE 5–47 (a)   Plot of $q(\gamma) = e^{-\gamma}: \gamma \equiv \alpha t$;   (b)   Plot of $w(\gamma) = 1 - e^{-\gamma}: \gamma \equiv \alpha t$; (c) Plot of $d(\varphi) = 1.00 - \dfrac{1}{\sqrt{1 - \zeta^2}} e^{-(\zeta/\sqrt{1-\zeta^2})\varphi} \sin(\varphi + \phi)$, where $\phi = \cos^{-1}\zeta$;   (d)   Plot of $\theta(x) =$
$$1 - \frac{1}{2}\left[\left(\frac{\zeta}{\sqrt{\zeta^2 - 1}} + 1\right)e^{-[(\zeta/\sqrt{\zeta^2-1}-1)]x} + \left(\frac{\zeta}{\sqrt{\zeta^2 - 1}} - 1\right)e^{-[(\zeta/\sqrt{\zeta^2-1})+1]x}\right]$$

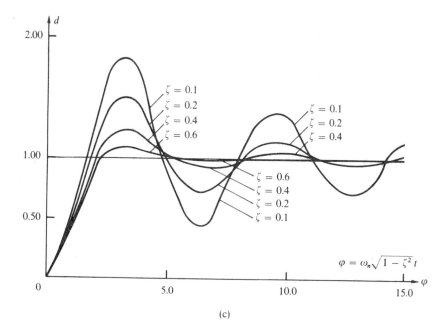

$$\varphi = \omega_n\sqrt{1 - \zeta^2}\, t$$

(c)

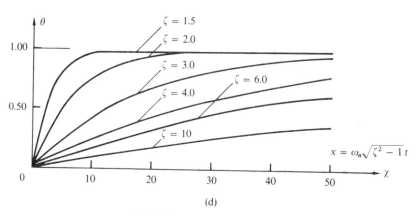

$$x = \omega_n\sqrt{\zeta^2 - 1}\, t$$

(d)

FIGURE 5–47   (cont'd)

$$f(t) = \frac{K}{\omega_n^2}\left[1 - \left(\frac{\zeta + \sqrt{\zeta^2 - 1}}{2\sqrt{\zeta^2 - 1}}\right) e^{-\omega_n(\zeta - \sqrt{\zeta^2 - 1})t}\right.$$

$$\left. + \left(\frac{\zeta - \sqrt{\zeta^2 - 1}}{2\sqrt{\zeta^2 - 1}}\right) e^{-\omega_n(\zeta + \sqrt{\zeta^2 - 1})t} \right]$$

$$= \frac{K}{\omega_n^2}\left\{ 1 - \frac{e^{-\omega_n\zeta t}}{2\sqrt{\zeta^2 - 1}}[(\zeta + \sqrt{\zeta^2 - 1})e^{\omega_n\sqrt{\zeta^2 - 1}t}\right.$$

$$\left. + (\zeta - \sqrt{\zeta^2 - 1})e^{-\omega_n\sqrt{\zeta^2 - 1}t}]\right\} \text{ for } t > 0$$

Normalizing and defining $x \equiv \omega_n \sqrt{\zeta^2 - 1} t$, as we did in plotting Fig. 5–34(a), also defining our new dependent variable as θ, we have

$$\theta(x) \equiv \frac{\omega_n^2 f(t)}{K} = 1 - \frac{e^{-(\zeta \sqrt{\zeta^2-1})x}}{2\sqrt{\zeta^2 - 1}} [\zeta + \sqrt{\zeta^2 - 1})e^x + (\zeta - \sqrt{\zeta^2 - 1})e^{-x}]$$

$$= 1 - \frac{1}{2}\left[\left(\frac{\zeta}{\sqrt{\zeta^2 - 1}} + 1\right)e^{-(\zeta/\sqrt{\zeta^2-1})x} + \left(\frac{\zeta}{\sqrt{\zeta^2 - 1}} - 1\right)e^{-(\zeta\sqrt{\zeta^2-1}+1)x}\right]$$

$$(5\text{–}142)$$

The plot of Eq. (5–142) is shown in Fig. 5–47(d).

We now have those universal graphs of Fig. 5–47 added to our library of graphs. These graphs will expand our capabilities for graphical approaches to plotting curves. For our next example let us consider some circuit which will utilize these graphs. The circuit we will consider is a linear two-stage transistor amplifier, which means we will use the ac equivalent model of a transistor as shown in Fig. 2–45(g) to develop an equivalent circuit. We will suppose that the amplifier is properly dc biased.

Example 5–16   Given the linear two-stage amplifier shown in Fig. 5–48:
(a) Determine the general equation for v_o.
(b) Determine the graph of v_o if $h_{fe} = 50$, $h_{ie} = 1 \text{ k}\Omega$, $h_{re} = 5 \times 10^{-4}$, $h_{oe} = 85 \times 10^{-6}$ ℧, $R_1 = 57 \text{ k}\Omega$, $R_2 = 1 \text{ k}\Omega$, $R_3 = 1.5 \text{ k}\Omega$, $R_L = 500 \Omega$, and $C_C = 10 \mu\text{F}$.
(c) If v_o is distorted for part (a) adjust C_C to correct that situation.

The reason we are interested in finding v_0 is that we wish to make certain we are not getting distortion from our coupling capacitance C_C. In other words, we are going to look at the speed of the RC time constant of this circuit as compared to the time of t_d and T of e_{in}.

Solution   (a) The first thing we will want to do is to put the circuit of Fig. 5–48(a) in its ac equivalent model. Thus we have Fig. 5–49(a), where the dc component of $v'_o(t)$ has been omitted. The dc component of $v'_o(t)$ is the result of the dc biasing of the circuit.

Since we are interested in the input voltage to the second stage let us replace that stage with its input resistance r_{in}, where

$$r_{in} = \frac{h_{ie} + \Delta h^e R_L}{1 + h_{oe}R_L} = \frac{h_{ie} + (h_{ie}h_{oe} - h_{re}h_{fe})R_L}{1 + h_{oe}R_L}$$

Also we see that e_{in} is across R_{eq} of the first stage, therefore R_{eq} need be considered only to determine if the

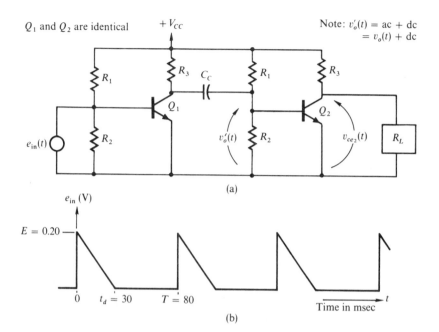

Q_1 and Q_2 are identical

Note: $v_o'(t)$ = ac + dc
= $v_o(t)$ + dc

(a)

(b)

FIGURE 5–48

voltage generator e_{in} can supply the current demands of $i_b(t) + e_{in}(t)/R_{eq}$. Then Fig. 5–49(a) may be simplified to that of Fig. 5–49(b), where the nodal voltage polarities of Fig. 5–49(b) were assumed.

Writing the necessary nodal equations to solve for v_o we have,

$$-h_{fe}i_{b_1}(t) - \frac{v_{ce_1}(t)}{R_{eq_2}} + C_C\frac{d}{dt}[v_o(t) - v_{ce_1}(t)] = 0$$

and

$$C_C\frac{d}{dt}[v_{ce_1}(t) - v_o(t)] - \frac{v_o(t)}{R_{eq_3}} = 0$$

where

$$R_{eq_3} = \frac{r_{in}R_{eq_1}}{r_{in} + R_{eq_1}}$$

Performing the Laplace transform,

$$-h_{fe}I_{b_1}(s) - \frac{V_{ce_1}(s)}{R_{eq_2}} + C_C[sV_o(s) - v_o(0^+) - sV_{ce_1}(s)$$
$$+ v_{ce_1}(0^+)] = 0 \qquad (5\text{–}143)$$

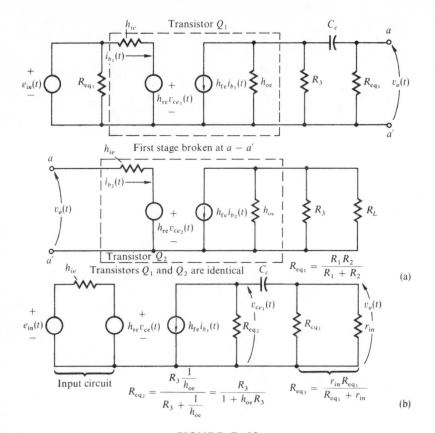

FIGURE 5–49

and

$$C_c[sV_o(s) - v_{ce_1}(0^+) - sV_o(s) + v_o(0^+)] - \frac{V_o(s)}{R_{eq_3}} = 0$$

From Fig. 5–49(a) or (b) and Fig. 5–48 we can determine $v_{ce_1}(0^+) = v_o(0^+) = 0$ since no potential is applied to the circuit until $t > 0$. Thus

$$-h_{fe}I_{b_1}(s) - \frac{V_{ce}(s)}{R_{eq_2}} + C_c[sV_o(s) - sV_{ce_1}(s)] = 0$$

and

$$C_c[sV_{ce_1}(s) - sV_o(s)] - \frac{V_o(s)}{R_{eq_3}} = 0$$

Putting these equations in determinate form

$$-h_{fe}I_{b_1}(s) = \left(\frac{1}{R_{eq_2}} + C_Cs\right)v_{ce_1}(s) - C_Csv_o(s) \quad \text{(5-144a)}$$

$$0 = -C_CsV_{ce_1}(s) + \left(\frac{1}{R_{eq_3}} + C_Cs\right)V_o(s) \quad \text{(5-144b)}$$

Then

$$\Delta = \begin{vmatrix} \left(\dfrac{1}{R_{eq_2}} + C_Cs\right) & -C_Cs \\ -C_Cs & \left(\dfrac{1}{R_{eq_3}} + C_Cs\right) \end{vmatrix}$$

$$= \left(\frac{1}{R_{eq_2}} + C_Cs\right)\left(\frac{1}{R_{eq_3}} + C_Cs\right) - (C_Cs)^2$$

$$= \frac{1}{R_{eq_2}R_{eq_3}} + \left(\frac{1}{R_{eq_2}} + \frac{1}{R_{eq_3}}\right)C_Cs$$

Since we know Δ always ends up as the denominator let's put it in a nicer form. Thus

$$\Delta = \frac{1}{R_{eq_2}R_{eq_3}} + \frac{(R_{eq_2} + R_{eq_3})C_Cs}{R_{eq_2}R_{eq_3}}$$

$$= \frac{(R_{eq_2} + R_{eq_3})C_C}{R_{eq_2}R_{eq_3}}\left[s + \frac{1}{(R_{eq_2} + R_{eq_3})C_C}\right]$$

Solving for $V_o(s)$ we find

$$V_o(s) = \frac{\begin{vmatrix} \dfrac{1}{R_{eq_2}} + C_Cs & -h_{fe}I_{b_1} \\ -C_Cs & 0 \end{vmatrix}}{\Delta} = -\frac{h_{fe}C_CsI_{b_1}(s)}{\Delta}$$

therefore

$$V_o(s) = -\frac{h_{fe}R_{eq}sI_{b_1}(s)}{s + \dfrac{1}{(R_{eq_2} + R_{eq_3})C_C}} \quad \text{(5-145)}$$

where

$$R_{eq} = \frac{R_{eq_2}R_{eq_3}}{R_{eq_2} + R_{eq_3}}$$

From Eq. (5-145) we see that we must determine $I_{b_1}(s)$. Investigating Fig. 5-49(b) we see that i_{b_1} may be determined from the input circuit of that figure. Usually h_{re} is such a small number that the quantity $h_{re}v_{ce_1}(t)$ can be approximated as zero, hence

$$i_{b_1}(t) \cong \frac{e_{in}(t)}{h_{ie}} \text{ if } h_{re} \cong 0 \qquad (5\text{--}146a)$$

If h_{re} cannot be approximated as zero we have

$$i_{b_1}(t) = \frac{e_{in}(t) - h_{re}v_{ce_1}(t)}{h_{ie}} \qquad (5\text{--}146b)$$

Thus from Eq. (5–146a)

$$I_{b_1}(s) \cong \frac{E_{in}(s)}{h_{ie}} \qquad (5\text{--}147a)$$

and from Eq. (5–146b)

$$I_{b_1}(s) = \frac{E_{in}(s) - h_{re}V_{ce_1}(s)}{h_{ie}} \qquad (5\text{--}147b)$$

If we are to use Eq. (5–147b) we must determine $V_{ce_1}(s)$. Then returning to our nodal equations of Eqs. (5–144) we find

$$V_{ce_1}(s) = \frac{\begin{vmatrix} -h_{fe}I_{b_1}(s) & -C_C s \\ 0 & \left(\dfrac{1}{R_{eq_3}} + C_C s\right) \end{vmatrix}}{\Delta} = \frac{-h_{fe}I_{b_1}(s)\left(\dfrac{1}{R_{eq_3}} + C_C s\right)}{\Delta}$$

$$(5\text{--}148)$$

Substituting Eq. (5–148) into Eq. (5–147b)

$$I_{b_1}(s) = \frac{E_{in}(s)}{h_{ie}} + \frac{h_{re}}{h_{ie}}\frac{h_{fe}}{\Delta}\left(\frac{1}{R_{eq_3}} + C_C s\right)I_{b_1}(s)$$

$$I_{b_1}(s) = \left[1 - \frac{h_{re}}{h_{ie}}\frac{h_{fe}}{\Delta}\left(\frac{1}{R_{eq_3}} + C_C s\right)\right] = \frac{E_{in}(s)}{h_{ie}}$$

or

$$I_{b_1}(s) = \frac{E_{in}(s)}{h_{ie} - \dfrac{h_{re}h_{fe}C_C}{\Delta}\left(s + \dfrac{1}{R_{eq_3}C_C}\right)} \qquad (5\text{--}149)$$

Fortunately for our case and the majority of cases $h_{re} \cong 0$ and Eq. (5–147a) may be used. Substituting Eq. (5–147b) into Eq. (5–145) results in

$$V_o(s) = -\frac{h_{fe}R_{eq}}{h_{ie}}\frac{sE_{in}(s)}{s + \dfrac{1}{(R_{eq_2} + R_{eq_3})C_C}} \qquad (5\text{--}150)$$

which is a general solution for $V_o(s)$ when $h_{re} \cong 0$.

To make Eq. (5–150) an explicit equation we must determine the explicit equation for $E_{in}(s)$. From Fig. 5–48(b),

$$e_{in_1}(t) = \left(-\frac{E}{t_d} t + 0.20\right)u(t) + \frac{E}{t_d}(t - t_d)u(t - t_d)$$

so

$$E_{in_1}(s) = -\frac{E}{t_d}\frac{1}{s^2} + \frac{0.20}{s} + \frac{Ee^{-t_d s}}{t_d s^2} \qquad (5\text{–}151)$$

And from Eq. (22) of Table 4–2 and Eq. (5–151) we can write for $E_{in}(s)$,

$$E_{in}(s) = \left[-\frac{E}{t_d s^2} + \frac{0.20}{s} + \frac{Ee^{-t_d s}}{t_d s^2}\right]\sum_{n=0}^{m} e^{-nTs}$$

$$= \left(-\frac{E}{t_d s^2} + \frac{0.20}{s}\right)\sum_{n=0}^{m} e^{-nTs} + \frac{E}{t_d s^2}\sum_{n=0}^{m} e^{-(t_d + nT)s}$$

$$(5\text{–}152)$$

You will find it tempting to group equations describing the functions, such as Eq. (5–152), according to like coefficients, that is, writing Eq. (5–152) as

$$E_{in}(s) = \left[\frac{E}{t_d s^2}(e^{-t_d s} - 1) + \frac{0.20}{s}\right]\sum_{n=0}^{m} e^{-nTs} \qquad (5\text{–}153)$$

Mathematically this is correct, but you'll find it confusing to plot v_o after the inverse of $V_o(s)$ has been found. Always group your driving function terms in the order of their time displacement, such as they appear in Eq. (5–152).

Substituting Eq. (5–152) into Eq. (5–150) we have

$$V_o(s) = -\frac{h_{fe}R_{eq}}{h_{ie}}\left[\frac{\left(-\dfrac{E}{t_d s} + 0.20\right)\displaystyle\sum_{n=0}^{m} e^{-nTs}}{s + \dfrac{1}{(R_{eq_2} + R_{eq_3})C_C}}\right.$$

$$\left. + \frac{\dfrac{E}{t_d s}\displaystyle\sum_{n=0}^{m} e^{-(t_d + nT)s}}{s + \dfrac{1}{(R_{eq_2} + R_{eq_3})C_C}}\right] \qquad (5\text{–}154)$$

To find v_o we must find the inverse Laplace of Eq. (5–154). To simplify matters let us expand the summation terms. So

$$V_o(s) = -\frac{h_{fe}R_{eq}}{h_{ie}}\Biggl\{\Biggl[-\frac{E}{t_d}\frac{1}{s\left(s+\frac{1}{\tau}\right)} + \frac{0.20}{s+\frac{1}{\tau}}\Biggr. $$

$$\Biggl. + \frac{Ee^{-t_d s}}{t_d s\left(s+\frac{1}{\tau}\right)}\Biggr]$$

$$\underbrace{\hspace{6cm}}_{n=0:\ 1\text{st period}}$$

$$+\Biggl[-\frac{E}{t_d}\frac{e^{-Ts}}{s\left(s+\frac{1}{\tau}\right)} + \frac{0.20e^{-Ts}}{s+\frac{1}{\tau}} + \frac{Ee^{-(t_d+T)s}}{t_d s\left(s+\frac{1}{\tau}\right)}\Biggr]$$

$$\underbrace{\hspace{7cm}}_{n=1:\ 2\text{nd period without historical term}}$$

$$+\Biggl[-\frac{Ee^{-2T}}{t_d s\left(s+\frac{1}{\tau}\right)} + \frac{0.20e^{-2Ts}}{s+\frac{1}{\tau}} + \frac{Ee^{-(t_d-2T)s}}{t_d s\left(s+\frac{1}{\tau}\right)}\Biggr]$$

$$\underbrace{\hspace{7cm}}_{n=2:\ 3\text{rd period without historical term}}$$

$$+\cdots+\Biggl[-\frac{Ee^{-mTs}}{t_d s\left(s+\frac{1}{\tau}\right)} + \frac{0.20e^{-mTs}}{s+\frac{1}{\tau}} + \frac{Ee^{-(t_d+mT)s}}{t_d s\left(s+\frac{1}{\tau}\right)}\Biggr]\Biggr\}$$

$$(5\text{-}155)$$

where $\tau = (R_{eq_2} + R_{eq_3})C_C$. Hence

$$v_o(t) = -\frac{h_{fe}R_{eq}}{h_{ie}}\Biggl\{\Biggl[-\frac{E\tau}{t_d}(1-e)^{-t/\tau}u(t) + 0.20e^{-t/\tau}u(t)\Biggr.$$

$$\Biggl. + \frac{E\tau}{t_d}(1-e^{-(t-t_d)/\tau})u(t-t_d)\Biggr]$$

$$+\Biggl[-\frac{E\tau}{t_d}(1-e^{-(t-T)/\tau})u(t-T)\Biggr.$$

$$+ 0.20e^{-(t-T)/\tau}u(t-T)$$

$$\Biggl. + \frac{E\tau}{t_d}(1-e^{-[t-(t_d+T)]/\tau})u[t-(t_d+T)]\Biggr]$$

$$+\Biggl[-\frac{E\tau}{t_d}(1-e^{-(t-2T)/\tau})u(t-2T)\Biggr.$$

$$+ 0.20e^{-(t-2T)/\tau}u(t-2T)$$

$$\Biggl. + \frac{E\tau}{t_d}(1-e^{-[t-(t_d+2T)]/\tau})u[t-(t_d+2T)]\Biggr]$$

$$+\cdots+\Biggl[-\frac{E\tau}{t_d}(1-e^{-(t-mT)/\tau})u(t-mT)\Biggr.$$

$$+ 0.20e^{-(t-mT)/\tau}u(t-mT)$$

$$\Biggl. + \frac{E\tau}{t_d}(1-e^{-[t-(t_d+mT)]/\tau})u[t-(t_d+mT)]\Biggr]\Biggr\}$$

$$= -\frac{h_{fe}R_{eq}}{h_{ie}}\left[-\frac{E\tau}{t_d}\sum_{n=0}^{m}(1 - e^{-(t-nT)/\tau})u(t - nT)\right.$$

$$+ 0.20\sum_{n=0}^{m} e^{-(t-nT)/\tau}u(t - nT)$$

$$\left.+ \frac{E\tau}{t_d}\sum_{n=0}^{m}(1 - e^{-[t-(t_d+nT)]/\tau})u[t - (t_d + nT)]\right.$$

$$(5\text{–}156)$$

This is the solution for part (a).

(b) Next let us determine v_o for various ranges of time as suggested by the procedures previously outlined. Hence:

For $0 < t < t_d$

$$v_o(t) = -\frac{h_{fe}R_{eq}}{h_{ie}}\left[-\frac{E\tau}{t_d}(1 - e^{-t/\tau}) + 0.20e^{-t/\tau}\right]$$

$$(5\text{–}157)$$

For $t_d < t < T$

$$v_o(t) = -\frac{h_{fe}R_{eq}}{h_{ie}}\left[-\frac{E\tau}{t_d}(1 - e^{-t/\tau}) + 0.20e^{-t/\tau}\right.$$

$$\left.+ \frac{E\tau}{t_d}(1 - e^{-(t-t_d)/\tau})\right]$$

$$(5\text{–}158)$$

For $T < t < t_d + T$

$$v_o(t) = -\frac{h_{fe}R_{eq}}{h_{ie}}\left\{\left[-\frac{E\tau}{t_d}(1 - e^{-t/\tau}) + 0.20e^{-t/\tau}\right.\right.$$

$$\left.+ \frac{E\tau}{t_d}(1 - e^{-(t-t_d)/\tau})\right]$$

$$\left.+ \left[\frac{E\tau}{t_d}(1 - e^{-(t-\tau)/\tau}) + 0.20e^{-(t-T)/\tau}\right]\right\}$$

$$(5\text{–}159)$$

For $t_d + T < t < 2T$

$$v_o(t) = -\frac{h_{fe}R_{eq}}{h_{ie}}\left\{\left[-\frac{E\tau}{t_d}(1 - e^{-t/\tau}) + 0.20e^{-t/\tau}\right.\right.$$

$$\left.+ \frac{E\tau}{t_d}(1 - e^{-(t-t_d)/\tau}) + \left[\frac{E\tau}{t_d}(1 - e^{-(t-T)/\tau})\right.\right.$$

$$\left.\left.+ 0.20e^{-(t-T)/\tau} + \frac{E\tau}{t_d}(1 - e^{-[t-(t_d+T)]/\tau})\right]\right\}$$

$$(5\text{–}160)$$

To carry out procedure 2 under Procedures for Graphical Techniques we must identify the individual terms (this part is a little different from our last example) with one of our universal curves. Examining Eq. (5–157) we see that the term $1 - e^{-t/\tau}$ fits Fig. 5–47(b) while the term $e^{-t/\tau}$ fits Fig. 5–47(a). So

$$v_o(t) = -\frac{h_{fe}R_{eq}}{h_{ie}}\left[-\frac{E\tau}{t_d}(1 - e^{-t/\tau}) + 0.20e^{-t/\tau}\right]$$

$$= -\frac{h_{fe}R_{eq}}{h_{ie}}\left[-\frac{E\tau}{t_d}w(\gamma) + 0.20q(\gamma)\right]$$

since $w(\gamma) = 1 - e^{-t/\tau}$ and $q(\gamma) = e^{-t/\tau}$ if we define $\gamma \equiv t/\tau$. Then let us state:

For $0 < t < t_d$

$$v_o(t) = -\frac{h_{fe}R_{eq}}{h_{ie}}\left[-\frac{E\tau}{t_d}w(\gamma) + 0.20q(\gamma)\right] \qquad \textbf{(5–161)}$$

where

$$\gamma \equiv \frac{t}{\tau}$$

For our next range $t_d < t < T$ we see the dominant term is $1 - e^{-(t-t_d)/\tau}$. As procedure 3 indicates we must reference our universal graphs to this term's time reference, which is $t - t_d$, hence define $t' \equiv t - t_d$. Thus $t = t' + t_d$ and $t/\tau = (t' + t_d)/\tau = \gamma = \gamma' + \gamma_d$ where $\gamma = t'/\tau$ and $\gamma_d = t_d/\tau$. So,

For $t_d < t < T$:

$$v_o(t) = -\frac{h_{fe}R_{eq}}{h_{ie}}\left[-\frac{E\tau}{t_d}w(\gamma = \gamma' + \gamma_d)\right.$$
$$\left. + 0.20q(\gamma = \gamma' + \gamma_d) + \frac{E\tau}{t_d}w(\gamma')\right]$$

$$= -\frac{h_{fe}R_{eq}}{h_{ie}}\left[-\frac{E\tau}{t_d}w(\gamma' + \gamma_d)\right.$$
$$\left. + 0.20q(\gamma' + \gamma_d) + \frac{E\tau}{t_d}w(\gamma')\right] \qquad \textbf{(5–162)}$$

where

$$\gamma' = \frac{t'}{\tau} = \frac{t - t_d}{\tau}$$

Continuing,

For $T < t < t_d + T$

Defining $t'' \equiv t - T$ then

$$\gamma'' = \frac{t''}{\tau} = \frac{t - T}{\tau} = \gamma - \gamma_T$$

Since $\gamma = t/\tau$, where $\gamma_T = T/\tau$. Also since

$$t = t'' + T = t' + t_d$$

then
$$t' = t'' + (T - t_d)$$
or
$$\gamma' = \gamma'' + (\gamma_T - \gamma_d)$$
So
$$v_o(t) = -\frac{h_{fe}R_{eq}}{h_{ie}} \left\{ \left[-\frac{E\tau}{t_d}w(\gamma) + 0.20q(\gamma) + \frac{E\tau}{t_d}w(\gamma') \right] \right.$$
$$\left. + \left[-\frac{E\tau}{t_d}w(\gamma'') + 0.20q(\gamma'') \right] \right\}$$
or
$$v_o(t) = -\frac{h_{fe}R_{eq}}{h_{ie}} \left\{ \left[-\frac{E\tau}{t_d}w(\gamma'' + \gamma_T) + 0.20q(\gamma'' + \gamma_T) \right. \right.$$
$$\left. + \frac{E\tau}{t_d}w[\gamma'' + (\gamma_T - \gamma_d)] \right]$$
$$\left. + \left[-\frac{E\tau}{t_d}w(\gamma'') + 0.20q(\gamma'') \right] \right\} \qquad (5\text{-}163)$$
where
$$\gamma'' = \frac{t''}{\tau} = \frac{t - T}{\tau}$$

For $t_d + T < t < 2T$

Defining $t''' \equiv t - (t_d + T)$ then
$$\gamma''' = \frac{t'''}{\tau} = \frac{t - (t_d + T)}{\tau} = \gamma - (\gamma_d + \gamma_T)$$
or
$$\gamma = \gamma''' + (\gamma_d + \gamma_T)$$
Also $t = t' + t_d$ and $t = t''' + (t_d + T)$ then $t' = t'' + T$ or $\gamma' = \gamma''' + \gamma_T$. Lastly
$$t = t'' + T = t''' + (t_d + T)$$
therefore
$$t'' = t''' + t_d$$
or
$$\gamma'' = \gamma''' + \gamma_d$$
Hence
$$v_o(t) = -\frac{h_{fe}R_{eq}}{h_{ie}} \left\{ \left[-\frac{E\tau}{t_d}w[\gamma''' + (\gamma_d + \gamma_T)] \right. \right.$$
$$\left. + 0.20q[\gamma''' + (\gamma_d + \gamma_T)] + \frac{E\tau}{t_d}w(\gamma''' + \gamma_T) \right]$$
$$\left. + \left[-\frac{E\tau}{t_d}w(\gamma''' + \gamma_d) + 0.20q(\gamma''' + \gamma_d) \right. \right.$$
$$\left. + \frac{E\tau}{t_d}w(\gamma''') \right] \qquad (5\text{-}164)$$

where

$$\gamma''' = \frac{t'''}{\tau} = \frac{t - (t_d + T)}{\tau}$$

Our work to this point has been general. Now let us become specific and consider the values for part (b). For our values we find

$R_{eq_1} \cong R_2 = 1 \text{ k}\Omega, \ R_{eq_2} \cong R_3 = 1.5 \text{ k}\Omega, \ R_{eq_3} = 500 \ \Omega,$
$R_{eq} = 380 \ \Omega, \ \Delta h^e \cong 1 \text{ k}\Omega$

and

$$r_{in} \cong 1 \text{ k}\Omega$$

Then

$$\tau = (R_{eq_2} + R_{eq_3})C_C = 2 \times 10^3(10 \times 10^{-6})$$
$$= 20 \times 10^{-3} = 20 \text{ ms},$$

$$\frac{h_{fe}R_{eq}}{h_{ie}} = \frac{50(38)}{1 \times 10^3} = 19$$

and

$$\frac{E\tau}{t_d} = \frac{0.20(20 \times 10^{-3})}{30 \times 10^{-3}} = 0.133$$

Then

$$\frac{h_{fe}R_{eq}}{h_{ie}}\frac{E\tau}{t_d} = 19(0.133) = 2.52$$

and

$$\frac{h_{fe}R_{eq}}{h_{ie}}(0.20) = 3.8$$

So,

For $0 < t < t_d = 30$ ms or $0 < \gamma < \gamma_d = 1.5$

From Eq. (5–161) we have

$$v_o(t) = 2.52w(\gamma) - 3.8q(\gamma) \qquad \textbf{(5–165)}$$

where

$$\gamma = \frac{t}{20 \times 10^{-3}}$$

For $t_d = 30$ ms $< t < 80$ ms $= T$, or $0 < \gamma' < (\gamma_T - \gamma_d)$
$= 2.5$

$$v_o(t) = 2.52w(\gamma' + \gamma_d) - 3.8q(\gamma' + \gamma_d) - 2.52w(\gamma')$$
$$\textbf{(5–166)}$$

where

$$\gamma' = \frac{t'}{20 \times 10^{-3}} = \frac{t - 30 \times 10^{-3}}{20 \times 10^{-3}}$$

For $T = 80$ ms $< t < (t_d + T) = 110$ ms or $0 < \gamma'' <$
$\gamma_d = 1.5$

$$v_o(t) = 2.52w(\gamma'' + \gamma_T) - 3.8q(\gamma'' + \gamma_T)$$
$$- 2.52w[\gamma'' + (\gamma_T - \gamma_d)] + 2.52w(\gamma'') - 3.8q(\gamma'')$$

$$(5\text{-}167)$$

where

$$\gamma'' = \frac{t''}{20 \times 10^{-3}} = \frac{t - T}{20 \times 10^{-3}}$$

For $t_d + T = 100$ ms $< t < 160$ ms $= 2T$ or $0 < \gamma'' <$
$(\gamma_T - \gamma_d) = 2.5$

$$v_o(t) = 2.52w[\gamma''' + (\gamma_d + \gamma_T)] - 3.8q[\gamma''' + (\gamma_d + \gamma_T)]$$
$$- 2.52w(\gamma''' + \gamma_T) + 2.52w(\gamma''' + \gamma_d)$$
$$- 3.8q(\gamma''' + \gamma_d) - 2.52w(\gamma''')$$

$$(5\text{-}168)$$

where

$$\gamma''' = \frac{t'''}{20 \times 10^{-3}} = \frac{t - (t_d + T)}{20 \times 10^{-3}}$$

We are now ready to make a set of tables for Eqs. (5–165), (5–166), (5–167), and (5–168). These are Tables 5–22, 5–23, and 5–24.

TABLE 5–22   For $0 < t < 30$ ms or
$0 < \gamma < 1.5$ to plot Eq. (5–165)

γ	$w(\gamma)$	$q(\gamma)$	$t = \gamma\tau$ $= 20\tau \times 10^{-3}$ t in ms	$v_o(t) = 2.52w(\gamma)$ $- 3.8q(\gamma)$ v_o in volts
0^+	0.00^+	1.00	0.00	-3.80
0.4	0.34	0.66	8.00	-1.64
1.0	0.62	0.38	20.00	0.12
1.5	0.78	0.22	30.00	1.14

And for

$$(t_d + T) = 100 \text{ ms} < t < 100 \text{ ms} = 2T$$

or

$$0 < \gamma''' < (\gamma_T - \gamma_d) = 2.5$$

we have

$$v_o(t) \cong 2.52w(\gamma''' + \gamma_d) - 3.80q(\gamma''' + \gamma_d) - 2.52w(\gamma''')$$

TABLE 5–23   For 30 ms $< t <$ 80 ms or
$0 < \gamma' < (\gamma_T - \gamma_d) = 2.5$ to plot Eq. (5–166)

γ'	$\gamma = $ $\gamma' + \gamma_d$	$t = \gamma'\tau$ $+ t_d$ t in ms	$w(\gamma')$	$w(\gamma'$ $+ \gamma_d)$	$q(\gamma'$ $+ \gamma_d)$	$v_o(t)$ v_o in volts
0	1.5	30.00	0.00	0.78	0.22	1.14
0.4	1.9	38.00	0.34	0.86	0.14	0.77
1.0	2.5	50.00	0.62	0.92	0.08	0.63
1.5	3.0	60.00	0.78	0.95	0.05	0.43
2.0	3.5	70.00	0.88	1.00^-	0.00^+	0.30
2.5	4.0	80.00	0.91	1.00^-	0.00^+	0.22

TABLE 5–24   For 80 ms $< t <$ 100 ms or
$0 < \gamma'' < \gamma_d = 1.5$ to plot Eq. (5–167)

γ''	$\gamma' = $ $\gamma'' +$ $(\gamma T - \gamma_d)$	$w(\gamma'')$	$w[\gamma'' +$ $(\gamma_T - \gamma_d)]$	$q(\gamma'')$	$t = \tau\gamma''$ $+ T$ t in ms	$v_o(t)$ v_o in volts
0^+	2.5	0.00^+	0.91	1.00	80.00^+	-3.58
0.4	2.9	0.34	0.95	0.66	88.00	-1.52
1.0	3.5	0.62	0.98	0.38	100.00	0.19
1.5	4.0	0.78	0.99	0.22	110.00	1.12

which is the same basic equation as

$$v_o(t) = 2.52w(\gamma' + \gamma_d) - 3.80q(\gamma' + \gamma_d) - 2.52w(\gamma')$$

for the range $t_d < t < T$. Hence, v_o is repetitive beginning with the second period. Then the equation for v_o can be written from Eq. (5–156) and is

$$
\begin{aligned}
v_o(t) &= v_o(t)_{\text{tr}} + v_o(t)_{\text{ss}} \\
&= -\frac{h_{\text{fe}} R_{\text{eq}}}{h_{\text{ie}}} \left\{ \left[-\frac{E\tau}{t_d}(1 - e^{-t/\tau})u(t) + 0.20e^{-t/\tau}u(t) \right. \right. \\
&\quad \left. + \frac{E\tau}{t_d}(1 - e)^{-(t-t_d)/\tau}u(t - t_d) \right] \\
&\quad + \left[\frac{E\tau}{t_d} \sum_{n=1}^{m} (1 - e^{-(t-nT)/\tau})u(t - nT) \right. \\
&\quad \left. \left. + 0.20 \sum_{n=1}^{m} e^{-(t-nT)/\tau}u(t - nT) \right] \right\}
\end{aligned}
$$

$$(5\text{–}169)$$

where

$$v_o(t)_{tr} = -\frac{h_{fe}R_{eq}}{h_{ie}}\left[-\frac{E\tau}{t_d}(1 - e^{-t/\tau})u(t) + 0.20e^{-t/\tau}\right.$$

$$\left.+ \frac{E\tau}{t_d}(1 - e^{-(t-t_d)/\tau})u(t - t_d)\right] \qquad (5\text{-}170)$$

and

$$v_o(t)_{ss} = -\frac{h_{fe}R_{eq}}{h_{ie}}\left[-\frac{E\tau}{t_d}\sum_{n=1}^{m}(1 - e^{-(t-nT)/\tau})u(t - nT)\right.$$

$$\left.+ 0.20\sum_{n=1}^{m}e^{-(t-nT)/\tau}u(t - nT)\right] \qquad (5\text{-}171)$$

Notice that the summation $\sum_{n=0}^{m}$ of Eq. (5–156) differs from Eq. (5–169) in that n no longer starts at 0 but rather at 1. This is so since $n = 0$ is the first period, or the transient term.

The graph of v_o appears in Fig. 5–50(b). As can be seen by comparing Fig. 5–50(a) and (b) e_{in} and v_o are 180° out of phase, which we expected; however, we also see that v_o is distorted. For part (c) we are to adjust C_C to remove most of this distortion.

(c) We know that no distortion would be present if we could remove C_C, but removing C_C would put a dc bias on our second-stage transistor different than designed for. So we must make C_C appear as an ac short circuit so that it "blocks" the dc but not the ac. This is accomplished by making its time constant slow compared to the time duration of the applied voltage, which is t_d for this case. Making the time constant τ five times slower than t_d we have

$$\tau = 5t_d = 5(30 \times 10^{-3}) = 150\,\text{ms} \qquad (5\text{-}172)$$

And from

$$\tau = (R_{eq_2} + R_{eq})C_C = 2 \times 10^3 C_C = 150 \times 10^{-3}$$

or

$$C_C = 75\mu\text{F} \qquad (5\text{-}173)$$

Fortunately most of our work has already been done for us in part (b). We may refer back to Eqs. (5–161), (5–162), (5–163), and (5–164). For convenience let us rewrite those equations.

For $0 < t < t_d$

$$v_o(t) = -\frac{h_{fe}R_{eq}}{h_{ie}}\left[-\frac{E\tau}{h_{ie}}w(\gamma) + 0.20q(\gamma)\right] \qquad (5\text{-}161)$$

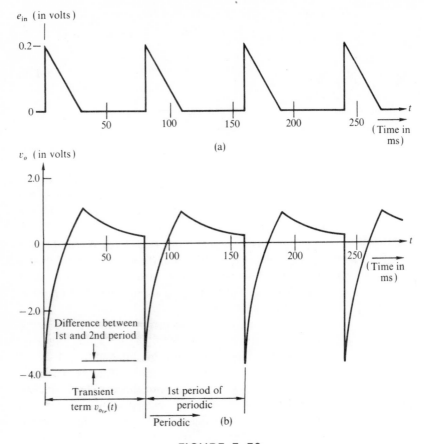

FIGURE 5–50

where $\gamma \equiv \dfrac{t}{\tau}$.

For $t_d < t < T$

$$v_o(t) = -\frac{h_{fe}R_{eq}}{h_{ie}}\left[-\frac{E\tau}{t_d}w(\gamma' + \gamma_d) + 0.20q(\gamma'' + \gamma_d)\right.$$

$$\left. + \frac{E\tau}{t_d}w(\gamma')\right] \qquad \textbf{(5-162)}$$

where $\gamma' = \dfrac{t'}{\tau} = \dfrac{t - t_d}{\tau}$.

For $T < t < t_d + T$

$$v_o(t) = -\frac{h_{fe}R_{eq}}{h_{ie}}\left\{\left[-\frac{E\tau}{t_d}w(\gamma'' + \gamma_T) + 0.20q(\gamma'' + \gamma_T)\right.\right.$$

$$\left.+ \frac{E\tau}{t_d}w[\gamma'' + (\gamma_T - \gamma_d)]\right]$$

$$\left.+ \left[-\frac{E\tau}{t_d}w(\gamma'') + 0.20q(\gamma'')\right]\right\} \qquad (5\text{-}163)$$

where $\gamma'' = \dfrac{t''}{\tau} = \dfrac{t - T}{\tau}$.

For $t_d + T < t < 2T$

$$v_o(t) = -\frac{h_{fe}R_{eq}}{h_{ie}}\left\{\left[-\frac{E\tau}{t_d}w[\gamma'' + (\gamma_d + \gamma_T)]\right.\right.$$

$$\left.+ 0.20q[\gamma''' + (\gamma_d + \gamma_T)] + \frac{E\tau}{t_d}w(\gamma''' + \gamma_T)\right]$$

$$+ \left[-\frac{E\tau}{t_d}w(\gamma''' + \gamma_d) + 0.20q(\gamma''' + \gamma_d)\right.$$

$$\left.\left.+ \frac{E\tau}{t_d}w(\gamma''')\right]\right] \qquad (5\text{-}164)$$

where $\gamma''' = \dfrac{t'''}{\tau} = \dfrac{t - (t_d + T)}{\tau}$.

Also, from before,

$R_{eq_1} \cong R_2 = 1\text{k}\Omega,\ R_{eq_2} \cong R_3 = 1.5\text{k}\Omega,\ R_{eq_3} = 500\Omega,$
$R_{eq} = 380\Omega,\ \Delta h^e \cong 1\text{k}\Omega,$ and $r_{in} \cong 1\text{k}\Omega.$

Then

$$\tau = (R_{eq_2} + R_{eq_3})C_C = 2 \times 10^3(75 \times 10^{-6}) = 150\text{ms}$$

$$\frac{h_{fe}R_{eq}}{h_{ie}} = 19 \text{ and } \frac{E\tau}{t_d} = 1.00$$

Thus,

$$\frac{h_{fe}R_{eq}}{h_{ie}}\frac{E\tau}{t_d} = 19 \text{ and } \frac{h_{fe}R_{eq}}{h_{ie}}(0.20) = 3.8$$

So from Eqs. (5-161), (5-162), (5-163), and (5-164)

For $0 < t < 30$ ms, or $0 < \gamma < \gamma_d = 0.20$

$$v_o(t) = 19w(\gamma) - 3.8q(\gamma) \qquad (5\text{-}174)$$

where $\gamma = \dfrac{t}{\tau}$.

For 30 ms $< t <$ 80 ms or $0 < \gamma' < (\gamma_T - \gamma_d) = 0.33$

$$v_o(t) = 19w(\gamma' + \gamma_d) - 3.8q(\gamma' + \gamma_d) - 19w(\gamma')$$
$$\text{(5-175)}$$

where $\gamma' = \dfrac{t'}{\tau} = \dfrac{t - t_d}{\tau}.$

For 80 ms $< t <$ 110 ms, or $0 < \gamma'' < 0.20$

$$v_o(t) = 19w(\gamma'' + \gamma_T) - 3.8q(\gamma'' + \gamma_T)$$
$$- 19w[\gamma'' + (\gamma_T - \gamma_d)] + 19w(\gamma'')$$
$$- 3.8q(\gamma'') \qquad\qquad \text{(5-176)}$$

where $\gamma'' = \dfrac{t''}{\tau} = \dfrac{t - T}{\tau}.$

For 110 ms $< t <$ 160 ms, or $0 < \gamma''' < 0.33$

$$v_o(t) = 19w[\gamma''' + (\gamma_d + \gamma_T)] - 3.8q[\gamma''' + (\gamma_d + \gamma_T)]$$
$$- 19w(\gamma''' + \gamma_T) + 19w(\gamma''' + \gamma_d)$$
$$- 3.8q(\gamma''' + \gamma_d) - 19w(\gamma''') \qquad \text{(5-177)}$$

where $\gamma''' = \dfrac{t'''}{\tau} = \dfrac{t - (t_d + T)}{\tau}$

Setting up our tables for the preceding time ranges we have the results shown in Table 5–25.

TABLE 5–25   For $0 < t <$ 30 ms or $0 < \gamma < 0.20$

γ	$w(\gamma)$	$q(\gamma)$	$t = \gamma\tau$ $= 150\gamma \times 10^{-3}$ t in ms	$v_o(t)$ v_o in volts
0.00	0.00	1.00	0.00	−3.8
0.20	0.20	0.80	30.00	0.78

Notice over the range of γ with which we are working Figs. 5–47(a) and (b) appear linear; therefore we are dealing with straight lines.

Comparing the points of v_o in Table 5–26 (30 ms $< t$ $<$ 80 ms) and Table 5–28 (110 ms $< t <$ 160 ms) we see that for all practical purposes they are the same. This tells us we are repetitive after the first period. From Tables 5–25, 5–26, 5–27, and 5–28 we may determine the Again notice we are essentially dealing with straight lines over the range of γ' with which we are working.

TABLE 5–26   For 30 ms $< t <$ 80 ms or $0 < \gamma' < 0.33$

γ'	$\dfrac{w(\gamma' + \gamma_d)}{w(\gamma' + 0.20)}$	$\dfrac{q(\gamma' + \gamma_d)}{q(\gamma' + 0.20)}$	$w(\gamma')$	$t = 150\gamma$ $\times 10^{-3} + t_d$ t in ms	$v_o(t)$ v_o in volts
0.00	0.20	0.80	0.00	30.00	0.80
0.20	0.34	0.66	0.20	60.00	0.10
0.33	0.40	0.60	0.30	80.00	−0.40

TABLE 5–27   For 80 ms $< t <$ 110 ms or $0 < \gamma'' < 0.20$

γ''	$\dfrac{w(\gamma'' + \gamma_T)}{w(\gamma'' + 0.53)}$	$\dfrac{q(\gamma' + \gamma_T)}{q(\gamma' + 0.53)}$	$\dfrac{w[\gamma'' + (\gamma_T - \gamma_d)]}{w(\gamma'' + 0.33)}$	$w(\gamma'')$	$q(\gamma'')$	$t = 150\gamma''$ $\times 10^{-3} + T$ t in ms	$v_o(t)$ v_o in volts
0.00	0.40	0.60	0.30	0.00	1.00	80.00	−4.20
0.20	0.50	0.50	0.40	0.20	0.80	110.00	0.80

TABLE 5–28   For 110 ms $< t <$ 160 ms or $0 < \gamma''' < 0.33$

γ'''	$\dfrac{w[\gamma''' + (\gamma_d + \gamma_T)]}{w(\gamma'' + 0.73)}$	$\dfrac{q[\gamma''' + (\gamma_d + \gamma_T)]}{q(\gamma''' + 0.73)}$	$\dfrac{w(\gamma''' + \gamma_T)}{w(\gamma''' + 0.53)}$	$\dfrac{w(\gamma''' + \gamma_d)}{w(\gamma''' + 0.20)}$
0.00	0.50	0.50	0.40	0.20
0.20	0.58	0.42	0.50	0.34
0.33	0.65	0.35	0.58	0.40

TABLE 5–28 (*con't*)   For 110 ms $< t <$ 160 ms

γ'''	$\dfrac{q(\gamma''' + \gamma_d)}{q(\gamma''' + 0.20)}$	$w(\gamma''')$	$t = 150\gamma'''$ $\times 10^{-3} + (t_d + T)$ t in ms	$v_o(t)$ v_o in volts
0.00	0.80	0.00	110.00	0.80
0.20	0.66	0.20	140.00	0.10
0.33	0.60	0.30	160.00	−0.52

graph of v_o. The graph of v_o is shown in Fig. 5–51(b), and the equation for v_o is the same as Eq. (5–171).

As we see from Fig. 5–51 we have a minimum of distortion, where the distortion present is near the t-axis. We will always have some distortion present due to the capacitor's charging and discharging. What happens is the capacitor charges to approximately $+0.80$ volts during the time the sawtooth voltage is applied from $nT < t < nT + t_d$ and as a result we get an overshoot because of this charge. Then for the time periods $nT + t_d < t < (n + 1)T$, e_{in} is applying zero volts (ac); hence the capacitor becomes the energy source and during this time the capacitor attempts to discharge and causes a current to flow, thus creating a voltage drop of about -0.40 volts. So when speaking of distortion we will have to ignore overshoot so long as we keep the overshoot to a tolerable level. One way to reduce the overshoot is to increase the time constant more so that C_C does not have sufficient time to charge up to even $+0.80$ volts during $nT < t < nT + t_d$.

We should realize the waveforms of Fig. 5–50(b) and 5–51(b) are ac voltage outputs. That is, from an absolute standpoint the zero reference of these figures might be 5.0 volts. Case in point: for our example we are using an NPN device, which requires positive V_{CC} volts as a bias supply. Then our output voltage must be positive, yet Figs. 5–50(b) and 5–51(b) show a negative voltage output. Recall from section 2–6 the ac equivalent circuit is referenced to the Q-point. Hence, if $V_{CC} = 15$ volts and our Q-point was approximately centered we would have Fig. 5–52. Figure 5–52 shows v_{ce_1}, which would be v_o if C_C were an ac short circuit. v_o is also shown if C_C were added, which is the case of Fig. 5–51.

5–9   Application of Unit Impulse Function

For the next example we will attempt to approach a unit impulse function as our driving force. We will then examine the results and draw some conclusions.

Example 5–17   Given the circuit in Fig. 5–53 solve for and graph v_o: (a) by writing an exact equation for e_{in}; (b) by using the unit impulse function δ.

Before solving part (a) or (b) let us determine the general equation for $V_o(s)$. Writing a nodal equation,

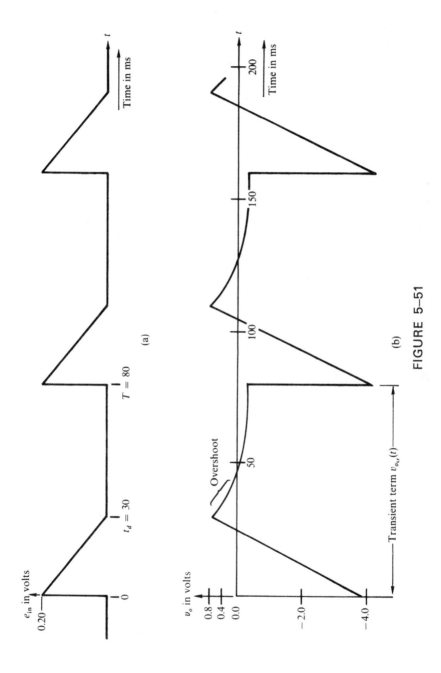

FIGURE 5-51

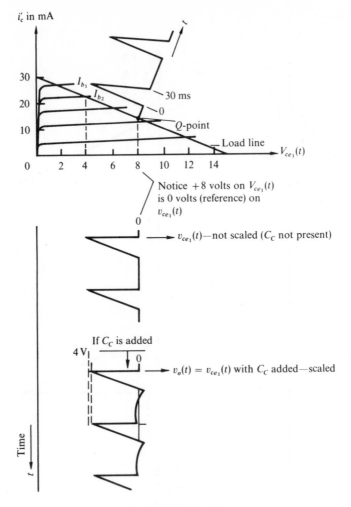

FIGURE 5–52

where e_{in} and v_o polarities are assumed,

$$\frac{e_{in}(t) - v_o(t)}{R} = C \frac{dv_o(t)}{dt}$$

So

$$V_o(s) = \frac{E_{in}(s) + RCv_o(0^+)}{RC\left(s + \dfrac{1}{RC}\right)}$$

which is the general equation we sought.

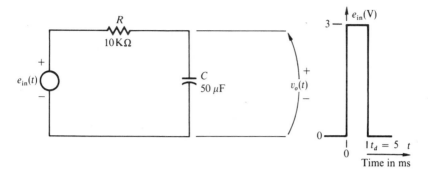

FIGURE 5–53

Solution   (a) Writing an equation for e_{in},

$$e_{in}(t) = 3u(t) - 3u(t - 5 \times 10^{-3})$$

Therefore,

$$E_{in}(s) = \frac{3}{s}(1 - e^{-5 \times 10^{-3}s})$$

So

$$V_o(s) = \frac{3(1 - e^{-5 \times 10^{-3}s})}{RCs\left(s + \dfrac{1}{RC}\right)}$$

since $v_o(0^+) = 0$. Finding the inverse Laplace transform we have,

$$v_o(t) = 3(1 - e^{-t/RC})u(t)$$
$$- 3(1 - e^{-(t-5\times10^{-3})/RC})u(t - 5 \times 10^{-3})$$
$$= 3(1 - e^{-t/0.5})u(t)$$
$$- 3(1 - e^{-(t-5\times10^{-3})/0.5})u(t - 5 \times 10^{-3}) \quad \textbf{(5–178)}$$

since $RC = 0.5$ s.

Graphing Eq. (5–178) we consider the ranges of t and identify which universal graph to use.

For $0 < t < 5 \times 10^{-3}$ s

$$v_o(t) = 3(1 - e^{-t/0.5}) = 3w(\gamma) \quad \textbf{(5–179a)}$$

by defining $1 - e^{-t/0.5} \equiv 1 - e^{-\gamma}$ of Fig. 5–47(b). Because of this definition then $\gamma = t/0.5$.

For $t > 5 \times 10^{-3}$ s

$$v_o(t) = 3(1 - e^{-t/0.5}) - 3(1 - e^{-t-5\times10^{-3}/0.5})$$
$$= 3w(\gamma) - 3w(\gamma')$$

where

$$\gamma' = \frac{t'}{0.5} = \frac{t - 5 \times 10^{-3}}{0.5} = \gamma - 10 \times 10^{-3}$$

Thus

$$v_o(t) = 3[w(\gamma' + 10 \times 10^{-3}) - w(\gamma')] \quad \text{(5-179b)}$$

since $\gamma = \gamma' + 10 \times 10^{-3}$.

Forming our table of points we have those shown in Table 5-29.

TABLE 5–29   For $0 < t < 5 \times 10^{-3}$ s, or $0 < \gamma <$ 10^{-2}, of Eq (5–179a)

γ	$w(\gamma)$	$t = 0.5\gamma$ t in ms	$v_o(t)$ v_o in volts
0	0	0.00	0.00
10^{-2}	0.00⁺	5.00	0.00⁺

Notice that we cannot interpret the graph of Fig. 5–47(b) at $\gamma = 10^{-2}$ except to approximate $w(\gamma)$ as being something "a little greater than zero." And for $t > 5 \times 10^{-3}$ s we have the table of points in Table 5–30.

TABLE 5–30   For $t > 5 \times 10^{-3}$ s or $\gamma > 10^{-2}$, of Eq. (5–179b)

γ'	$w(\gamma' + 10$ $\times 10^{-3}) =$ $w(\gamma)$	$w(\gamma')$	$t = 0.5\gamma$ t in ms	$v_o(t)$ v_o in volts
0.4	0.34⁺	0.34	0.20	0.00⁺
1.0	0.62⁺	0.62	0.50	0.00⁺
1.5	0.78⁺	0.78	0.75	0.00⁺
2.0	0.88⁺	0.88	1.00	0.00⁺
3.0	0.95⁺	0.95	1.50	0.00⁺

From our two tables we see that our graphical techniques fail. They cannot be used because of the relatively short duration of the pulse when compared to the circuit's RC time constant. Notice the ratio of time constant to pulse duration is

$$\frac{\text{pulse duration}}{\text{circuit time constant}} = \frac{t_d}{\tau} = \frac{5 \times 10^{-3}}{0.5} = 10^{-2} \quad \text{(5–180)}$$

And when Eq. (5–180) is written in terms of the coordinate γ we see that $\gamma_d = t_d/\tau = 10^{-2}$, which is too small to interpret on the graph of Fig. 5–47(b). In fact, we could say that in order to interpret Fig. 5–47(b) it is required that $\gamma > 0.1$, which in terms of t_d and τ is saying $t_d/\tau > 0.1$ or

$$t_d > 0.1\tau \quad \text{(5–181)}$$

In words Eq. (5–181) is saying that the pulse duration must be at least a tenth of the circuit's time constant in order to interpret our universal graph. Similar analysis can be made for our other universal graphs.

(b) To use the unit impulse function δ our first reaction might be to reason that since the duration of the pulse t_d is so small compared to the circuit's time constant that we could approximate $t_d \rightarrow 0$. This reasoning is sound and quite correct from a practical point of view. Then we might continue to reason that we could form the product $3\delta(t)$ to represent e_{in}. This would be wrong. From Eq. (4–52) we see that $\delta(t)$ has the units of 1/sec for $t = 1$ sec. Thus $3\delta(t) = (3 \text{ V})(1/\text{sec}) = 3 \text{ V/sec} \neq 3 \text{ V}$, that is, e_{in} must be expressed in units of volts rather than volts/second. Then to use δ as a multiplier its coefficient, or strength of δ as termed in section 4–14, must have the units of volts-second, for then the product would be volts. That is, if $e_{\text{in}}(t) = $ units of volts $= k\delta(t)$, then $k \equiv$ strength $=$ volt$/\delta(t) =$ volt$/(1/\text{sec}) =$ volt·sec, which is the area under the pulse. Thus for the strength of the pulse of e_{in} we are interested in its area, which is for this case

$$k = Et_d = 3 \text{ volts} \cdot 5 \times 10^{-3} \text{ sec} = 15 \times 10^{-3} \text{ volt·sec} \quad \text{(5–182)}$$

So

$$e_{\text{in}}(t) = 15 \times 10^{-3}\delta(t) \text{ volts} \quad \text{(5–183)}$$

and

$$E_{\text{in}}(s) = 15 \times 10^{-3}\mathcal{L}[\delta(t)] = 15 \times 10^{-3} \quad \text{(5–184)}$$

To evaluate $v_o(0^+)$ when using the unit impulse we must return to section 4–8 where we are reminded that the initial condition being evaluated at $t = 0^+$ was due to the nonexistence of $f(t)$ at $t = 0$. However, for $f(t) = \delta(t)$ the function $f(t)$ exists at $t = 0$. Then for an initial condition where the unit impulse is being applied we must think in terms of $t = 0^-$. For our particular case $v_o(0^-) = 0$. Substituting Eq. (5–184) into the equation for $V_o(s)$ we have

$$V_o(s) = \frac{15 \times 10^{-3}}{RC\left(s + \dfrac{1}{RC}\right)} = \frac{30 \times 10^{-3}}{\left(s + \dfrac{1}{0.5}\right)} \qquad (5\text{–}185)$$

where $v_o(0^-) = 0$. And then find the inverse

$$v_o(t) = 30 \times 10^{-3}e^{-t/0.5}u(t) \qquad (5\text{–}186)$$

Now we see why we could not interpret the graphs. We were attempting to read magnitudes of approximately 10^{-3}.

To graph Eq. (5–186) we refer to Fig. 5–47(a). Then Eq. (5–186) can be written as

$$v_o(t) = 30 \times 10^{-3}q(\gamma) \qquad (5\text{–}187)$$

where $\gamma = t/0.5$. Hence, we determine Table 5–31.

TABLE 5–31   For plotting Eq. (5–187)

γ	$q(\gamma)$	$t = 0.5\gamma$ t in s	$v_o(t)$ v_o in mV
0.0	1.00	0.00	30.00
0.4	0.66	0.20	20.00
1.0	0.38	0.50	11.40
1.5	0.22	0.75	6.60
2.0	0.12	1.00	2.64
3.0	0.05	1.50	1.50
5.0	0.00$^+$	2.50	0.00

The points for plotting Eq. (5–187) are plotted in Fig. 5–54.

In order to compare the results of v_o by using $\delta(t)$, where we approximated t_d to be zero, for e_{in}, versus writing e_{in} with no approximations, let us make a point-by-point plot of Eq. (5–178), where Eq. (5–178) is written here.

$$v_o(t) = 3(1 - e^{-t/0.5})u(t)$$
$$- 3(1 - e^{-(t-5\times10^{-3})/0.5})u(t - 5 \times 10^{-3})$$

$$\text{(5–178)}$$

For $0 < t < 5 \times 10^{-3}$ s

$$v_o(t) = 3(1 - e^{-t/0.5})$$

$$v_o(t = 0) = 3(1 - 1) = 0$$

$$v_o(t = 2 \times 10^{-3}) = 3(1 - e^{-0.2\times10^{-3}/0.5})$$
$$= 3(1 - e^{-4\times10^{-3}}) = 12 \text{ mV}$$

$$v_o(5 \times 10^{-3}) = 3(1 - e^{-5\times10^{-3}/0.5}) = 30 \text{ mV}$$

For $t > 5 \times 10^{-3}$ s

$$v_o(t) = 3[(1 - e^{-t/0.5}) - (1 - e^{-(t-5\times10^{-3})/0.5})]$$
$$= 3e^{-t/0.5}(e^{5\times10^{-3}/0.5} - 1)$$
$$= 3e^{-t/0.5}(1.010 - 1.000 = 30 \times 10^{-3}e^{-t/0.5}$$

Notice this is the same equation as Eq. (5–186). Then we may use Eq. (5–187) and the points collected for Eq. (5–187). However, we must understand that the collection of points is for $t > 5 \times 10^{-3}$ rather than $t > 0$. Hence, we must add 5×10^{-3} to t of that table. Our modified table would appear as on Table 5–32. These points are plotted in Fig. 5–54(b).

TABLE 5–32   For Plotting Fig. 5–54(b)

γ	$q(\gamma)$	$t = 0.5\gamma$ $+ 0.005$ t in s	$v_o(t)$ v_o in mV
0.0	1.00	0.005	30.00
0.4	0.66	0.205	20.00
1.0	0.38	0.505	11.40
1.5	0.22	0.755	6.60
2.0	0.12	1.005	2.64
3.0	0.05	1.505	1.50
5.0	0.00+	2.505	0.00

The results shown in Fig. 5–54(a) and (b) are very important. Notice that Fig. 5–54(a) and (b) are the exact

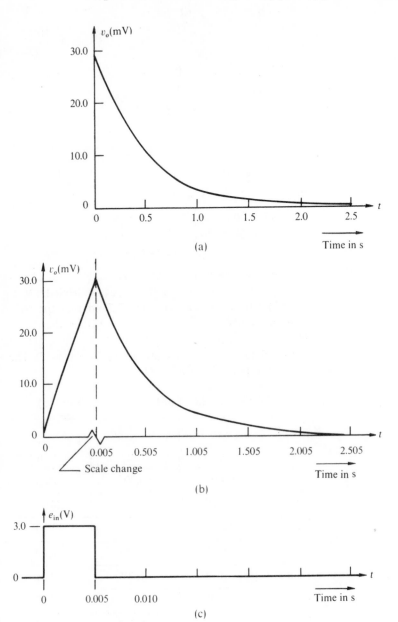

(a)

Time in s

(b)

Scale change

Time in s

(c)

Time in s

FIGURE 5–54

same if you change your time reference to 0.005 s for Fig.
5–54(b) and ignore the portion of the graph for $t <$
0.005 s. That is, let us define 0.005 as zero. Then the
0.505-s point for t becomes 0.500 s, which is the same as
for Fig. 5–54(a). Likewise for all the other points shown
in Fig. 5–54(b). And as for the portion of Fig. 5–54(b) we
are ignoring $(0 < t < 0.005)$ in Fig. 5–54(b) (notice the
scale change). We are in effect saying that we do not care
how v_o reached a value of 30 mV at $t = 0.005$ s. If one
would try to plot the points of v_o for $0 < t < 0.005$ s on
the same scale as for $t > 0.005$ s they would find indeed
Fig. 5–54(a) is a very realistic approximation to Fig.
5–54(b). In conclusion, then, we are justified in using δ as
we did to approximate e_{in} when the pulse duration of e_{in}
is much faster than the time constant τ of the circuit;
stated mathematically $\tau \gg t_d$.

5–10   Circuits Containing Diodes

Circuits containing diodes deserve special mention since a diode is ideally a
digital device in the sense it is either fully ON or fully OFF. As a result, we
must analyze circuits containing diodes during the ON and OFF conditions separately. Then a major problem will be to determine the state of the
diode. To do this we shall write the necessary equation to solve for the
voltage across the diode and if this voltage polarity is such as to forward-
bias the diode then we know the diode is ON, otherwise the diode is OFF.
As an example consider the diode shown in Fig. 5–55. The voltage across

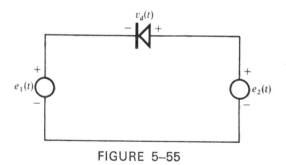

FIGURE 5–55

the diode v_d was *assumed* to have the polarity shown, which is a forward-
bias polarity. The voltage generators e_1 and e_2 polarities are also assumed.
Writing a loop equation so that we may solve for v_o we have

$$e_2(t) - v_d(t) - e_1(t) = 0$$

or
$$v_d(t) = e_2(t) - e_1(t) \qquad \textbf{(5-188)}$$

Now clearly if $e_2(t) > e_1(t)$ then v_d of Eq. (5–188) has a positive value, which means our assumed polarity is correct and the diode is forward biased or, simply, is ON. However, for when $e_1(t) > e_2(t)$ Eq. (5–188) has a negative value, which states the polarity is the reverse of that shown and the diode is reverse biased, or OFF.

In Fig. 5–56 waveforms were drawn for e_1 and e_2. Below those waveforms it is labeled whether the ideal diode is ON or OFF. When viewing Fig. 5–56 recall that for $e_2(t) > e_1(t)$ the diode is ON and for $e_1(t) > e_2(t)$ the diode is OFF.

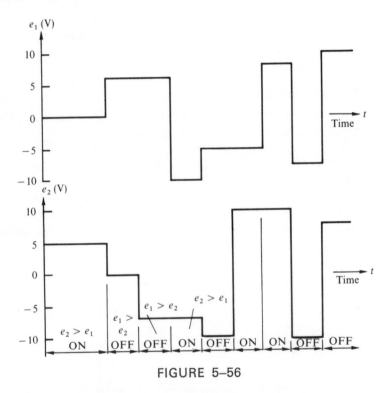

FIGURE 5–56

When a diode is ON it ideally appears as a short circuit; however, all forward-biased diodes contain some resistance. In contrast, a reverse-biased diode ideally appears as an open circuit, but all reverse-biased diodes have finite resistance. Then when a diode is forward-biased, it can be replaced by either a resistor of small value or a short circuit. If one has a circuit where a few ohms make a noticeable difference in the results, then the small-valued resistor should be inserted to replace the ON diode. If, however, the results are about the same whether the diode is replaced with a short circuit versus being replaced with a small-valued resistance, the short circuit is preferred. And when the diode is reverse-biased, that is, OFF, it may be replaced by either an open circuit or very large resistance. The choice would again depend on how exact we must be. If the circuit under analysis contained very large resistance, then the diode would probably have to be replaced with its actual reverse-biased resistance. If, however, the circuit contains values of resistance of 50 kΩ or less it is usually safe to assume an open circuit for the diode replacement.

Another important point for us to understand concerning diodes is that the current flow is *never* instantaneous. If a forward-biased voltage is applied across a diode there is a time delay before current will flow. The time delay may be very very small, but nevertheless it is there.

In summary, the concepts we will be using in our analysis of circuits containing diodes are that: (1) ON diodes can ideally be replaced with short circuits; (2) OFF diodes ideally are replaceable with open circuits; (3) when a diode is forward biased a time delay exists before current flows.

Let us now analyze the circuit given in Ex. 5–18 and use the principles which apply.

Example 5–18   Analyze the circuit given in Fig. 5–57 assuming ideal conditions for the diode.

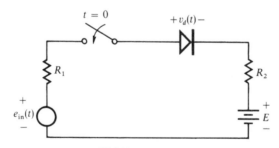

FIGURE 5–57

Solution   As shown in the circuit a polarity has already been assumed for e_{in} and v_d. Our first task is to determine the conditions for the diode to be ON or OFF as a function of the potentials e_{in} and E. In doing this we will utilize the two facts that if the diode is OFF no current flows or if the diode is ON no current flows for some small time delay. Then to determine the state of the diode we will analyze the circuit in the time range of $0 < t < 0^+$. Notice this eliminates any current considerations from our determining the state of the diode since no current is flowing through the diode; that is, if the diode is reverse biased no current flows and if it is forward biased no current flows for the time delay of $0 < t < 0^+$. Then writing a loop equation in this time range we have

$$e_{in}(t) - v_d(t) - E = 0$$

Solving for v_d

$$v_d(t) = e_{in}(t) - E \qquad (5\text{-}189)$$

Equation (5-189) states that: for $e_{in}(t) > E$ the assumed voltage polarity of v_d is true and therefore the diode is ON and current will be flowing through it for $t > 0^+$ and for $e_{in}(t) < E$ the voltage polarity of v_d is the reverse of that assumed and hence the diode is reverse biased and current will not flow through the diode so long as $e_{in}(t) < E$ exists. The circuit conditions are shown in Fig. 5-58(a) and (b) for these two conditions.

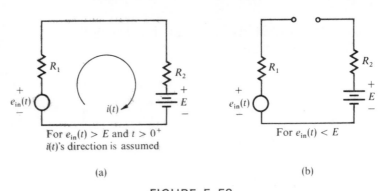

For $e_{in}(t) > E$ and $t > 0^+$
$i(t)$'s direction is assumed

(a)   (b)

FIGURE 5–58

Example 5-19 Analyze the circuit given in Fig. 5-59 for v_o if e_{in} is as shown.

Solution Let us begin by determining the conditions for the two states of the diode. Assuming the voltage polarities for e_{in}, v_d, and v_o we have the circuit shown in Fig. 5-60.

Now writing a loop equation in order to determine v_d we have, $E - v_d(t) - v_o(t) = 0$, or

$$v_d(t) = E - v_o(t) \qquad (5\text{-}190)$$

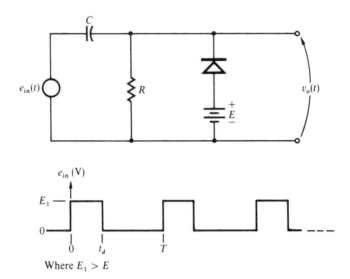

Where $E_1 > E$

FIGURE 5–59

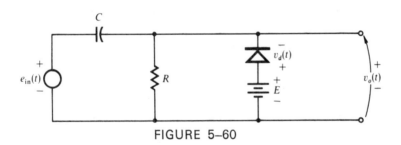

FIGURE 5–60

Then for $E > v_o(t)$ the diode is ON and for $E < v_o(t)$ the diode is OFF. The equivalent circuit for each of these conditions appears in Fig. 5–61.

As we can see, so long as $E > v_o(t)$ exists, then $v_o(t) = E$. This seems to be a contradiction for E to be greater than v_o and at the same time for v_o to be equal to E. This contradiction points up the difference between the ideal and the practical diode. Actually a drop of about 0.7 volts is across the diode, due to its resistance; hence, E is greater than v_o by 0.7 volts. If we fully understand that we do not have an ideal diode (the diode is actually equivalent to a small-value resistance), then this contradiction resolves itself. And as far as the 0.7-volt error

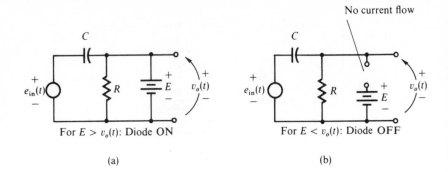

For $E > v_o(t)$: Diode ON   For $E < v_o(t)$: Diode OFF

(a)   (b)

FIGURE 5-61

is concerned, for most analyses an 0.7-volt error presents no problems.

Our approach will be to assume the diode is OFF, since this is true for some small time even if the diode is biased ON, and solve for v_o. Recall this delay is due to the delay in turn-on-time of the diode. Once we have the equation for v_o under OFF conditions we will apply the inequality $E > v_o(t)$ to see if the diode is ON or OFF.

We will now solve for v_o using Fig. 5-61(b). Writing a nodal equation we have

$$C \frac{d}{dt}[e_{\text{in}}(t) - v_o(t)] = \frac{v_o(t)}{R}$$

Taking the Laplace we find

$$CsE_{\text{in}}(s) - C[e_{\text{in}}(0^+) - v_o(0^+)] = \left(\frac{1}{R} + Cs\right)V_o(s)$$

Solving for $V_o(s)$,

$$V_o(s) = \frac{sE_{\text{in}}(s)}{s + \frac{1}{RC}} - \frac{e_{\text{in}}(0^+) - v_o(0^+)}{s + \frac{1}{RC}} \qquad \textbf{(5-191)}$$

To determine the initial conditions $e_{\text{in}}(0^+)$ and $v_o(0^+)$ we reason that the capacitor acts as a short to any change in potential across it and since it has no initial charge then $e_{\text{in}}(0^+) = v_o(0^+)$. To reiterate, even if the diode turns ON we can assume it OFF momentarily because of the turn-on delay of the diode. So for now (this will change later) Eq. (5-191) may be written as

$$V_o(s) = \frac{sE_{in}(s)}{s + \dfrac{1}{RC}} \tag{5-192}$$

due to $e_{in}(0^+) - v_o(0^+) = 0$.

We must now become specific and determine v_o in order that we may determine the state of the diode. This means we must write an explicit equation for $E_{in}(s)$ so that v_o may be found from Eq. (5–192). From the problem we see that

$$e_{in_1}(t) = E_1 u(t) - E_1 u(t - t_d)$$

so

$$e_{in}(t) = E_1 \sum_{n=0}^{m} \{u(t - nT) - u[t - (t_d + nT)]\}$$

thus

$$E_{in}(s) = \frac{E_1}{s} \sum_{n=0}^{m} [e^{-nTs} - e^{-(t_d+nT)s}]$$

Substituting this into Eq. (5–192) we have

$$V_o(s) = \frac{E_1 \sum_{n=0}^{m} [e^{-nTs} - e^{-(t_d+nT)s}}{s + \dfrac{1}{RC}}$$

Now we know that our circuit analysis changes every time the diode switches states; hence there is every possibility that the $V_o(s)$ we just expressed is valid only for some short period of time. For that reason let us investigate $V_o(s)$ for $n = 0$ first, which is $0 < t < T$ in the t-plane, and evaluate the ON condition $E > v_o(t)$. Thus

$$V_o(s) = \frac{E_1(1 - e^{-t_d s})}{s + \dfrac{1}{RC}} = \frac{E_1}{s + \dfrac{1}{RC}} - \frac{E_1 e^{-t_d s}}{s + \dfrac{1}{RC}} \tag{5-193}$$

Finding the inverse Laplace we have

$$v_o(t) = E_1 e^{-t/RC} u(t) - E_1 e^{-(t-t_d)/RC} u(t - t_d) \tag{5-194}$$

Taking the first t-range indicated by Eq. (5–194):
For $0 < t < t_d$

$$v_o(t) = E_1 e^{-t/RC} = E_1 q(\gamma) \tag{5-195}$$

where $\gamma \equiv t/RC$. Substituting Eq. (5–195) into $E > v_o(t)$ we have

$$E > E_1 q(\gamma) \quad \text{or} \quad \frac{E}{E_1} > q(\gamma)$$

The inequality $E/E_1 > q(\gamma)$ states that in order for the diode to turn ON the quantity E/E_1 must be greater than $q(\gamma)$. Now the quantity E/E_1 is always less than unity, since the problem states $E_1 > E$, and $q(\gamma)$ starts at unity and decays to zero; therefore, the diode is initially OFF but may turn ON if the condition $E/E_1 > q(\gamma)$ is met. We can determine when the diode would turn ON. To do this substitute $q(\gamma) = e^{-t/RC}$ back into the equation and define the time at which the diode turns ON as t_{ON}, hence $E/E_1 > e^{-t_{\text{ON}}/RC}$, where t_{ON} is just when $e^{-t/RC}$ becomes less than E/E_1. Taking ln we have

$$\ln \frac{E}{E_1} > -\frac{t_{\text{ON}}}{RC} \quad \text{or} \quad \ln \frac{E_1}{E} < \frac{t_{\text{ON}}}{RC}$$

So we can state $t_{\text{ON}} > RC \ln E_1/E$, or verbally, t_{ON} is greater than the time $[RC \ln E_1/E]$ (check units). Of course a very close approximation would be

$$t_{\text{ON}} \cong RC \ln \frac{E_1}{E} \qquad (5\text{-}196)$$

Then the diode is OFF for t_{ON} units of time and during this OFF time Eq. (5-195) describes v_o. Figure 5-62 indicates what we might expect for a circuit-time constant of about $RC \cong t_d$.

At $t = t_{\text{ON}}$ the diode turns ON and Eq. (5-195) is no longer valid. Then Fig. 5-61(a) becomes the equivalent circuit. From Fig. 5-61(a) we see that

$$v_o(t) = E \qquad (5\text{-}197)$$

Notice also from Fig. 5-61(a) that the voltage across the capacitor, let us designate it v_C, is

$$v_C(t) = e_{\text{in}}(t) - v_o(t)$$

Then at $t = 0^+$

$$v_C(0^+) = e_{\text{in}}(0^+) - v_o(0^+)$$

so we see that Eq. (5-191) can be written as

$$V_o(s) = \frac{sE_{\text{in}}(s)}{s + \dfrac{1}{RC}} - \frac{v_C(0^+)}{s + \dfrac{1}{RC}} \qquad (5\text{-}198)$$

where $e_{\text{in}}(0^+) - v_o(0^+)$ is the initial voltage across the capacitor.

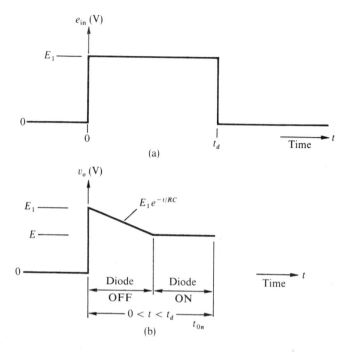

FIGURE 5–62

Our next analysis will be for the next time range of $t_d < t < T$. Hence:

For $t_d < t < T$: Again assume the diode OFF. Now $e_{in}(t) = Eu(t) - Eu(t - t_d)$ for the first period, then for $t_d < t < T$, $e_{in}(t) = 0$. Therefore, $E_{in}(s) = 0$. Substituting this into Eq. (5–198) we have

$$V_o(s) = - \frac{v_C(0^+)}{s + \dfrac{1}{RC}} \qquad (5\text{–}199)$$

From our previous work $v_C(0^+) = 0$, but not for this case. This can be seen from Fig. 5–61(a) and the equation $v_C(t) = e_{in}(t) - v_o(t)$ evaluated at $t = 0^+$. Now, each time the diode switches state we define that time as our new zero reference insofar as determining initial conditions. So, if the diode turned OFF at $t = t_d$ we would define t_d as zero, thus

$$v_C(t_d^+) \equiv v_C(0^+) = e_{in}(0^+) - v_o(0^+)$$

From our illustration of e_{in} and v_o we see at $t = t_d \equiv 0$

that

$$v_o(0^+) = E \quad \text{and} \quad e_{in}(0^+) = E_1$$

Therefore $v_C(0^+) = E_1 - E$ and Eq. (5–199) becomes

$$V_o(s) = -\frac{E_1 - E}{s + \dfrac{1}{RC}} \qquad (5\text{–}200)$$

From Eq. (5–200) we find

$$v_o(t) = -(E_1 - E)e^{-t/RC}u(t) \qquad (5\text{–}201)$$

Since this is for the t-range $t_d < t < T$ then $u(t) = 1$ and

$$v_o(t) = -(E_1 - E)e^{-t/RC}$$

Putting this into the inequality $E > v_o(t)$ we have the condition

$$E > (E - E_1)e^{-t/RC}$$

or

$$E(1 - e^{-t/RC}) > -E_1 e^{-t/RC}$$

in order to turn the diode ON. Now $E(1 - e^{-t/RC})$ is always greater than $-E_1 e^{-t/RC}$, so the condition necessary to turn the diode ON is met and it turns ON, and $v_o(t) = E$ as stated in Eq. (5–197). The waveform of v_o for $0 < t < t_d$ and $t_d < t < T$ is shown in Fig. 5–63.

For $T < t < t_d + T$

The analysis of the next time range of $T < t < t_d + T$ is the same as analyzing the range $0 < t < t_d$ if we define $T \equiv 0$ and re-evaluate our initial conditions. For this range of time $e_{in}(t) = E_1$ so $E_{in}(s) = E_1/s$. Then from Eq. (5–198)

$$V_o(s) = \frac{E_1}{s + \dfrac{1}{RC}} - \frac{v_C(0^+)}{s + \dfrac{1}{RC}} \qquad (5\text{–}202)$$

The initial conditions $v_C(0^+)$ can be found by evaluating $v_C(T^-)$ which is $v_C(0^-)$ if we define $T \equiv 0$. Again, the reason we are making this definition is only for evaluating initial conditions. At $t = T^- \equiv 0^-$ we are dealing with Fig. 5–61(b), so

$$v_C(T^-) \equiv v_C(0^-) = e_{in}(0^-) - v_o(0^-)$$

and at T^-, or 0^-, $e_{in}(0^-) = 0$ and $v_o(0^-) = E$. Then $v_C(0^-) = -E$, and since $v_C(0^-) \cong v_C(0^+)$ Eq. (5–202)

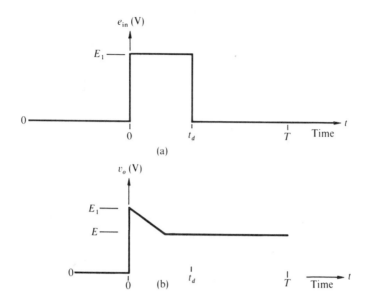

FIGURE 5–63

becomes

$$V_o(s) = \frac{E_1}{s + \dfrac{1}{RC}} + \frac{E}{s + \dfrac{1}{RC}}$$

so

$$v_o(t) = E_1 e^{-t/RC} u(t) + E e^{-t/RC} u(t)$$

where $T \equiv 0$. Since we are dealing with the range $T < t < t_d + T$

$$v_o(t) = (E_1 + E)e^{-t/RC} \qquad (5\text{-}203)$$

Substituting this into $E > v_o(t)$ in order to determine the diode's state we have $E > (E_1 + E)e^{-t/RC}$ or $E(1 - e^{-t/RC}) > E_1$. Now $E_1 > E$ from the statement of the problem and at $t = 0$ $E(1 - e^0) = 0 > E_1$, which is not true; likewise, as t approaches infinity $E(1 - e^{-\infty}) = E > E_1$, which also is not true. Therefore the diode is OFF for $t_d < t < t_d + T$ and $v_o(t)$ is described by Eq. (5–203). So far we have the waveform shown in Fig. 5–64(b).

For $t_d + T < t < 2T$

For the next range of $t_d + T < t < 2T$ we will again assume the diode is OFF and then test the validity of our

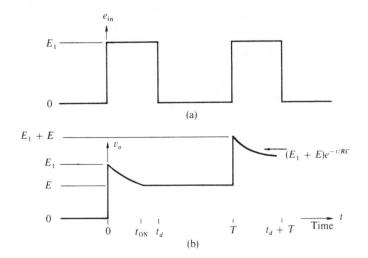

FIGURE 5–64

assumption using the condition $E > v_o(t)$ for ON. From the waveform of e_{in} we see that $e_{in}(t) = 0$ for this range, hence $E_{in}(s) = 0$. We now evaluate $v_C(0^+)$, the initial condition. The voltage still present on the capacitor at $t = (t_d + T)^+ = 0^+$, where $t_d + T$ is now defined as zero, is

$$v_C(0^+) = e_{in}(0^+) - v_o(0^+) = 0 - (E + E_1)e^{-(t_d+T)^+/RC}$$

since

$$v_o[(t_d + T)^+] = (E + E_1)e^{-t/RC}\Big|_{t=(t_d+T)^+} = (E + E_1)e^{-(t_d+T)^+/RC}$$

as stated by Eq. (5–203) and seen in Fig. 5–61(b). To understand, recall $v_C(0^-) \cong v_C(0^+)$ and for $t = 0^- = (t_d + T)^-$ the diode is OFF. So from Eq. (5–198)

$$V_o(s) = -\frac{(E + E_1)e^{-(t_d+T)/RC}}{s + \dfrac{1}{RC}}$$

or

$$v_o(t) = -[(E + E_1)e^{-(t_d+T)/RC}]e^{-t/RC}$$

Then for an ON diode

$$-[(E + E_1)e^{-(t_d+T)/RC}] < E$$

which is always true. Therefore at $t = (t_d + T)^+$ the diode is ON and $v_o(t) = E$. From this point on we will find periodicity. The waveform will appear as shown in Fig. 5-65(b).

(a)

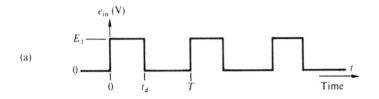

(b)

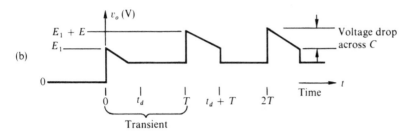

FIGURE 5-65

The next example will be basically the same circuit as Ex. 5-19; however, the time constant will be such as to make it perform a particular function. Its function is to add a desired dc level to the ac term $e_{in}(t)$. That is, it clamps the ac input to a dc level. This will be pointed out at the end of the analysis.

Example 5-20   Determine the mathematical expression for v_o given e'_{in} and the circuit of Fig. 5-66, where the polarities of e'_{in}, v_d, and v_o are assumed and $E_1 < E < E_2$.

Solution   Writing the loop equation for determining the state of diode

$$E - v_d(t) - v_o(t) = 0$$

therefore

$$v_d(t) = E - v_o(t) \qquad (5\text{-}204)$$

So, for the diode to turn ON requires that $E > v_o(t)$. The equivalent circuits for the diode ON and OFF are shown in Fig. 5-67(a) and (b). The equation describing the circuit for the OFF condition is

$$C \frac{d}{dt}[e'_{in}(t) - v_o(t)] + \frac{E - v_o(t)}{R} = 0$$

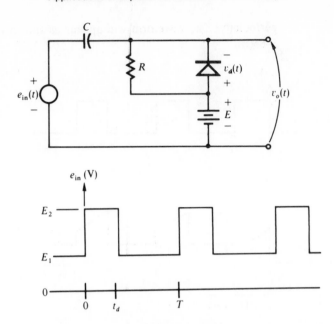

FIGURE 5–66

as found from Fig. 5–67(a). Taking the Laplace transform

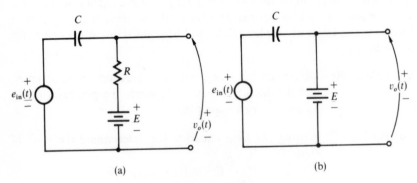

FIGURE 5–67

of this equation and solving for $V_o(s)$,

$$CsE'_{in}(s) + \frac{E}{Rs} = \left(\frac{1}{R} + Cs\right)V_o(s)$$

or

$$V_o(s) = \frac{sE'_{in}(s)}{s + \dfrac{1}{RC}} + \frac{E}{RCs\left(s + \dfrac{1}{RC}\right)} \qquad (5\text{--}205)$$

for initial conditions of zero. For e'_{in} as shown we may write

$$e_{in_{1ac}}(t) = \Delta E u(t) - \Delta E u(t - t_d)$$

therefore

$$e'_{in}(t) = E_1 u(t) + \Delta E \sum_{n=0}^{m} \{u(t - nT) - u[t - (t_d + nT)]\}$$
(5–206)

We will investigate the circuit for various t-ranges of e'_{in}, hence from Eq. (5–206) let $n = 0$,

$$e'_{in}(t)\Big|_{n=0} = E_1 u(t) + \Delta E u(t) - \Delta E u(t - t_d) \qquad (5\text{–}207)$$

The quantity $e'_{in}(t)|_{n=0}$ describes the first period e'_{in_1}, therefore we are investigating the t-range $0 < t < T$. Then

$$E'_{in_1}(s) = E'_{in}(s)\Big|_{n=0} = \frac{E_1}{s} + \frac{\Delta E}{s}(1 - e^{-t_d s})$$

$$= \frac{E_2}{s} - \frac{\Delta E e^{-t_d s}}{s} \qquad (5\text{–}208)$$

Substituting Eq. (5–208) into Eq. (5–205) we have

$$V_o(s) = \frac{E_2}{s + \dfrac{1}{RC}} - \frac{\Delta E e^{-t_d s}}{s + \dfrac{1}{RC}} + \frac{E}{RCs\left(s + \dfrac{1}{RC}\right)}$$

So

$$v_o(t) = [E_2 e^{-t/RC} + E(1 - e^{-t/RC})]u(t)$$
$$- \Delta E e^{-(t-t_d)/RC} u(t - t_d) \qquad (5\text{–}209)$$

To determine if the diode is ON or OFF during the time $0 < t < t_d$ we investigate Eq. (5–209) for this range and then compare it with E volts as stated by the inequality $E > v_o(t)$ resulting from Eq. (5–204).

For $0 < t < t_d$

$$v_o(t) = E_2 e^{-t/RC} + E(1 - e^{-t/RC})$$
$$= E_2 q(\gamma) + E w(\gamma) \qquad (5\text{–}209)$$

by defining $\gamma = t/RC$ for Fig. 5–47(a) and (b). And from the ON condition $E > v_o(t)$ we have

$$E > E_2 e^{-t/RC} + E(1 - e^{-t/RC}) \qquad (5\text{–}210)$$

or $E e^{-t/RC} > E_2 e^{-t/RC}$ which simply states

$$E > E_2 \qquad (5\text{–}211)$$

Now in order for the diode to turn ON E has to be greater than E_2, which is not true for this example. Therefore the diode is OFF for $0 < t < t_d$ and v_o behaves according to Eq. (5–209).

Let us make the RC time constant large ($RC \cong 10t_d$) so that for the entire range $0 < t < t_d$ we would find $w(\gamma) \cong 0$ and $q(\gamma) \cong 1.0$ of Eq. (5–210). Thus for $0 < t < t_d$ we may write

$$v_o(t) \cong E_2 \qquad\qquad (5\text{--}212)$$

For the next time range we have:

For $t_d < t < T$

From Eq. (5–209)

$$v_o(t) = E_2 e^{-t/RC} + E(1 - e^{-t/RC}) - \Delta E e^{-(t-t_d)/RC}$$
$$\cong E_2 e^{-t/RC} + E(1 - e^{-t/RC}) - \Delta E^{-t/RC}$$

since

$$e^{-t_d/RC} = e^{0.1} \cong 1.0$$

So

$$v_o(t) \cong E_1 e^{-t/RC} + E(1 - e^{-t/RC}) \qquad (5\text{--}213)$$

Testing to see if the diode is ON we evaluate the inequality $E > v_o(t)$, which is

$$E > [E_1 e^{-t/RC} + E(1 - e^{-t/RC})]$$
$$E e^{-t/RC} > E_1 e^{-t/RC}$$

or

$$E > E_1$$

From the statement of the problem it is true that $E > E_1$, hence the diode is turned ON at $t = t_d$. Then at $t = t_d$ Fig. 5–67(b) is valid and $v_o(t) = E$.

For the next time range we are essentially repeating the steps we have already performed in deriving Eq. (5–205) except that our initial conditions have changed. That is, taking the Laplace of the differential equation describing the OFF condition we have

$$CsE'_{in}(s) - C[e_{in}(0^+) - v_o(0^+)] + \frac{E}{Rs} = \left(\frac{1}{R} + Cs\right)V_o(s)$$
$$(5\text{--}214)$$

Now, look at Fig. 5–67(b) and write a loop equation such that one solves for the voltage drop across the capacitor C. Labeling this voltage v_C we have

$$v_C(t) = v_o(t) - e_{\text{in}}(t)$$

so

$$v_C(0^+) = v^o(0^+) - e_{\text{in}}(0^+)$$

Then Eq. (5–214) can be written as

$$CsE'_{\text{in}}(s) + Cv_C(0^+) + \frac{E}{Rs} = \left(\frac{1}{R} + Cs\right)V_o(s)$$

To determine the initial voltage across the capacitance, we recall that $v_C(0^-) = v_C(0^+)$ for capacitance, where this is true since capacitors resist change in potential across them. To find $v_C(0^-)$ return to Fig. 5–67(b) for $t_d < t < T$. Now at $t = T^-$ we find $v_C(T^-) = E - E_1$ and since time is relative we define $T \equiv 0$ so $v_C(0^-) = E - E_1$, then $v_C(0^+) = E - E_1$.

Hence,

$$V_o(s) = \frac{sE'_{\text{in}}(s)}{s + \dfrac{1}{RC}} + \frac{E - E_1}{s + \dfrac{1}{RC}} + \frac{E}{RCs\left(s + \dfrac{1}{RC}\right)} \qquad (5\text{–}215)$$

or

$$V_o(s) = \frac{E_2}{s + \dfrac{1}{RC}} - \frac{\Delta E e^{-t_d s}}{s + \dfrac{1}{RC}} + \frac{E - E_1}{s + \dfrac{1}{RC}} + \frac{E}{RCs\left(s + \dfrac{1}{RC}\right)}$$

Thus

$$V_o(s) = \frac{E_2 - E_1}{s + \dfrac{1}{RC}} - \frac{\Delta E e^{-t_d s}}{s + \dfrac{1}{RC}} + \frac{E}{s + \dfrac{1}{RC}} + \frac{E}{RCs\left(s + \dfrac{1}{RC}\right)}$$

$$= \frac{\Delta E}{s + \dfrac{1}{RC}} - \frac{\Delta E e^{-t_d s}}{s + \dfrac{1}{RC}} + \frac{E}{s + \dfrac{1}{RC}} + \frac{E}{RCs\left(s + \dfrac{1}{RC}\right)}$$

$$(5\text{–}216)$$

since $\Delta E = E_2 - E_1$. Finding v_o from Eq. (5–216) we have

$$v_o(t) = \Delta E e^{-t/RC} u(t) - \Delta E e^{-(t-t_d)/RC} u(t - t_d)$$
$$+ E e^{-t/RC} u(t) + E(1 - e^{-t/RC}) u(t)$$
$$= \Delta E e^{-t/RC} u(t) - \Delta E e^{-(t-t_d)/RC} u(t - t_d) + E u(t)$$

$$(5\text{–}217)$$

Now for $T < t < t_d + 2T$, or $0 < t < t_d$ defining $T \equiv 0$, we have from Eq. (5–217)

$$v_o(t) = \Delta E e^{-t/RC} + E$$

since $u(t - t_d) = 0$. And for a long RC time constant $\Delta E e^{-t/RC} \cong \Delta E$ over the entire range of $T < t < t_d + 2T$ (recall for $t = t_d$ we have $t_d \cong RC/10$, or $e^{-0.1} \cong 1.0$) then we may approximate

$$v_o(t) \cong \Delta E + E \quad \text{for} \quad T < t < t_d + 2T \qquad \textbf{(5–218)}$$

if the diode is OFF. To determine the diode state we again evaluate $E > v_o(t)$ for the ON condition. Thus $E > \Delta E + E$, which says $0 > \Delta E$. From this we know the diode is OFF for $T < t < t_d + 2T$. At $t = 2T$ we would find that again $v_o(t) = E$. It can be said that v_o is periodic after the first period and appears as shown in Fig. 5–68.

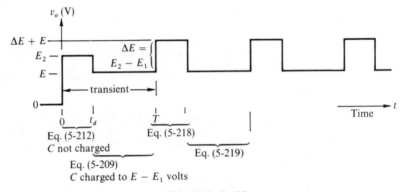

FIGURE 5–68

In viewing Fig. 5–68 we see that the transient term is due to the charging of C in the time range $0 < t < t_d$. Once the capacitor is charged the circuit's time constant is too large for that value of charge to change, hence the output voltage v_0 becomes steady. This type of circuit goes by the name of Clamper for it clamps the ac input ΔE at the dc level E [see Eq. (5–218)]. For the periodic portion of v_o (steady state) we could write the equation,

$$v'_{o_{ss}}(t) = v_o(t > T)$$
$$= Eu(t) + \Delta E \sum_{n=0}^{m} \{u(t - nT) - u[t - (t_d + nT)]\} \qquad \textbf{(5–219)}$$

where we have redefined $t = 0$ to be at T of the original problem and we primed $v_{o_{ss}}$ in keeping with our notation when a voltage is composed of both ac and dc terms.

5–11   Miscellaneous Examples

In all the previous sections a certain concept has been presented. For this section we wish to present some examples which are "just problems." In this section we hope the reader will be able to do much of the analysis. For this reason we will work the example problems with very little comment concerning procedure, etc. Some of the solutions are bulky and definitions of quantities will be made in order to simplify.

Example 5–21   For the circuit shown in Fig. 5–69 find v_0.

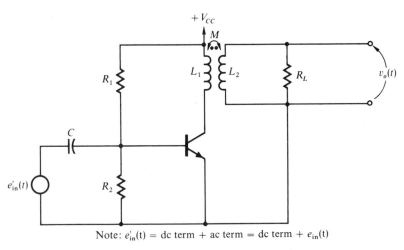

Note: $e'_{in}(t)$ = dc term + ac term = dc term + $e_{in}(t)$

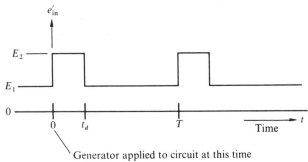

Generator applied to circuit at this time

FIGURE 5–69

Solution   The ac circuit for this problem is given in Fig. 5–70. Writing the differential equations for the circuit:

Output circuit

$$-h_{fe}i_b(t) - h_{oe}v_{ce}(t) - \Gamma_1 \int v_{ce}(t)\, dt - \Gamma_M \int v_0(t)\, dt = 0$$

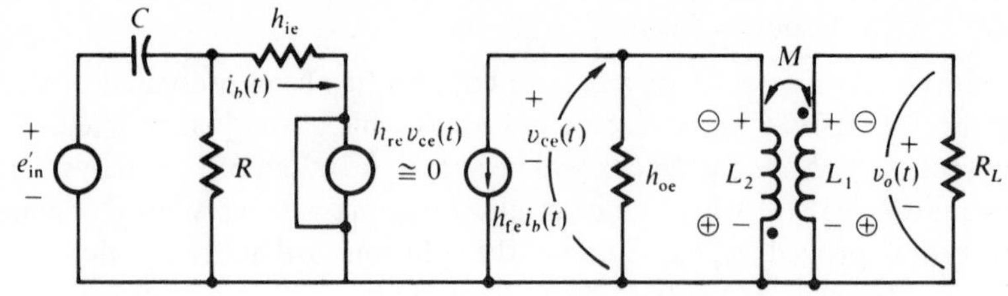

$$R = \frac{R_1 R_2}{R_1 + R_2}$$

$h_{re}v_{ce}(t)$ is short-circuited since $h_{re} \cong 0$
$v_o(t)$ is an assumed polarity

FIGURE 5–70

and

$$-\Gamma_2 \int v_o(t)\,dt - \Gamma_M \int v_{ce}(t)\,dt - \frac{v_o(t)}{R_L} = 0$$

Then

$$-h_{fe}I_b(s) = \left(h_{oe} + \frac{\Gamma_1}{s}\right)V_{ce}(s) + \frac{\Gamma_M}{s}V_o(s)$$

and

$$0 = \frac{\Gamma_M}{s}V_{ce}(s) + \left(\frac{1}{R_L} + \frac{\Gamma_2}{s}\right)V_o(s)$$

Solving for $V_o(s)$

$$
\Delta = \begin{vmatrix} \left(h_{oe} + \dfrac{\Gamma_1}{s}\right) & \dfrac{\Gamma_M}{s} \\[2mm] \dfrac{\Gamma_M}{s} & \left(\dfrac{1}{R_L} + \dfrac{\Gamma_2}{s}\right) \end{vmatrix}
$$

$$= \left(h_{oe} + \frac{\Gamma_1}{s}\right)\left(\frac{1}{R_L} + \frac{\Gamma_2}{s}\right) - \left(\frac{\Gamma_M}{s}\right)^2$$

$$= \frac{h_{oe}}{R_L} + \left(\frac{\Gamma_1}{R_L} + h_{oe}\Gamma_2\right)\frac{1}{s} + (\Gamma_1\Gamma_2 - \Gamma_M^2)\frac{1}{s^2}$$

$$= \frac{s^2\dfrac{h_{oe}}{R_L} + \left(\dfrac{\Gamma_1}{R_L} + h_{oe}\Gamma_2\right)s + (\Gamma_1\Gamma_2 + \Gamma_M^2)}{s^2}$$

$$= \frac{h_{oe}\left[s^2 + \dfrac{R_L}{h_{oe}}\left(\dfrac{\Gamma_1}{R_L} + h_{oe}\Gamma_2\right)s + \dfrac{R_L}{h_{oe}}(\Gamma_1\Gamma_2 - \Gamma_M^2)\right]}{R_L s^2}$$

$$= \frac{h_{oe}\left[s^2 + \left(\dfrac{\Gamma_1}{h_{oe}} + R_L\Gamma_2\right)s + (\Gamma_1\Gamma_2 - \Gamma_M^2)\dfrac{R_L}{h_{oe}}\right]}{R_L s^2}$$

and

$$\Delta V_o(s) = \begin{vmatrix} h_{oe} + \dfrac{\Gamma_1}{s} & -h_{fe}I_b(s) \\[2ex] \dfrac{\Gamma_M}{s} & 0 \end{vmatrix} = \dfrac{h_{fe}\Gamma_M I_b(s)}{s}$$

therefore,

$$V_o(s) = \frac{h_{fe}\Gamma_M R_L}{h_{oe}} \left[\frac{sI_b(s)}{s^2 + \left(\dfrac{\Gamma_1}{h_{oe}} + R_L\Gamma_2\right)s + (\Gamma_1\Gamma_2 - \Gamma_M^2)\dfrac{R_L}{h_{oe}}} \right]$$

We now solve for $I_b(s)$:

<u>Input circuit</u>

Writing loop equations from Fig. 5–71 we have,

$$e'_{in}(t) - Ri_1(t) + Ri_b(t) = 0$$

$$Ri_1(t) - \frac{1}{C} \int i_b(t)\, dt - (R + h_{ie})i_b(t) = 0$$

$$E'_{in}(s) = RI_1(s) - RI_b(s)$$

$$0 = -RI_1(s) + \left[\frac{1}{Cs} + (R + h_{ie}) \right] I_b(s)$$

$$\Delta = \begin{vmatrix} R & -R \\ -R & \left[\dfrac{1}{Cs} + (R + h_{ie})\right] \end{vmatrix} = R\left[\frac{1}{Cs} + (R + h_{ie})\right] - R^2$$

$$= Rh_{ie} + \frac{R}{Cs} = \frac{Rh_{ie}\left(s + \dfrac{1}{h_{ie}C}\right)}{s}$$

$$\Delta I_b(s) = \begin{vmatrix} R & E'_{in}(s) \\ -R & 0 \end{vmatrix} = RE'_{in}(s)$$

$$I_b(s) = \frac{sE'_{in}(s)}{h_{ie}\left(s + \dfrac{1}{h_{ie}C}\right)}$$

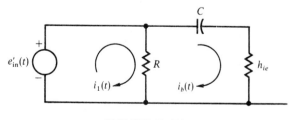

FIGURE 5–71

Then

$$V_o(s) = \frac{h_{fe}\Gamma_M R_L}{h_{ie}h_{oe}}$$

$$\times \frac{s^2 E'_{in}(s)}{\left(s+\dfrac{1}{h_{ie}C}\right)\left[s^2+\left(\dfrac{\Gamma_1}{h_{oe}}+h_{oe}\Gamma_2\right)s+(\Gamma_1\Gamma_2-\Gamma_M^2)\dfrac{R_L}{h_{oe}}\right]}$$

Writing an equation for $E'_{in}(s)$,

$$e'_{in}(t) = E_1 u(t) + \Delta E \sum_{n=0}^{m} \{u(t-nT) - u[t-(t_d+nT)]\}$$

so,

$$E'_{in}(s) = \frac{E_1}{s} + \frac{\Delta E}{s} \sum_{n=0}^{m} (e^{-nTs} - e^{-(t_d+nT)s})$$

Therefore,

$$V_o(s) = \frac{h_{fe}\Gamma_M R_L}{h_{ie}h_{oe}}$$

$$\times \frac{s\left[E_1 + \Delta E \sum_{n=0}^{m} (e^{-nTs} - e^{-(t_d+nT)s})\right]}{\left(s+\dfrac{1}{h_{ie}C}\right)\left[s^2+\left(\dfrac{\Gamma_1}{h_{oe}}+h_{oe}\Gamma_2\right)s+(\Gamma_1\Gamma_2-\Gamma_M^2)\dfrac{R_L}{h_{oe}}\right]}$$

We will use partial fractions, which means we are to factor the quadratic into $(s+\alpha)(s+\beta)$. We know that for this quadratic $\zeta > 1$ since there is no C present in the quadratic. Hence,

$$s_{1,2} = -\frac{1}{2}\left(\frac{\Gamma_1}{h_{oe}} + h_{oe}\Gamma_2\right)$$

$$\pm \frac{1}{2}\sqrt{\left(\frac{\Gamma_1}{h_{oe}} + h_{oe}\Gamma_2\right)^2 - \frac{4R_L}{h_{oe}}(\Gamma_1\Gamma_2 - \Gamma_M^2)}$$

which can be numerically evaluated once numerical values are known for the components. For simplification we define

$$\alpha \equiv \frac{1}{2}\left[\left(\frac{\Gamma_1}{h_{oe}} + h_{oe}\Gamma_2\right) - \sqrt{\left(\frac{\Gamma_1}{h_{oe}} + h_{oe}\Gamma_2\right)^2 - \frac{4R_L}{h_{oe}}(\Gamma_1\Gamma_2 - \Gamma_M^2)}\right]$$

and

$$\beta \equiv \frac{1}{2}\left[\left(\frac{\Gamma_1}{h_{oe}} + h_{oe}\Gamma_2\right) + \sqrt{\left(\frac{\Gamma_1}{h_{oe}} + h_{oe}\Gamma_2\right)^2 - \frac{4R_L}{h_{oe}}(\Gamma_1\Gamma_2 - \Gamma_M^2)}\right]$$

Then

$$V_o(s) = \frac{h_{fe} \Gamma_M R_L}{h_{ie} h_{oe}} \frac{s \left[E_1 + \Delta E \sum_{n=0}^{m} (e^{-nTs} - e^{-(t_d + nT)s}) \right]}{\left(s + \frac{1}{h_{ie}C} \right)(s + \alpha)(s + \beta)}$$

On investigation we see that we want the partial fraction of

$$\frac{s}{\left(s + \frac{1}{h_{ie}C} \right)(s + \alpha)(s + \beta)}$$

since $e^{-\gamma s}$ in the numerator only indicates shifting. Hence

$$\frac{s}{\left(s + \frac{1}{h_{ie}C} \right)(s + \alpha)(s + \beta)} = \frac{K_1}{s + \frac{1}{h_{ie}C}} + \frac{K_2}{s + \alpha} + \frac{K_3}{s + \beta}$$

where

$$K_1 = \frac{-\frac{1}{h_{ie}C}}{\left(-\frac{1}{h_{ie}C} + \alpha \right)\left(-\frac{1}{h_{ie}C} + \beta \right)}$$

$$= -\frac{1}{\left[\frac{1 + \alpha\beta}{h_{ie}C} - (\alpha + \beta) \right]}$$

$$K_2 = \frac{-\alpha}{\left(-\alpha + \frac{1}{h_{ie}C} \right)(-\alpha + \beta)}$$

$$= -\frac{1}{\left[\left(\alpha + \frac{\beta}{\alpha h_{ie}C} \right) - \left(\beta + \frac{1}{h_{ie}C} \right) \right]}$$

$$K_3 = \frac{-\beta}{\left(-\beta + \frac{1}{h_{ie}C} \right)(-\beta + \alpha)}$$

$$= -\frac{1}{\left[\left(\beta + \frac{\alpha}{\beta h_{ie}C} \right) + \left(\alpha + \frac{1}{h_{ie}C} \right) \right]}$$

Now, once numerical values are known for the circuit, K_1, K_2, and K_3 are just numbers. For convenience we will determine the inverse Laplace in terms of K_1, K_2, and K_3. Hence,

$$V_o(s) = \frac{h_{fe} \Gamma_M R_L}{h_{ie} h_{oe}} \left[\frac{K_1}{s + \frac{1}{h_{ie}C}} + \frac{K_2}{s + \alpha} + \frac{K_3}{s + \beta} \right]$$

$$\times \left[E_1 + \Delta E \sum_{n=0}^{m} (e^{-nTs} e^{-(t_d + nT)s}) \right]$$

where the negative signs from K_1, K_2, and K_3 were factored to show we assumed the wrong polarity for $v_o(t)$. Finding v_o from $V_o(s)$ we have,

$$v_o(t) = -\left\{\frac{h_{fe}\Gamma_M R_L E_1}{h_{ie}h_{oe}}(K_1 e^{-t/h_{ie}C} + K_2 e^{-\alpha t} + K_3 e^{-\beta t})u(t)\right.$$

$$+ \underbrace{\frac{h_{fe}\Gamma_M R_L \Delta E}{h_{ie}h_{oe}}(K_1 e^{-t/h_{ie}C} + K_2 e^{-\alpha t} + K_3 e^{-\beta t})u(t)}_{n=0}$$

$$+ \frac{h_{fe}\Gamma_M R_L \Delta E}{h_{ie}h_{oe}}[(K_1 e^{-(t-T)/h_{ie}C} + K_2 e^{-\alpha(t-T)}$$

$$+ K_3 e^{-\beta(t-T)})u(t-T) - (K_1 e^{-[t-(t_d+T)]/h_{ie}C}$$

$$+ K_2 e^{-\alpha[t-(t_d+T)]} + K_3 e^{-\beta[t-(t_d+T)]})u[t-(t_d+T)]]$$

$$+ \cdots + \frac{h_{fe}\Gamma_M R_L \Delta E}{h_{ie}h_{oe}}[(K_1 e^{-(t-mT)/h_{ie}C} + K_2 e^{-\alpha(t-mT)}$$

$$+ K_3 e^{-\beta(t-mT)})u(t-mT) - (K_1 e^{-[t-(t_d+mT)]/h_{ie}C}$$

$$+ K_2 e^{-\alpha[t-(t_d+mT)]} + K_3 e^{-\beta[t-(t_d+mT)]})u[t-(t_d+mT)]]$$

or

$$v_o(t) = -\frac{h_{fe}\Gamma_M R_L}{h_{ie}h_{oe}}\left\{\underbrace{(K_1 e^{-t/h_{ie}C} + K_2 e^{-\alpha t} + K_3 e^{-\beta t})E_1}_{\text{the dc term}}\right.$$

$$+ \Delta E \sum_{n=0}^{m}[(K_1 e^{-(t-nT)/h_{ie}C} + K_2 e^{-\alpha(t-nT)}$$

$$+ K_3 e^{-\beta(t-nT)})u(t-nT) - (K_1 e^{-[t-(t_d+nT)]h_{ie}C}$$

$$+ K_2 e^{-\alpha[t-(t_d+nT)]} + K_3 e^{-\beta[t-(t_d+nT)]})u[t-(t_d+nT)]$$

To graph v_o we would return to using our universal graphs.

Notice the dc term of v_o is a transient; that is, as t approaches infinity the dc term approaches zero. Of course we knew this would happen since neither the capacitor nor the transformer will pass dc. In fact, we see both components causing E to decay to zero, that is, $K_1 E_1 e^{-t/h_{ie}C}$ for the capacitor and $E_1(K_2 e^{-\alpha t} + K_3 e^{-\beta t})$ for the transformer.

Example 5–22 For a circuit with a gain, $G(s)$, find v_o for the e_{in} shown in Fig. 5–72.

Solution $V_o(s) = E_{in}(s)/\{RC[s + (1/RC)]\}$ as seen from $G(s)$. Hence,

$$e_{in}(t) = \frac{E}{t_d}tu(t) - \frac{E}{t_d}(t-t_d)u(t-t_d) - Eu(t-t_d)$$

$$E_{in}(s) = \frac{E}{t_d}\left(\frac{1}{s^2} - \frac{e^{-t_d s}}{s^2}\right) - \frac{Ee^{-t_d s}}{s}$$

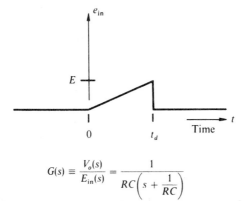

$$G(s) \equiv \frac{V_o(s)}{E_{in}(s)} = \frac{1}{RC\left(s + \dfrac{1}{RC}\right)}$$

FIGURE 5–72

$$V_o(s) = \frac{E}{RCt_d}\left[\frac{1}{s^2\left(s + \dfrac{1}{RC}\right)} - \frac{e^{-t_d s}}{s^2\left(s + \dfrac{1}{RC}\right)}\right]$$
$$- \frac{Ee^{-t_d s}}{RCs\left(s + \dfrac{1}{RC}\right)}$$

Since Table 4–2 contains no quantities which appear as [constant/$s^2(s + $ constant$)$] we will use partial fractions. Using partial fractions to determine $\mathcal{L}^{-1}\{1/s^2[s + (1/RC)]\}$ we have,

$$\frac{1}{s^2\left(s + \dfrac{1.}{RC}\right)} = \frac{A_{11}}{s} + \frac{A_{12}}{s^2} + \frac{B_1}{s + \dfrac{1}{RC}}$$

Evaluating the constants,

$$A_{11} = \frac{d}{ds}\left(\frac{1}{s + \dfrac{1}{RC}}\right)\Bigg|_{s=0} = \frac{\left(s + \dfrac{1}{RC}\right)\cdot 0 - 1}{\left(s + \dfrac{1}{RC}\right)^2}\Bigg|_{s=0} = -(RC)^2$$

$$A_{12} = \frac{d^0}{ds^0}\left(\frac{1}{s + \dfrac{1}{RC}}\right)\Bigg|_{s=0} = RC$$

and

$$B_1 = \frac{1}{s^2}\Bigg|_{s=-1/RC} = (RC)^2$$

Therefore,

$$\frac{1}{s^2\left(s + \dfrac{1}{RC}\right)} = -\frac{(RC)^2}{s} + \frac{RC}{s^2} + \frac{(RC)^2}{s + \dfrac{1}{RC}}$$

so

$$\mathcal{L}^{-1}\left[\frac{1}{s^2\left(s + \dfrac{1}{RC}\right)}\right] = \mathcal{L}^{-1}\left[-\frac{(RC)^2}{s} + \frac{RC}{s^2} + \frac{(RC)^2}{s + \dfrac{1}{RC}}\right]$$

$$= [-(RC)^2 + RCt + (RC)^2 e^{-t/RC}]u(t)$$

$$= [(RC)^2(1 - e^{-t/RC}) + RCt]u(t)$$

$$= RC[RC(1 - e^{-t/RC}) + t]u(t)$$

Thus

$$v_o(t) = \frac{E}{RCt_d}\{RC[RC(1 - e^{-t/RC}) + t]u(t)$$
$$- RC[RC(1 - e^{-(t-t_d)/RC} + (t - t_d)]u(t - t_d)\}$$
$$- E(1 - e^{-(t-t_d)/RC})u(t - t_d)$$

$$v_o(t) = \frac{E}{t_d}\{[RC(1 - e^{-t/RC}) + t]u(t)$$
$$- [RC(1 - e^{-(t-t_d)/RC}) + (t - t_d)]u(t - t_d)\}$$
$$- E(1 - e^{-(t-t_d)/RC})u(t - t_d)$$

Example 5–23 Find i_3 from the circuit shown in Fig. 5–73, where the loop currents are already shown.

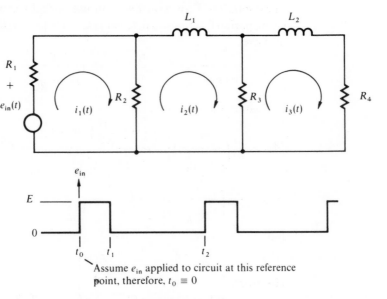

Assume e_{in} applied to circuit at this reference point, therefore, $t_0 \equiv 0$

FIGURE 5–73

Solution   Writing the loop equations we have

$$e_{in}(t) = (R_1 + R_2)i_1(t) - R_2i_2(t)$$

$$0 = -R_2i_1(t) + (R_2 + R_3)i_2(t) + L_1\frac{di_2(t)}{dt} - R_3i_3(t)$$

$$0 = -R_3i_2(t) + (R_3 + R_4)i_3(t) + L_2\frac{di_3(t)}{dt}$$

Taking the Laplace transform,

$$E_{in}(s) = (R_1 + R_2)I_1(s) - R_2I_2(s)$$

$$0 = -R_2I_1(s) + [(R_2 + R_3) + L_1s]I_2(s) - R_3I_3(s)$$

$$0 = -R_3I_2(s) + [(R_3 + R_4) + L_2s]I_3(s)$$

since

$$i_1(0^+) = i_2(0^+) = i_3(0^+) = 0$$

Now solving for $I_3(s)$

$$\Delta = \begin{vmatrix} (R_1 + R_2) & -R_2 & 0 \\ -R_2 & [(R_2+R_3)+L_1s] & -R_3 \\ 0 & -R_3 & [(R_3+R_4)+L_2s] \end{vmatrix}$$

$$\Delta = (R_1 + R_2)\begin{vmatrix} [(R_2 + R_3) + L_1s] & -R_3 \\ -R_3 & [(R_3 + R_4) + L_2s] \end{vmatrix}$$

$$- (-R_2)\begin{vmatrix} -R_2 & 0 \\ -R_3 & [(R_3 + R_4) + L_2s] \end{vmatrix}$$

$$= (R_1 + R_2)\{[(R_2 + R_3) + L_1s][(R_3 + R_4) + L_2s] - R_3^2\}$$
$$+ R_2\{-R_2[(R_3 + R_4) + L_2s]\}$$

$$= (R_1 + R_2)\{(R_2 + R_3)(R_3 + R_4) + [L_1(R_3 + R_4)$$
$$+ L_2(R_2 + R_3)s + L_1L_2s^2 - R_3^2\}$$
$$- R_2^2[(R_3 + R_4) + L_2s]$$

$$= (R_1 + R_2)(R_2 + R_3)(R_3 + R_4) - R_3^2(R_1 + R_2)$$
$$- R_2^2(R_3 + R_4)(R_1 + R_2)[L_1(R_3 + R_4)$$
$$+ L_2(R_2 + R_3) - R_2^2L_2]s + (R_1 + R_2)L_1L_2s^2$$

Factoring $(R_1 + R_2)L_1L_2$ so as to force the coefficient of s^2 to unity

$$\Delta = (R_1 + R_2)L_1L_2\left[\frac{(R_1 + R_2)(R_2 + R_3)(R_3 + R_4)}{(R_1 + R_2)L_1L_2} - R_3^2(R_1 + R_2) - R_2^2(R_3 + R_4)}{}\right.$$

$$\left.\frac{[L_1(R_3 + R_4) + L_2(R_2 + R_3) - R_2^2L_2]}{L_1L_2}s + s^2\right]$$

which is of the same form as $s^2 + 2\zeta\omega_n s + \omega_n^2$. Since no capacitance is present, then $\zeta > 1$. So let us conveniently write

$$\Delta = (R_1 + R_2)L_1 L_2(s + \alpha)(s + \beta)$$

and

$$\Delta I_3(s) = \begin{vmatrix} (R_1 + R_2) & -R_2 & E_{in}(s) \\ -R_2 & [(R_2 + R_3) + L_1 s] & 0 \\ 0 & -R_3 & 0 \end{vmatrix}$$

$$= -(-R_2)[R_3 E_{in}(s)] = R_2 R_3 E_{in}(s),$$

so

$$I_3(s) = \frac{R_2 R_3 E_{in}(s)}{(R_1 + R_2)L_1 L_2(s + \alpha)(s + \beta)}$$

Writing the necessary equation for $e_{in}(t)$ we have,

$$e_{in_1}(t) = Eu(t) - Eu(t - t_1)$$

therefore,

$$e_{in}(t) = E \sum_{n=0}^{m} \{u(t - nt_2) - u[t - (t_1 + nt_2)]\}$$

So

$$E_{in}(s) = \frac{E}{s} \sum_{n=0}^{m} (e^{-nt_2 s} - e^{-(t_1 + nt_2)s})$$

Then

$$I_3(s) = \frac{R_2 R_3 E}{(R_1 + R_2)L_1 L_2} \frac{\sum_{n=0}^{m} (e^{-nt_2 s} - e^{(t_1 + nt_2)s}}{s(s + \alpha)(s + \beta)}$$

Finding $i_3(t)$ we have

$$i_3(t) = \frac{R_2 R_3 E}{(R_1 + R_2)L_1 L_2} \left\{ \frac{1}{\alpha\beta} \left[\left(1 \sum_{n=0}^{m} u(t - nt_2) \right. \right. \right.$$

$$\left. - \frac{\beta e^{-\alpha t} \sum_{n=0}^{m} e^{n\beta t_2} u(t - nt_2)}{\beta - \alpha} + \frac{\alpha e^{-\beta t} \sum_{n=0}^{m} e^{n\beta t_2} u(t - nt)_2}{\beta - \alpha} \right)$$

$$- \left(1 \sum_{n=0}^{m} u[t - (t_1 + nt_2)] \right.$$

$$- \frac{\beta e^{-\alpha t} \sum_{n=0}^{m} e^{\alpha(t_1 + nt_2)} u[t - (t_1 + nt_2)]}{\beta - \alpha}$$

$$\left. \left. \left. + \frac{\alpha e^{-\beta t} \sum_{n=0}^{m} e^{\beta(t_1 + nt_2)} u[t - (t_1 + nt_2)]}{\beta - \alpha} \right) \right] \right\}$$

While i_3 appears to be very difficult to graph, remember we would only consider a period at a time until periodicity was established. Also we would use our universal graphs. That is, for $n = 0$ we would write i_3 as

$$i_3(t) = \frac{R_2 R_3 E}{(R_1 + R_2) L_1 L_2 \alpha \beta} \left\{ \left(1 - \frac{\beta e^{-\alpha t}}{\beta - \alpha} + \frac{\alpha e^{-\beta t}}{\beta - \alpha}\right) u(t) \right.$$
$$\left. - \left(1 - \frac{\beta e^{-\alpha(t - t_1)}}{\beta - \alpha} + \frac{\alpha e^{-\beta(t - t_1)}}{\beta - \alpha}\right) u(t - t_1) \right\}$$

or

$$i_3(t) = \frac{R_2 R_3 E}{(R_1 + R_2) L_1 L_2 \alpha \beta} [\theta(x) u(x) - \theta(x') u(x')]$$

where

$$x' = x - x_1 = \omega_n \sqrt{\zeta^2 - 1}(t - t_1)$$

and then continue as before.

6 Application of Laplace Transform to Network Analysis

6-1 Introduction

This chapter will treat topics related to network analysis. We will begin in section 6–2 by investigating transfer functions, which will give us an even greater appreciation for the algebraic qualities of Laplace transforms. We will also have use for the transfer function concept in other sections to be presented.

From our treatment of transfer functions we will make an introductory investigation into circuit synthesis. Because of the space available to treat such an involved topic we can hope for little more than an introduction. It is hoped that by this introduction one will have gained enough knowledge to continue his studies in this area as the need arises.

The next topic is ac impedance concepts developed from Laplace transforms. This section will help the reader to tie his elementary ac circuit analysis to the more complex Laplace transform analysis.

Our last topic of this chapter is two-network analysis, where we will work in the s-plane.

6-2 Transfer Functions

There is an important point to be derived from Exs. 5–17 and 5–19. Refer back to the general expression derived for $V_o(s)$ in Ex. 5–17; that is,

$V_o(s) = [1/RC(s + 1/RC)]E_{in}(s)$. Now, if you wanted to know the behavior of the circuit, in the time domain, regardless of e_{in}, you would simply like to form the ratio of output to input, which is termed gain, and then find the inverse Laplace of the gain. That is

$$\frac{V_o(s)}{E_{in}(s)} \equiv \text{Gain} = G(s) = \frac{1}{RC\left(s + \dfrac{1}{RC}\right)} \tag{6-1}$$

where the quantity $1/RC(s + 1/RC)$ is called the transfer function of the circuit since it could be looked upon as transferring the input $E_{in}(s)$ to the output $V_o(s)$. When we wish to express the transfer function we will use the symbol T. If we are in the s-plane we will write $T(s)$ and if in the t-plane $T(t)$. We will always write the transfer function in implicit form so as to distinguish it from the period T. One might notice that we could be accused of double naming the same term, that is, Eq. (6–1) states that $G(s) = 1/RC(s + 1/RC)$ and we just defined $T(s) = 1/RC(s + 1/RC)$. Well, we have in the one sense double named them but the difference lies in the meaning of definitions. The term "transfer function" is a general terminology while the term gain is a specific type of transfer function. When speaking of voltage or current gains we use $G(s)$ and form the ratio of output/input. However, when referring to putting a driving force into a circuit and having it "transferred" to some output force we define the equation which describes the circuit as being the transfer function $T(s)$ or $T(t)$. Then for this example

$$G(s) = T(s) = \frac{1}{RC\left(s + \dfrac{1}{RC}\right)}$$

We will see in not all instances $G(s) = T(s)$. The inverse Laplace of $T(s)$ is

$$T(t) = \frac{1}{RC}e^{-t/RC}u(t) \tag{6-2}$$

This approach would allow us to examine the characteristics of the circuit in the time domain.

We have witnessed in practice the means to carry out just such an investigation, that is the use of the unit impulse function. Consider again the equation

$$V_o(s) = \frac{E_{in}(s)}{RC\left(s + \dfrac{1}{RC}\right)} = T(s)E_{in}(s)$$

For e_{in} apply a pulse that has its pulse duration time t_d much much less than the circuit's time constant τ. Then e_{in} can be written as

$$e_{in}(t) = Et_d\,\delta(t)$$

and so

$$E_{in}(s) = Et_d$$

Then

$$V_o(s) = \frac{1}{RC\left(s + \frac{1}{RC}\right)} Et_d = Et_d T(s)$$

where

$$T(s) = \frac{1}{RC\left(s + \frac{1}{RC}\right)}$$

so

$$v_o(t) = \frac{Et_d}{RC} e^{-t/RC} u(t)$$

By forming the ratio $v_o(t)/Et_d$, we have a physical way to graph the transfer function of Eq. (6–2) in the time domain. Hence,

$$T(t) = \frac{v_o(t)}{Et_d} = \frac{1}{RC} e^{-t/RC} u(t) \qquad (6–3)$$

Then Fig. 5–54(a) could serve as a graph of $T(t)$, or $g(t)$ if gain is preferred, for the circuit used in Ex. 5–17 if we would divide the vertical axis by $Et_d = 15 \times 10^{-3} Rd/s$, or,

$$T(t) = \frac{v_o(t)}{15 \times 10^{-3}} = \frac{1}{0.50} e^{-t/0.5} u(t)$$

Example 6–1   For the circuit shown in Fig. 6–1 devise a means to display the voltage transfer function.

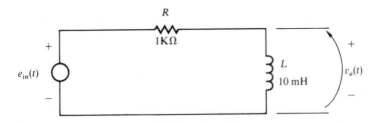

FIGURE 6–1

Solution   To determine the transfer function we will need to find $V_o(s) = T(s) E_{in}(s)$, which says to use nodal analysis. We must next determine t_d, which is found from the circuit's time constant given in $T(s)$. Lastly we will divide v_0 by the constants necessary to yield us $T(t)$. Hence:

$$\frac{e_{in}(t) - v_o(t)}{R} = \frac{1}{L} \int v_o(t)dt$$

$$\frac{E_{in}(s) - V_o(s)}{R} = \frac{1}{Ls}V_o(s) \text{ since } v_o^{-1}(0^+) = 0$$

Then

$$\frac{E_{in}(s)}{R} = \left(\frac{1}{R} + \frac{1}{Ls}\right)V_o(s) = \frac{1}{RLs}(Ls + R)V_o(s)$$

so

$$V_o(s) = \frac{sE_{in}(s)}{s + \dfrac{R}{L}} \qquad (6\text{-}4)$$

From Eq. (6–4) we see the circuit's time constant τ is L/R, or $\tau = L/R = 10^{-2}/10^3 = 10^{-5}$s. And from Eq. (5–181) we found it was required that $t_d > 0.1\tau$ in order to interpret our universal graph. Then we can reason $t_d < 0.1\tau$ would be required to apply the unit impulse function concept. Thus

$$t_d < 0.1(10^{-5}) = 10^{-6} = 1\mu s$$

so let us choose $t_d = 0.1\mu s$. Hence, for a *single pulse* we could express e_{in} as $e_{in}(t) = Et_d\delta(t)$, where E is the amplitude of the pulse. But since we want to display the voltage transfer function possibly on an oscilloscope we will need a repetitive driving force e_{in}. So e_{in} will be periodic, expressed as

$$e_{in}(t) = Et_d \sum_{n=0}^{m} \delta(t - nT)$$

where the period T must be large enough so that the circuit has sufficient time to reach a stable state between pulses. To be safe let us make the period five time constants or, mathematically, $T = 5\tau$. Thus $T = 5 \times 10^{-5}$ s, and

$$e_{in}(t) = Et_d \sum_{n=0}^{m} \delta(t - nT)$$

$$= E \times 10^{-7} \sum_{n=0}^{m} \delta(t - n5 \times 10^{-5}) \qquad (6\text{-}5a)$$

Taking the Laplace transform of Eq. (6–5) we have

$$E_{in}(s) = E \times 10^{-7} \sum_{n=0}^{m} e^{-n5 \times 10^{-5}s} \qquad (6\text{-}5b)$$

Substituting Eq. (6–6) into Eq. (6–4)

$$V_o(s) = \frac{s}{s + \dfrac{R}{L}} E \times 10^{-7} \sum_{n=0}^{m} e^{-n5 \times 10^{-5}s}$$

$$= \frac{s}{s + \dfrac{R}{L}} E \times 10^{-7} + \frac{se^{-5 \times 10^{-5}s}}{s + \dfrac{R}{L}} E \times 10^{-7} + \cdots$$

$$+ \frac{se^{-m5 \times 10^{-5}s}}{s + \dfrac{R}{L}} E \times 10^{-7} \tag{6-6}$$

From Eq. (6–4) we see that the transfer function $T(s)$ is $T(s) = s/(s + R/L)$, hence we will want to operate on Eq. (6–6) so that it appears as

$$\text{transfer function } T(s) = \frac{V_o(s)}{E \times 10^{-7}}$$

$$= \frac{s}{s + \dfrac{R}{L}} \sum_{n=0}^{m} e^{-n5 \times 10^{-5}s} \tag{6-7}$$

where we need the repetitiveness of $\sum_{n=0}^{m} e^{-n5 \times 10^{-5}s}$ so as to retain a trace on the scope. Then to find $T(t)$ we take the inverse of Eq. (6–7)

$$T(t) = \frac{v_o(t)}{E \times 10^{-7}} = \mathcal{L}^{-1} \left[\left(1 - \frac{\dfrac{R}{L}}{s + \dfrac{R}{L}} \right) \sum_{n=0}^{m} e^{-n5 \times 10^{-5}s} \right]$$

$$= \sum_{n=0}^{m} \left[\delta(t - n5 \times 10^{-5}) \right.$$

$$\left. - \frac{R}{L} e_{-(t - n5 \times 10^{-5})/(L/R)} u(t - n5 \times 10^{-5}) \right] \tag{6-8}$$

since $s/(s + R/L)$ is an improper fraction and is equal to $1 - [(R/L)/(s + R/L)]$ in proper form.

Since scopes trace potentials and not transfer functions we will have to modify Eq. (6–8). From Eq. (6–8) we find

$$v_o(t) = T(t)E \times 10^{-7}$$

$$= E \times 10^{-7} \sum_{n=0}^{m} \left[\delta(t - 5 \times 10^{-5}n) \right.$$

$$\left. - \frac{R}{L} e^{-t - 5 \times 10^{-5}n/(L/R)} u(t - n5 \times 10^{-7}) \right] \tag{6-9}$$

which can be displayed on a CRT. So v_0 is what we will display and to determine $T(t)$ we simply divide the vertical axis by $E \times 10^{-7}$.

It is now time to choose a value for E. This choice was purposefully held off until Eq. (6–9) was derived. This was done so we could make an intelligent choice for E's magnitude. From Eq. (6–9) we see that

$$v_o(t) = E \times 10^{-7}\delta(t) = \frac{RE \times 10^{-7}}{L}e^{-t/(R/L)}u(t) + \cdots$$

$$= E \times 10^{-7}\delta(t) - E \times 10^{-2}e^{-t/10^{-5}}u(t) + \cdots$$

Now, the magnitude of E will determine how sensitive a scope we must have. If we choose $E = 10$ volts we would have

$$v_o(t) = 10^{-6}\delta(t) - 10^{-1}e^{-t/10^{-5}}u(t) + \cdots$$

Where the term

$$E \times 10^{-7}\delta(t) = 10^{-6}\delta(t) = Et_d\delta(t)$$

$$= Et_d\left\{\frac{1}{t_d}\lim_{t_d \to 0}[u(t) - u(t - t_d)]\right\}$$

$$= E\lim_{t_d \to 0}[u(t) - u(t - t_d)]$$

realizing the width of δ is t_d (recall we are approximating t_d as zero). So

$$E \times 10^{-7}\delta(t)\Big|_{t=0} = E \times 10^{-7}\left(\frac{1}{t_d}\right)\Big|_{t_d=0} = Et_d\left(\frac{1}{t_d}\right)\Big|_{t=0}$$

$$= E\Big|_{t=0} = E = 10 \text{ V}$$

Thus $v_o(t) = 10|_{t=0} - 10^{-1}e^{-t/10^{-5}}u(t) + \ldots +$. The second term $10^{-1}e^{-t/10^{-5}}$ has a maximum value at $t = 0$, which is 10^{-1} volts. Since most scopes can detect 0.1 volt fairly accurately $E = 10$ volts would be a good choice. In effect we are using the magnitude of E as a scaling function for the height of v_o on our scope display.

With the choice $E = 10$ volts Eq. (6–9) can be written as

$$v_o(t) = 10^{-6}T(t)$$

$$= 10^{-6}\sum_{n=0}^{m}[\delta(t - 5 \times 10^{-5}n)$$

$$- 10^{5}e^{-(t-5\times10^{-5}n)/10^{-5}}u(t - 5 \times 10^{-5}n)]$$

$$= 10^{-6}\delta(t) - 0.1e^{-t/10^{-5}}u(t) + 10^{-6}\delta(t - 5 \times 10^{-5})$$

$$- 0.1e^{-(t-5\times10^{-5})/10^{-5}}u(t - 5 \times 10^{-5}) + \cdots$$

$$+ 10^{-6}\delta(t - 5 \times 10^{-5}m)$$

$$- 0.1e^{-(t-5\times10^{-5}m)/10^{-5}}u(t - 5 \times 10^{-5}m)$$

$$\tag{6–10}$$

Because of the magnitude we chose for the period T we know no initial conditions will be carried from one period to the next; hence we only need to determine points for the first period. This is so since our waveform will be periodic starting with the first period. Hence,

For $t = 0$: $u(t) = 0$ and $10^{-6}\delta(t) = E$

$$v_o(t) = 10^{-6}T(t) = 10^{-6}\delta(t) = E = 10 \text{ V} \qquad (6\text{–}11)$$

For $0 < t < T$: $u(t) = 1$ and $\delta(t) = 0$

$$v_o(t) = 10^{-6}T(t) = 0.1e^{-t/10^{-5}} = 0.1q(\gamma) \qquad (6\text{–}12)$$

where $\gamma = t/10^{-5}$ as seen from Fig. 5–47(a). It is important to point out that $10^{-6}\delta(t) = 10\big|_{t=0}$ volts means that we have 10 volts present *only* at $t = 0$. Finding the points for $q(\gamma)$ we refer to Fig. 5–47(a).

TABLE 6–1   For $0 < t < T = 5 \times 10^{-5}$, or
$0 < \gamma < \gamma_T = 5$ to plot Eq. (6–12)

γ	$q(r)$	$t = \gamma$ $\times 10^{-5}$ t in μs	$v_o(t)$ v_o in volts	$T(t) = \dfrac{v_o(t)}{Et_d} = \dfrac{v_o(t)}{10^{-6}}$ T in 10^6 dimensionless units
0.00^+	1.00	0.00	-0.100	-0.100
0.40	0.66	4.00	-0.066	-0.066
1.00	0.38	10.00	-0.038	-0.038
1.50	0.22	15.00	-0.022	-0.022
2.00	0.12	20.00	-0.012	-0.012
3.00	0.05	30.00	-0.005	-0.005
5.00	0.00^+	50.00	-0.000	-0.000

The graph of Eq. (6–10), which is the periodic of the first period expressed in Eqs. (6–11) and (6–12), appears in Fig. 6–2(b).

We should understand that v_o is what we will display on our oscilloscope. However, to interpret into $T(t)$ we need merely to divide v_o by 10^{-6} as was done for the extreme left-hand vertical axis of Fig. 6–2(b).

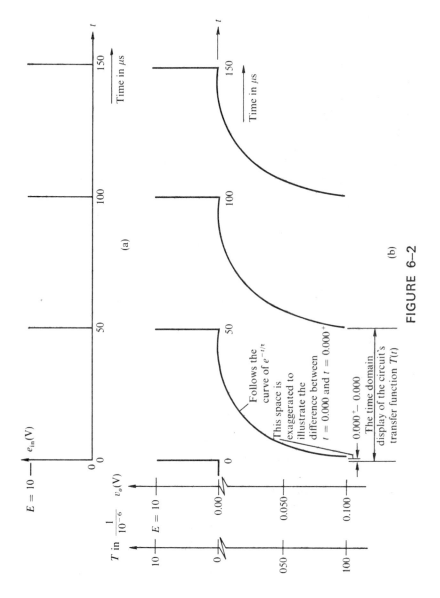

FIGURE 6-2

(a)

(b)

$e_{in}(V)$

$E = 10$

0

Time in μs

50   100   150 t

$v_o(V)$

$E = 10$

T in $\dfrac{1}{10^{-6}}$

0.00

0.050

0.100

10

050

100

0

Time in μs

50   100   150 t

Follows the
curve of $e^{-t/\tau}$

This space is
exaggerated to
illustrate the
difference between
$t = 0.000$ and $t = 0.000^+$

$0.000^+ - 0.000$

The time domain
display of the circuit's
transfer function $T(t)$

Let us now view the circuit and Fig. 6–2(a) and reason the correctness of Fig. 6–2(b) using elementary techniques. Now, we know that when E volts are applied to the circuit at $t = 0$, $50\mu s$, $100\mu s$, etc., the inductor will appear as an open-circuit circuit. Hence, at these times we are in effect measuring the open-circuit voltage as if L were removed, which would be E volts, or 10 volts, in our specific case. This agrees with Fig. 6–2(b). And during the actual duration of E (time t_d) we established some current through L. And at $t = t_d$ ($t = 0.000^+$) the voltage source E was removed. Now inductors attempt to maintain the current magnitude and direction already established. Hence, the inductor now looks like a source of energy. In order for the inductor to be a source current must flow out of its positive side, which is a reverse of polarity for v_o. This voltage across L is described by $-0.1e^{-t/\tau}$ where τ is the circuit's time constant. This also agrees with Fig. 6–2(b). The space shown between $t = 0$ and $t = 0.000^+$ is to indicate in exaggerated fashion that there is a difference between $t = 0$ and $t = 0.000^+$. Also we have no curve shown between these points, which simply says we neither know nor care what path was followed in going from $v_o(t = 0) = 10$ volts to $v_o(t = 0.000^+) = 0.1$ volt. If we did want this information we would have to make an analysis as we did to plot Fig. 5–54(b).

In view of the analysis just made let us discuss what we mean by "time-domain display of the circuit's transfer function." For the circuit of Ex. 6–1 we found that

$$\frac{e_{in}(t) - v_o(t)}{R} = \frac{1}{L} \int v_o(t)\, dt \tag{6–13}$$

Now, we would like to be able to perform some algebraic factoring on this equation and come up with the equation

$$v_o(t) = T(t)e_{in}(t) \tag{6–14}$$

where $T(t)$ is the circuit's transfer function. But this would be incorrect since we cannot properly factor Eq. (6–14). Recall this is the reason for Laplace transforms. So Eq. (6–14) is not valid in the way we are trying to use $T(t)$. Let us define a new symbol so that we can write $T(t)e_{in}(t)$ with some meaning. To develop and define this new symbol write Eq. (6–13) as

$$\frac{e_{in}(t)}{R} = \frac{1}{L} \int v_o(t)\, dt + \frac{v_o(t)}{R} = \left[\frac{1}{L} \int (\quad)\, dt + \frac{1}{R}\right] v_o(t)$$

or

$$v_o(t) = \left[\frac{1}{\dfrac{R}{L} \int (\quad)\, dt + 1}\right] e_{in}(t) = T(t)e_{in}(t) \tag{6–15}$$

where

$$T(t) = \cfrac{1}{\cfrac{R}{L} \int (\quad) \, dt + 1} \tag{6-16}$$

We may use Eq. (6–15) if we fully understand that $T(t)$ *is not* an algebraic quantity but rather an operational one. That is, when we see what appears as the product of $e_{in}(t)$ and $T(t)$, we realize that this is not a product as in algebra but rather $T(t)$ is operating upon $e_{in}(t)$. To give us a visual reminder we will use the symbol $\otimes$ as defined in section 1–3. The symbol $\otimes$ will mean ". . . operates upon. . . ." Thus

$$v_o(t) = T(t) \otimes e_{in}(t) \tag{6-17}$$

This means: $T(t)$ operates upon $e_{in}(t)$ to produce $v_o(t)$. Notice $T(t) \otimes e_{in}(t) \neq e_{in}(t) \otimes T(t)$ since $e_{in}(t) \otimes T(t)$ would be the same as saying $e_{in}(t)$ is operating upon $T(t)$.

Then from Eqs. (6–8) and (6–16)

$$T(t) = \cfrac{1}{\cfrac{R}{L} \int (\quad) \, dt + 1} = \delta(t) - \frac{R}{L} e^{-t/(L/R)} u(t) \tag{6-18}$$

where we need only consider $n = 0$ for Eq. (6–8). Recall the repetition of Eq. (6–8) was done so that we could display $T(t)$ on a scope. The equal sign of Eq. (6–18) means equivalence; that is, the operation $[1/(R/L)\int (\quad) dt + 1]$ is graphically equivalent to

$$\delta(t) - \frac{R}{L} e^{-t/(L/R)} u(t)$$

The primary use of $T(t)$ will be to circuit model a "black box." If we have some system, or black box, for which the circuit components are unknown, under our mode of operation we may model that system by finding $T(t)$. There is a point we wish to discuss concerning what we mean by "mode of operation." We know as frequency increases circuits look less and less like their component construction. And this is due to such phenomena as stray capacitance, interelectrode capacitance, component coupling, etc. Then to properly model a system we need it in operation in our time range of operation, or, as we termed it, "mode of operation." To model a circuit in this manner can be of great benefit since it is under operating conditions while being modeled. We will term this type of modeling *dynamic modeling*.

To determine t_d for a simulated unit impulse for dynamic modeling we will refer back to previous work. Recall earlier we specified that for a pulse to qualify as a unit impulse its pulse duration t_d must meet the requirement that $t_d < 0.1\tau$. Choosing t_d to be a tenth less we have

$$t_d = 0.01\tau \tag{6-19}$$

Also we specified that $T = 5\tau$; hence, from this and Eq. (6–19) we find $T = 500t_d$. Since this is not a hard and fast rule we will write this last equation as an approximation, thus

$$T \cong 500t_d \qquad \textbf{(6–20)}$$

Then our manner of approach will be to apply a periodic pulse to the black box where the period T of the pulse is the same as our intended mode of operation. The pulse duration will be determined by Eq. (6–20).

Example 6–2   Suppose we operate the black box shown in Fig. 6–3(a) at a frequency of 10×10^9 repetitions/second. To find

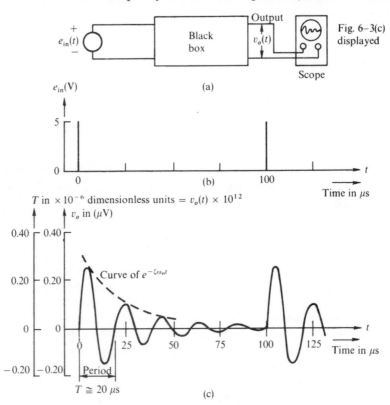

FIGURE 6–3

$T(t)$ we applied the unit impulses at this same frequency, which required

$$t_d \cong \frac{T}{500} = \frac{10^{-10}}{500} = 0.2 \times 10^{-12} \text{ s}$$

We arbitrarily pick $E = 5$ volts, so $Et_d = 5(0.2 \times 10^{-12})$ $= 10^{-12}\text{V}\cdot\text{s}$. Under these conditions the output voltage v_o was found to be as shown in Fig. 6–3(c). From Fig. 6–3(c) we ask ourselves "what can you tell about the black box?"

From Fig. 6–3(c) we see that v_o behaves as a damped sine wave which is generally described as

$$v_o(t) = \frac{k}{\omega_d} e^{-\zeta\omega_n t} \sin \omega_d t \, u(t) \text{ V} \qquad (6\text{–}21)$$

Recall $\omega_d = \omega_n \sqrt{1 - \zeta^2}$ and is termed the damp resonant frequency. To determine this frequency we merely refer to Fig. 6–3(c) and measure the period T, which is 20 μs. Thus

$$\omega_d = \frac{2\pi}{T} = \frac{2\pi}{20 \times 10^{-6}} = 0.314 \times 10^6 \text{ rad/s} \qquad (6\text{–}22)$$

Also from Fig. 6–3(c) we can determine the circuit time constant τ since $\zeta\omega_n = 1/\tau$. $\zeta\omega_n$ can be determined because of the presence of the curve of $e^{-\zeta\omega_n t}$, which is shown in dotted lines. We are able to do this since at maximum and minimum points $\sin \omega_d t = +1$ and -1 respectively, and this in effect removes $\sin \omega_d t$ from the equation. So at $t \cong 5\mu s = t_s$ we have $v_o(t_s) = 0.25 \times 10^{-6} = (k/\omega_d)e^{-\zeta\omega_n t_s}$, where $v_o(t_s)$ was determined graphically from Fig. 6–3(c). Also $v_o(t = 25\mu s) = 0.10 \times 10^{-6} = (k/\omega_d)e^{-\zeta\omega_n t_{25}}$. Solving each equation for k/ω_d and equating we have $k/\omega_d = 0.25 \times 10^{-6}e^{\zeta\omega_n t_s} = 0.10 \times 10^{-6}e^{\zeta\omega_n t_{25}}$. Therefore $0.25/0.10 = e^{\zeta\omega_n t_{25}}/e^{\zeta\omega_n t_s} = e^{\zeta\omega_n(t_{25}-t_s)} = 2.5$.

Taking $\log_e = \ln$ we find

$$\zeta\omega_n(t_{25} - t_s) = \ln 2.5$$

or

$$\zeta\omega_n = \frac{1}{\tau} = \frac{1}{t_{25} - t_s} \ln 2.5 = \frac{10^6}{20}(0.916) = 0.046 \times 10^6 \frac{1}{\text{s}}$$

$$(6\text{–}23)$$

Now that we know $\zeta\omega_n$ we may solve for K. Since we have already found $(K/\omega_d)e^{-\zeta\omega_n t_s} = 0.25 \times 10^{-6}$, where $\zeta\omega_n = 0.046 \times 10^6$ then $(K/\omega_d)e^{-0.046\times10^6 t_s} = 0.25 \times 10^{-6}$V, and $(K/\omega_d) = 0.25 \times 10^{-6}e^{0.046\times10^6 t_s} = 0.25e^{0.23} \times 10^{-6}$, or

$$\frac{K}{\omega_d} = 0.316 \times 10^{-6} \qquad (6\text{–}24)$$

Substituting Eqs. (6–22), (6–23), and (6–24) into Eq. (6–21) we have

$$v_o(t) = \frac{K}{\omega_d} e^{-\zeta\omega_n t} \sin \omega_d t$$

$$= 0.316 \times 10^{-6}e^{-0.046\times10^6 t} \sin 0.314 \times 10^6 t \, u(t)$$

$$(6\text{–}25)$$

Equation (6–25) is the mathematical expression for Fig. 6–3(c).

To determine $T(t)$ from Eq. (6–25) let us examine the transform of Eq. (6–25). Hence, taking the transform of Eq. (6–25)

$$V_o(s) = \frac{K}{s^2 + 2\zeta\omega_n s + \omega_n^2} \tag{6-26}$$

Now we know that the general equation for $V_o(s)$, valid for any e_{in} [remember the $V_o(s)$ of Eq. (6–26) was for the unit impulse being applied], is $T(s) = V_o(s)/E_{in}(s)$, or

$$V_o(s) = \frac{kE_{in}(s)}{s^2 + \zeta\omega_n s + \omega_n^2} = T(s)E_{in}(s) \tag{6-27}$$

where the constant K of Eq. (6–26) is different than the constant k of Eq. (6–27). And when we made e_{in} become a unit impulse we required $e_{in}(t) = Et_d\delta(t)$V looking only at the first period. Then $E_{in}(s) = Et_d$ and Eq. (6–27) becomes

$$V_o(s) = \frac{kEt_d}{s^2 + 2\zeta\omega_n s + \omega_n^2} \tag{6-28}$$

Equations (6–26) and (6–28) are the same, therefore $K = kEt_d$. From before we know $Et_d = 10^{-12}$, and from Eqs. (6–24) and (6–22) we can find

$$K = 0.316 \times 10^{-6}\omega_d = 0.316 \times 10^{-6}(0.314 \times 10^6)$$
$$= 0.10$$

So

$$k = \frac{K}{Et_d} = \frac{10^{-1}}{10^{-12}} = 10^{11} \tag{6-29}$$

Equation (6–27) states that

$$T(s) = \frac{k}{s^2 + 2\zeta\omega_n s + \omega_n^2} \tag{6-30}$$

so

$$T(t) = \frac{k}{\omega_d}e^{-\zeta\omega_n t}\sin\omega_d t$$

which can be found from Eq. (6–25) by substituting $K = kEt_d$ and then solving for $I(t)$ by dividing v_o by Et_d. Thus

$$v_o(t) = \frac{kEt_d}{\omega_d}e^{-\zeta\omega_n t}\sin\omega_d t$$

so

$$T(t) = \frac{v_o(t)}{Et_d} = \frac{k}{\omega_d}e^{-\zeta\omega_n t}\sin\omega_d t = \frac{v_o(t)}{10^{-12}}$$
$$= 0.317 \times 10^6 e^{-0.046\times10^6 t}\sin 0.314 \times 10^6 t \tag{6-31}$$

The graph of $T(t)$ is also shown in Fig. 6–3(c) where the extreme left-hand vertical scale applies.

In summary, we were able to write the expression for the output voltage v_o, which is expressed in Eq. (6–25). And from this equation we were able to develop an expression for $T(t)$ which is expressed in Eq. (6–31). We understand that the wave form of Fig. 6–3(c) is what we would view on our scope, assuming our scope is sensitive enough to read μ volts. If one wishes to increase the amplitude of v_o the value of E and t_d could be increased. Increasing t_d would be the most reasonable approach, but of course we do have to approach satisfying Eqs. (6–19) and (6–20).

We will consider one more example and then we will attempt to synthesize a circuit from $T(t)$.

In the example to be undertaken we will derive $T(t)$ as we did before; however, for this example we shall determine t_d experimentally. Given some circuit for which we wish to find $T(t)$ let us begin by applying some pulse which satisfies Eq. (6–20). Now if we wish $T(t)$ for the actual component and not those effects from stray capacitance, component coupling, etc., we must apply pulses which are as wide as possible in pulse duration. However, we must still approach $t_d \ll \tau$. In order to determine t_d we will apply a periodic pulse with an adjustable pulse duration t_d to the circuit and monitor the output voltage v_o. We will adjust t_d until the circuit is just unable to reach a steady state of zero volts for $nT < t < t_d + nT$. We will assume this is approximately five of the circuit's time constant τ. Then $5\,\tau \cong t_d$ or $\tau = t_d/5$. We will then take that value of τ and apply Eq. (6–19), which is $t_d = 0.01\,\tau$, which will indicate what value t_d should be adjusted to. After that we will adjust t_d to its new value and make the period T according to Eq. (6–20).

As an illustration of what we are saying look at Ex. 5–14. Now refer to Fig. 5–43 and recall we had just stated that we would widen t_d of e_{in} until steady state was just reached. From Fig. 5–43(b) we see that for a steady state to be reached in the time range $nT < t < t_d + nT$ for $n = 0$ or, $0 < t < t_d$, that t_d will have to be increased to approximately $40\eta s$. Then as we stated before $5\tau = 40 \times 10^{-9}$, so $\tau \cong 8 \times 10^{-9}$. To find its actual value we can refer to Eq. (5–107). From the term $e^{-82.5 \times 10^6 t}$ we know that $\tau = 1/82.5 \times 10^6 = 0.0121 \times 10^{-6} = 12.1 \times 10^{-9}$. Hence, for an "eye ball" guess $8\eta s$ is correct. Then in order to comply with the equation $t_d = 0.01\,\tau$ we must adjust t_d to $t_d = 0.01\,(8 \times 10^{-9}) = 80\eta s$. And from Eq. (6–19) we would make $T \cong 500\,t_d = 500(80 \times 10^{-12}) = 40\eta s$.

Example 6–3   Using the techniques described determine $T(t)$ for the black box of Fig. 6–4(a). Also display $T(t)$ graphically.

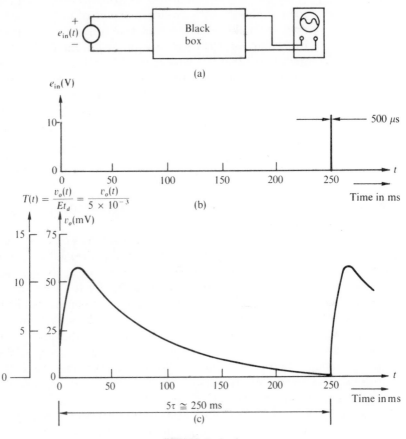

$$T(t) = \frac{v_o(t)}{Et_d} = \frac{v_o(t)}{5 \times 10^{-3}}$$

FIGURE 6–4

Solution   We must begin by applying an e_{in} such that v_o just reaches a steady state of zero volts for each time range of $nT < t < t_d + nT$. This was done and v_o appeared as illustrated in Fig. 6–4(c). From Fig. 6–4(c) we see then $5\tau \cong 250$ ms, therefore $\tau \cong 250 \times 10^{-3}/5 = 50$ ms. Let us now calculate the value of t_d for e_{in} that it took to accomplish v_o of Fig. 6–4(c) [if we had e_{in} displayed on a scope as shown in Fig. 6–4(b) we would simply expand the scale of the horizontal axis and determine t_d directly]. From the equation $t_d \cong 0.01\tau$ we calculate t_d to be $t_d \cong 0.01(50 \times 10^{-3}) = 500$ ms. From Fig. 6–4(b) a t_d

of 500 μs could be correct. As a check we also know that $T \cong 500\, t_d$, which for this case would be $T \cong 500(500 \times 10^{-6}) = 250$ ms, which agrees with the experimental value of T.

We can now write an equation for e_{in}. We begin by writing an equation for the first period of e_{in}, which is $e_{in_1}(t) = Et_d\delta(t)$. From Fig. 6–4(b) we see that $E = 10$ volts and we calculated $t_d = 500\,\mu$s so $Et_d = 10(500 \times 10^{-6}) = 5 \times 10^{-3}$ V·s. Hence,

$$e_{in}(t) = Et_d \sum_{n=0}^{m} \delta(t - nT)$$

$$= 5 \times 10^{-3} \sum_{n=0}^{m} \delta(t - n250 \times 10^{-3}) \quad \text{(6-32)}$$

We now search our universal curves to try and find a matching graph to Fig. 6–4(c) so that we may express v_o mathematically. We see that either one of the curves from Fig. 5–34(a) or Fig. 5–34(b) could be the curve for which we search. Probably the easiest and quickest way to determine which it might be is to assume that one of the curves is correct and then see if v_o behaves according to our assumption. That is, if $\zeta = 1$ then

$$v_{o_1}(t) = Kp(y) = ye^{-y} = K\omega_n t e^{-\omega_n t}$$

for the first period. Hence at

$$v_{o_1}(t = 10\text{ms}) = 55 \times 10^{-3} = K\omega_n(10 \times 10^{-3})e^{-\omega_n \times 10^{-2}}$$

To determine ω_n we know from Fig. 5–34(b) that $y_{max} = 1.00$ and from Fig. 6–4(c) $t_{max} = 15 \times 10^{-3}$s. Then from the relationship $y = \omega_n t$ we have

$$\omega_n = \frac{y_{max}}{t_{max}} = \frac{1.00}{15 \times 10^{-3}} = 0.067 \times 10^3 = 67$$

So

$$55 \times 10^{-3} = K(0.67)e^{-0.67} = K(0.67)(0.51) = 0.342K$$

or

$$K = \frac{55 \times 10^{-3}}{0.342} = 0.161$$

Picking a second point with which to determine K and see if it agrees with the value just determined let $t = 100$ ms. Thus

$$v_{o_1}(t = 100 \text{ ms}) = K(67)(100 \times 10^{-3})e^{-6.7}$$

$$= 13.4 \times 10^{-3}K$$

From Fig. 6–4(c)

$$v_{o_1}(t = 100 \text{ ms}) = 19 \times 10^{-3}$$

therefore

$$19 \times 10^{-3} = 13.4 \times 10^{-3} K$$

or

$$K = \frac{19 \times 10^{-3}}{13.4 \times 10^{-3}} = 1.42$$

As we see the Ks do not agree, which eliminates the graph for $\zeta = 1$.

For Fig. 5–34(a) we would have

$$v_{o_1}(t) = K[e^{-(\zeta\sqrt{\zeta^2-1}-1)x} - e^{-(\zeta\sqrt{\zeta^2-1}+1)x}]$$
$$= K[e^{-(\zeta\omega_n - \omega_n\sqrt{\zeta^2-1})t} - e^{-(\zeta\omega_n + \omega_n\sqrt{\zeta^2-1})t}$$

Or we could option to write v_o as

$$v_o(t) = Kg(x) \tag{6–33}$$

where $x = \omega_n\sqrt{\zeta^2 - 1}\, t$. From Fig. 6–4(c) we see that $v_{o_{max}}$ occurs at $t = 15$ ms and from Fig. 5–34(a) we can determine g_{max} for each ζ. And from $v_{o_1}(t) = Kg(x)$ we know

$$v_{o_1}(t = 15 \text{ ms}) = v_{o_{max}} = Kg_{max}$$

so

$$K = \frac{v_{o_{max}}}{g_{max}} = \frac{57.5 \times 10^{-3}}{g_{max}}$$

Then for:

$$\underline{\zeta = 1.5} \quad K = \frac{57.5 \times 10^{-3}}{0.60} = 96.0 \times 10^{-3}$$

$$\text{and} \quad \omega_n\sqrt{\zeta^2 - 1} = \frac{x_{max}}{t_{max}} = \frac{0.963}{15 \times 10^{-3}} = 64$$

$$\underline{\zeta = 2.0} \quad K = \frac{57.5 \times 10^{-3}}{0.75} = 76.8 \times 10^{-3}$$

$$\omega_n\sqrt{\zeta^2 - 1} = \frac{1.31}{15 \times 10^{-3}} = 87.5$$

$$\underline{\zeta = 3.0} \quad K = \frac{57.5 \times 10^{-3}}{0.86} = 66.9 \times 10^{-3}$$

$$\omega_n\sqrt{\zeta^2 - 1} = \frac{1.76}{15 \times 10^{-3}} = 117$$

and so on.

With this information we may assume a ζ and then see if this assumption agrees with Eq. (6–33). If it does we will be able to write an explicit equation for v_o, and, if not, we will keep trying. Obviously the accuracy with which this method works depends on one's patience to keep trying different ζs. To be practical one would only hope to come within some predetermined tolerance, where this tolerance would depend on the specific physical problem. In other words, "... how much error can you live with?"

First let us try $\zeta = 1.5$, then $K = 96.0 \times 10^{-3}$ and $\omega_n \sqrt{\zeta^2 - 1} = 64$, or $x = 64\,t$. As a check for these points let us try $t = 100$ ms. We will be using Eq. (6–33) to determine $v_{o_1}(t = 100$ ms), therefore $x(t = 100$ ms) must first be found. Hence,

$$x(t = 100 \text{ ms}) = \omega_n \sqrt{\zeta^2 - 1}\,t \Big|_{t=100\text{ms}} = 64(100 \times 10^{-3}) = 6.4$$

At $x = 6.4$ the corresponding value of $g(x)$ is 0.13. Evaluating Eq. (6–33) we have

$$v_{o_1}(t = 100 \text{ ms}) = Kg(x = 6.4) = 96.0 \times 10^{-3}(0.13)$$
$$= 12.5 \text{ mV}$$

Comparing this value with Fig. 6–4(c) at $t = 100$ ms we find that they disagree. The value for Fig. 6–4(c) at $t = 100$ ms is $v_{o_1}(t = 100$ ms) $= 19.0$ mV.

Next we will try $\zeta = 2.0$. Then $K = 76.8 \times 10^{-3}$, $\omega_n \sqrt{\zeta^2 - 1} = 87.5$, $x = 87.5\,t$, and $v_{o_1}(t) = 76.8 \times 10^{-3} \times g(x)$. Find x, say at $t = 100$ ms. We have $x = 87.5 \times (100 \times 10^{-3}) = 8.75$. And $g(x = 8.75) = 0.26$, so $v_{o_1}(t = 100$ ms) $= 76.8 \times 10^{-3} (0.26) = 19.9$ mV. When comparing this value with $v_{o_1}(t = 100$ ms) $= 19.0$ mV of Fig. 6–4(c) we find a difference of about 4.3%, which is certainly acceptable in most cases. But, to be certain that we have found the correct ζ let us determine v_{o_1} at one more point and then compare that point with the same point in time on Fig. 6–4(c). Choosing $t = 25$ ms we calculate $x = 87.5(25 \times 10^{-3}) = 2.2$ and $g(x = 2.2) = 0.70$. Then $v_{o_1}(t = 25$ ms) $= 76.8 \times 10^{-3}(0.70) = 53.8$ mV. For $v_{o_1}(t = 25$ ms) on Fig. 6–4(c) we find $v_{o_1}(t = 25$ ms) $= 54.0$ mV, which is a 0.37% difference. Then we can conclude that for Fig. 6–4(c) $\zeta = 2.0$, $K = 76.8 \times 10^{-3}$, and $\omega_n \sqrt{\zeta^2 - 1} = 87.5$, or $\omega_n = 87.5/\sqrt{3} = 50.6$. And $v_{o_1}(t)$ can be written as

$$v_{o_1}(t) = K(e^{-\omega_n(\zeta - \sqrt{\zeta^2 - 1})t} - e^{-\omega_n(\zeta + \sqrt{\zeta^2 - 1})t})$$
$$= 76.8 \times 10^{-3}(e^{-14.0t} - e^{-188.4t}) \quad \textbf{(6–34)}$$

In order to determine $T(t)$ from Eq. (6–34) we must determine the composition of K. To do this let's take the Laplace of Eq. (6–34) using Eq. (10) of Table 4–2,

$$V_{o_1}(s) = \frac{(\beta - \alpha)K}{(s + \alpha)(s + \beta)} \qquad (6\text{–}35)$$

where
$$\beta \equiv \omega_n(\zeta + \sqrt{\zeta^2 - 1})$$
$$\alpha \equiv \omega_n(\zeta - \sqrt{\zeta^2 - 1})$$

Then for a general equation

$$V_{o_1}(s) = \frac{kE_{in_1}(s)}{(s + \alpha)(s + \beta)} = T(s)E_{in}(s)$$

or

$$T(s) = \frac{k}{(s + \alpha)(s + \beta)} \qquad (6\text{–}36)$$

where $k \equiv (\beta - \alpha)K$. Since $e_{in_1}(t) = Et_d\delta(t)$ then

$$V_{o_1}(s) = \frac{kEt_d}{(s + \alpha)(s + \beta)} \qquad (6\text{–}37)$$

Thus from Eqs. (6–35) and (6–37) we find $(\beta - \alpha)K = kEt_d$ so $\hfill (6\text{–}37)$

$$k = \frac{(\beta - \alpha)K}{Et_d} = \frac{2\omega_n\sqrt{\zeta^2 - 1}\,K}{Et_d} = \frac{2(87.5)(76.8 \times 10^{-3})}{5 \times 10^{-3}}$$
$$= 2690 \qquad (6\text{–}38)$$

And from Eq. (6–36)

$$T(t) = \frac{k}{\beta - \alpha}(e^{-\alpha t} - e^{-\beta t})$$

and from Eq. (6–35)

$$v_o(t) = K(e^{-\alpha t} - e^{-\beta t})$$

As determined from Eq. (6–38)

$$K = \frac{Et_d k}{\beta - \alpha}$$

so

$$v_{o_1}(t) = \frac{Et_d k}{\beta - \alpha}(e^{-\alpha t} - e^{-\beta t})$$

thus

$$T(t) = \frac{v_{o_1}(t)}{Et_d} = \frac{k}{\beta - \alpha}(e^{-\alpha t} - e^{-\beta t}) = \frac{v_{o_1}(t)}{5 \times 10^{-3}}$$
$$= 15.3(e^{-14.0t} - e^{-188.4t}) \qquad (6\text{–}39)$$

The extreme right-hand scale of Fig. 6–4(c) is $T(t)$.

6-3   Introduction to Circuit Synthesis

This section will concern itself with introducing circuit synthesis. As specific examples of our techniques we will synthesize equivalent circuits from the derived transfer function $T(s)$ of Exs. 6–2 and 6–3. However, before undertaking these specific examples let us consider some general problems so that we may formulate our approach. Suppose that for some black box we found

$$T(s) = \frac{K}{s + \alpha} \tag{6-40}$$

where the same techniques of finding $T(s)$ in Exs. 6–2 and 6–3 were used. We know that

$$V_o(s) = T(s)E_{in}(s)$$

therefore

$$V_o(s) = \frac{KE_{in}(s)}{s + \alpha} \tag{6-41}$$

Then

$$KE_{in}(s) = (s + \alpha)V_o(s) = sV_o(s) + \alpha V_o(s) \tag{6-42}$$

Next collect coefficients of like powers of s. Thus

$$KE_{in}(s) - \alpha V_o(s) = sV_o(s) \tag{6-43}$$

You will want to always keep your driving force $E_{in}(s)$ positive and that is why we did not write Eq. (6–43) as $\alpha V_o(s) - KE_{in}(s) = -sV_o(s)$. The reason for this will be apparent shortly. To continue, we will perform the inverse Laplace transform on Eq. (6–43), hence,

$$Ke_{in}(t) - \alpha v_o(t) = \frac{d}{dt}v_o(t) \tag{6-44}$$

Since initial conditions do not exist under the circumstances we determine $T(s)$. That is, when we determined $T(s)$ using the techniques of Exs. 6–2 and 6–3 we used the unit impulse with a period large enough so that no initial conditions existed. Since Eq. (6–44) has the term $dv_o(t)/dt$, which is current since $C(dv_o(t)/dt) = i_c(t)$, we know that it is a nodal equation. Hence Eq. (6–44) written in component form must be

$$\frac{e_{in}(t)}{R_1} - \frac{v_o(t)}{R_2} = C\frac{dv_o(t)}{dt}$$

in order to have units of current, where $R_1 = 1/K$, $R_2 = 1/\alpha$, and $C = 1$. But we cannot construct a physical circuit from this equation. Next let us divide Eq. (6–44) by some constant k. Then

$$\frac{K}{k}e_{in}(t) - \frac{\alpha}{k}v_o(t) = \frac{1}{k}\frac{dv_o(t)}{dt}$$

where in an *actual numerical* problem we would find $K/k = \alpha/k$ or

$K = \alpha$. Then $K/k = \alpha/k = 1/R$ and $C = 1/k$, so

$$\frac{e_{\text{in}}(t) - v_o(t)}{R} = C\frac{dv_o(t)}{dt} \tag{6-45}$$

Equation (6-45) yields the circuit in Fig. 6-5.

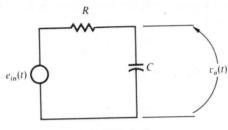

FIGURE 6-5

Next let us consider a general problem which has as its transfer function $T(s)$,

$$T(s) = \frac{K}{s^2 + 2\zeta\omega_n s + \omega_n^2} \tag{6-46}$$

hence

$$V_o(s) = T(s)E_{\text{in}}(s) = \frac{KE_{\text{in}}(s)}{s^2 + 2\zeta\omega_n s + \omega_n^2} \tag{6-47}$$

So

$$s^2 V_o(s) + 2\zeta\omega_n s V_o(s) + \omega_n^2 V_o(s) = KE_{\text{in}}(s) \tag{6-47}$$

or

$$s^2 V_o(s) + 2\zeta\omega_n s V_o(s) = KE_{\text{in}}(s) - \omega_n^2 V_o(s) \tag{6-48}$$

We know there is no component which would yield s to a power other than s^{-1}, s^1, or s^0. That is

$$i_L(t) = \frac{1}{L}\int v_o(t)dt \quad \text{so} \quad I_L(s) = \frac{1}{L}s^{-1}V_o(s), \quad i_C(t) = C\frac{dv_o(t)}{dt}$$

$$\text{so} \quad I_C(s) = CsV_o(s), \quad \text{and} \quad i_R(t) = \frac{v_o(t)}{R} \quad \text{so} \quad I_R(s) = \frac{1}{R}s^0 V_o(s)$$

Then we must require that the power of s be either ± 1 or 0. We will divide Eq. (6-48) by s in order to fulfill that requirement. Hence,

$$sV_o(s) + 2\zeta\omega_n V_o(s) = \frac{1}{s}[KE_{\text{in}}(s) - \omega_n^2 V_o(s)]$$

Since we are performing $KE_{\text{in}}(s) - \omega_n^2 V_o(s)$ then K must have the same units as ω_n. In an actual numerical problem we would find $K = \omega_n^2$, then let us write

$$sV_o(s) + 2\zeta\omega_n V_o(s) = \frac{\omega_n^2}{s}[E_{\text{in}}(s) - V_o(s)] \tag{6-49}$$

We now take the inverse Laplace of Eq. (6–49) and we get

$$\frac{dv_o(t)}{dt} + 2\zeta\omega_n v_o(t) = \omega_n^2 \int [e_{in}(t) - v_o(t)]\, dt \qquad (6\text{-}50)$$

We know then that Eq. (6–50) is

$$C\frac{dv_o(t)}{dt} + \frac{v_o(t)}{R} = \frac{1}{L} \int [e_{in}(t) - v_o(t)]\, dt \qquad (6\text{-}51)$$

From Eq. (6–51) we derive the circuit shown in Fig. 6–6. Notice the values of C, R, and L are not unique. That is, Eq. (6–50) says $C = 1$, $R = 1/2\zeta\omega_n$,

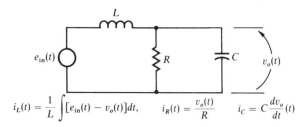

$$i_L(t) = \frac{1}{L} \int [e_{in}(t) - v_o(t)]dt, \qquad i_R(t) = \frac{v_o(t)}{R} \qquad i_C = C\frac{dv_o}{dt}(t)$$

FIGURE 6–6

and $L = 1/\omega_n^2$ which is not realistic for C; however, we could adjust these values by dividing by some constant K_1. Then Eq. (6–50) would appear as

$$\frac{1}{K_1}\frac{dv_o(t)}{dt} + \frac{2\zeta\omega_n}{K_1}v_o(t) = \frac{\omega_n^2}{K_1} \int [e_{in}(t) - v_o(t)]\, dt$$

hence under these conditions

$$C = \frac{1}{K_1}, \quad R = \frac{K_1}{2\zeta\omega_n}, \quad \text{and} \quad L = \frac{K_1}{\omega_n^2}$$

In conclusion, we can draw an equivalent circuit but we are unable to assign unique values to those components.

Following is a list of the steps performed in synthesizing the two circuits.

1. Find the product of the output, which was $V_o(s)$ in our case, and the denominator of $T(s)$. That is, if $T(s) = N(s)/D(s)$ then perform $D(s)\cdot V_o(s)$ for $V_o(s) =$ output.

2. Collect like coefficients of s keeping $E_{in}(s)$ positive.

3. If an s-term is present in the second step which is raised to a power other than ± 1 or 0, perform the necessary algebra to make its power $+1$, -1, or 0.

4. Take the inverse Laplace transform of the equation from step 3.

5. Synthesize the circuit from equation resulting in step 4. These steps are shown in the flow diagram of Fig. 6–7.

As demonstration of our discussion let us synthesize equivalent circuits for Exs. 6–2 and 6–3.

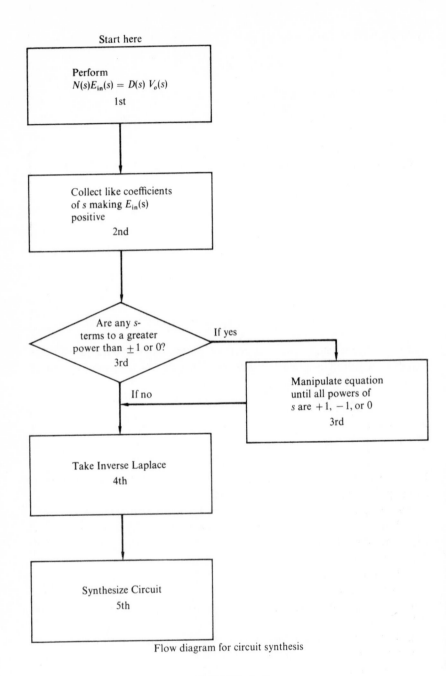

Flow diagram for circuit synthesis

FIGURE 6–7

Example 6–4   From Eq. (6–31) of Ex. 6–2

$$T(s) = \mathcal{L}[T(t)] = \mathcal{L}[0.317 \times 10^6 e^{-0.046 \times 10^6 t} \sin 0.314 \\ \times 10^6 t] \text{ for } t > 0 \qquad (6\text{–}52)$$

which is the same as

$$\mathcal{L}\left[\frac{K}{\omega_n\sqrt{1 - \zeta^2}} e^{-\zeta\omega_n t} \sin \omega_n\sqrt{1 - \zeta^2} t u(t)\right]$$

$$= \frac{K}{s^2 + 2\zeta\omega_n s + \omega_n^2}$$

This equation can be manipulated to appear as

$$\mathcal{L}[Ke^{-\zeta\omega_n t} \sin \omega_n\sqrt{1 - \zeta^2} t u(t)]$$

$$= \frac{K\omega_n\sqrt{1 - \zeta^2}}{s^2 + 2\zeta\omega_n s + \omega_n^2} \qquad (6\text{–}53)$$

since $\omega_n\sqrt{1 - \zeta^2}$ is a constant. Letting $K = 0.317 \times 10^6$, $\zeta\omega_n = 0.046 \times 10^6$, and $\omega_n\sqrt{1 - \zeta^2} = 0.314 \times 10^6$ then Eq. (6–51) and Eq. (6–52) are the same, hence

$$\mathcal{L}[0.317 \times 10^6 e^{-0.046 \times 10^6 t} \sin 0.314 \times 10^6 t u(t)]$$

$$= \frac{0.317 \times 10^6 (0.314 \times 10^6)}{s^2 + 0.092 \times 10^6 s + \omega_n^2}$$

To determine ω_n^2 we will use two equations

$$\omega_d = \omega_n\sqrt{1 - \zeta^2} = 0.314 \times 10^6$$

and

$$\zeta\omega_n = 0.046 \times 10^6$$

Solution   We will first solve for ζ and then use the relationship $\zeta\omega_n = 0.046 \times 10^6$ to solve for ω_n. Then

$$\zeta\omega_n = \frac{\zeta\omega_d}{\sqrt{1 - \zeta^2}} = 0.046 \times 10^6$$

$$= \frac{\zeta}{\sqrt{1 - \zeta^2}}(0.314 \times 10^6)$$

or

$$\frac{\zeta}{\sqrt{1 - \zeta^2}} = \frac{0.046 \times 10^6}{0.314 \times 10^6} = 0.147$$

Solving for ζ

$$\frac{\zeta^2}{1 - \zeta^2} = (0.147)^2 = 0.0216$$

or

$$\zeta^2(1 + 0.0216) = 0.0216$$

so

$$\zeta = \sqrt{\frac{0.0216}{1.0216}} = 0.145$$

Solving for ω_n

$$\omega_n = \frac{0.046 \times 10^6}{\zeta} = \frac{0.046 \times 10^6}{0.145} = 0.317 \times 10^6$$

and

$$\omega_n^2 = 10^{11}$$

Therefore,

$$T(s) = \mathcal{L}[0.317 \times 10^6 e^{-0.046 \times 10^6 t} \sin 3.14 \times 10^6 t u(t)]$$

$$= \frac{10^{11}}{s^2 + 0.092 \times 10^6 s + 10^{11}} \tag{6-54}$$

Now that we have the explicit equation for $T(s)$ we may follow the flow diagram of Fig. 6–7.

Step 1:

$$V_o(s) = T(s)E_{in}(s) = \frac{10^{11}E_{in}(s)}{s^2 + 0.092 \times 10^6 s + 10^{11}}$$

or

$$s^2 V_o(s) + 0.092 \times 10^6 s V_o(s) + 10^{11} V_o(s) = 10^{11} E_{in}(s)$$

Return briefly to Eq. (6–48) and Eq. (6–49) and notice that indeed $K = \omega_n^2$.

Step 2:

$$s^2 V_o(s) + 0.092 \times 10^6 s V_o(s) = 10^{11}[E_{in}(s) - V_o(s)]$$

Step 3:

$$s V_o(s) + 0.092 \times 10^6 V_o(s) = \frac{10^{11}}{s}[E_{in}(s) - V_o(s)] \tag{6-55}$$

Step 4:

$$\frac{d}{dt}v_o(t) + 0.092 \times 10^6 v_o(t) = 10^{11} \int [e_{in}(t) - v_o(t)]\, dt \tag{6-56}$$

which is

$$C\frac{dv_o(t)}{dt} + \frac{v_o(t)}{R} = \frac{1}{L}\int [e_{in}(t) - v_o(t)]\, dt \tag{6-57}$$

As we see, Eqs. (6–49) and (6–55) are the same; likewise for (6–50) and (6–56), and (6–51) and (6–57). Recall in our earlier analysis it was pointed out that the values for R, L, and C are not unique. Now, looking at Eqs. (6–56) and (6–57) we know they are very impractical as they stand. That is,

$$C = 1\,\text{F}$$

$$R = \frac{1}{0.092 \times 10^6} \cong 10^{-5}\,\Omega$$

and $L = 10^{-11}\text{H}$

Therefore let us adjust these components to more reasonable values.

To make this adjustment let us construct the circuit as dictated by Eq. (6–57) and then write the equation for $T(s)$ using these components. This will allow us to know what relating ζ and ω_n have to R, L, and C, which we hope will aid us in adjusting the values of R, L, and C to reasonable values. From Eq. (6–57) we have the circuit of Fig. 6–8.

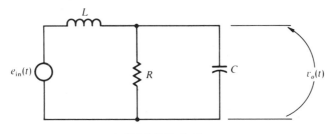

FIGURE 6–8

For this circuit we find

$$V_o(s) = T(s)E_{in}(s) = \frac{E_{in}(s)}{LC\left(s^2 + \dfrac{1}{RC}s + \dfrac{1}{LC}\right)}$$

therefore,

$$T(s) = \frac{1}{LC\left(s^2 + \dfrac{1}{RC}s + \dfrac{1}{LC}\right)} \tag{6–57}$$

Comparing this with

$$T(s) = \frac{10^{11}}{s^2 + 0.092 \times 10^6 s + 10^{11}}$$

we find

$$\frac{1}{LC} = 10^{11} \quad \text{and} \quad \frac{1}{RC} = 0.092 \times 10^6$$

which gives us two relationships between R, L, and C. We also know that $\zeta = 1/2R\sqrt{L/C}$ by equating like coefficients of s, that is, $2\zeta\omega_n = 1/RC$, but you will find this equation is of no help since it was determined from the other two relationships. What we need for a unique solution for R, L, and C is one other relationship between L, R, and C, which we do not have. Therefore for this equivalent circuit let us choose a reasonable value for R, say $R = 100\,\Omega$. Then as a result we may calculate $C = 1/0.092 \times 10^6 \cong 10^{-7} = 0.1\,\mu$F and $L = 1/C \times 10^{11} = 10^{-4} = 0.1$mH, which are reasonable component values. To modify Eq. (6–56) to agree with this result we must divide Eq. (6–56) by some constant K_1. Thus Eq. (6–56) becomes

$$\frac{1}{K_1}\frac{dv_o(t)}{dt} + \frac{0.092 \times 10^6}{K_1}v_o(t) = \frac{10^{11}}{K_1}\int [e_{\text{in}}(t) - v_o(t)]\,dt$$

The numerical value of K_1 is then determined by equating like coefficients of Eq. (6–56), divided by K_1, and Eq. (6–57) and using our previous results of $C = 0.1\mu$F, $L = 0.1$ mH, and $R = 100\,\Omega$. Under these conditions from Eq. (6–56), divided by K_1, and Eq. (6–57) we find $C = 1/K_1, R = K_1/(0.092 \times 10)^6$, and $L = K_1/10^{11}$. Now, we previously calculated that for R, C, and L adjusted we wanted $C = 0.1 \times 10^{-6}$, $L = 0.1 \times 10^{-3}$, and $R = 10^2$. So, solving for K_1 from any one of these three equations we find $K_1 = 1/C$, $K_1 = 0.092 \times 10^6 R$, or $K_1 = 10^{11}/L$. Hence from any one of these equations and a desire for $C = 0.1 \times 10^{-6}$, $R = 10^2$, and $L = 0.1 \times 10^{-3}$ we find $K_1 = 1/C = 10^7, K_1 = 0.092 \times 10^6 R = 0.092 \times 10^6 (10^2) \cong 10^7$, and $K_1 = 10^{11}/10^{-4} = 10^7$; therefore $K_1 = 10^7$ in order that C, R, and L be adjusted to the desired values. Therefore

$$10^{-7}\frac{dv_o(t)}{dt} + 0.092 \times 10^{-1}v_o(t)$$

$$= 10^4 \int [e_{\text{in}}(t) - v_o(t)]\,dt \qquad (6\text{–}58)$$

Comparing coefficients of Eqs. (6–57) and (6–58)

$$C = 10^{-7} = 0.1\mu\text{F}, \quad R \cong 100\Omega,$$

and

$$L = 10^{-4} = 0.1\text{mH}$$

For the next example we will synthesize an equivalent circuit from $T(t)$ of Ex. 6–3.

Example 6–5   To synthesize a circuit for Ex. 6–3 we will find the Laplace transform of Eq. (6–39). Hence

$$T(s) = \mathcal{L}[15.3(e^{-14.0t} - e^{-188.4t})u(t)] \qquad \textbf{(6–59)}$$

which identifies with Eq. (10) of Table 4–2. Then

$$\mathcal{L}[K(e^{-\alpha t} - e^{-\beta t})u(t)] = \frac{(\beta - \alpha)K}{(s + \alpha)(s + \beta)}$$

$$= \mathcal{L}[15.3(e^{-14.0t} - e^{-188.4t})u(t)] \quad \text{where} \quad \beta > \alpha.$$

$$\textbf{(6–60)}$$

Solution   From Eq. (6–60) we can determine that

$$K = 15.3, \quad \alpha = 14.0, \quad \text{and} \quad \beta = 188.4$$

So

$$T(s) = \frac{(188.4 - 14.0)15.3}{(s + 14.0)(s + 188.4)} = \frac{2660}{(s + 14.0)(s + 188.4)}$$

or

$$T(s) = \frac{2660}{s^2 + 202.4s + 2640} \qquad \textbf{(6–61)}$$

We may now refer to the flow diagram of Fig. 6–7. Hence

Step 1

$$V_o(s) = \frac{2660E_{in}(s)}{s^2 + 202.4s + 2640}$$

or

$$s^2V_o(s) + 202.4sV_o(s) + 2640V_o(s) = 2660E_{in}(s)$$

Step 2

$$s^2V_o(s) + 202.4sV_o(s) = 2660E_{in}(s) - 2640V_o(s)$$

For all practical purposes 2660 and 2640 are the same. Remember, everything we have done has been to graphical and/or slide-rule accuracy. Then

$$s^2V_o(s) + 202.4sV_o(s) = 2660[E_{in}(s) - V_o(s)]$$

Step 3

$$sV_o(s) + 202.4V_o(s) = \frac{2660}{s}[E_{in}(s) - V_o(s)]$$

Step 4

$$\frac{dv_o(t)}{dt} + 202.4v_o(t) = 2660 \int [e_{in}(t) - v_o(t)] \, dt$$

Step 5. As we see we have the exact circuit of Ex. 6–4 except now $\zeta > 1$. Choosing $R = 100 \ \Omega$ again but this time finding

$$C = \frac{1}{202.4R} = \frac{10^{-2}}{202.4} = 49.5 \times 10^{-6} \cong 50 \ \mu F$$

$$L = \frac{1}{2640C} = \frac{10^6}{2640(50)} = 7.64 \ H$$

The circuit is as shown in Fig. 6–9.

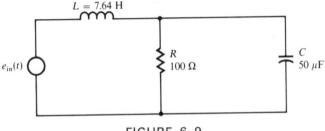

FIGURE 6–9

The reason that both examples were of the same circuit is that it was believed these to be the most difficult examples we could consider. We must remember we are limited because of the limited universal curves we have to work. For instance, we have no universal curve for such functions as $Ks/(S^2 + 2\zeta\omega_n s + \omega_n^2)$. This is not to mean we cannot graph this function using the universal graphs we already have. We can apply partial fractions, which breaks the function into parts which will fit our universal curves. However, if our library were expanded to include this function, and many more, life would be a little simpler. But the purpose of this text is to acquaint the reader with the theory and applications of Laplace transform in circuit analysis and not to be an all inclusive handbook. If one finds he wants to generate more universal curves it was earlier shown how these curves were developed.

As our last example we will consider a transfer function which yields a circuit configuration other than Exs. 6–4 and 6–5.

Example 6–6   Given the output voltage v_o of Fig. 6–10(b), which resulted from the input voltage e_{in} of Fig. 6–10(a), synthesize an equivalent circuit from the transfer function $T(s)$.

Comparing Fig. 6–10(b) for the t-range $0 < t < 5.0$ ms with our universal curves we find it identifies with Fig. 5–47(a); hence

$$v_{o_1}(t) = Kq(\gamma) = Ke^{-\gamma} \quad \text{and} \quad \gamma = \alpha t \qquad \text{(6–62)}$$

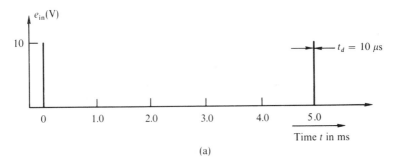

(a)

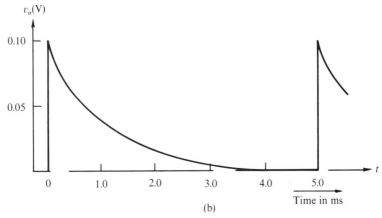

(b)

FIGURE 6–10

(v_{o_1} means first period). At $t = 0$ the γ value of γ is zero, so

$$v_{o_1}(t = 0) = Ke^{-0} = K$$

From Fig. 6–10(b) we see

$$v_{o_1}(t = 0) = 0.10 \text{ V}$$

then

$$K = 0.10$$

Equation (6–62) becomes

$$v_{o_1}(t) = 0.10e^{-at}$$

To determine the value of α we will pick some arbitrary point for t and find its corresponding value of v_{o_1}. Choosing the point $t = 1\text{ms}$ we find

$$v_{o_1}(t = 1 \times 10^{-3}) = 0.038\text{V}$$

hence

$$v_{o_1}(t = 1\text{ms}) = 0.038 = 0.10e^{-\alpha(10^{-3})}$$

So

$$e^{-\alpha \times 10^{-3}} = \frac{0.038}{0.10} = 0.38$$

or

$$-\alpha \times 10^{-3} = \ln 0.38 = -0.97$$

thus

$$\alpha = 0.97 \times 10^{-3} \qquad (6\text{–}63)$$

Equation (6–52) can now be expressed as

$$v_{o_1}(t) = 0.1e^{-0.97 \times 10^3 t} \qquad (6\text{–}64)$$

If we wish to write an expression for v_o we would write

$$v_o(t) = 0.1 \sum_{n=0}^{m} e^{-0.97 \times 10^3 (t - nT)} u(t - nT)$$

$$= 0.1 \sum_{n=0}^{m} e^{-0.97 \times 10^3 (t - n5 \times 10^{-3})} u(t - 5 \times 10^{-3} n) \qquad (6\text{–}65)$$

To find $T(s)$ we take the Laplace transform of Eq. (6–64),

$$V_{o_1}(s) = \mathcal{L}[0.1e^{-0.97 \times 10^3 t} u(t)] = \frac{0.1}{s + 0.97 \times 10^3} \qquad (6\text{–}66)$$

We realize that for a general equation Eq. (6–66) would be expressed as

$$V_o(s) = \frac{K}{s + \alpha} E_{\text{in}}(s) = T(s)E_{\text{in}}(s) \qquad (6\text{–}67)$$

or

$$T(s) = \frac{K}{s + \alpha} \qquad (6\text{–}68)$$

Since for this case $E_{\text{in}_1}(s) = Et_d$ then

$$V_{o_1}(s) = \frac{KEt_d}{s + \alpha} \qquad (6\text{–}69)$$

where

$$\alpha = 0.97 \times 10^3$$

Equating Eqs. (6–66) and (6–69) we find

$$KEt_d = 0.1$$

Since

$$Et_d = 10(10 \times 10^{-6}) = 10^{-4}\text{V}\cdot\text{s}$$

then

$$K = \frac{0.1}{Et_d} = \frac{0.1}{10^{-4}} = 10^3 \qquad (6\text{-}70)$$

Substituting Eq. (6–70) into Eq. (6–68) then

$$T(s) = \frac{10^3}{s + 0.97 \times 10^3} \qquad (6\text{-}71)$$

We may now apply the flow graph of Fig. 6–7. Hence:

Step 1

$$V_o(s) = T(s)E_{in}(s) = \frac{10^3}{s + 0.97 \times 10^3} E_{in}(s)$$

or

$$sV_o(s) + 0.97 \times 10^3 V_o(s) = 10^3 E_{in}(s)$$

Step 2

$$sV_o(s) = 10^3[E_{in}(s) - V_o(s)] \text{ since } 0.97 \times 10^3 \cong 10^3$$

Step 3   No. Therefore, continue to Step 4.

Step 4

$$\frac{dv_o(t)}{dt} = 10^3[e_{in}(t) - v_o(t)]$$

Step 5

$$C\frac{dv_o(t)}{dt} = \frac{e_{in}(t) - v_o(t)}{R}$$

The equation in the fourth step yields the circuit in Fig. 6–11. To adjust for reasonable values we will find $T(s)$ from this circuit. That is,

$$T(s) = \frac{1}{RC\left(s + \dfrac{1}{RC}\right)}$$

so

$$RC \cong 10^3$$

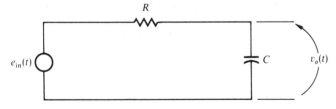

FIGURE 6–11

Let us choose to divide our differential equation by 10^6, hence

$$\frac{1}{10^6}\frac{dv_o(t)}{dt} = 10^{-3}[e_{in}(t) - v_o(t)]$$

Under this condition

$$C = 10^{-6} = 1\mu F \quad \text{and} \quad R = 10^3 \, \Omega$$

6–4 Impedance

Earlier we defined gain as being the output force divided by input force and we designated this ratio as G. We then decided that G could be termed as a transfer function since it "transferred" the input voltage to the output voltage. We now wish to consider another transfer function, which is the ratio of voltage and current. This transfer function is given the name of impedance and is designated with z. We will use Z for a transformed impedance. Impedance is, of course, the resistance offered to current flow.

Let us consider the circuit in Fig. 6–12 and determine input impedance in both the t-plane and s-plane.

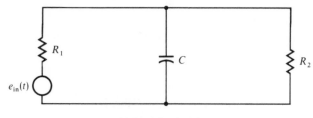

FIGURE 6–12

Now input impedance is defined as the ratio of driving potential e_{in} to current supplied by that driving source. This means we are going to be solving for a current, the current supplied by e_{in}, as a function of the voltage supply e_{in}. Then we will want to write loop equations and solve for the current in question. To demonstrate we assume loop currents for the circuit in Fig. 6–12 and assume a voltage polarity for e_{in} as shown in Fig. 6–13. We then write loop equations describing this circuit, which are:

$$e_{in}(t) - R_1 i_1(t) - \frac{1}{C}\int i_1(t)\,dt + \frac{1}{C}\int i_2(t)\,dt = 0$$

and

$$\frac{1}{C}\int i_1(t)\,dt - \frac{1}{C}\int i_2(t)\,dt - R_2 i_2(t) = 0$$

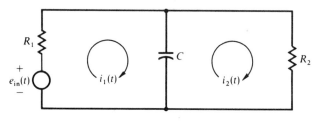

FIGURE 6–13

Taking the Laplace transform and requiring initial conditions to be zero,

$$E_{in}(s) - R_1 I_1(s) - \frac{1}{Cs} I_1(s) + \frac{1}{Cs} I_2(s) = 0$$

$$\frac{1}{Cs} I_1(s) - \frac{1}{Cs} I_2(s) - R_2 I_2(s) = 0$$

Arranging in determinate form and solving for $I_1(s)$, which is the current we seek, we have

$$E_{in}(s) = \left(R_1 + \frac{1}{Cs}\right) I_1(s) - \frac{1}{Cs} I_2(s)$$

$$0 = -\frac{1}{Cs} I_1(s) + \left(R_2 + \frac{1}{Cs}\right) I_2(s)$$

$$\Delta = \begin{vmatrix} \left(R_1 + \frac{1}{Cs}\right) & -\frac{1}{Cs} \\ -\frac{1}{Cs} & \left(R_2 + \frac{1}{Cs}\right) \end{vmatrix} = \left(R_1 + \frac{1}{Cs}\right)\left(R_2 + \frac{1}{Cs}\right) - \frac{1}{(Cs)^2}$$

$$= R_1 R_2 + (R_1 + R_2)\frac{1}{Cs} + \frac{1}{(Cs)^2} - \frac{1}{(Cs)^2}$$

$$= R_1 R_2 + (R_1 + R_2)\frac{1}{Cs}$$

Knowing Δ will be in the denominator of $I_1(s)$ we usually put Δ in a "nice" form for taking the inverse. However, for this specific instance we will leave it as is except for factoring the quantity $(R_1 + R_2)$. Our reason for making this exception is to later demonstrate a point. Then

$$\Delta = R_1 R_2 + (R_1 + R_2)\frac{1}{Cs} = (R_1 + R_2)\left(\frac{R_1 R_2}{R_1 + R_2} + \frac{1}{Cs}\right)$$

or

$$\Delta = R_{eq2}\left(R_{eq1} + \frac{1}{Cs}\right) \tag{6-72}$$

by defining $R_{eq1} = R_1 R_2/(R_1 + R_2)$ and $R_{eq2} = R_1 + R_2$. Now solving for $I_1(s)$,

$$\Delta I_1(s) = \begin{vmatrix} E_{in}(s) & -\dfrac{1}{Cs} \\ 0 & \left(R_2 + \dfrac{1}{Cs}\right) \end{vmatrix} = E_{in}(s)\left(R_2 + \dfrac{1}{Cs}\right)$$

so

$$I_1(s) = \frac{E_{in}(s)\left(R_2 + \dfrac{1}{Cs}\right)}{R_{eq2}\left(R_{eq1} + \dfrac{1}{Cs}\right)} = \frac{\left(R_2 + \dfrac{1}{Cs}\right)E_{in}(s)}{\left(R_{eq1} + \dfrac{1}{Cs}\right)R_{eq2}} \tag{6-73}$$

Then the input impendance $Z_{in}(s)$, which is defined as $Z_{in}(s) \equiv E_{in}(s)/I_1(s)$, is

$$Z_{in}(s) \equiv \frac{E_{in}(s)}{I_1(s)} = \frac{\left(R_{eq1} + \dfrac{1}{Cs}\right)R_{eq2}}{R_2 + \dfrac{1}{Cs}} \tag{6-74}$$

It is from Eq. (6–74) we shall learn why we made the exception to putting Δ in nice form. In the beginning, s was defined to be $s = \sigma + j\omega$, where $\omega = 2\pi f$. Let us require that for Eq. (6–74) e_{in} be sinusoidal. This means that $\sigma = 0$, or $s = j\omega$. Under this condition Eq. (6–74) becomes

$$\frac{E_{in}(j\omega)}{I_1(j\omega)} = \frac{\left(R_{eq1} + \dfrac{1}{j\omega C}\right)R_{eq2}}{R_2 + \dfrac{1}{j\omega C}} = \frac{(R_{eq1} - jX_c)R_{eq2}}{R_2 - jX_c} \tag{6-75}$$

which is the ac input impedance of the circuit. To verify this statement we will determine $Z_{in}(j\omega)$ assuming e_{in} is sinusoidal, or, stated another way, the driving force is $E_{in}(j\omega)$.

$$\begin{aligned} Z(j\omega) &= R_1 + \frac{-jX_C R_2}{R_2 - jX_C} = \frac{R_1(R_2 - jX_C) - jX_C R_2}{R_2 - jX_C} \\ &= \frac{R_1 R_2 - jR_1 X_C - jR_2 X_C}{R_2 - jX_C} = \frac{R_1 R_2 - j(R_1 + R_2)X_C}{R_2 - jX_C} \\ &= \frac{(R_1 + R_2)\left(\dfrac{R_1 R_2}{R_1 + R_2} - jX_C\right)}{R_2 - jX_C} = \frac{R_{eq2}(R_{eq1} - jX_C)}{R_2 - jX_C} \end{aligned}$$

The point to this demonstration is that $Z_{in}(j\omega)$ is just a specific case of $Z_{in}(s)$.

Returning now to Eq. (6–74) and putting it into a nice form we have

$$Z_{in}(s) = \frac{(R_{eq1}Cs + 1)R_{eq2}}{R_2 Cs + 1} = \frac{R_{eq1}R_{eq2}\left(s + \dfrac{1}{R_{eq1}C}\right)}{R_2\left(s + \dfrac{1}{R_2 C}\right)}$$

$$= \frac{R_1\left(s + \frac{1}{R_{eq1}C}\right)}{s + \frac{1}{R_2C}} \tag{6-76}$$

To use Eq. (6–76) as a transfer function, an impedance transfer function to be specific, we simply recall its definition as stated in Eq. (6–74) and use it to transform the input voltage e_{in} to the supply current i_1. However, we must perform this transform in the s-plane. Hence,

$$I_1(s) = \frac{E_{in}(s)}{Z_{in}(s)} = \frac{E_{in}(s)\left(s + \frac{1}{R_2C}\right)}{R_1\left(s + \frac{1}{R_{eq1}C}\right)} \tag{6-77}$$

Of course, to actually perform the specific transformation to the t-plane we must have an explicit expression for $E_{in}(s)$. Suppose $e_{in}(t) = Eu(t)$, then $E_{in}(s) = E/s$ and then

$$I_1(s) = \frac{E\left(s + \frac{1}{R_2C}\right)}{R_1 s\left(s + \frac{1}{R_{eq1}C}\right)} = \frac{E}{R_1\left(s + \frac{1}{R_{eq1}C}\right)} + \frac{E}{R_1 R_2 C s\left(s + \frac{1}{R_{eq1}C}\right)}$$

Thus

$$i_1(t) = \frac{E}{R_1}e^{-t/R_{eq1}C}u(t) + \frac{ER_{eq1}}{R_1 R_2}(1 - e^{-tR_{eq1}C})u(t)$$

$$= \frac{Eu(t)}{R_1 + R_2} + \left(\frac{1}{R_1} - \frac{1}{R_1 + R_2}\right)Ee^{-tR_{eq1}C}u(t)$$

$$= \frac{E}{R_1 + R_2}\left(1 + \frac{R_2}{R_1}e^{-t/R_{eq1}C}\right)u(t) \tag{6-78}$$

To verify Eq. (6–77) we know at $t = 0^+$ the capacitor will appear as a short circuit; therefore, $i_1(0^+) = E/R_1$. And for time much greater than the circuit's time constant the capacitor appears as an open circuit. Then for $t \to \infty$ $i_1(\infty) = E/(R_1 + R_2)$. To test Eq. (6–78) we shall evaluate i_1 at $t = 0^+$ and as $t \to \infty$. Thus from Eq. (6–78)

$$i_1(0^+) = \frac{E}{R_1 + R_2}\left(1 + \frac{R_2}{R_1}\right) = \frac{E}{R_1}$$

which agrees, and

$$i_1(\infty) = \frac{E}{R_1 + R_2}\left(1 + \frac{R_2}{R_1} \cdot 0\right) = \frac{E}{R_1 + R_2}$$

which also agrees.

For another example of impedance being considered as a transfer function return back to Eq. (5–73), which is

$$I_L(s) = -\frac{M}{L_1 L_2 - M^2} \frac{s E_{in}(s)}{s^2 + \dfrac{RL_2 + R_L L_1}{L_1 L_2 - M^2} s + \dfrac{RR_L}{L_1 L_2 - M^2}} \quad (5\text{-}73)$$

We should realize from our definition of impedance in general, voltage/current, we could have written Eq. (5–73) as

$$I_L(s) = -\frac{E_{in}(s)}{Z(s)}$$

where we defined impedance to be $Z(s) \equiv E(s)/I(s)$, hence

$$Z(s) = \frac{(L_1 L_2 - M^2)\left(s^2 + \dfrac{RL_2 - R_L L_1}{L_1 L_2 - M^2} s + \dfrac{RR_L}{L_1 L_2 - M^2}\right)}{Ms} \quad (6\text{-}79)$$

Putting Eq. (6–79) in terms of $j\omega$, which means the driving force is sinusoidal, we have

$$Z(j\omega) = \frac{(L_1 L_2 - M^2)\left[(j\omega)^2 + \dfrac{RL_2 - R_L L_1}{L_1 L_2 - M^2} j\omega + \dfrac{RR_L}{L_1 L_2 - M^2}\right]}{Mj\omega}$$

$$= \frac{[j\omega L_1 j\omega L_2 - (j\omega M)^2] + (Rj\omega L_2 - R_L j\omega L_1) + RR_L}{j\omega M}$$

Recalling from ac circuits $j\omega M = jX_M$, $j\omega L_1 = jX_1$ and $j\omega L_2 = jX_2$, then

$$Z(j\omega) = \frac{jX_1 jX_2 - (jX_M)^2 + jRX_2 - jR_L X_1 + RR_L}{jX_M}$$

$$= \frac{(RX_2 - R_L X_1) + j(X_1 X_2 - X_M^2 - RR_L)}{X_M}$$

$$= \text{Real} + j\text{Im}$$

where

$$Im = \frac{X_1 X_2 - X_M^2 - RR_L}{X_M}$$

$$\text{Real} = \frac{RX_2 - R_L X_1}{X_M}$$

Since impedance is heavily stressed in elementary circuit analysis we will consider enough has been said here.

6–5   Two-Port Network Analysis in s-Plane

In section 1–4 we developed the technique of two-port network analysis in the t-plane and the ω-plane. We wish to extend our use now to include the s-plane.

To refresh our memories, we took the black box of Fig. 1–3(a), shown in Fig. 6–14 with only the ac components of the currents and voltages, and wrote several equations describing that black box. Our equations were the

FIGURE 6–14

result of choosing two independent variables and two dependent variables from the four variables of the black box and operating upon them according to the equation

$$df = \frac{\partial f}{\partial x} dx + \frac{\partial f}{\partial y} dy$$

If we choose

$$v_1 = v_1[i_1(t), i_2(t)]$$

and

$$v_2 = v_2[i_1(t), i_2(t)]$$

which are the ac components of Eqs. (1–9) we arrived at Eqs. (1–11), which are repeated here.

$$v_1(t) = \frac{\partial v_1}{\partial i_1} i_1(t) + \frac{\partial v_1}{\partial i_2} i_2(t) \qquad \text{(1–11a)}$$

$$v_2(t) = \frac{\partial v_2}{\partial i_1} i_1(t) + \frac{\partial v_2}{\partial i_2} i_2(t) \qquad \text{(1–11b)}$$

To transform Eqs. (1–11) into the s-plane requires we take the Laplace transform of $(\partial v/\partial i)i(t)$, which is

$$\int_0^\infty \frac{\partial v}{\partial i} i(t) e^{-st} \, dt = \frac{\partial v}{\partial i} \int_0^\infty i(t) e^{-st} \, dt = \frac{\partial v}{\partial i} I(s)$$

Then Eqs. (1–11) can be written as

$$V_1(s) = \frac{\partial v_1}{\partial i_1} I_1(s) + \frac{\partial v_1}{\partial i_2} I_2(s) \qquad \text{(6–80a)}$$

$$V_2(s) = \frac{\partial v_2}{\partial i_1} I_1(s) + \frac{\partial v_2}{\partial i_2} I_2(s) \qquad \text{(6–80b)}$$

To evaluate $\partial v/\partial i$ we will proceed as in section 1–4. We force $I_2(s) = 0$ to evaluate $\partial v_1/\partial i_1$ and $\partial v_2/\partial i_1$, and $I_1(s) = 0$ to evaluate $\partial v_1/\partial i_2$ and $\partial v_2/\partial i_2$. Hence

$$\frac{\partial v_1}{\partial i_1}\bigg|_{I_2(s)=0} = \frac{V_1(s)}{I_1(s)}, \quad \frac{\partial v_2}{\partial i_1}\bigg|_{I_2(s)=0} = \frac{V_2(s)}{I_1(s)}, \quad \frac{\partial v_1}{\partial i_2}\bigg|_{I_1(s)=0} = \frac{V_1(s)}{I_2(s)}$$

and

$$\left.\frac{\partial v_2}{\partial i_2}\right|_{I_1(s)=0} = \frac{V_2(s)}{I_2(s)}$$

From the units we see these quantities are impedances and since they are evaluated from quantities in the s-plane they also are in the s-plane. Thus, Eqs. (6–80) can now be written as

$$V_1(s) = Z_{11}(s)I_1(s) + Z_{12}(s)I_2(s) \qquad \textbf{(6–81a)}$$
$$V_2(s) = Z_{21}(s)I_1(s) + Z_{22}(s)I_2(s) \qquad \textbf{(6–81b)}$$

If we would require that the driving forces be sinusoidal then $s = j\omega$ and Eqs. (6–81) become

$$V_1(j\omega) = Z_{11}(j\omega)I_1(j\omega) + Z_{12}(j\omega)I_2(j\omega) \qquad \textbf{(6–82a)}$$
$$V_2(j\omega) = Z_{21}(j\omega)I_1(j\omega) + Z_{22}(j\omega)I_2(j\omega) \qquad \textbf{(6–82b)}$$

Equations (6–82) are, of course, the type of equations which appear in elementary ac circuit analysis. Let us now consider an example using Eqs. (6–82).

Example 6–7   From the circuit given in Fig. 6–15 determine the various impedances Z_{11}, Z_{12}, etc.

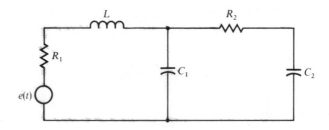

FIGURE 6–15

Solution   Writing the necessary loop equations we have

$$e(t) = R_1 i_1(t) + L\frac{di_1(t)}{dt} + \frac{1}{C_1}\int i_1(t)dt - \frac{1}{C_1}\int i_2(t)\,dt$$

$$0 = \frac{1}{C_1}\int i_1(t)\,dt + R_2 i_2(t) + \left(\frac{1}{C_1} + \frac{1}{C_2}\right)\int i_2(t)\,dt$$

Taking the Laplace transform we find

$$E(s) = \left(R_1 + Ls + \frac{1}{C_1 s}\right)I_1(s) - \frac{1}{C_1 s}I_2(s)$$

$$0 = -\frac{1}{C_1 s}I_1(s) + \left(R_2 + \frac{C_1 + C_2}{C_1 C_2 s}\right)I_2(s)$$

where initial conditions are ignored. Requiring that the

driving force be sinusoidal means that $s = j\omega$, so

$$E(j\omega) = \left(R_1 + j\omega L + \frac{1}{j\omega C_1}\right)I_1(j\omega) - \frac{1}{j\omega C_1}I_2(j\omega)$$

$$(6\text{-}83\text{a})$$

$$0 = -\frac{1}{j\omega C_1}I_1(j\omega) + \left(R_2 + \frac{1}{j\omega C_{eq}}\right)I_2(j\omega)$$

$$(6\text{-}83\text{b})$$

where

$$C_{eq} = \frac{C_1 C_2}{C_1 + C_2}$$

From Eqs. (6-82) and (6-83) we see that

$$Z_{11}(j\omega) = R + j\omega L_1 + \frac{1}{j\omega C_1}$$

$$Z_{12}(j\omega) = Z_{21}(j\omega) = -\frac{1}{j\omega C_1}$$

and

$$Z_{22}(j\omega) = R_2 + \frac{1}{j\omega C_{eq}}$$

If we would have had to determine $Z_{kn}(j\omega)$ by circuit analysis according to the definition of $Z_{kn}(j\omega)$ we would have had to perform for $Z_{11}(j\omega)$,

$$Z_{11}(j\omega) = \frac{E(j\omega)}{I_1(j\omega)}\bigg|_{I_2(j\omega)=0} \qquad (6\text{-}84)$$

This would require an open circuit in the second loop so that $I_2(j\omega) = 0$. Let us open the circuit at the junction of R_2 and C_2 and then find $Z_{11}(j\omega)$. Opening the circuit at the junction of R_2 and C_2 results in the circuit shown in Fig. 6-16. As we see from this circuit the impedance $Z_{11}(j\omega)$ determined by Eq. (6-84) is $R_1 + j\omega L + 1/j\omega C_1$ which agrees with $Z_{11}(j\omega)$ derived from Eqs. (6-82) and (6-83). It is up to the reader to verify the other Zs.

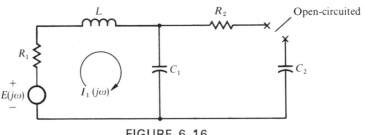

FIGURE 6–16

As we did in section 1–4 we may determine equivalent circuits in the form of T- and π-networks. As an example let us find the equivalent T-network for a transformer.

Example 6–8   Determine the equivalent T-network for the transformer circuit shown in Fig. 6–17.

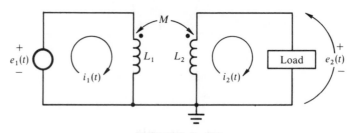

FIGURE 6–17

Solution: Writing the loop equations we have

$$e_1(t) = L_1\frac{di_1(t)}{dt} - M\frac{di_2(t)}{dt}$$

$$-e_2(t) = -M\frac{di_2(t)}{dt} + L_2\frac{di_2(t)}{dt}$$

Therefore

$$E_1(j\omega) = j\omega L_1 I_1(j\omega) - j\omega M I_2(j\omega)$$
$$= jX_{L_1}I_1(j\omega) - jX_M I_2(j\omega)$$
$$-E_2(j\omega) = -j\omega M I_1(j\omega) + j\omega L_2 I_2(j\omega)$$
$$= -jX_M I_1(j\omega) + jX_{L_2}I_2(j\omega)$$

From Eqs. (6–81) we find

$$Z_{11} = jX_{L_1}, \quad Z_M = -jX_M, \quad \text{and} \quad Z_{22} = jX_{L_2}$$

To derive our equivalent T-network we refer to Fig. 1–5(d) and find that

$$Z_1 \equiv Z_{11} - Z_{12} = j(X_{L_1} - X_M) = j\omega(L_1 - M)$$
$$Z_2 \equiv Z_{22} - Z_{12} = j(X_{L_2} - X_M) = j(L_2 - M)$$

and

$$Z_3 \equiv jX_M = j\omega M$$

Then our equivalent circuit is as shown in Fig. 6–18.

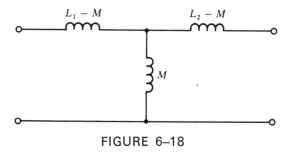

FIGURE 6–18

We should realize that we are not restricted to working with z-parameters. We could just as well transform y-parameters, h-parameters, or any other derived from two-port analysis into the s-plane.

7 Bode Plot

7-1 Introduction

For some circuit analysis it is desirable to determine how a circuit behaves according to frequency rather than how it behaves according to time. As an example of how we determined a circuit's behavior according to time recall our analysis of $T(t)$ in section 6–2. The most common frequency analysis is to graph the gain G of a circuit as a function of frequency. This is known as the circuit's frequency response. Bode plot is an approximation technique which will enable us to quickly make a graph of this response. Bode plot is the subject of this chapter and will be presented on an introductory level.

7-2 Frequency Response

Before getting into Bode plot we should first cover the method for graphing a circuit's exact frequency response. Suppose we determined that the gain of a circuit in the s-plane is

$$G(s) \equiv \frac{\text{Output}}{\text{Input}} = \frac{V_o(s)}{E_{\text{in}}(s)} = \frac{1}{RCs\left(s + \dfrac{1}{RC}\right)} \qquad (7\text{–}1)$$

where we define gain to be the ratio of output to input. Now $s = \sigma + j\omega$, so if we wish to make a frequency analysis we must require $\sigma = 0$ so that $s = j\omega$. From elementary circuit analysis we recall that ω is the frequency of a sinusoidal waveform, expressed in units of radians/second, hence for $s = j\omega$ we are making a sinusoidal analysis. Under the condition that $s = j\omega$ Eq. (7–1) becomes

$$G(j\omega) = \frac{V_0(j\omega)}{E_{in}(j\omega)} = \frac{1}{RCj\omega\left(j\omega + \dfrac{1}{RC}\right)} \tag{7-2}$$

Equation (7–2) is the mathematical expression for the frequency response of the circuit described in Eq. (7–1).

Next let us see how to evaluate Eq. (7–2). For each frequency, Eq. (7–2) can be expressed in terms of a magnitude and phase angle. That is, suppose that the numerical value for RC was 10^{-3} and the gain was to be found for $\omega = 1.5$ krad/s, thus,

$$G(j\omega = j1.5 \times 10^3) = \frac{1}{10^{-3}j\omega(j\omega + 10^3)}\bigg|_{\omega=1.5\times10^3}$$

$$= \frac{10^3}{j1.5 \times 10^3(j1.5 \times 10^3 + 10^3)}$$

where

$$j1.5 \times 10^3 = 1.5 \times 10^3 \angle 90° \text{ and } j1.5 \times 10^3 + 10^3 = 1.80 \times 10^3 \angle 56.2°$$

So

$$G(j1.5 \times 10^3) = \frac{10^3}{1.5 \times 10^3 \angle 90°(1.8 \times 10^3 \angle 56.2°)} = \frac{1}{2.70 \times 10^3 \angle 146.2°}$$

$$= \frac{1}{2.70 \times 10^3} \angle -146.2° \tag{7-3}$$

Then to determine the gain for various frequencies we would repeat the steps followed in Eq. (7–3).

From Eq. (7–3) we see that Eq. (7–2) can be represented as a magnitude and a phase angle, where for Eq. (7–3) the magnitude is $1/(2.70 \times 10^3)$ and the phase angle is $-146.2°$. Let us represent the magnitude of Eq. (7–2) as $M(\omega)$ and the phase angle as $\theta(\omega)$, where ω indicates that each of those terms are functions of frequency ω. Therefore

$$G(j\omega) = \frac{1}{RCj\omega\left(j\omega + \dfrac{1}{RC}\right)} = M(\omega) \angle \theta(\omega) \tag{7-4}$$

Now we shall define the units with which we will be working. The gain of a circuit is usually measured and described in units of decibels, where

$$\text{decibels} = 20 \log_{10} M(\omega) \tag{7-5}$$

The symbol for decibels is dB, hence let us represent Eq. (7–5) as

$$dB(\omega) = 20 \log_{10} M(\omega) \qquad (7\text{–}6)$$

where $dB(\omega)$ is the dependent variable and shows that the dBs are a function of ω. To work an example, the gain of Eq. (7–2) at a frequency of $\omega = 1.5 \times 10^3$ is

$$dB(\omega = 1.5 \times 10^3) = 20 \log_{10} \frac{1}{2.70 \times 10^3} = -20 \log_{10} 2.70 \times 10^3$$

$$= -20 \log_{10} 2.70 - 20 \log_{10} 10^3$$

$$= -20(0.99) - 20(3) = -19.80 - 60.00 = -79.80 \, dB$$

Usually when one makes a frequency response it is over a large range of frequencies and therefore difficult to graph on standard linear graph paper. That is, if you were graphing from 10 rad/s to 10^4 rad/s on linear graph paper it would be difficult to find a suitable scale for the independent variable that would allow you to show any detail of the dependent variable and still use a reasonable size graph paper. For that reason frequency responses are graphed on semilog paper using the log portion for the frequency ω and the linear portion for $dB(\omega)$. Under these circumstances to graph from 10 rad/s to 10^4 rad/s three-cycle semilog paper could be used and reasonable detail of $dB(\omega)$ for all ω in the range of $10 < \omega < 10^4$ could be expected.

Since for each value of ω we get not only the magnitude of the gain but the phase as well we could plot phase on the same graph as the dBs and we would then have the complete graphical picture of the circuit's frequency response.

To give concreteness to our discussion we will make a graph of the frequency response from Eq. (7–2) for $RC = 10^{-3}$ over the frequency range of $10^2 < \omega < 10^4$, which will require two-cycle semilog paper.

Sample Calculations

For $\omega = 10^2$

$$G(j\omega = j10^2) = \frac{1}{10^{-3}(j10^2)(j10^2 + 10^3)} \cong \frac{1}{10^{-3}(10^2 \angle 90°)(10^3 \angle 0°)}$$

$$= \frac{1}{10^2} \angle -90°, \text{ where } M(\omega = 10^2) = \frac{1}{10^2} \text{ and } \theta(\omega = 10^2) = -90°$$

So

$$dB(\omega = 10^2) = 20 \log_{10} \frac{1}{10^2} = -20 \log_{10} 10^2$$

$$= -40 \, dB \text{ at an angle of } -90°$$

For $\omega = 2 \times 10^2$

$$G(j\omega = 2 \times 10^2) = \frac{1}{10^{-3}(j200)(j200 + 10^3)}$$

$$= \frac{10^3}{200\angle 90°(1.02 \times 10^3 \angle 11.3°)} = \frac{10^3}{204\angle 90° + 11.3°}$$

$$= \frac{1}{204} \angle -101.3°$$

$$dB(\omega = 200) = 20 \log_{10} \frac{1}{204} = -20 \log_{10} 204 = -20(2.31) = -46.5\,dB$$

at an angle of $-101.3°$.

For $\omega = 5 \times 10^2$

$$G(j\omega = j5 \times 10^2) = \frac{10^3}{j500(j500 + 10^3)} = \frac{10^3}{500\angle 90°(1.12 \times 10^3 \angle 26.5°)}$$

$$= \frac{1}{560\angle 90° + 26.5°} = \frac{1}{560} \angle -116.5°$$

$$dB(\omega = 500) = 20 \log_{10} \frac{1}{560} = -20 \log_{10} 560 = -20(2.747) = -55.4\,dB$$

at an angle of -116.5, or

$$dB(\omega = 500) = -55.4\,dB \text{ at } \angle -116.5°$$

For $\omega = 10^3$

$$G(j\omega = j10^3) = \frac{10^3}{j10^3(j10^3 + 10^3)} = \frac{10^3}{10^3 \angle 90°(1.41 \times 10^3 \angle 45°)}$$

$$= \frac{1}{1.41 \times 10^3 \angle 135°} = \frac{1}{1.41 \times 10^3} \angle -135°$$

$$dB(\omega = 10^3) = -20 \log_{10} 1.41 \times 10^3 = -20(3.15) = -63\,dB$$
$$@\angle -135°$$

For $\omega = 2 \times 10^3$

$$G(j\omega = j2 \times 10^3) = \frac{10^3}{j2 \times 10^3(j2 \times 10^3 + 10^3)}$$

$$= \frac{10^3}{2 \times 10^3 \angle 90°(2.25 \times 10^3 \angle 63.6°)}$$

$$= \frac{1}{4.50 \times 10^3} \angle -153.6°$$

$$dB(\omega = 2 \times 10^3) = -20 \log_{10} 4.50 \times 10^3 = -20(3.652)$$
$$= -72.5\,dB \quad @\angle -153.6°$$

For $\omega = 5 \times 10^3$

$$G(j\omega = j5 \times 10^3) = \frac{10^3}{j5 \times 10^3(j5 \times 10^3 + 10^3)}$$

$$= \frac{1}{5 \angle 90°(5.1 \times 10^3 \angle 78.7°)}$$

$$= \frac{1}{25.5 \times 10^3} \angle -168.7°$$

$$dB(\omega = 5 \times 10^3) = -20 \log_{10} 25.5 \times 10^3 = -20(4.406)$$

$$= -88.1 \text{ dB at } \angle -168.7°$$

For $\omega = 10^4$

$$G(j\omega = j10^4) \cong \frac{10^3}{j10^4(j10^4)} = \frac{1}{10^5} \angle -180°$$

$$dB(\omega = 10^4) = -20 \log_{10} 10^5 = -100 \text{ dB at } \angle -180°$$

Putting our calculated points in table form we have Table 7–1. The plot of these points is shown in Fig. 7–1.

TABLE 7–1

ω rad/s	$dB(\omega)$ dB(ω) in dB	$\theta(\omega)$ θ in degrees
10^2	−40.0	−90.0
2×10^2	−46.5	−101.3
5×10^2	−55.4	−116.5
1×10^2	−63.0	−135.0
2×10^3	−72.5	−153.6
5×10^3	−88.1	−168.7
10×10^3	−100.0	−180.0

Figure 7–1 is the exact graphical representation of the circuit described by Eq. (7–2). We see that at a frequency of $\omega = 800$ rad/s we can expect a loss of 61 dB in magnitude from input to output (negative dB means loss). Also at $\omega = 800$ rad/s we see that a phase shift of $-127°$ between input and output can be expected.

Since this type of material is usually covered in elementary circuit theory it is believed that we need not say any more here.

7–3　Magnitude Approximation

In the previous section we saw what an exact frequency response of a circuit is and how to graph it. We will now develop Bode plot techniques

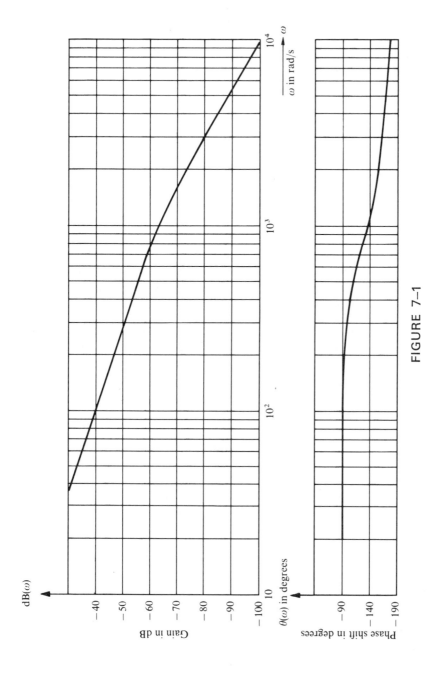

FIGURE 7-1

465

with which we can quickly make these same plots. We will first consider the dB(ω) magnitude approximations and then the phase. As was previously stated Bode plot is an approximation technique, and for all practical purposes is a rather accurate approximation.

Before beginning on Bode plot let us review some concepts concerning logarithms since it will be necessary to manipulate equations in log form.

$$\log \frac{u}{v} = \log u - \log v$$

$$\log \frac{u^a}{v^b} = a \log u - b \log v$$

$$\log uv = \log u - \log v$$

$$\log u^a v^b = a \log u + b \log v$$

Let us return now to the development of Bode plot. The basic principle of Bode plot is that of considering each quantity in $G(j\omega)$ that is composed of a real and an imaginary number and neglecting *either* the real or the imaginary number. The basis for determining which term gets neglected is based upon the frequency range we are considering. For instance, Eq. (7–2) is composed of the quantities $1 + j0$ in the numerator and $RC + j0$, $j\omega + 0$, $j\omega + 1/RC$ in the denominator. If we single out the quantity $j\omega + 1/RC$, for some ranges of ω we approximate the quantity $j\omega + 1/RC$ to be $j\omega$ and for other ω-ranges $j\omega + 1/RC$ will be approximated to be $1/RC$.

The quantities which have neither their imaginary nor real terms *equal to zero* determine what ω-ranges we shall consider. The real parts of these terms are called corner frequencies and as we will see later all changes in the trend of the frequency response occur at these corner frequencies. For Eq. (7–2) we have one corner frequency, which is at $1/RC$, since the quantity $j\omega + 1/RC$ is the only quantity having neither its real nor imaginary term equal to zero.

To determine the ω-ranges based upon the corner frequencies we simply consider ω-ranges as existing in between each pair of corner frequencies where the corner frequencies are arranged in increasing numerical order. The ω-ranges also include the ranges of ω below the lowest value corner frequency and those above the highest value corner frequency. Then if we had corner frequencies at 10, 150, 10^3, 10^4, we would have ω-ranges of $0 < \omega < 10, 10 < \omega < 150, 150 < \omega < 10^3, 10^3 < \omega < 10^4$, and $\omega > 10^4$. When zero is a corner frequency it is never expressed. The reason $\omega = 0$ (dc) is never explicitly written is that we are graphing ω on a log scale and the $\log_{10}$ of 0 is $-\infty$. Thus our ω-range would actually be written as $\omega < 10, 10 < \omega < 150, 150 < \omega < 10^3, 10^3 < \omega < 10^4$, and

$\omega > 10^4$. For Eq. (7–2) we have the ω-ranges of $\omega < 1/RC$ and $\omega > 1/RC$. Notice in each case here we have considered ω from approximately zero to approaching $+\infty$. Of course it depends on the specific problem how much one would go below the lowest corner frequency or above the highest corner frequency. That is, for the case given, how much below $\omega = 10$ and how much above $\omega = 10^4$?

Once we have our ranges of ω determined our next step is to approximate $G(j\omega)$ for *each* of these ranges. The manner in which we approximate $G(j\omega)$ is to consider each quantity in $G(j\omega)$ which has no zero real or imaginary term for each ω-range. Now each of these quantities will contain some real and imaginary term; we must, in *every* case, neglect one or the other of these terms. The manner in which we judge which to drop is to simply ask ourselves "for the ω-range I am considering which one is *always* the larger in magnitude?" and we neglect the smaller magnitude term. That is, if we have the quantity $j\omega + 10$ and are considering the ω-range of $\omega < 10$ then we would neglect the $j\omega$ term since ω is always less than the corner frequency 10 for this ω-range. Hence, we would state $j\omega + 10 \cong 10$ for $\omega < 10$. And for the ω-range $10 < \omega < 90$ we would neglect 10 since for this ω-range ω is always greater than the corner frequency 10. This approximation for the various ω-ranges is why Bode plot is an approximation technique. Other examples of approximation are shown here.

For $10 < \omega < 50$

$$j\omega + 10^3 \cong 10^3 \text{ since } \omega < 10^3$$

$$j\omega + 5 \cong j\omega \text{ since } \omega > 5$$

$$j\omega + 50 \cong 50 \text{ since } \omega < 50$$

$$j\omega + 3 \cong j\omega \text{ since } \omega > 3$$

After we have approximated $G(j\omega)$ for each ω-range we will determine the gain in dB and phase shift as we did in section 7–2. We will see that $dB(\omega)$ will give us a straight equation which will allow us to graph our approximated $G(j\omega)$ for that ω-range rather quickly and with great ease. To better illustrate the concepts previously discussed and develop further concepts we will now work an example.

Example 7–1   Make a Bode plot of Eq. (7–2) for $RC = 10^{-3}$ and compare the results with Fig. 7–1.

$$G(j\omega) = \frac{1}{RCj\omega\left(j\omega + \dfrac{1}{RC}\right)} = \frac{1}{10^{-3}j\omega(j\omega + 10^3)} \quad (7\text{–}2)$$

Solution

We must first identify the corner frequencies which are: just 10^3 since the quantity $j\omega + 10^3$ is the only quantity which has no zero term. Then ω-ranges will be $0 < \omega < 10^3$ and $\omega > 10^3$, or simply $\omega < 10^3$ and $\omega > 10^3$. Next we approximate $G(j\omega)$ for each ω-range.

For $\omega < 10^3$

$$G(j\omega) \cong \frac{1}{10^{-3}j\omega(10^3)} = \frac{1}{\omega} \angle -90°, \text{ where } j\omega + 10^3 \cong 10^3$$

For $\omega > 10^3$

$$G(j\omega) \cong \frac{1}{10^{-3}j\omega(j\omega)} = \frac{1}{\omega^2 \times 10^{-3}} \angle -180°,$$
$$\text{where } j\omega + 10^3 \cong j\omega$$

We now determine the magnitude in dBs as we did in section 7–2. Hence

For $\omega < 10^3$

$$dB(\omega) = 20 \log_{10} \frac{1}{\omega} = -20 \log_{10} \omega \ @ \angle -90° \qquad \text{(7-7)}$$

For $\omega > 10^3$

$$dB(\omega) = 20 \log_{10} \frac{1}{\omega^2 \times 10^{-3}}$$
$$= -20 \log_{10} \omega^2 - 20 \log_{10} 10^3$$
$$= -40 \log_{10} \omega + 60 \ @ \angle -180° \qquad \text{(7-8)}$$

We stated earlier that we were to plot ω on log paper; therefore we are plotting $\log_{10} \omega$ on the horizontal axis and not just ω. Let us define the variable x equal to the variable $\log_{10} \omega$, that is $x = \log_{10} \omega$. Under this condition Eqs. (7–7) and (7–8) can be written as $dB(\omega) = -20 x$ and $dB(\omega) = -40 x + 60$ respectively. We recognize these two equations to be expressions for a straight line. Therefore, plotting on semilog paper with ω plotted on the log portion Eqs. (7–7) and (7–8) are equations of straight lines. To plot any straight line all we need is two points, so let us find two points for Eqs. (7–7) and (7–8) and then plot them. When picking these two points let us make one of the points at the corner frequency and try to make the other point at some convenient point, say at ten raised to some power. The reason we want to pick the corner frequency is to check our dB(ω) equations. This provides a check since the Bode plot *must* be continuous; then Eq. (7–7) must equal Eq. (7–8) when both equations are evaluated at the corner frequency, or ω = corner frequency = $1/10^{-3}$ = 10^3. Our reason for picking the second point at 10^a is the convenience of finding $\log_{10} 10^a = a$.

Evaluating Eq. (7–7) at $\omega = 10^3$ we have

$$dB(\omega = 10^3) = -20 \log_{10} 10^3 = -60 \, dB$$

And Eq. (7–8) also evaluated at $\omega = 10^3$, dB($\omega = 10^3$) = $-40 \log_{10} 10^3 + 60 = -120 + 60 = -60dB$, hence Eqs. (7–7) and (7–8) check out at the corner frequency. For Eq. (7–7) let us pick $\omega = 10^2$ for the second point. Our only criteria for picking $\omega = 10^2$ are that ω must be less than 10^3 and we would like $\omega = 10^a$, where a = some rational number. Thus

$$dB(\omega = 10^2) = -20 \log_{10} 10^2 = -40 \, dB$$

For Eq. (7–8) let us pick $\omega = 10^4$ for the second point. Then

$$dB(\omega = 10^4) = -40 \log_{10} 10^4 + 60 = -160 + 60$$
$$= -100 \, dB$$

We can now graph each of these equations. The graph of Eq. (7–7) is shown in Fig. 7–2(a) while Eq. (7–8) is shown in Fig. 7–2(b). The complete Bode plot, which is the composite of Eqs. (7–7) and (7–8) for each one's ω-range, is shown in Fig. 7–2(c).

Notice that the graphs of the gain $G(j\omega)$ in Figs. 7–1 and 7–2 agree very closely. For $\omega = 10^2$ dB($\omega = 10^2$) = -40 dB for Fig. 7–1 and dB($\omega = 10^2$) = -40 dB for Fig. 7–2. At $\omega = 10^3$ Fig. 7–1 shows -63 dB while Fig. 7–2 shows -60 dB, which is an error of -3 dB. And for $\omega = 10^4$ both graphs show -100 dB. The greatest error exists at the corner frequency, and it is -3 dB difference. This will be true for all Bode approximation; the greatest error occurs at the corner frequencies and that error will usually be about 3 dB in magnitude, which is no serious problem since an error of 3 dB is acceptable for most practical cases. We will see later that we will be able to even reduce this error. Later we will also see how to approximate the phase shift, but for now we will concern ourselves with only the gain.

We will now consider another example.

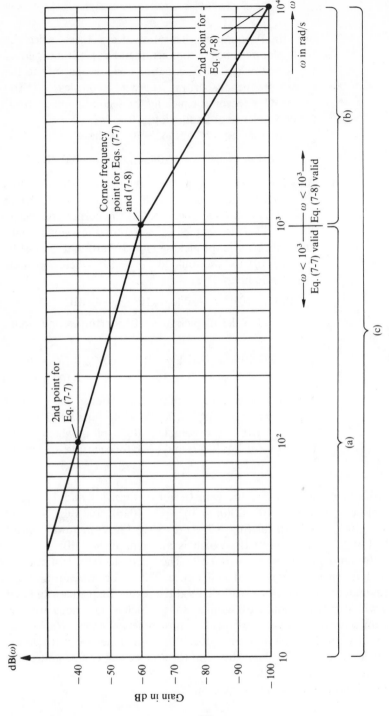

FIGURE 7-2

Example 7–2   Make a Bode plot for

$$G(s) = \frac{10(s + 50)}{s(s + 250)(s + 10^3)}$$

Solution   Require $s = j\omega$ so

$$G(j\omega) = \frac{10(j\omega + 50)}{j\omega(j\omega + 250)(j\omega + 10^3)}$$

The corner frequencies are determined from the quantities $j\omega + 50, j\omega + 250$, and $j\omega + 10^3$. The corner frequencies are the real terms of these quantities, hence corner frequencies = 50, 250, and 10^3 rad/s. Then the ω-ranges are

$$\omega < 50, \ 50 < \omega < 250, \ 250 < \omega < 10^3, \ \text{and} \ \omega > 10^3$$

based upon the corner frequencies. Approximating $G(j\omega)$ for each ω-range we have:

For $\omega < 50$

$$G(j\omega) \simeq \frac{10(50)}{j\omega(250)10^3} \quad \text{since} \quad j\omega + 50 \simeq 50$$

$j\omega + 250 \simeq 250$ and $j\omega + 10^3 \simeq 10^3$ for the range $\omega < 50$.
So

$$G(j\omega) \simeq \frac{2 \times 10^{-3}}{\omega} \angle -90°$$

and

$$\begin{aligned}
\text{dB}(\omega) &= 20 \log_{10} \frac{2 \times 10^{-3}}{\omega} \\
&= -20 \log_{10} \omega + 20 \log_{10} 2 \times 10^{-3} \\
&= -20 \log_{10} \omega + 20(0.30 - 3.00) \\
&= -20 \log \omega - 54 \, \text{dB at} \ \angle -90° \qquad (7\text{–}9)
\end{aligned}$$

For $50 < \omega < 250$

$$G(j\omega) \simeq \frac{10j\omega}{j\omega(250)10^3} = \frac{1}{250 \times 10^2} \angle 0°$$

$$\begin{aligned}
\text{dB}(\omega) &= 20 \log_{10} \frac{1}{250 \times 10^2} = -20 \log_{10} 250 \times 10^2 \\
&= -20(4.398) \simeq -88 \, \text{dB at} \ \angle 0° \qquad (7\text{–}10)
\end{aligned}$$

For $250 < \omega < 10^3$

$$G(j\omega) \cong \frac{10j\omega}{j\omega(j\omega)10^3} = \frac{10}{j\omega10^3} = \frac{10^{-2}}{\omega} \angle -90°$$

$$dB(\omega) = 20 \log_{10} \frac{10^{-2}}{\omega} = -20 \log_{10} \omega - 40 \text{ dB at } \angle -90°$$

(7–11)

For $\omega > 10^3$

$$G(j\omega) \cong \frac{10j\omega}{j\omega(j\omega)j\omega} = \frac{10}{\omega^2} \angle -180°$$

$$dB(\omega) = 20 \log_{10} \frac{10}{\omega^2} = -40 \log_{10} \omega + 20 \text{ dB at } \angle -180°$$

(7–12)

We will now get two points per straight-line equation, where our points will be at corner frequencies so as to serve as a check on the continuity of Eqs. (7–9), (7–10), (7–11), and (7–12). For Eq. (7–9) let us choose the convenient point of $\omega = 10$ for the lower frequency point since no lower corner frequency is expressed, so $dB(\omega = 10) = -20 \log_{10} 10 - 54 = -74dB$. For the upper frequency point we have the corner frequency $\omega = 50$, hence $dB(\omega = 50) = -20 \log_{10} 54 - 54 = -88.6dB$. For Eq. (7–10) we have an equation of a constant, which is -88 dB. We see that Eqs. (7–9) and (7–10) give continuity at $\omega = 50$ since for all practical purposes both equations equal -88 dB when evaluated at $\omega = 50$. We next evaluate Eq. (7–11) at $\omega = 250$ and 10^3. Thus

$$dB(\omega = 250) = -20 \log_{10} 250 - 40 = -20(2.398) - 40$$
$$= -87.8 \text{ dB}$$

which agrees with Eq. (7–10). Evaluating Eq. (7–11) at $\omega = 10^3$ we have $dB(\omega = 10^3) = -20 \log_{10} 10^3 - 40 = -100$ dB. We next determine two points for Eq. (7–12), where one point is to be determined by the corner frequency $\omega = 10^3$ and the other point is one of convenience, where $\omega > 10^3$, so let us pick $\omega = 10^4$. Hence, $dB(\omega = 10^3) = -40 \log_{10} 10^3 + 20 = -100$ dB, which agrees with Eq. (7–11) evaluated also at $\omega = 10^3$, and $dB(\omega = 10^4) = -40 \log_{10} 10^4 + 20 = -140$ dB. We now plot these points and draw our straight line between the points, where these straight lines are expressed in Eqs. (7–9), (7–10), (7–11), and (7–12). The Bode plot of $G(j\omega)$ is shown in Fig. 7–3.

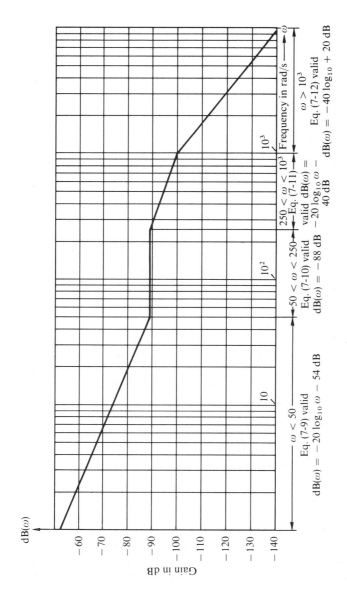

FIGURE 7-3

473

We previously stated the Bode plot has its greatest error at the corner frequencies and this is approximately 3-dB error. Let us verify this by calculating $G(j\omega)$ exactly at one of the corner frequencies. Choosing the corner frequency of 10^3 we have

$$G(j\omega = j10^3) = \frac{10(j10^3 + 50)}{j10^3(j10^3 + 250)(j10^3 + 10^3)}$$

$$\cong \frac{10(10^3 \angle 90°)}{10^3 \angle 90°(1.03 \times 10^3 \angle 76°)(1.41 \times 10^3 \angle 45°)}$$

$$= \frac{10}{1.45 \times 10^6} \angle -121° = \frac{1}{1.45 \times 10^5} \angle -121°$$

$$dB(\omega = 10^3) = 20 \log_{10} \frac{1}{1.45 \times 10^5} = -20(5.162) = -103 \text{ dB}$$

From Fig. 7–3 we see at $\omega = 10^3$ that $dB(\omega = 10^3) = -100 \text{ dB}$, which is a difference of -3 dB. It is suggested that the reader check the corner frequencies 50 and 250 rad/s.

7–4   Calculated Error in Bode Plot

Now that we have demonstrated that Bode plot has approximately 3-dB error at the corner frequencies, and this a maximum difference between the exact plot and the Bode plot, let us verify this mathematically so as to draw some conclusions which will aid us in bettering our Bode plot.

Let us consider some general quantity $s + \alpha$, which for $s = j\omega$ would be written as $j\omega + \alpha$. We know that for this quantity the corner frequency would be α. Then for $\omega < \alpha$ we would approximate the quantity as being equal to α. So the magnitude in dBs for $\omega < \alpha$ would be $20 \log_{10} \alpha$ dB. Now at $\omega = \alpha$ the actual quantity would be $j\alpha + \alpha$. The magnitude of this quantity is $\sqrt{\alpha^2 + \alpha^2} = \alpha\sqrt{2}$, so the dB expression is $20 \log \alpha\sqrt{2}$ $= 20 \log_{10} \alpha + 20 \log_{10} 2^{1/2} = 20 \log_{10} \alpha + 3$ dB. We see the difference between the approximated ($20 \log_{10} \alpha$ dB) and the exact ($20 \log_{10} \alpha + 3$ dB) is 3 dB, so we have 3-dB difference. If the quantity $j\omega + \alpha$ were in the numerator the difference would be positive and if in the denominator it would be negative. Then to make our Bode plots more accurate let us add 3 dB to the Bode plot at numerator corner frequencies and add -3 dB at denominator corner frequencies. We will see later that this 3-dB correction is to be more of an "eyeball fudge factor" than an absolute correction. However, for now we will treat it as absolute.

With our 3-dB correction factor return to Ex. 7–1 and make the Bode plot of Fig. 7–2 more accurate. From Eq. (7–2) of Ex. 7–1 we were given

$$G(j\omega) = \frac{1}{10^{-3}j\omega(j\omega + 10^3)}$$

Our only corner frequency of 10^3 is in the denominator, so we add -3 dB to our graph at $\omega = 10^3$. This puts a point at -63 dB, which agrees exactly with Fig. 7-1 at $\omega = 10^3$. Now to complete the Bode plot curve we take a French curve, or similar instrument, and draw a line through our new point converging with the straight-line approximations on each side of $\omega = 10^3$. This concept is shown in Fig. 7-4.

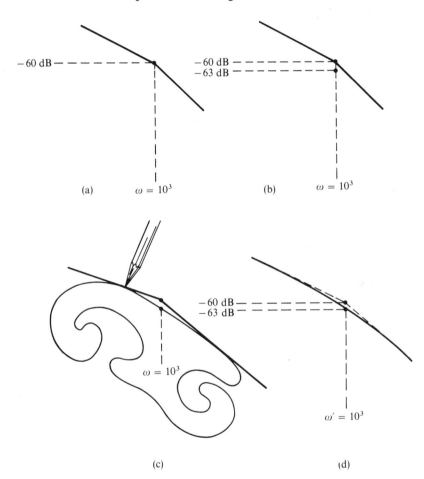

FIGURE 7–4   (a) Fig. 7–2 at corner frequency $\omega = 10^3$; (b) -3 dB
                   added to Fig. 7–2 at $\omega = 10^3$;   (c) Drawing correc-
                   tion for Bode plot;   (d) Corrected Bode plot

If the reader will actually perform the correction on Fig. 7–2 and then compare this with Fig. 7–1 he will see his Bode plot is now more accurate.

Let us next determine the error an octave away from the corner frequencies. Again consider the quantity $j\omega + \alpha$, where α is the corner frequency. Going an octave up in frequency (an octave up is for $\omega = 2\alpha$ and an octave down would be $\omega = \alpha/2$) we have $j2\alpha + \alpha$. So the magnitude is $\sqrt{(2\alpha)^2 + \alpha^2} = \alpha\sqrt{5}$ and in dB we have $20\log\alpha\sqrt{5} = 20\log_{10}\alpha + 20\log_{10}\sqrt{5} = 20\log_{10}\alpha + 10\log_{10}5 = 20\log_{10}\alpha + 7$ dB. To approximate $j\omega + \alpha$ for Bode plots we would have said $j\omega + \alpha \cong j\omega = \omega\angle 90°$ since $\omega > \alpha$. The dB equation would be $20\log_{10}\omega$ so at $\omega = 2\alpha$ we have $20\log_{10}2\alpha = 20\log_{10}\alpha + 20\log_{10}2 = 20\log_{10}\alpha + 6$ dB. We see the difference between the exact and Bode equation is $+1$ dB. Then for an octave up a $+1$-dB error is present if the quantity $j\omega + \alpha$ is in the numerator; and if $j\omega + \alpha$ is in the denominator it is -1 dB. So at an octave up from the corner frequency let us add $+1$-dB correction factor to our Bode plot for corner frequencies in the numerator and a -1-dB correction factor for denominator corner frequencies. To verify this compare dB(ω) of Figs. 7-1 and 7-2 at $\omega = 2 \times 10^3$. For Fig. 7-1 we see dB($\omega = 2 \times 10^3$) $\cong -73$ dB and for Fig. 7-2 dB($\omega = 2 \times 10^3$) $= -72$ dB, an error of -1 dB. Hence, since the corner frequency is a denominator corner frequency adding -1 dB to the Bode plot would remove any error. The reader can prove for himself the same can be said for an octave down in frequency.

In summary, our Bode plots in general will have a 1-dB error at an octave up and an octave down from the corner frequencies. An error of 3 dB will exist at the corner frequencies. For denominator corner frequencies and associated octaves we correct the Bode plot by adding -3 dB at corner frequencies and -1 dB at the corner frequency octaves. We correct at numerator corner frequency and associated octaves by adding $+3$ dB and $+1$ dB respectively.

Our procedure for making a Bode plot will be to first graph the Bode plot as we have done in the past. Then we will correct this Bode plot at the corner frequencies and associated octaves. Next we take a French curve, or similar instrument, and draw in the corrected Bode plot. To illustrate this concept we have redone the Bode plot of Fig. 7-3 in Fig. 7-5.

There is an important observation to be made from Fig. 7-3. Notice the octave correction points at $\omega = 100$ and $\omega = 125$ serve only as guides. That is, the actual curve was "eyeballed" so that the graphic average was taken. Averaging will always occur when corner frequencies come close to each other, where "close" means that before a corrected curve can converge with the straight-line approximation the down octave correction point of the next corner frequency appears. This same thing occured for the corner frequencies 250 rad/s and 10^3 rad/s. Then we can conclude that our correction technique may still have to be "eyeballed" in. But notice

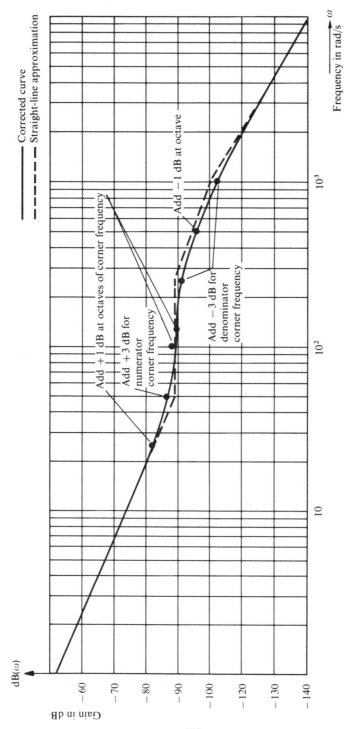

FIGURE 7-5

477

even the straight-line approximation without any correction is fairly accurate.

Let us consider another example.

Example 7–3   For the circuit shown in Fig. 7–6 determine the Bode plot, where by Bode plot we will now mean "with corrections."

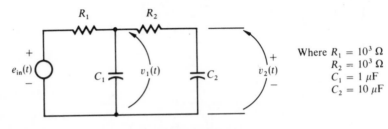

Where $R_1 = 10^3 \, \Omega$
$R_2 = 10^3 \, \Omega$
$C_1 = 1 \, \mu\text{F}$
$C_2 = 10 \, \mu\text{F}$

FIGURE 7–6

Solution

$$\frac{e_{in}(t) - v_1(t)}{R} - C_1 \frac{dv_1(t)}{dt} + \frac{v_o(t) - v_1(t)}{R_2} = 0$$

$$\frac{v_1(t) - v_o(t)}{R_2} - C_2 \frac{dv_o(t)}{dt} = 0$$

$$\frac{E_{in}(s)}{R_1} = \left(\frac{1}{R_1} + \frac{1}{R_2} + C_1 s\right) V_1(s) - \frac{1}{R_2} V_o(s)$$

$$0 = -\frac{1}{R_2} V_1(s) + \left(\frac{1}{R_2} + C_2 s\right) V_o(s)$$

where initial conditions are *never* considered for Bode plot cases.

$$\Delta = \begin{vmatrix} \dfrac{1}{R_1} + \dfrac{1}{R_2} + C_1 s & -\dfrac{1}{R_2} \\[2ex] -\dfrac{1}{R_2} & \dfrac{1}{R_2} + C_2 s \end{vmatrix}$$

$$= \left(\frac{1}{R_1} + \frac{1}{R_1} + C_1 s\right)\left(\frac{1}{R_2} + C_2 s\right) - \left(\frac{1}{R_2}\right)^2$$

$$= \frac{1}{R_1 R_2} + \left(\frac{C_1}{R_2} + \frac{C_2}{R_1} + \frac{C_2}{R_2}\right) s + C_1 C_2 s^2$$

Putting Δ in nice form, that is, the coefficient of s^2 equal to unity, we have

$$\Delta = C_1 C_2 \left[s^2 + \frac{1}{C_1 C_2} \left(\frac{C_1}{R_2} + \frac{C_2}{R_1} + \frac{C_2}{R_2} \right) s + \frac{1}{C_1 R_1 C_2 R_2} \right]$$

$$= C_1 C_2 \left[s^2 + \left(\frac{1}{R_2 C_2} + \frac{1}{R_1 C_1} + \frac{1}{R_2 C_1} \right) s + \frac{1}{C_1 R_1 C_2 R_2} \right]$$

Now solving for $V_o(s)$,

$$\Delta V_o(s) = \begin{vmatrix} \frac{1}{R_1} + \frac{1}{R_2} + C_1 s & \dfrac{E_{in}(s)}{R_1} \\[2mm] -\dfrac{1}{R_2} & 0 \end{vmatrix} = \frac{E_{in}(s)}{R_1 R_2}$$

or

$$\frac{V_o(s)}{E_{in}(s)} = G(s) = \frac{1}{R_1 R_2 \Delta}$$

$$= \frac{1}{R_1 C_1 R_2 C_2 \left[s^2 + \left(\dfrac{1}{R_2 C_2} + \dfrac{1}{R_1 C_1} + \dfrac{1}{R_2 C_1} \right) s + \dfrac{1}{R_1 C_1 R_2 C_2} \right]}$$

$$(7\text{–}13)$$

For Bode plot we must have our gain equation in the form

$$G(s) = \frac{K(s + a)(s + b)(s + c) \cdots}{(s + \alpha)(s + \beta)(s + \gamma) \cdots} \qquad (7\text{–}14)$$

Then Eq. (7–13) must be factored in order to appear as Eq. (7–14). Hence,

$$s_{1,2} = -\frac{1}{2} \left(\frac{1}{R_2 C_2} + \frac{1}{R_1 C_1} + \frac{1}{R_2 C_1} \right)$$

$$\pm \frac{1}{2} \sqrt{\left(\frac{1}{R_2 C_2} + \frac{1}{R_1 C_1} + \frac{1}{R_2 C_1} \right)^2 - \frac{4}{R_1 C_1 R_2 C_2}}$$

where

$$R_1 C_1 = 10^3 (10^{-6}) = 10^{-3} \text{ s}, \quad R_2 C_2 = 10^3 (10^{-5}) = 10^{-2} \text{ s},$$
$$R_2 C_1 = 10^3 (10^{-6}) = 10^{-3} \text{ s}$$

So

$$s_{1,2} = -\frac{1}{2} (10^2 + 10^3 + 10^3)$$

$$\pm \frac{1}{2} \sqrt{(10^2 + 10^3 + 10^3)^2 + 4 \times 10^5}$$

$$= -\frac{2.1 \times 10^3}{2} \pm \frac{1}{2} \sqrt{4.4 \times 10^6 - 0.4 \times 10^6}$$

$$= (-1.05 \pm 1.00) \times 10^3$$

or $s_1 = -0.05 \times 10^3 = -50$ and $s_2 = -2.05 \times 10^3$.
And since $(s + \alpha)\big|_{s=s_1} = 0 = s_1 + \alpha$ and $(s + \beta)\big|_{s=s_2} = 0 = s_2 + \beta$ then $\alpha = -s_1 = 50$ and $\beta = -s_2 = 2.05 \times 10^3$.
So from Eq. (7–13)

$$G(s) = \frac{1}{10^{-5}(s + 50)(s + 2.05 \times 10^3)}$$

$$\cong \frac{10^5}{(s + 50)(s + 2 \times 10^3)} \qquad (7\text{–}15)$$

Then for $s = j\omega$ Eq. (7–15) becomes

$$G(j\omega) = \frac{10^5}{(j\omega + 50)(j\omega + 2.0 \times 10^3)} \qquad (7\text{–}16)$$

To make our Bode plot we see from Eq. (7–15) that the corner frequencies are 50 rad/s, and 2.0×10^3 rad/s. From the corner frequencies we determine the ω-range of $\omega < 50$, $50 < \omega < 2.0 \times 10^3$ and $\omega > 2.0 \times 10^3$. Then for

$\underline{\omega < 50}$

$$G(j\omega) \cong \frac{10^5}{50(2.0 \times 10^3)} = 1.0 \angle 0°$$

$$dB(\omega) = 20 \log_{10} 1.0 = 0 \, dB \text{ at } \angle 0° \qquad (7\text{–}17)$$

$\underline{50 < \omega < 2.0 \times 10^3}$

$$G(j\omega) \cong \frac{10^5}{j\omega(2.0 \times 10^3)} = \frac{50}{\omega} \angle -90°$$

$$dB(\omega) = -20 \log_{10} \omega + 20 \log_{10} 50$$
$$= -20 \log_{10} \omega + 34 \, dB \text{ at } \angle -90° \qquad (7\text{–}18)$$

$\underline{\omega > 2.0 \times 10^3}$

$$G(j\omega) \cong \frac{10^5}{(j\omega)^2} = \frac{10^5}{\omega^2} \angle -180°$$

$$dB(\omega) = -20 \log_{10} \omega^2 + 20 \log_{10} 10^5$$
$$= -40 \log_{10} \omega + 100 \, dB \text{ at } \angle -180° \qquad (7\text{–}19)$$

Notice in Eq. (7–19) we did not leave $-20 \log \omega^2$ in that form but wrote it as $-40 \log \omega$. Our reason is that we are *not* plotting $\log \omega^2$ on the horizontal axis but rather $\log \omega$. So, for us to plot anything but $\log \omega$ on the horizontal is incorrect. Always put your equations in the form of $20 \, a \log_{10} \omega$, where the magnitude is ω^a.

We now plot Eqs. (7–17), (7–18), and (7–19) on Fig. 7-7 and then put our correction points at the corner frequencies and octaves. We then can draw our corrected Bode plot as shown in Fig. 7-7. The two points for Eqs. (7–17), (7–18), and (7–19) are calculated here.

For Eq. (7–17)
We do not need any since $dB(\omega) = 0\,dB = $ constant.

For Eq. (7–18)
$dB(\omega = 50) = -20 \log_{10} 50 + 34 = -34 + 34 = 0\,dB$, which agrees with Eq. (7–17). And

$$dB(\omega = 2.0 \times 10^3) = -20 \log_{10} 2.0 \times 10^3 + 34$$
$$= -66 + 34 = -32\,dB$$

For Eq. (7–19)

$$dB(\omega = 2.0 \times 10^3) = -40 \log_{10} 2.0 \times 10^3 + 100$$
$$= -132 + 100 = -32\,dB,$$

which agrees with Eq. (7–18) evaluated at $\omega = 2.0 \times 10^3$. And

$$dB(\omega = 10^4) = -40 \log_{10} 10^4 + 100 = -60\,dB$$

When determining the gain equation $G(s)$ notice we use much of the same procedures as for finding the inverse Laplace transform. Notice especially that our s-terms have coefficients of one in each quantity $s + \alpha$.

Our next topic of discussion is the slope of our straight-line equations. We will see this information can speed up our plotting of the Bode plot.

7–5   Slopes of Straight-Line Approximations

When working with Bode plots it is sometimes convenient to know the slopes of the straight-line equations. As we will see we will be able to make our Bode plots by knowing just the slopes of each equation; this method will speed our making a Bode plot.

Each straight-line equation we have seen thus far has the form of either $\pm 20 \log_{10} \omega + b$ or $\pm 40 \log_{10} \omega + b$. Recalling that $\log_{10} \omega$ is our independent variable we would state that the slope of our first expression is ± 20 and the slope of the second is ± 40. We could become general and write the general expression for $dB(\omega)$ as

$$dB(\omega) = 20 \log_{10} \omega^k + b = 20k \log_{10} \omega + b, \text{ where } k = 0, \pm 1, \pm 2, \text{ etc.}$$
$$(7\text{–}20)$$

For Eq. (7–20) we have a slope of $20k$.

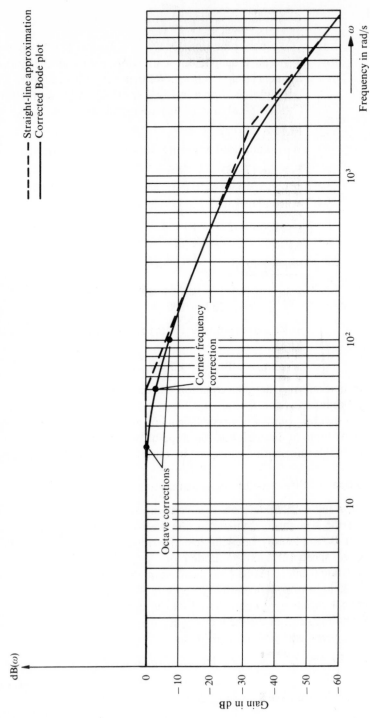

FIGURE 7-7

We will want to arrive at an expression for the slope of Eq. (7–20) expressed in decibels/octave. We know that

$$\text{slope} = \frac{\text{opposite}}{\text{adjacent}} = \frac{\Delta\, dB(\omega)}{\Delta\omega} \tag{7–21}$$

If we want the slope to be dB/octave then $\Delta\omega$ must be an octave, so we will express $\Delta\omega = \omega_2 - \omega_1$, where $\omega_2 = 2\omega_1$, for an octave up and $\Delta\omega = \omega_1 - \omega_1/2$ for an octave down. We will limit discussion to an octave up and leave it for the reader to verify for an octave down. From Eq. (7–21) we want $\Delta\, dB(\omega)$ so for an octave up $\Delta\, dB(\omega) = dB(2\omega_1) - dB(\omega_1)$. Hence Eq. (7–21) can be written as

$$\text{slope} = \frac{\Delta\, dB(\omega)}{\Delta\omega} = \frac{dB(2\omega_1) - dB(\omega_1)}{\omega_2 - \omega_1} = \frac{dB(2\omega_1) - dB(\omega_1)}{\text{octave}} \tag{7–22}$$

To determine the slope for Eq. (7–20) we substitute Eq. (7–20) into Eq. (7–22), hence,

$$\text{slope} = \frac{[20k \log_{10} 2\omega_1 + b] - [20k \log_{10} \omega_1 + b]}{\text{octave}}$$

$$= \frac{20k(\log_{10} 2\omega_1 - \log_1 \omega_1)}{\text{octave}} = \frac{20k \log_{10}\dfrac{2\omega_1}{\omega_1}}{\text{octave}}$$

$$= \frac{20k \log_{10} 2}{\text{octave}} = \frac{6k\, dB}{\text{octave}}$$

So the slope can be expressed as

$$\text{slope} = \frac{6k}{\text{octave}}, \text{ where } k = 0, \pm 1, \pm 2, \pm 3, \text{ etc.} \tag{7–23}$$

As some examples of Eq. (7–23) consider these equations:

$$20 \log_{10} \omega + 50 \text{ the slope is } + \frac{6\, dB}{\text{octave}} \text{ since } k = 1$$

$$20 \log_{10} \omega^2 - 50 = 40 \log_{10} \omega - 50, \text{ slope} = \frac{12\, dB}{\text{octave}}, \; k = 2$$

$$20 \log_{10} \omega^3 = 60 \log_{10} \omega, \text{ slope} = \frac{18\, dB}{\text{octave}}, \; k = 3$$

$$20 \log_{10} \omega^{-1} = -20 \log_{10} \omega, \text{ slope} = -\frac{6\, dB}{\text{octave}}, \; k = -1$$

$$20 \log_{10} \omega^{-5} + 10 = -100 \log_{10} \omega + 10, \text{ slope} = -\frac{30\, dB}{\text{octave}}, \; k = -5$$

$$20 \log_{10} \omega^{-2} - 5 = -40 \log_{10} \omega - 5, \text{ slope} = -\frac{12\, dB}{\text{octave}}, \; k = -2$$

So for $\pm 20 \log_{10} \omega$ we have ± 6 dB/octave slope and for $\pm 40 \log_{10} \omega$ we have ± 12 dB/octave slope, and so on.

The manner in which we can use the slope of these straight-line equations to make our Bode plot is to first determine a point in the lowest ω-range at least an octave down from the lowest corner frequency. Then by knowing the slope for that ω-range we can determine the second point by going an octave up from that point since from Eq. (7–23) we see that $6\,k$ dB/octave $\cdot$ octave $= 6\,k$ (dB). Once we have these two points we can draw our straight line for this ω-range. In drawing this line we have graphically calculated the lower corner frequency point for the next ω-range since our straight-line approximations must be continuous. So this graphically determined point will serve as our first point of the next ω-range straight line. For the second point we will go up an octave from this lower corner frequency and determine its relative dB position using Eq. (7–23). We continue with this method until our Bode plot is finished.

As an example of this technique consider Ex. 7–1. Our lowest ω-range is $\omega < 10^3$ for which Eq. (7–7) is valid. For a first point let us choose a convenient point, such as 10^2. Then for our first, and *only point to be calculated*, we find

$$\mathrm{dB}(\omega = 10^2) = -20 \log_{10} 10^2 = -40\ \mathrm{dB}$$

So we place a point at -40 dB for $\omega = 10^2$. For the second point we reason that since Eq. (7–7) has a slope of -6dB/octave, then for one octave up, which is at $\omega = 2 \times 10^2$, we should drop 6 dB down from the value at $\omega = 10^2$. Thus, at $\omega = 2 \times 10^2$ we have the point -46 dB. We now draw a line through -40 dB at $\omega = 10^2$ and -46 dB at $\omega = 2 \times 10^2$. We see this line intersects -60 dB at $\omega = 10^3$ from Fig. 7–2 and this point is the point of the lower corner frequency for the next ω-range. For the next ω-range we see the slope for that range is -12dB/octave from Eq. (7–8). Then going an octave up from $\omega = 10^3$, which is $\omega = 2 \times 10^3$, we drop -12 dB from -60 dB, or -72 dB. We now draw a line through the points -60 dB at $\omega = 10^3$ and -72 dB at $\omega = 2 \times 10^3$ and extend that line as far as we wish. This completes our Bode plot for Ex. 7–1.

We will now work another example using the slope technique to make a Bode plot.

Example 7–4   Make a Bode plot, using the slope technique, for $G(s)$ given here.

$$G(s) = \frac{5.5 \times 10^3 s + 27.6 \times 10^4}{(30s + 2.2 \times 10^3)(10s + 10^4)}$$

Solution   First we put $G(s)$ into a better form by making the coefficients of s equal to unity. Then

$$G(s) = \frac{5.5 \times 10^3 \left(s + \dfrac{27.6 \times 10^4}{5.5 \times 10^3}\right)}{30 \left(s + \dfrac{2.2 \times 10^3}{30}\right) 10(s + 10^3)}$$

$$= \frac{18.4(s + 50)}{(s + 73)(s + 10^3)}$$

Therefore

$$G(j\omega) = \frac{18.4(j\omega + 50)}{(j\omega + 73)(j\omega + 10^3)}$$

for which the corner frequencies are 50, 73, 10^3. Therefore, the ω-ranges are $\omega < 50$, $50 < \omega < 73$, $73 < \omega < 10^3$, and $\omega > 10^3$. Thus,

$\underline{\omega < 50}$

$$G(j\omega) \simeq \frac{18.4(50)}{73(10^3)} = \frac{12.6}{10^3} \angle 0°$$

$$dB(\omega) = 20 \log_{10} 12.6 - 60 = -38\,dB \text{ at } \angle 0°$$

$$(7\text{-}24)$$

$\underline{50 < \omega < 73}$

$$G(j\omega) \simeq \frac{18.4\,j\omega}{73(10^3)} = \frac{0.25\,\omega}{10^3} \angle 90°$$

$$dB(\omega) = 20 \log_{10} \omega - 72\,dB \text{ at } \angle 90° \quad (7\text{-}25)$$

$\underline{73 < \omega < 10^3}$

$$G(j\omega) \simeq \frac{18.4\,j\omega}{j\omega(10^3)} = \frac{18.4}{10^3} \angle 0°$$

$$dB(\omega) = 20 \log_{10} \frac{18.4}{10^3} = -34.8\,dB \text{ at } \angle 0° \quad (7\text{-}26)$$

$\underline{\omega > 10^3}$

$$G(j\omega) \simeq \frac{18.4\,j\omega}{j\omega(j\omega)} = \frac{18.4}{\omega} \angle -90°$$

$$dB(\omega) = -20 \log_{10} \omega + 20 \log_{10} 18.4$$

$$= -20 \log_{10} \omega + 25.3\,dB \text{ at } \angle -90° \quad (7\text{-}27)$$

The first slope to consider is the slope of Eq. (7-24). Its slope is 0 dB/octave; therefore we draw a line of slope zero for the range $\omega < 50$. This is shown in Fig. 7-8. Then for $50 < \omega < 73$ the slope is 6 dB/octave, so from $\omega = 50$ we go up one octave, which is $\omega = 100$, and add 6 dB to -38 dB. This gives us -32 dB at $\omega = 100$.

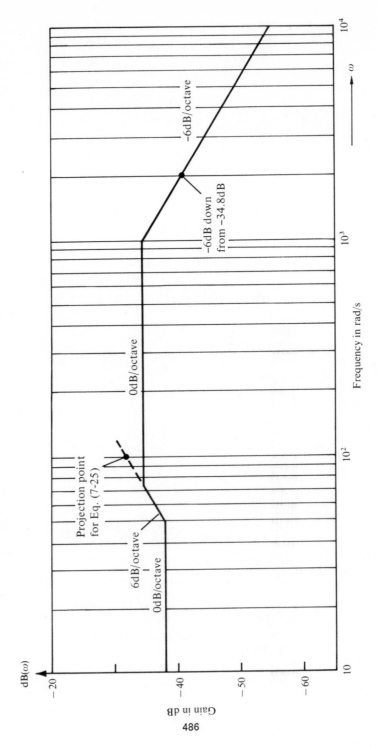

FIGURE 7-8

However, $\omega = 100$ is out of the ω-range valid for Eq. (7–25) so this point can serve only as a projection point. After drawing in the line for Eq. (7–25) we then proceed to Eq. (7–26), which describes the range $73 < \omega < 10^3$. Now Eq. (7–25) graphically intersected $\omega = 73$ at -34.8 dB so this is to be the point for Eq. (7–26) evaluated at $\omega = 73$. We see that Eq. (7–26) indeed does intersect at -34.8 dB for $\omega = 73$. Equation (7–26) has a zero slope so we draw a straight line of -34.8 dB for Eq. (7–26) on Fig. 7–8. For our last equation, Eq. (7–27), we begin at -34.8 dB for $\omega = 10^3$ and show a -6 dB/octave slope. Hence, for an octave up from 10^3 we add -6 dB to -34.8, which gives us -40.8 dB at $\omega = 2 \times 10^3$. Putting our point at -40.8 dB for $\omega = 2 \times 10^3$ allows us to draw the straight line for Eq. (7–27). No correction will be shown on the Bode plot of Fig. 7–8 so as not to add confusion to the concept of slope techniques of making a Bode plot. In practice we would make our corrections.

There is one major problem with the slope technique. It provides no check on the validity of the equations derived for the Bode plot. That is, when we plot these straight-line equations by determining two points at the corner frequencies we are automatically checking the equations' validity by determining their continuity. Whereas the slope technique does not provide this check since one only goes by the slopes and not the absolute magnitudes. For that reason we will not use the slope technique to any extent in this text.

7–6 Phase Approximation

Thus far we have made no phase approximation on our Bode plots. This section will undertake the task of making a phase plot from the same gain approximations we used to derive our straight-line equations, which are technically known as asymptotes. In order that we may have something concrete to discuss let us return to Ex. 7–1, where

$$G(j\omega) = \frac{1}{10^{-3}j\omega(j\omega + 10^3)}$$

For our ω-ranges we found that:
For $\omega < 10^3$

$$dB(\omega) = -20 \log_{10} \omega \text{ at } \angle -90° \tag{7–7}$$

and

For $\omega > 10^3$

$$dB(\omega) = -40 \log_{10} \omega + 60 \text{ at } \angle -180° \qquad \textbf{(7–8)}$$

Now the phase angle $-90°$ for Eq. (7–7) is a constant over the ω-range $\omega < 10^3$ and likewise for $-180°$ for Eq. (7–8) over the ω-range $\omega > 10^3$. Then for $G(j\omega)$ the phase $\theta(\omega)$ would appear as shown in Fig. 7–9.

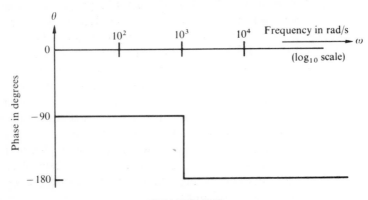

FIGURE 7–9

In viewing Fig. 7–9 we know that no phase relation behaves in this discontinuous manner. We will see that the phase lines of Fig. 7–9 are to serve as phase asymptotes for the actual phase angle. To see this we will analyze the quantity $j\omega + \alpha$ at the corner frequency $\omega = \alpha$. For as in the case of our greatest error in decibels occurring at the corner frequency the greatest error in phase also occurs there. That is,

$$j\omega + \alpha \bigg|_{\omega = \alpha} = j\alpha + \alpha = \sqrt{\alpha^2 + \alpha^2} \angle \tan^{-1}\frac{\alpha}{\alpha} = \alpha\sqrt{2} \angle 45°$$

So our phase angle is 45°, but in our approximation we would have stated $j\omega + \alpha \cong \alpha \angle 0°$ for $\omega < \alpha$ and $j\omega + \alpha \cong j\omega = \omega \angle 90°$ for $\omega > \alpha$. So at $\omega = \alpha$ we would have the discontinuity shown in Fig. 7–10(a). Now since an actual plot would have given us 45° then we may correct Fig. 7–10(a) by placing a point at 45° and using the straight lines as asymptotes. This is shown in Fig. 7–10(b).

There is an even better way to use our asymptotes and that is to get a correction point an octave up and an octave down. Thus

For an octave up

$$(j\omega + \alpha) \bigg|_{\omega = 2\alpha} = j2\alpha + \alpha = \alpha\sqrt{5} \angle \tan^{-1} 2 = \alpha\sqrt{5} \angle 63.5°$$

and

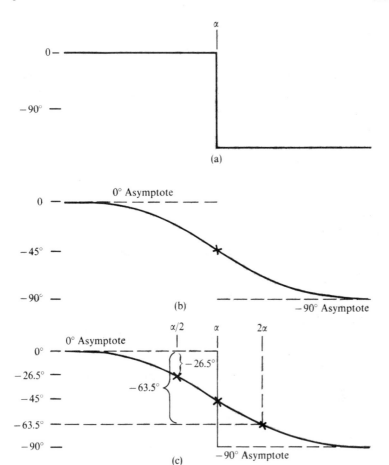

Note: The 0° asymptote is the reference asymptote since it is the asymptote just below the corner frequency.

FIGURE 7–10

For an octave down

$$(j\omega + \alpha)\Big|_{\omega=\alpha/2} = j\frac{\alpha}{2} + \alpha = \frac{\alpha}{2}\sqrt{5} \angle \tan^{-1} 0.5 = \frac{\alpha}{2}\sqrt{5} \angle 26.5°$$

So we now have three correction points, 26.5° an octave down from the corner frequency, 45° at the corner frequency, and 63.5° an octave up from the corner frequency. These corrections are to be referenced to the phase asymptote just below the corner frequency under consideration. Our new correction is shown in Fig. 7–10(c).

If the quantity $j\omega + \alpha$ is in the denominator the phase shift is negative and if in the numerator positive. Then all corrections for denominator corner frequencies are negative and those for numerator corner frequencies are positive. We shall see also that these phase corrections may still have to be averaged graphically, or eyeballed in, for cases where the corner frequencies are close to each other. We saw this situation in Fig. 7–5 when correcting the dB gain.

We will now make a phase plot for Exs. 7–2 and 7–3. Considering Ex. 7–2 first we have

$$G(j\omega) = \frac{10(j\omega + 50)}{j\omega(j\omega + 250)(j\omega + 10^3)}$$

from which we found:

For $\omega < 50$

$$dB(\omega) = -20 \log_{10} \omega - 54 \, dB \text{ at } \angle -90° \qquad (7\text{–}9)$$

For $50 < \omega < 250$

$$dB(\omega) = -88 \, dB \text{ at } \angle 0° \qquad (7\text{–}10)$$

For $250 < \omega < 10^3$

$$dB(\omega) = -20 \log_{10} \omega - 40 \, dB \text{ at } \angle -90° \qquad (7\text{–}11)$$

For $\omega > 10^3$

$$dB(\omega) = -40 \log_{10} \omega + 20 \, dB \text{ at } \angle -180° \qquad (7\text{–}12)$$

Then we have the asymptotes of $-90°$ for $\omega < 50$, $0°$ for $50 < \omega < 250$, $-90°$ for $250 < \omega < 10^3$, and $-180°$ for $\omega > 10^3$. We plot these asymptotes as dotted lines as shown in Fig. 7–11(a). Next we put the correction points on our phase plot where we will reference our corrections from the phase asymptote just below the corner frequency under consideration. Then for the corner frequency $\omega = 50$ the reference phase is $-90°$. Since this is a numerator corner frequency the phase corrections are positive, hence we have $-90° + 45° = -45°$ for the corner frequency correction, $-90° + 26.5° = -63.5°$ for an octave down from $\omega = 50$, and $-90° + 63.5° = -26.5°$ for an octave up from $\omega = 50$. Correcting next for the denominator corner frequency $\omega = 250$, the asymptote phase reference is $0°$; hence, for an octave down $\theta(250/2 = 125) = 0° - 26.5° = -26.5°$, at the corner frequency $\theta(250) = 0° - 45° = -45°$, and at an octave up $\theta(2 \times 250 = 500) = 0° - 63.5° = -63.5°$. And for denominator corner frequency $\omega = 10^3$ we have the asymptote phase reference of $-90°$. Then

$$\theta\left(\frac{10^3}{2} = 500\right) = -90° - 26.5° = -116.5°$$

$$\theta(10^3) = -90° - 45° = -135°$$

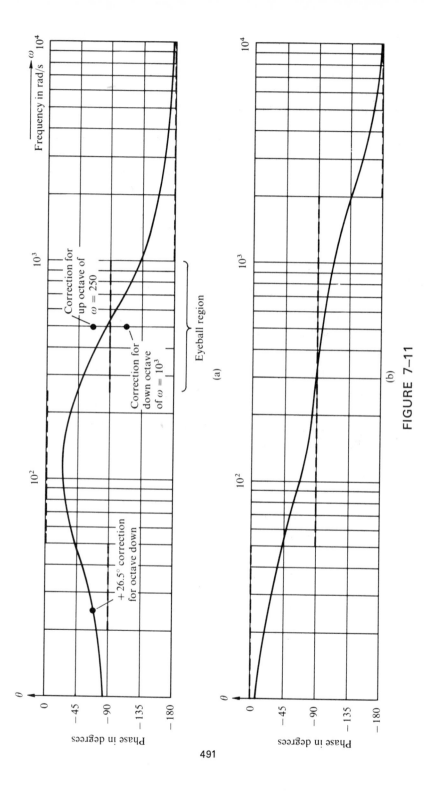

FIGURE 7-11

491

and

$$\theta(2 \times 10^3) = -90° - 63.5° = -153.5°$$

Notice from Fig. 7–11(a) that in the ω-range from approximately $200 < \omega < 10^3$ we had to use our correction points to "eyeball in" the corrected phase plot. Recall this same eyeballing was necessary for the Bode correction of Fig. 7–5. As in the case of Fig. 7–5 the necessity to graphically average Fig. 7–11(a), or eyeball in, is due to corner frequencies being close to each other.

For Ex. 7–3 we determined that

$$G(j\omega) = \frac{10^5}{(j\omega + 50)(j\omega + 2 \times 10^3)}$$

and for

$\underline{\omega < 50}$

$$dB(\omega) = 0 \, dB \text{ at } \angle 0° \tag{7-17}$$

$\underline{50 < \omega < 2 \times 10^3}$

$$dB(\omega) = -20 \log_{10} \omega + 34 \, dB \text{ at } \angle -90° \tag{7-18}$$

$\underline{\omega > 2 \times 10^3}$

$$dB(\omega) = -40 \log_{10} \omega + 100 \, dB \text{ at } \angle -180° \tag{7-19}$$

Therefore we have the asymptotes of 0° for $\omega < 50$, $-90°$ for $50 < \omega < 2 \times 10^3$, and $-180°$ for $\omega > 2 \times 10^3$. These asymptotes are shown in Fig. 7–11(b). Making our phase corrections for the denominator corner frequency $\omega = 50$ we have

$$\theta \left(\frac{50}{2} = 25 \right) = 0° - 26.5° = -26.5°, \quad \theta(50) = 0° - 45° = -45°$$

and

$$\theta(100) = 0° - 63.5° = -63.5°$$

where 0° is our reference phase asymptote. And correcting for corner frequency 2.0×10^3 we have

$$\theta \left(\frac{2 \times 10^3}{2} = 10^3 \right) = -90° - 26.5° = -116.5°$$

$$\theta(2 \times 10^3) = -90° - 45° = -135°$$

and

$$\theta(4 \times 10^3) = -90° - 63.5° = -153.5°$$

These corrections are made and the corrected phase plot is shown. It is suggested the reader verify this phase plot by actual calculation of $G(j\omega)$ for various values of ω.

We will now consider an example where the phase and Bode plot are to be plotted.

Example 7–5   Make a Bode and phase plot for the circuit shown in
Fig. 7–12.

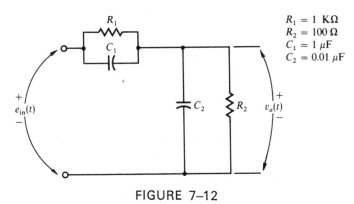

$R_1 = 1\ \mathrm{K\Omega}$
$R_2 = 100\ \Omega$
$C_1 = 1\ \mu\mathrm{F}$
$C_2 = 0.01\ \mu\mathrm{F}$

FIGURE 7–12

Solution

$$\frac{e_{in}(t) - v_0(t)}{R_1} + C_1 \frac{d}{dt}[e_{in}(t) - v_o(t)] - C_2 \frac{dv_o(t)}{dt} - \frac{v_o(t)}{R_2}$$
$$= 0$$

$$\left(\frac{1}{R_1} + C_1 s\right) E_{in}(s) = \left[\frac{1}{R_1} + \frac{1}{R_2} + (C_1 + C_2)s\right] V_o(s)$$

$$G(s) = \frac{V_o(s)}{E_{in}(s)} = \frac{\left(\dfrac{1}{R_1} + C_1 s\right)}{\dfrac{1}{R_1} + \dfrac{1}{R_2} + (C_1 + C_2)s}$$

$$= \frac{C_1}{C_1 + C_2}\frac{s + \dfrac{1}{R_1 C_1}}{\left[s + \dfrac{R_1 + R_2}{R_1 R_2 (C_1 + C_2)}\right]}$$

$$= \frac{10^{-6}}{10^{-6} + 10^{-8}}\frac{s + \dfrac{1}{10^{-3}}}{s + \dfrac{1}{91(10^{-6} + 10^{-8})}}$$

$$\cong \frac{s + \dfrac{1}{10^{-3}}}{s + \dfrac{1}{91 \times 10^{-6}}}$$

$$G(j\omega) = \frac{j\omega + 10^3}{j\omega + 11 \times 10^3}$$

Corner frequencies are: 10^3 and 11×10^3. ω-ranges are:

$\omega < 10^3,\ 10^3 < \omega < 11 \times 10^3,\ \omega > 10^3$

For $\omega < 10^3$

$$G(j\omega) \cong \frac{10^3}{11 \times 10^3} = \frac{1}{11} \angle 0°$$

$\text{dB}(\omega) = -20 \log_{10} 11 = -20.8 \text{ dB at } \angle 0°$

For $10^3 < \omega < 11 \times 10^3 = 1.1 \times 10^4$

$$G(j\omega) \cong \frac{j\omega}{11 \times 10^3} = \frac{\omega}{11 \times 10^3} \angle 90°$$

$$\text{dB}(\omega) = 20 \log_{10} \omega - 20 \log_{10} 11 \times 10^3$$
$$= 20 \log_{10} \omega - 80.8 \text{ dB at } \angle 90°$$

For $\omega > 1.1 \times 10^4$

$$G(j\omega) \cong \frac{j\omega}{j\omega} = 1 \angle 0°$$

These straight-line asymptotes for both magnitude and phase are shown in Fig. 7–13. Also shown in Fig. 7–13 are the correction points and the corrected curves.

If it is desired to make the driving force e_{in} a voltage generator (as it appears now it could be the output voltage of some Thevenin equivalent circuit) the internal resistance of the generator should be put into the circuit. In fact it is recommended for the reader to add the internal resistance R_s and make a Bode plot. The main difference will be that a negative dB slope will be present for high frequencies.

7–7   Bode Plot of Quadratics with $\zeta \leq 1$

Our Bode plots thus far have been for quantities which have the form $(s + \alpha)$. We will now investigate those quantities appearing as $(s + j\gamma + \alpha)(s - j\gamma + \alpha)$ and $(s + \alpha)^2$; that is, the quadratic with $\zeta < 1$, or $\zeta = 1$.

Consider the quadratic $s^2 + 2\zeta\omega_n s + \omega_n^2$, which can be factored such that

$$s^2 + 2\zeta\omega_n s + \omega_n^2 = (s + j\omega_n\sqrt{1 - \zeta^2} + \zeta\omega_n)(s - j\omega_n\sqrt{1 - \zeta^2} + \zeta\omega_n) \tag{7-28}$$

for $\zeta < 1$.

Then for $s = j\omega$ Eq. (7–28) becomes

$$[j(\omega + \omega_n\sqrt{1 - \zeta^2} + \zeta\omega_n][j(\omega - \omega_n\sqrt{1 - \zeta^2}) + \zeta\omega_n] \tag{7-29}$$

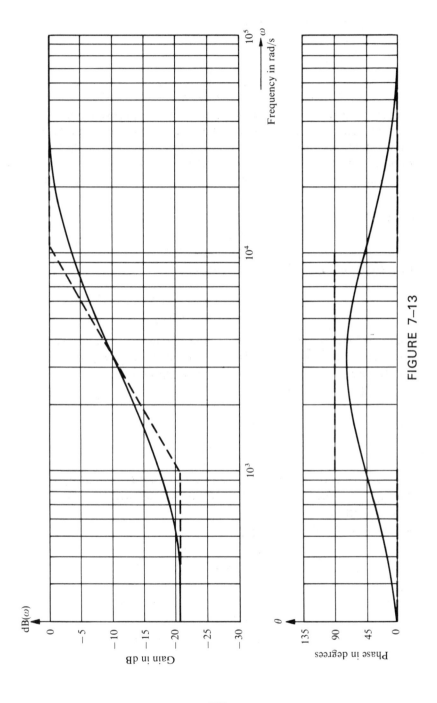

FIGURE 7-13

495

So, for a gain $G(s)$ having a quadratic in the denominator we would have

$$G(j\omega) = \frac{1}{s^2 + 2\zeta\omega_n s + \omega_n^2}\bigg|_{s=j\omega}$$

$$= \frac{1}{[j(\omega + \omega_n\sqrt{1 - \zeta^2}) + \zeta\omega_n][j(\omega - \omega_n\sqrt{1 - \zeta^2} + \zeta\omega_n]} \qquad (7\text{--}30)$$

Trying to make a Bode plot of Eq. (7–30) by approximation is not a practical technique. For this reason when plotting quadratic functions other techniques will be used. We will graph quadratics using the same graphical approach as our universal curves of chapter 5.

To make a universal curve for a quadratic with $\zeta < 1$ we begin with the quadratic $s^2 + 2\zeta\omega_n s + \omega_n^2\big|_{s=j\omega} = (j\omega)^2 + 2\omega_n\zeta j\omega + \omega_n^2$. Let us now divide by ω_n^2, thus

$$\omega_n^2\left[\left(j\frac{\omega}{\omega_n}\right)^2 + j2\zeta\frac{\omega}{\omega_n} + 1\right]$$

Then $G(j\omega)$ of Eq. (7–30) can be written as

$$G(j\omega) = \frac{1}{\omega_n^2\left[\left(j\frac{\omega}{\omega_n}\right)^2 + j2\zeta\frac{\omega}{\omega_n} + 1\right]} \qquad (7\text{--}31)$$

Using procedures similar to those used in chapter 5, for plotting universal curves let us multiply Eq. (7–31) by ω_n^2 and then define $F(j\omega) \equiv \omega_n^2 G(j\omega)$ and define $f \equiv \omega/\omega_n$. Then Eq. (7–31) will appear as

$$F(jf) = \frac{1}{j2\zeta f + (1 - f^2)} \qquad (7\text{--}32)$$

where

$$f = \frac{\omega}{\omega_n}$$

We will now choose a value for ζ and then plot $dB(f) = 20 \log_{10}|F(jf)|$ and $\theta(f)$ for various values of f. Notice we can write $F(j\omega)$ or $F(jf)$ since $\omega = \omega(f)$.

Sample calculations for $\zeta = 0.1$

$$F(jf) = \frac{1}{j0.2f + (1 - f^2)}$$

$f = 0.1$

$$F(j0.1) = \frac{1}{j0.02 + 1 - 0.01} \cong 1\angle 0°$$

$$dB(f = 0.1) = 20 \log_{10} 1 = 0\ dB \text{ and } \theta(f = 0.1) = 0°$$

$\underline{f = 0.2}$

$$F(j0.2) = \frac{1}{j0.04 + (1 - 0.04)} \cong 1\angle 0°$$

$$dB(f = 0.2) = 0 \text{ dB}, \quad \theta(f = 0.2) = 0°$$

$f = 0.5$

$$F(j0.5) = \frac{1}{j0.1 + (1 - 0.25)} = \frac{1}{j0.1 + 0.75} = 1.32\angle -7.6°$$

$$dB(0.5) = 20 \log_{10} 1.32 = 2.4 \text{ dB}; \quad \theta(0.5) = -7.6°$$

$f = 0.7$

$$F(j0.7) = \frac{1}{j0.14 + (1 - 0.49)} = \frac{1}{j0.14 + 0.51} = 1.9\angle -15.4°$$

$$dB(0.7) = 20 \log_{10} 1.9 = 5.6 \text{ dB}; \quad \theta(0.7) = -15.4°$$

$f = 1.0$ (resonance since $\omega = \omega_n$)

$$F(j1.0) = \frac{1}{j0.2} = 5\angle -90°$$

$$dB(1.0) = 20 \log_{10} 5 = 14 \text{ dB}; \quad \theta(1.0) = -90°$$

$f = 2.0$

$$F(j2.0) = \frac{1}{j0.4 + (1 - 4)} = \frac{1}{j0.4 - 3} = \frac{1}{3.02\angle 172.4°}$$

$$dB(2.0) = -20 \log_{10} 3.02 = -9.52 \text{ dB}; \quad \theta(2.0) = -172.4°$$

Since our phase changed from $-90°$ to $-172.4°$ in going from $f = 1.0$ to 2.0 we had better determine a point in between.

$f = 1.4$

$$F(j1.4) = \frac{1}{j0.28 - 0.96} = 1\angle -163.7°$$

$$dB(1.4) = 0 \text{ dB}; \quad \theta(1.4) = -163.7°$$

$f = 4.0$

$$F(j4.0) = \frac{1}{j0.8 - 15} \cong \frac{1}{15} \angle -180°$$

$$dB(4.0) = -20 \log_{10} 15 = -23.5 \text{ dB}; \quad \theta(4.0) = -180°$$

The plots of our universal curve F for various values of ζ are shown in Fig. 7–14.

Notice there is no need to discuss curves for $\zeta > 1$ since $s^2 + 2\zeta\omega_n s + \omega_n^2 = (s + \alpha)(s + \beta)$, which is the type we have already handled in our Bode plots.

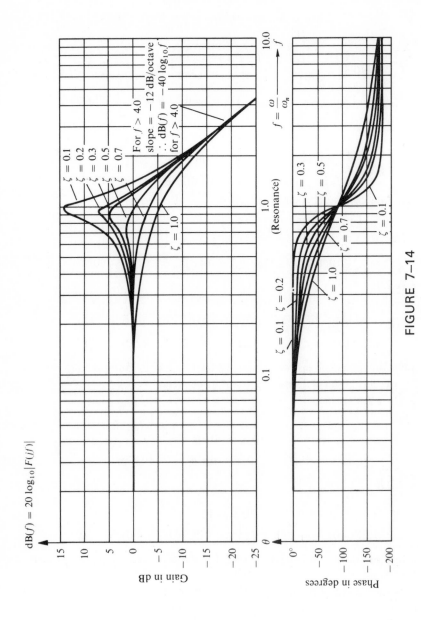

FIGURE 7–14

There are two very important observations to make of Fig. 7–14 and these are: for $f < 0.1$, $dB(f) \cong 0 \, dB$ and $\theta(f) \cong 0°$; and for $f > 4.0$, $dB(f) \cong -40 \log_{10} f$ and $\theta(f)$ approaches $-180°$. Now since $f = \omega/\omega_n$ we may say:

For $\omega < 0.1 \, \omega_n$ (derived from $f < 0.1$)

$$dB(f) \cong 0 \, dB \text{ at } \angle 0°$$

which says

$$F(jf) \cong 1 \ \angle 0° \tag{7-33}$$

For $\omega > 4 \, \omega_n$ (derived from $f > 4$)

$$dB(f) \cong -40 \log_{10} f \Rightarrow \angle 180°$$

or

$$F(jf) \cong \frac{1}{f^2} = \left(\frac{\omega_n}{\omega}\right)^2 \tag{7-34}$$

Equations (7–33) and (7–34) can be verified from Eq. (7–31) by considering ω as very small and ω as large relative to ω_n. We will make good use of Eqs. (7–33) and (7–34) in Bode plots containing quadratics. To demonstrate just how we shall use them let us work an example.

Example 7–6   Make a Bode plot for $G(s)$.

$$G(s) = \frac{10^5(s + 50)}{s^2 + 0.2 \times 10^3 s + 10^6}$$

Solution   First let $s = j\omega$, hence

$$G(j\omega) = \frac{10^5(j\omega + 50)}{(j\omega)^2 + 0.2 \times 10^3 j\omega + 10^6}$$

Putting the denominator in the form of Eq. (7–31) we have

$$G(j\omega) = \frac{j\omega + 50}{10\left[\left(j\frac{\omega}{10^3}\right)^2 + 0.2j\left(\frac{\omega}{10^3}\right) + 1\right]} \tag{7-35}$$

We may write Eq. (7–35) as

$$G(j\omega) = \frac{j\omega + 50}{10} F(jf) \tag{7-36}$$

by defining

$$f = \frac{\omega}{10^3}$$

and then referring to Eq. (7–32).

By applying the conditions of Eqs. (7–33) and (7–34)

and considering the corner frequency of Eq. (7–36) we may determine our ω-range. From $\omega < 0.1\,\omega_n$ we have $\omega < 0.1 \times 10^3 = 10^2$, which gives us a *pseudo-corner frequency* and likewise for $\omega > 4\,\omega_n = 4 \times 10^3$. Then we are interested in the ranges formed from $\omega = 50$, 10^2, and 4×10^3. Forming the ω-ranges we have $\omega < 50$, $50 < \omega < 10^2$, $10^2 < \omega < 4 \times 10^3$, and $\omega > 4 \times 10^3$. We may now approximate $G(j\omega)$ for these ranges.

For $\omega < 50$

$$G(j\omega) \cong \frac{50}{10} F(jf) = 5(1\angle 0°) = 5\angle 0°$$

according to Eq. (7–33). Thus

$$\text{dB}(\omega) = 20\log_{10} 5 = 14\,\text{dB at } \angle 0° \qquad (7\text{–}37)$$

For $50 < \omega < 10^2$

$$G(j\omega) \cong \frac{j\omega}{10} F(jf) = \frac{\omega}{10}\angle 90° \text{ since } F(jf) \cong 1\angle 0°$$

for this ω-range also. Therefore

$$\text{dB}(\omega) = 20\log_{10} \omega - 20 \text{ at } \angle 90° \qquad (7\text{–}38)$$

For $10^2 < \omega < 4 \times 10^3$

$$G(j\omega) \cong j\frac{\omega}{10} F(jf) = \frac{\omega}{10} F(jf)\angle 90°$$

where $F(jf)$ is different than $1\angle 0°$. Using the notation $|F(jf)|$ for the magnitude of $F(jf)$ and using $\theta(f)$ for the phase we may write the gain equation for this range as

$$G(j\omega) = \frac{\omega}{10}|F(jf)|\ \underline{/90° + \theta(f)}$$

Thus

$$\text{dB}(\omega) = 20\log_{10}\frac{\omega|F(jf)|}{10}$$

$$= 20\log_{10}\omega - 20 + 20\log_{10}|F(jf)|$$

Now from Fig. 7–14 we see that $\text{dB}(f) = 20\log_{10}|F(jf)|$ so

$$\text{dB}(\omega) = 20\log_{10}\omega - 20 + \text{dB}(f) \text{ at } \underline{/90° + \theta(f)}$$
$$(7\text{–}39)$$

where

$$f = \omega/\omega_n = \omega/10^3$$

Do not confuse Eq. (7–39) as an equation of a straight

line for the term dB(f) makes it otherwise.
For $\omega > 4 \times 10^3$

$$G(j\omega) \cong \frac{j\omega}{10} F(jf) \cong \frac{\omega}{10} \angle 90° \left(\frac{\omega_n^2}{\omega^2} \angle -180°\right)$$

$$= \frac{10^5}{\omega} \angle -90°$$

since

$$F(jf) \cong \frac{1}{f^2} \Longrightarrow \angle -180° \text{ for } \omega > 4\omega_n$$

as seen from Eq. (7–34). Thus

$$dB(\omega) = 20 \log_{10} \frac{10^5}{\omega} = -20 \log_{10} \omega + 100 \text{ dB}$$

at $\angle -90°$

$$(7\text{--}40)$$

To graph the Bode plot of $G(j\omega)$ we will proceed as before except for Eq. (7–39). To plot Eq. (7–39) we will first plot the straight equation $20 \log_{10} \omega - 20$ [shown in Fig. 7–15(a) as a dotted line] and then add the values of dB(f) to this straight line. The values of dB(f) are determined from Fig. 7–14 for the various values of ω in the range $10^2 < \omega < 4 \times 10^3$. In other words we will treat dB(f) the same as a correction factor for the straight-line equation $20 \log_{10} \omega - 20$.

Making our Bode plot for $G(j\omega)$ we begin by plotting the straight lines, or asymptotes, of Eqs. (7–37) and (7–38) as shown on Fig. 7–15(a). We will also put in the +3-dB correction at the numerator corner frequency $\omega = 50$ and +1 dB an octave down and up from $\omega = 50$. Since $\omega = 50$ is the only corner frequency this is the only place where this 1-dB and 3-dB correction occurs. Next we plot the straight-line portion of Eq. (7–39), which we see is just a continuation of Eq. (7–38) (an important point to remember). We must now determine the value of ζ so that we may know which curve of Fig. 7–14 applies. Comparing Eqs. (7–31) and (7–35) we see that $2\zeta = 0.2$, or $\zeta = 0.1$. We next decide what the important points of f are for the curve $\zeta = 0.1$. This may vary from individual to individual except that all should agree that the maximum value of dB(f) for $\zeta = 0.1$ is necessary. The points chosen by the author

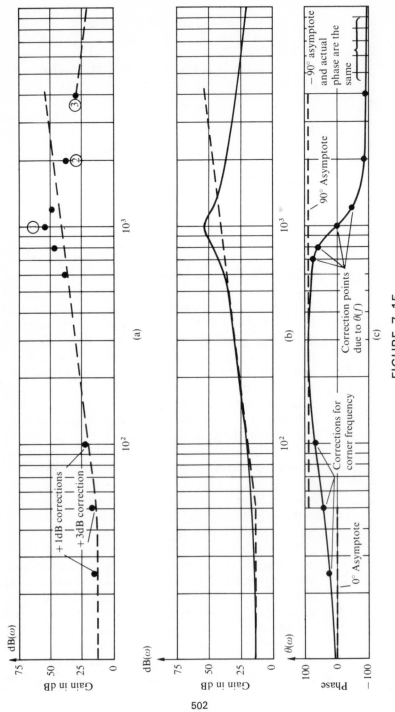

FIGURE 7-15

are given in Table 7–2 where the author looked for "rapid change" as his guide. Adding the dB points under the dB(f) column and the asymptote of Fig. 7–15(a) at the frequencies indicated we have the correction points shown in Fig. 7–15(a). As an example of the calculations for these corrections the calculations for points 1, 2, and 3 of Fig. 7–15 are offered. At $\omega = 10^3$ we see the straight line has a dB value of 40 dB. Our correction from Fig. 7–14 at $\omega = 10^3$ is 14 dB, as shown in Table 7–2. Adding these quantities together, as indicated in Eq. (7–39), we have a corrected value of 54 dB, which is point ①. For

TABLE 7–2   for $\zeta = 0.1$

f	dB(f) in dB	$\theta(f)$ in degrees	$\omega = \omega_n f$ $= f \times 10^3$ ω in rad/s	Example correction points of Fig. 7–15(a)
0.1	0	0	0.1×10^3	
0.6	+3.8	−6	0.6×10^3	
0.7	+5.5	−15	0.7×10^3	
0.8	+8.5	−30	0.8×10^3	
1.0	+14.0	−90	1.0×10^3	1
1.2	+6.0	−140	1.2×10^3	
2.0	−9.2	−180	2.0×10^3	2
4.0	−23.5	−180	4.0×10^3	3

point ② we have 46 dB + (−9.2) $\cong$ 37 dB and for ③, 52 + (−23.5) = 28.5 dB. We now continue with Eq. (7–40), which is a familiar type. Checking the continuity of Eq. (7–40) we will evaluate it at $\omega = 4 \times 10^3$. Thus dB($\omega = 4 \times 10^3$) = $-20 \log_{10} 4 \times 10^3 + 100 = 28$ dB. We see that for all practical purposes the point 28.5 dB and 28 dB agree, hence continuity exists. Notice that we need only to correct at $\omega = 50$ for corner frequency error since this is the only actual corner frequency. The corrected curve for the gain of $G(j\omega)$ is shown in Fig. 7–15(b).

All that remains is to make the phase plot. From Eq. (7–37) we see the asymptote for $\omega < 50$ is 0°. And for

$50 < \omega < 10^2$ the asymptote is $90°$. These asymptotes are shown as dotted lines in Fig. 7–15(c). For the ω-range $10^2 < \omega < 4 \times 10^3$ the angle of Eq. (7–39) tells us to add the angle $\theta(f)$ of Table 7–2 to the $90°$ asymptote. Notice that the phase asymptotes of Eqs. (7–38) and (7–39) are the same, just as is the straight-line asymptote for the gain. So we draw our $90°$ asymptote from $50 < \omega < 4 \times 10^3$. We next put in the $-90°$ asymptote for $\omega > 4 \times 10^3$ as stated by Eq. (7–40). We can now put our correction points of $45°$ at the numerator corner frequency $\omega = 50$ and $26.5°$ for an octave down and $63.5°$ for an octave up. We may also put the phase corrections of $\theta(f)$ over the ω-range $10^2 < \omega < 4 \times 10^3$. From Table 7–2 we see that for $\omega = 700$, $\theta(f) = -15°$. Therefore $\theta(\omega = 700) = 90° + \theta(f) = 90° + (-15°) = 75°$. And for $\omega = 800$, $\theta(f) = -30°$, so $\theta(\omega = 800) = 90° + (-30°) = 60°$. Continuing with these corrections we have the corrected phase plot (solid line) as shown in Fig. 7–15(c).

Let us consider another example of a quadratic with $\zeta < 1$.

Example 7–7   Make a Bode and phase plot for $G(s) = V_o(s)/E_{in}(s)$ of the circuit in Fig. 7–16.

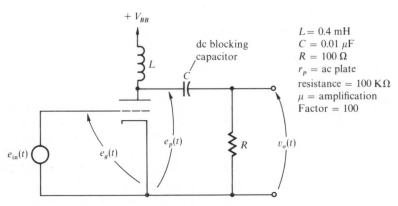

$$+ V_{BB}$$

dc blocking capacitor

$L = 0.4$ mH
$C = 0.01$ μF
$R = 100$ Ω
r_p = ac plate resistance = 100 KΩ
μ = amplification Factor = 100

Note: $e'_{in}(t)$ has the proper dc level for proper biasing.

FIGURE 7–16

Solution   The ac equivalent circuit is as shown in Fig. 7–17.

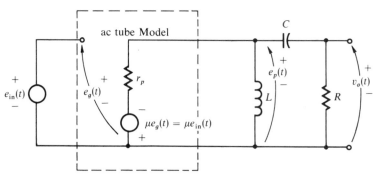

Note: We are considering *only* the ac portion of $e'_{in}(t)$ for this model.

FIGURE 7–17

Writing the necessary equations we have:

$$\frac{-\mu e_{in}(t) - e_p(t)}{r_p} - \frac{1}{L}\int e_p(t)\,dt + C\frac{d}{dt}[v_o(t) - e_p(t)] = 0$$

$$C\frac{d}{dt}[e_p(t) - v_o(t)] - \frac{v_o(t)}{R} = 0$$

Taking the Laplace:

$$-\frac{\mu}{r_p}E_{in}(s) = -CsV_o(s) + \left(\frac{1}{r_p} + \frac{1}{Ls} + Cs\right)E_p(s)$$

$$0 = \left(\frac{1}{R} + Cs\right)V_o(s) - CsE_p(s)$$

Solving for Δ,

$$\Delta = \begin{vmatrix} -Cs & \left(\dfrac{1}{r_p} + \dfrac{1}{Ls} + Cs\right) \\[2mm] \left(\dfrac{1}{R} + Cs\right) & -Cs \end{vmatrix}$$

$$= -\left(\frac{1}{R} + Cs\right)\left(\frac{1}{r_p} + \frac{1}{Ls} + Cs\right) + (Cs)^2$$

$$= -\left[\frac{Ls}{r_p} + RL\left(\frac{1}{r_p} + \frac{1}{R}\right)Cs^2 + 1 + RCs\right]\frac{1}{RLs}$$

$$= \frac{1}{RLs}\left[LC\left(\frac{R + r_p}{r_p}\right)s^2 + \left(\frac{L}{r_p} + RC\right)s + 1\right]$$

which has the form as the denominator of Eq. (7–31). Now solving for $V_o(s)$,

$$\Delta V_o(s) = \begin{vmatrix} -\dfrac{\mu}{r_p} E_{in}(s) & \left(\dfrac{1}{r_p} + \dfrac{1}{Ls} + Cs\right) \\ 0 & -Cs \end{vmatrix}$$

$$= \dfrac{\mu Cs}{r_p} E_{in}(s)$$

therefore

$$\dfrac{V_o(s)}{E_{in}(s)} = G(s) = \dfrac{\mu Cs}{\Delta r_p}$$

$$= -\dfrac{\mu RLCs^2}{\left[LC\left(\dfrac{R+r_p}{r_p}\right)s^2 + \left(\dfrac{L}{r_p} + RC\right)s + 1 \right]}$$

Letting $s = j\omega$ we have

$$G(j\omega) = -\dfrac{\mu RLC(j\omega)^2}{\left[LC\left(\dfrac{R+r_p}{r_p}\right)(j\omega)^2 + \left(\dfrac{L}{r_p} + RC\right)j\omega + 1 \right]}$$

$$= \dfrac{\mu RLC\omega^2}{\left[LC\left(\dfrac{R+r_p}{r_p}\right)(j\omega)^2 + \left(\dfrac{L}{r_p} + RC\right)j\omega + 1 \right]}$$

$$(7\text{--}41)$$

Comparing the form of the quadratic denominators of $G(j\omega)$ and Eq. (7–31) we find that

$$\dfrac{2\zeta}{\omega_n} = \dfrac{L}{r_p} + RC$$

and

$$\omega_n^2 = \dfrac{r_p}{LC(R + r_p)}$$

or

$$\omega_n = \dfrac{1}{\sqrt{LC}} \sqrt{\dfrac{r_p}{R + r_p}}$$

Then

$$\zeta = \dfrac{\omega_n}{2}\left(\dfrac{L}{r_p} + RC\right) = \dfrac{1}{2}\dfrac{1}{\sqrt{LC}}\sqrt{\dfrac{r_p}{R + r_p}}\left(\dfrac{L}{r_p} + RC\right)$$

Notice from values of R and r_p that $(R + r_p) \cong r_p$, hence

$$\zeta \cong \dfrac{1}{2\sqrt{LC}}\left(\dfrac{L}{r_p} + RC\right)$$

$$= \dfrac{1}{2\sqrt{0.4 \times 10^{-11}}}\left(\dfrac{0.4 \times 10^{-3}}{10^5} + 10^{-6}\right)$$

$$\cong \dfrac{10^{-6}}{2(2 \times 10^{-6})} = 0.25 \qquad (7\text{--}42)$$

Also we may define

$$f = \frac{\omega}{\omega_n} \cong \frac{\omega}{\frac{1}{\sqrt{LC}}}$$

since $r_p \gg R$, hence

$$f = \frac{\omega}{\frac{1}{2 \times 10^{-6}}}$$

or

$$\omega = 0.5f \times 10^6 \tag{7-43}$$

Then we may write Eq. (7–41) as

$$G(j\omega) = \mu RLC\omega^2 F(jf) \tag{7-44}$$

It is from Eq. (7–44) that we shall construct our Bode and phase plot. From Eq. (7–44) we see that we have no corner frequencies, only pseudo-corner frequencies which are due to $F(jf)$. These pseudo-corner frequencies occur at $f = 0.1$ and 4. To convert from f to ω we use Eq. (7–43), hence our pseudo-corner frequencies are: $\omega = 0.5(0.1) \times 10^6 = 5 \times 10^4$ and $\omega = 0.5(4) \times 10^6 = 2 \times 10^6$. Then our ω-ranges are: $\omega < 5 \times 10^4$, $5 \times 10^4 < \omega < 2 \times 10^6$, and $\omega > 2 \times 10^6$. And approximating $G(j\omega)$ we have,

For $\omega < 5 \times 10^4$

$$G(j\omega) \cong \mu RLC\omega^2(1 \angle 0°) = \mu RLC\omega^2 \angle 0°$$
$$dB(\omega) = 40 \log_{10} \omega + 20 \log_{10} \mu RLC \text{ dB at } \angle 0°$$
$$= 40 \log_{10} \omega + 2 \log_{10} 0.4 \times 10^{-7}$$

therefore

$$dB(\omega) = 40 \log_{10} \omega - 148 \text{ dB at } \angle 0° \tag{7-45}$$

For $5 \times 10^4 < \omega < 2 \times 10^6$

$$G(j\omega) = \mu RLC\omega^2 F(jf) = \mu RLC\omega^2 |F(jf)| \angle \theta(f)$$
$$dB(\omega) = 40 \log_{10} \omega + 20 \log_{10} \mu RLC + 20 \log_{10} |F(jf)|,$$

or

$$dB(\omega) = 40 \log_{10} \omega - 148 + dB(f) \text{ at } \angle \theta(f) \tag{7-46}$$

For $\omega > 2 \times 10^6$

$$G(j\omega) \cong \mu RLC\omega^2 \left(\frac{\omega_n}{\omega}\right)^2 \angle -180° = \mu RLC\omega_n^2 \angle -180°$$

$$\cong \mu RLC\left(\frac{1}{LC}\right) \angle -180° = \mu R \angle -180°$$

since

$$\omega_n \cong \frac{1}{\sqrt{LC}}$$

$$dB(\omega) = 20 \log_{10} \mu R = 80 \text{ dB at } \angle\, 0° \qquad (7\text{--}47)$$

To plot Eq. (7–45) we proceed as usual. That is, we find two points with which to draw our straight line. We notice that Eq. (7–46) is just Eq. (7–45) with a correction factor of dB(f), so we extend the asymptote of Eq. (7–45) to include the ω-range of Eq. (7–46). We next put the correction fraction dB(f) in for $40 \log_{10} \omega - 148$, where dB($f$) is determined from Fig. 7–14 and the points for $40 \log_{10} \omega - 148$ are determined graphically from the extension of Eq. (7–45) in Fig. 7–18. These corrections are shown in Table 7–3 and the corrected plots are shown in Fig. 7–18.

TABLE 7–3

f	$\omega = 0.5f$ $\times 10^6$ ω in rad/s	$40 \log \omega - 148$ dB (points determined graphically from Fig. 7–14)	dB(f) in dB	$\theta(f)$ $= \theta(\omega)$ in degree	dB(ω) (see Eq. 7–46)
0.1	5×10^4	40	0	0	40
0.6	3×10^5	72	3	−10	75
0.8	4×10^5	77	6.2	−45	83.2
0.96	4.7×10^5	79	dB(f)$_{max}$ = 8	−80	87
1.2	6×10^5	84	2.5	−130	86.5
2.0	1×10^6	92	−10	−170	82
4.0	2×10^6	104	−23.5	−180	80.5

As our last example of Bode plot we will plot $G(j\omega)$ of Ex. 7–8.

Example 7–8   Make a Bode and phase plot of

$$G(s) = \frac{10^6 s(s + 10^3)}{(s + 50)(s^2 + 12.2 \times 10^3 s + 64 \times 10^6)}$$

Solution   We begin by checking for the value of ζ to determine if we need to apply Fig. 7–14. From $s^2 + 2\zeta\omega_n s + \omega_n^2$ we

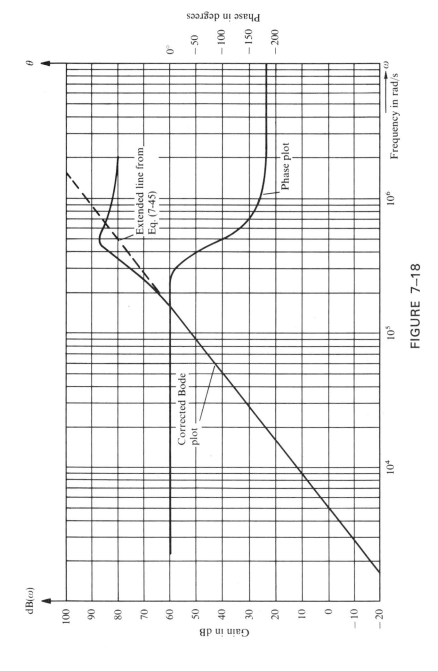

FIGURE 7–18

509

see that $2\zeta\omega_n = 12.2 \times 10^3$ and $\omega_n^2 = 64 \times 10^6$, therefore

$$\omega_n = 8 \times 10^3$$

and

$$\zeta = \frac{12.2 \times 10^3}{2(8 \times 10^3)} = 0.76$$

Hence we must estimate the curve $\zeta = 0.76$ from Fig. 7–14.

Putting $s^2 + 12.2 \times 10^3 s + 64 \times 10^6$ in the form of Eq. (7–31) we have

$G(s)$

$$= \frac{10^6 s(s + 10^3)}{64 \times 10^6(s + 50)\left[\left(\dfrac{s}{8 \times 10^3}\right)^2 + \dfrac{12.2 \times 10^3}{64 \times 10^6}s + 1\right]}$$

$$= \frac{s(s + 10^3)}{64(s + 50)\left[\left(\dfrac{s}{8 \times 10^3}\right)^2 + \dfrac{s}{5.25 \times 10^3} + 1\right]}$$

So

$$G(j\omega) = \frac{j\omega(j\omega + 10^3)}{64(j\omega + 50)\left[\left(\dfrac{j\omega}{8 \times 10^3}\right)^2 + j\dfrac{\omega}{5.25 \times 10^3} + 1\right]}$$

$$= \frac{j\omega(j\omega + 10^3)}{64(j\omega + 50)}F(jf), \qquad\qquad (7\text{–}48)$$

where

$$f = \frac{\omega}{8 \times 10^3}$$

The corner frequencies are 50 and 10^3, and the pseudo-corner frequencies are $\omega = 0.1\omega_n = 800$ and $\omega = 4\omega_n = 32 \times 10^3$. Then our ω-ranges are $\omega < 50$, $50 < \omega < 800$, $800 < \omega < 10^3$, $10^3 < \omega < 32 \times 10^3$, and $\omega > 32 \times 10^3$. Hence,

For $\omega < 50$

$$G(j\omega) \cong \frac{j\omega(10^3)}{64(50)} = \frac{\omega}{3.2} \angle 90° \text{ since } F(jf) \cong 1\angle 0°$$

$$\text{dB}(\omega) = 20 \log_{10} \omega - 20 \log_{10} 3.2$$

$$= 20 \log_{10} \omega - 10 \text{ dB at } \angle 90° \quad (7\text{–}49)$$

For $50 < \omega < 800$

$$G(j\omega) \cong \frac{j\omega(10^3)}{64(j\omega)} 1 \angle 0° = 15.6 \angle 0°$$

$$dB(\omega) = 20 \log_{10} 15.6 = 24 \text{ dB at } \angle 0° \qquad (7\text{–}50)$$

For $800 < \omega < 10^3$

$$G(j\omega) \cong \frac{j\omega(10^3)}{64(j\omega)} F(jf) = 15.6|F(jf)| \text{ at } \angle \theta(f)$$

$$dB(\omega) = 24 + dB(f) \text{ dB at } \angle \theta(f) \qquad (7\text{–}51)$$

For $10^3 < \omega < 32 \times 10^3 = 3.2 \times 10^4$

$$G(j\omega) \cong \frac{j\omega(j\omega)}{64(j\omega)} F(jf) = \frac{\omega}{64}|F(jf)| \angle 90° + \theta(f)$$

$$dB(\omega) = 20 \log_{10} \omega - 36.4 + dB(f) \text{ at } \angle 90° + \theta(f)$$
$$(7\text{–}52)$$

For $\omega > 3.2 \times 10^4$

$$G(j\omega) \cong \frac{j\omega(j\omega)}{64(j\omega)} \left(\frac{\omega_n}{\omega}\right)^2 \angle -180° = \frac{\omega_n^2}{64\omega} \angle 90° - 180°$$

$$= \frac{64 \times 10^6}{64\omega} \angle -90° = \frac{10^6}{\omega} \angle -90°$$

$$dB(\omega) = -20 \log_{10} \omega + 120 \text{ dB at } \angle -90° \qquad (7\text{–}53)$$

Let us first plot all the asymptotes for both gain and phase, that is, Eqs. (7–49), (7–50), 24dB of Eq. (7–51), $20 \log_{10} \omega - 36.4$ of Eq. (7–52) and Eq. (7–53). Then put in the corner frequency corrections. We notice that for the range of Eq. (7–51) we can eyeball the curve in. And for Eq. (7–52) we consult Fig. 7–14 for $\zeta = 0.76$ and correct $20 \log_{10} \omega - 36.4$ by adding $dB(f)$ to it. The completed graph is shown in Fig. 7–19.

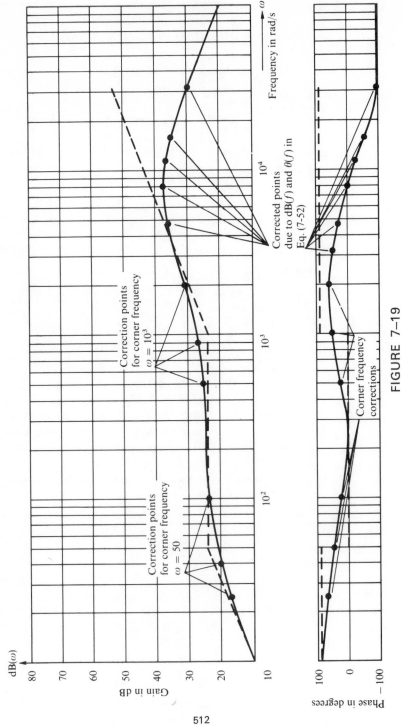

FIGURE 7-19

8 Diagrammatical Circuit Representation

8–1 Introduction

This chapter concerns itself with concepts of circuit representation using a diagram approach. We will mathematically analyze a circuit and then illustrate our analysis with a diagram. Our diagram will first be in block diagram form and later we will change it to what is termed a signal-flow diagram.

Representing a circuit in a diagrammatical form can have the advantage of speed and ease in analysis if the circuit analyzed is to be used in other analysis. That is, if one has a certain circuit, such as the ac model of a transistor, which may be placed in many other circuits, it may be beneficial for him to derive the circuit's signal-flow diagram model so that this model can replace the circuit. The speed and ease of analysis occur since signal-flow diagram is quick and easy to analyze. Diagrammatical representation also has the advantage that it gives a visual picture of the relationships between the driving sources and the resultant outputs.

An area where this material is of special interest is feedback control. Our approach to the subject matter will be introductory in hopes that the reader will be able to envision the broader applications and if need for the area arises he will be acquainted enough with the material to know what literature he must study.

8–2   Block Diagram

We have seen that by the use of Laplace transforms we can transform an equation from an operational type, that is a differential equation, to an algebraic type. The transformation transformed the equation from the t-plane to the s-plane. Once the transformation was performed we were able to algebraically manipulate the equation and solve for the unknown. This gave us a relationship between input (driving force) and output in the s-plane, which for input and output voltages we expressed as $V_o(s) = T(s) E_{in}(s)$. In chapter 6 we termed $T(s)$ the transfer function for it transferred the input driving force from $E_{in}(s)$ to $V_o(s)$, or mathematically expressed as

$$\text{transfer function} = \frac{\text{output}}{\text{input}} \qquad (8\text{–}1)$$

Equation (8–1) is diagrammatically represented as shown in Fig. 8–1(a).

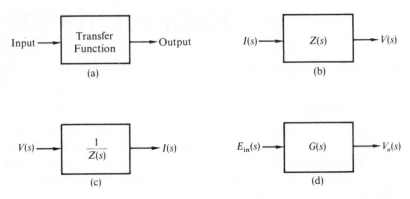

FIGURE 8–1

Under this type of definition impedance is just a special type of transfer function, as is gain. Impedance used as a transfer function can be expressed as $V(s) = Z(s)I(s)$ and represented as shown in Fig. 8–1(b). However, if we wanted I to be the dependent variable and V to be the independent variable we would write $I(s) = V(s)/Z(s)$ and represent the equation diagrammatically as shown in Fig. 8–1(c). The gain representation, $G(s) = V_o(s)/E_{in}(s)$, is shown in Fig. 8–1(d). From this one should conclude that the diagrammatical representation depends on the choice of independent and dependent variables.

It is possible for us to have several transfer functions all transferring the same input. That is, suppose we had the equations $V_{o_1}(s) = G_1(s)E_{in}(s)$, $V_{o_2}(s) = G_2(s)E_{in}(s)$, and $I(s) = E_{in}(s)/Z(s)$, which can be represented as shown in Fig. 8–2(a). Also we could have the product of several transfer

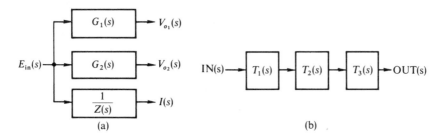

(a)   (b)

FIGURE 8–2

functions acting as a single transfer function, that is, $\text{IN}(s) = T_1(s) \, T_2(s)$
$T_3(s) = \text{OUT}(s)$. This is shown diagrammatically in the block diagram of
Fig. 8–2(b). Figure 8–2(b) can be easily verified by considering a single
transfer function at a time. Thus $\text{IN}(s) \, T_1(s) = O_1(s)$, $O_1(s)T_2(s) = O_2(s)$,
$O_2(s)T_3(s) = \text{OUT}(s)$, so $\text{OUT}(s) = O_2(s)T_3(s) = [O_1(s)T_2(s)]T_3(s) =$
$O_1(s)T_2(s)T_3(s) = [\text{IN}(s)T_1(s)]T_2(s)T_3(s) = T_1(s)T_2(s)T_3(s)\text{IN}(s)$.

We need to know one other symbol and that is a summer. It is written
using the Greek letter Σ and symbolically illustrated as shown in Fig.
8–3(a). The arrows going into the circle represent the input, or independent,
variables and the arrow coming out represents the dependent variable. The
sign of the independent variable is shown in the pie-shape portion of the
circle. Figure 8–3(a) shows three inputs but one may have as many as
needed. As an example suppose we wish to diagrammatically represent
$I(s) = I_1(s) - I_2(s) + I_3(s)$. We would use the summer as shown in Fig.
8–3(b). And to represent $V_o(s) = V_1(s) - V_2(s)$ we have Fig. 8–3(c).
Notice it is arbitrary as to which positions are used for inputs or output.

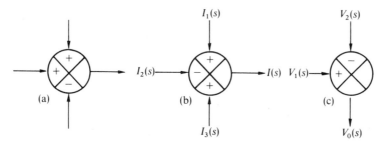

FIGURE 8–3

Let us now integrate the concepts previously discussed. Consider the
block diagram of the system shown in Fig. 8–4 where we wish to determine
the overall transfer function described by $O(s)/I(s)$. At point ① we have

$E(s)$, which can be expressed as

$$E(s) = I(s) - F(s) \tag{8-2}$$

And at points ② and ③ we have respectively

$$F(s) = H(s)O(s) \tag{8-3}$$

and

$$O(s) = G(s)E(s) \tag{8-4}$$

Let us eliminate the variables $E(s)$ and $F(s)$. Hence, substituting Eq. (8–3) into Eq. (8–2) we have

$$E(s) = I(s) - H(s)O(s) \tag{8-5}$$

We now solve Eq. (8–4) for $E(s)$ and substitute this into Eq. (8–5), which is $O(s)/G(s) = I(s) - H(s)O(s)$. Next solving for $O(s)/I(s)$,

$$O(s)\left[\frac{1}{G(s)} + H(s)\right] = \left[\frac{1 + G(s)H(s)}{G(s)}\right]O(s) = I(s),$$

or

$$\frac{O(s)}{I(s)} = \frac{G(s)}{1 + G(s)H(s)} \tag{8-6}$$

This equation is considered as the general mathematical representation of a block diagram with negative feedback, where the feedback occurs because of the transfer function $H(s)$. Figure 8–4 is the simplest general representation of a block diagram with feedback.

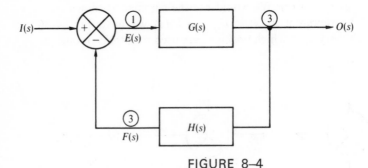

FIGURE 8–4

We will now consider some examples in order to gain practice in working with these block diagrams.

Example 8–1   Find $O(s)/I(s)$ for the block diagram given in Fig. 8–5.

Solution   At point ①: $I(s) + H(s)O(s)$

At point ②: $O(s) - G_1(s)[I(s) + H(s)O(s)]$

At point ③: $G_2(s)\{O(s) - G_1(s)[I(s) + H(s)O(s)]$
$$= O(s)$$

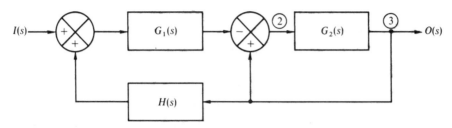

FIGURE 8–5

We now solve the equation from point ③ for our desired ratio $O(s)/I(s)$, hence

$$G_2(s)O(s) - G_1(s)G_2(s)I(s) + G_2(s)H(s)O(s) = O(s)$$
$$O(s)[G_2(s) + G_2(s)H(s) + 1] = G_1(s)G_2(s)I(s)$$

or

$$\frac{O(s)}{I(s)} = \frac{G_1(s)G_2(s)}{1 + G_2(s)[1 + H(s)]}$$

Example 8–2   Find $V_o(s)/E_{in}(s)$ from the block diagram given in Fig. 8-6.

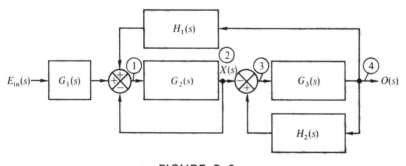

FIGURE 8–6

Solution   For convenience we will define the output of $G_2(s)$ as $X(s)$. Then at point ① we have

$$G_1(s)E_{in}(s) + H_1(s)O(s) - X(s)$$

At point ② we can write

$$X(s) = G_2(s)[G_1(s)E_{in}(s) + H_1(s)O(s) - X(s)]$$

therefore

$$X(s)[1 + G_2(s)] = G_1(s)G_2(s)E_{in}(s) + G_2(s)H_1(s)O(s)$$

or

$$X(s) = \frac{G_1(s)G_2(s)E_{in}(s) + G_2(s)H_1(s)O(s)}{1 + G_2(s)}$$

At point ③ we have

$$-X(s) + H_2(s)O(s)$$

$$= -\frac{G_1(s)G_2(s)E_{in}(s) + G_2(s)H_1(s)O(s)}{1 + G_2(s)} + H_2(s)O(s)$$

And for point ④:

$$O(s)$$

$$= G_3(s)\left[H_2(s)O(s) - \frac{G_1(s)G_2(s)E_{in}(s) + G_2(s)H_1(s)O(s)}{1 + G_2(s)} \right]$$

Solving point ④ for $O(s)/E_{in}(s)$ we have

$$O(s) = \frac{G_3(s)\{H_2(s)O(s)[1 + G_2(s)] - G_1(s)G_2(s)E_{in}(s)}{1 + G_2(s)}^{+ G_2(s)H_1(s)O(s)\}}$$

$$O(s)\left\{ 1 - \frac{G_3(s)H_2(s)[1 + G_2(s)] + G_2(s)G_3(s)H_1(s)}{1 + G_2(s)} \right\}$$

$$= -\frac{G_1(s)G_2(s)E_{in}(s)}{1 + G_2(s)}$$

therefore,

$$\frac{O(s)}{E_{in}(s)} =$$

$$-\frac{G_1(s)G_2(s)}{[1 + G_2(s)] - G_3(s)H_2(s)[1 + G_2(s)] + G_2(s)G_3(s)H_1(s)}$$

We will now consider the analysis of some physical problems and then put our analysis in block diagram form.

Example 8–3   For the circuit given in Fig. 8–7 represent the gain $G(s) = V_o(s)/E_{in}(s)$ and the input impedance $Z_{in}(s) = E_{in}(s)/I_{in}(s)$ in block diagram form. Use Eq. (8–6) and Fig. 8–4 as guides for the simplest representations.

Solution   Undertaking the problem of representing $G(s)$ in block diagram form we begin by writing the necessary nodal

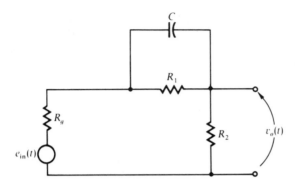

FIGURE 8-7

equations (assume nodal voltage v_1 for the node of R_g, R_1, and C).

$$\frac{e_{in}(t) - v_1(t)}{R_g} + C\frac{d}{dt}[v_o(t) - v_1(t)] + \frac{v_o(t) - v_1(t)}{R_1} = 0$$

$$C\frac{d}{dt}[v_1(t) - v_o(t)] + \frac{v_1(t) - v_o(t)}{R_1} - \frac{v_o(t)}{R_2} = 0$$

Taking the Laplace and considering the initial conditions to be zero,

$$\frac{E_{in}(s)}{R_g} = \left(\frac{1}{R_g} + \frac{1}{R_1} + Cs\right)V_1(s) - \left(\frac{1}{R_1} + Cs\right)V_o(s)$$

$$0 = -\left(\frac{1}{R_1} + Cs\right)V_1(s) + \left(\frac{1}{R_1} + \frac{1}{R_2} + Cs\right)V_o(s)$$

Solving for $V_o(s)$;

$$\Delta = \begin{vmatrix} \left(\frac{1}{R_g} + \frac{1}{R_1} + Cs\right) & -\left(\frac{1}{R_1} + Cs\right) \\ -\left(\frac{1}{R_1} + Cs\right) & \left(\frac{1}{R_1} + \frac{1}{R_2} + Cs\right) \end{vmatrix}$$

$$= \left(\frac{1}{R_g} + \frac{1}{R_1} + Cs\right)\left(\frac{1}{R_1} + \frac{1}{R_2} + Cs\right) - \left(\frac{1}{R_1} + Cs\right)^2$$

$$= \frac{1}{R_g R_1} + \frac{1}{R_g R_2} + \frac{1}{R_1 R_2} + \left(\frac{1}{R_g} + \frac{1}{R_2}\right)Cs$$

$$= \frac{(R_g + R_2)}{R_g R_2}C\left[\frac{1}{(R_g + R_2)C}\left(\frac{R_2}{R_1} + 1 + \frac{R_g}{R_1}\right) + s\right]$$

$$= \frac{(R_g + R_2)C}{R_g R_2}\left\{s + \frac{R_1 + R_2 + R_g}{R_1}\left[\frac{1}{(R_g + R_2)C}\right]\right\}$$

And

$$\Delta V_o(s) = \begin{vmatrix} \left(\dfrac{1}{R_g} + \dfrac{1}{R_1} + Cs\right) & \dfrac{E_{in}(s)}{R_g} \\[2mm] -\left(\dfrac{1}{R_1} + Cs\right) & 0 \end{vmatrix} = \dfrac{E_{in}(s)}{R_g}\left(\dfrac{1}{R_1} + Cs\right)$$

$$\frac{V_o(s)}{E_{in}(s)} = G(s) = \frac{C\left(s + \dfrac{1}{R_1 C}\right)}{\Delta R_g}$$

$$= \frac{R_2\left(s + \dfrac{1}{R_1 C}\right)}{(R_g + R_2)\left[s + \dfrac{R_1 + R_2 + R_g}{R_1(R_g + R_2)C}\right]} \qquad (8\text{-}7)$$

Now the equation we wish to model Eq. (8–7) after is Eq. (8–6), or we wish

$$\frac{G(s)}{1 + G(s)H(s)} = \frac{R_2\left(s + \dfrac{1}{R_1 C}\right)}{(R_g + R_2)\left[s + \dfrac{R_1 + R_2 + R_g}{R_1(R_g + R_2)C}\right]}$$

$$(8\text{-}8)$$

for then we can determine $G(s)$ and $H(s)$ of Fig. 8–4. We see that we need to manipulate the right-hand side's denominator in some manner so that we get it in the form $1 + G(s)H(s)$. Factoring an s we get

$$\frac{G(s)}{1 + G(s)H(s)} = \frac{R_2\left(s + \dfrac{1}{R_1 C}\right)}{(R_g + R_2)s\left[1 + \dfrac{R_1 + R_2 + R_g}{sR_1(R_g + R_2)C}\right]}$$

$$= \frac{\dfrac{R_2\left(s + \dfrac{1}{R_1 C}\right)}{(R_g + R_2)s}}{1 + \dfrac{R_1 + R_2 + R_g}{sR_1(R_g + R_2)C}} \qquad (8\text{-}9)$$

Then defining

$$G(s) \equiv \frac{R_2\left(s + \dfrac{1}{R_1 C}\right)}{(R_g + R_2)s} = \frac{R_2}{R_g + R_2}\left(1 + \frac{1}{sR_1 C}\right)$$

would require that

$$G(s)H(s) = \frac{R_1 + R_2 + R_g}{sR_1(R_g + R_2)C}$$

or

$$H(s) = \frac{R_1 + R_2 + R_g}{sR_1(R_g + R_2)C} \left[\frac{(R_g + R_2)s}{R_2\left(s + \dfrac{1}{R_1 C}\right)} \right]$$

$$= \frac{R_1 + R_2 + R_g}{R_1 R_2 C\left(s + \dfrac{1}{R_1 C}\right)}$$

For this definition of $G(s)$ we have Fig. 8–8(a).

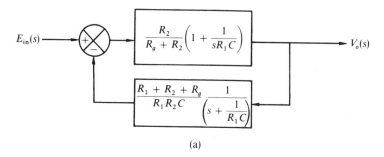

(a)

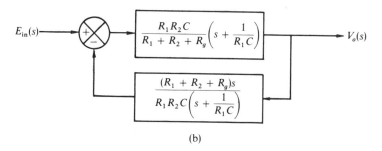

(b)

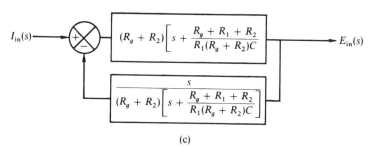

(c)

FIGURE 8–8

Suppose we had chosen to manipulate Eq. (8–8) such that

$$\frac{G(s)}{1 + G(s)H(s)} = \frac{R_2\left(s + \dfrac{1}{R_1C}\right)}{\left(\dfrac{R_1 + R_2 + R_g}{R_1C}\right)(s + 1)}$$

$$= \frac{\left[\dfrac{R_1R_2C\left(s + \dfrac{1}{R_1C}\right)}{R_1 + R_2 + R_g}\right]}{1 + s} \qquad (8\text{–}10)$$

We now define

$$G(s) \equiv \frac{R_1R_2C\left(s + \dfrac{1}{R_1C}\right)}{R_1 + R_2 + R_g}$$

hence

$$G(s)H(s) = s$$

or

$$H(s) = \frac{s}{G(s)} = \frac{(R_1 + R_2 + R_g)s}{R_1R_2C\left(s + \dfrac{1}{R_1C}\right)} \qquad (8\text{–}11)$$

Then the block diagram would appear as shown in Fig. 8–8(b). As we can see neither Fig. 8–8(a) nor (b) gives a very good representation of the physical circuit. In the next section we will discuss how to make these diagrammatical representations to approach a physical similarity to the circuit, but for now we will continue as we have been.

To find $Z_{in}(s)$ we must determine the current $i_{in}(t)$ furnished by $e_{in}(t)$ where this current is to be a function of $e_{in}(t)$. To accomplish this we will write loop equations, hence

$$e_{in}(t) - (R_g + R_1 + R_2)i_{in}(t) + R_1i_2(t) = 0$$

and

$$-R_1i_2(t) - \frac{1}{C}\int i_2(t)\,dt + R_1i_{in}(t) = 0$$

Taking the Laplace transform and arranging in determinate form we have

$$E_{in}(s) = (R_g + R_1 + R_2)I_{in}(s) - R_1I_2(s)$$

$$0 = -R_1I_{in}(s) + \left(R_1 + \frac{1}{Cs}\right)I_2(s)$$

Then

$$\Delta = \begin{vmatrix} (R_g + R_1 + R_2) & -R_1 \\ -R_1 & \left(R_1 + \dfrac{1}{Cs} \right) \end{vmatrix}$$

$$= (R_g + R_1 + R_2)\left(R_1 + \frac{1}{Cs} \right) - R_1^2$$

$$= R_1(R_g + R_2) + (R_g + R_1 + R_2)\frac{1}{Cs}$$

$$= \frac{R_1(R_g + R_2)Cs + (R_g + R_1 + R_2)}{Cs}$$

and

$$\Delta I_{\text{in}}(s) = \begin{vmatrix} E_{\text{in}}(s) & -R_1 \\ 0 & R_1 + \dfrac{1}{Cs} \end{vmatrix} = \left(R_1 + \frac{1}{Cs} \right) E_{\text{in}}(s)$$

or

$$Z_{\text{in}}(s) = \frac{E_{\text{in}}(s)}{I_{\text{in}}(s)} = \frac{\Delta}{R_1 + \dfrac{1}{Cs}}$$

$$= \frac{R_1(R_g + R_2)Cs + (R_g + R_1 + R_2)}{R_1Cs + 1}$$

$$= (R_g + R_2)\frac{\left[s + \dfrac{R_g + R_1 + R_2}{R_1(R_g + R_2)C} \right]}{s + 1} \qquad \textbf{(8–12)}$$

If we define

$$(R_g + R_2)\left[s + \frac{R_g + R_1 + R_2}{R_1(R_g + R_2)C} \right]$$

as $G(s)$ then $G(s)H(s) = s$, or

$$H(s) = \frac{s}{G(s)} = \frac{s}{(R_g + R_2)\left[s + \dfrac{R_g + R_1 + R_2}{R_1(R_g + R_2)C} \right]}$$

This mathematical interpretation of $Z_{\text{in}}(s)$ is shown in Fig. 8–8(c). To reiterate, the block diagrams of Fig. 8–8 and their mathematical representations are the results of mathematical manipulation with no regard for the physical characteristics of the circuit. The next section will consider circuit parameters in forming the representative block diagram.

8–3 Determining Diagrammatical Representation from Circuit Parameters

The ideal diagrammatical representation of a circuit should show the mathematical equivalent of each component, and/or show the cause-

effect relationships, hence this will be our goal. If we had the simple RC
circuit shown in Fig. 8–9 and we wished to diagrammatically show the

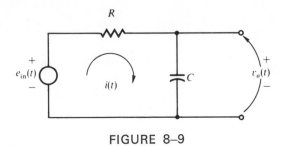

$$R$$

FIGURE 8–9

cause-effect relationship we realize we must begin with $E_{in}(s)$ (cause),
progress through some transfer function to $I(s)$ [effect of $E_{in}(s)$], and then
proceed through another transfer function to $V_o(s)$ [effect of cause $I(s)$].

Since we are looking for cause-effect relationships we will want to write
an equation which will relate e_{in} and i. Writing a loop equation we have

$$e_{in}(t) = Ri(t) + \frac{1}{C} \int i(t)\, dt$$

or

$$I(s) = \frac{1}{\left(R + \dfrac{1}{Cs}\right)} E_{in}(s) \tag{8–13}$$

The diagram for Eq. (8–13) is shown in Fig. 8–10(a). We next relate the
effect v_o to its cause i, which can be found by writing a loop equation in the
output circuit. Hence,

$$v_o(t) = \frac{1}{C} \int i(t)\, dt$$

Then

$$V_o(s) = \frac{1}{Cs} I(s) \tag{8–14}$$

The block diagram of Eq. (8–14) is shown in Fig. 8–10(b). Now let us
connect the $I(s)$ output of Figs. 8–10(a) and (b), which results in Fig.
8–10(c). Figure 8–10(c) has physical significance, in that, by visual inspection, we can see that by passing $E_{in}(s)$ through the transfer function
$1/[R + (1/Cs)]$ we get the current $I(s)$ and then by passing the current $I(s)$
through $1/Cs$ we get the output voltage $V_o(s)$.

Another way we could have represented this circuit is to return to Eq.
(8–13) and realize that since $Z_{in}(s) \equiv E_{in}(s)/I(s)$ then Eq. (8–13) is

$$I(s) = \frac{1}{Z_{in}(s)} E_{in}(s) = \frac{E_{in}(s)}{R + \dfrac{1}{Cs}} \tag{8–15}$$

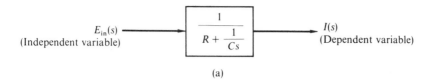

(a)

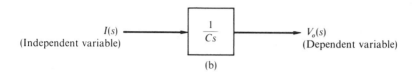

(b)

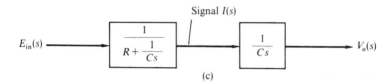

(c)

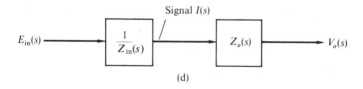

(d)

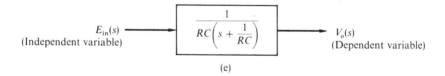

(e)

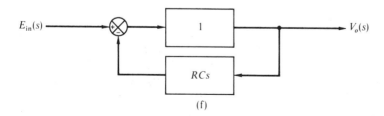

(f)

FIGURE 8–10

(check this by letting $s = j\omega$). And Eq. (8–14) can be written as $V_o(s) = Z_o(s)I(s)$ since $Z_o(s) \equiv V_o(s)/I(s) = 1/Cs$ (this can also be verified by letting $s = j\omega$), thus

$$V_o(s) = Z_o(s)I(s) \qquad (8\text{–}16)$$

Putting Eqs. (8–15) and (8–16) in block diagram form and connecting the common parameter $I(s)$ we have Fig. 8–10(d).

Suppose we next wish to represent the circuit as a block diagram showing just the input-output relationships. Writing a nodal equation we have

$$\frac{e_{\text{in}}(t) - v_o(t)}{R} = C\frac{dv_o(t)}{dt}$$

or

$$V_o(s) = \frac{E_{\text{in}}(s)}{R\left(\dfrac{1}{R} + Cs\right)} = \frac{1}{RC\left(s + \dfrac{1}{RC}\right)}E_{\text{in}}(s) \qquad (8\text{–}17)$$

Equation (8–17) is represented in Fig. 8–10(e).

Notice none of the block diagrams show feedback, which makes a better physical representation without it in these cases; however, let us now take Eq. (8–17) and force it through mathematical manipulation to show feedback. From Eq. (8–17)

$$\frac{V_o(s)}{E_{\text{in}}(s)} = \frac{1}{RC\left(s + \dfrac{1}{RC}\right)} = \frac{1}{1 + RCs} \qquad (8\text{–}18)$$

Comparing Eq. (8–18) with Eq. (8–6) we see we may define $G(s) = 1$, which would require $H(s) = RCs/G(s) = RCs$. This is shown in Fig. 8–10(f).

When deciding how the block diagram is to represent the circuit that is being analyzed one can start by determining what quantities he is interested in. Once this is determined he has in effect determined the quantities which will appear in the block diagram. That is, if we have a circuit for which we wish to develop a block diagram and this circuit has nodal voltages $v_1, v_2, v_3, \ldots, v_n$, and branch currents $i_1, i_2, i_3, \ldots, i_n$, we would probably want a block diagram which would show the relationships between the nodal voltages and the branch currents. Then these quantities would appear in our block diagram. To be specific let us make a block diagram equivalent for an FET. An FET is symbolically represented as shown in Fig. 8–11(a). As in all ac models of active components, to analyze them as a circuit component all one needs to know is simple circuit analysis; the FET is no exception. In the model of Fig. 8–11(b) we see the quantities $v_{gs}(t)$, $v_{ds}(t)$, and $i_d(t)$, which we will want in our block diagram. Then we must relate these mathematically. Writing a nodal equation we find

$$i_d(t) - g_f v_{gs}(t) - \frac{v_{ds}(t)}{r_d} = 0$$

or by taking the Laplace transform

$$I_d(s) - g_f V_{gs}(s) - \frac{1}{r_d} V_{ds}(s) = 0 \qquad (8\text{–}19)$$

Now, basically using the cause-effect criteria (cause-effect, cause-effect, etc.) we know that we want the input variable to be $V_{gs}(s)$ since it is responsible for the magnitudes of $I_d(s)$ and $V_{ds}(s)$ (see the characteristic curves). Now, the decision whether to make $I_d(s)$ or $V_{ds}(s)$ the output takes some reasoning since *both* are effects of $V_{gs}(s)$. We know that the output is usually thought of as a voltage, hence $V_{ds}(s)$ will be our dominant output, which means it will be the last to appear. So we will arrange our variables in the order of $V_{gs}(s)$, $I_d(s)$, and then $V_{ds}(s)$. Since $I_d(s)$ and $V_{ds}(s)$ both are really outputs we will arrange our block diagram so indicating. We will solve Eq. (8–19) for $I_d(s)$ and determine our block diagram from that equation. Thus

$$I_d(s) = g_f V_{gs}(s) + \frac{1}{r_d} V_{ds}(s) \qquad (8\text{–}20)$$

which yields the block diagram of Fig. 8–11(c).

Notice from Fig. 8–11(c) there appears to be a component missing between $I_d(s)$ and $V_{ds}(s)$. That is, returning to the cause-effect relationship there seems to be a transfer function missing between $I_d(s)$ and $V_{ds}(s)$ which, when added, would allow $I_d(s)$ to help determine the output voltage $V_{ds}(s)$. This missing component is the load for the FET. Suppose that a resistor was put in the source circuit; then the equivalent circuit would be that of Fig. 8–11(d). Since we have already analyzed the FET we need only look at the resistor R_s. The circuit we need to analyze is shown in Fig. 8–11(e). Notice all we had to do was to show how R_s fits into the picture relative to $i_d(t)$ and $v_{ds}(t)$. To show the mathematical relationship we write a nodal for Fig. 8–11(e), which is

$$i_d(t) - \frac{[-v_{ds}(t)]}{R_s} = 0$$

so

$$V_{ds}(s) = -R_s I_d(s) \qquad (8\text{–}21)$$

Putting Eq. (8–21) into the block diagram of Fig. 8–11(c) we have Fig. 8–11(f), where the negative sign means 180° phase shift. We would have put $-R_s$ in a single transfer function block and done away with the two blocks 1 and R_s; however, the single block containing $-R_s$ could be interpreted as negative resistance.

When viewing Fig. 8–11(f) we see that the input voltage $V_{gs}(s)$ is transferred to some current by passing through $g_f(g_f = 1/\text{ohms})$. Summed with that current to form $I_d(s)$ is some feedback current $V_{ds}(s)/r_d$ formed by $V_{ds}(s)$ passing through the transfer function $1/r_d$. And the current $I_d(s)$ has its effect upon the output voltage $V_{ds}(s)$ due to $I_d(s)$ passing through the transfer function -1 and R_s.

Let us now verify Fig. 8–11(f) by determining the gain $V_{ds}(s)/V_{gs}(s)$ from it. Hence, from Fig. 8–11(f)

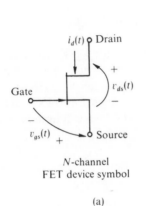

N-channel
FET device symbol

(a)

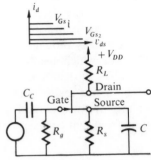

A possible circuit configuration
for FET amplifier

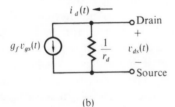

(b)

$g_f \equiv$ Forward transadmittance

$r_d \equiv$ Drain resistance

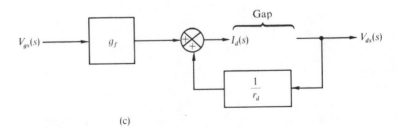

(c)

FIGURE 8–11

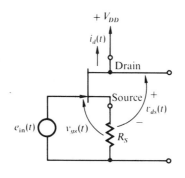

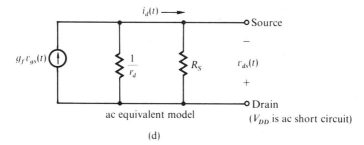

ac equivalent model

(V_{DD} is ac short circuit)

(d)

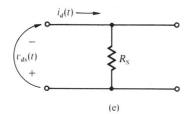

(e)

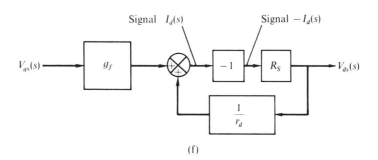

(f)

FIGURE 8–11   (continued)

$$I_{ds}(s) = g_f V_{gs}(s) + \frac{1}{r_d} V_{ds}(s)$$

and

$$V_{ds}(s) = -R_s I_{ds}(s) = -R_s \left[g_f V_{gs}(s) + \frac{1}{r_d} V_{ds}(s) \right]$$

or

$$g_f R_s V_{gs}(s) = -\left(1 + \frac{R_s}{r_d}\right) V_{ds}(s) = -\left(\frac{r_d + R_s}{r_d}\right) V_{ds}(s)$$

Then

$$\frac{V_{ds}(s)}{V_{gs}(s)} = -\frac{g_f r_d R_s}{r_d + R_s} = -g_f R_{eq}$$

which is the gain for an FET of the configuration we have.

In our representations one might notice that the only signals we can readily make available are those of the input and output. That is, in Fig. 8–11(f) we had to draw an arrow to a line and indicate that through this line $I(s)$ flowed, and for Fig. 8–10(c) and (d) we had to do much the same thing for $I(s)$. In this next section we will develop another diagrammatical representation which will allow us to have each variable available. This method will also enable us to speed up our analysis of a circuit, once we have the circuit in this diagrammatical form. The method is known as signal-flow analysis. And the diagrammatical representation is termed signal-flow diagrams.

8–4 Signal-Flow Diagrams

To construct a signal-flow diagram we consider each variable, or signal, that we wish to have present as a node regardless of the units of the variable. Then for each variable to be present in a signal-flow diagram a node, represented by a small circle, will be drawn. Each node is to be labeled as to which variable it represents. The nodes are connected by branches which are lines with arrowheads in their geometrical center to indicate direction of flow. If the direction of the arrow on a branch line is such as to indicate its going in the direction from input to output it is a forward path, and if the direction is the reverse of this it is termed a feedback path. Any transversing along a branch *must* be done in the direction of the arrow. Near the arrowhead the transfer function necessary to go from one node to another is to be written. As in the block diagram transfer functions act as multipliers. More than one branch may enter a node. The sign of the product of the variable transversing the entering branch and the transfer function indicates whether this product is to be added or subtracted at the node. Examples of this are shown in Fig. 8–12.

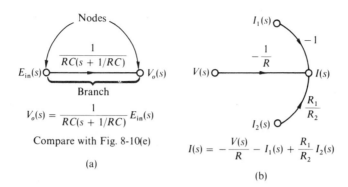

Nodes

$$V_o(s) = \frac{1}{RC(s + 1/RC)} E_{in}(s)$$

Compare with Fig. 8-10(e)

(a)

$$I(s) = -\frac{V(s)}{R} - I_1(s) + \frac{R_1}{R_2} I_2(s)$$

(b)

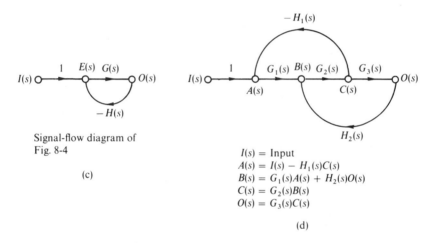

Signal-flow diagram of
Fig. 8-4

(c)

$I(s) =$ Input
$A(s) = I(s) - H_1(s)C(s)$
$B(s) = G_1(s)A(s) + H_2(s)O(s)$
$C(s) = G_2(s)B(s)$
$O(s) = G_3(s)C(s)$

(d)

FIGURE 8–12

Let us now make a signal-flow diagram of the FET of Fig. 8–11(c). We want variables $V_{gs}(s)$, $I_d(s)$, and $V_{ds}(s)$ to appear in that order. So we put a node for each variable and label it as such. This is shown in Fig. 8–13(a). We next consult Eq. (8–20) to determine the branch connections. Equation (8–20) states that $I_d(s)$ is the sum of two branches, one *from* $V_{gs}(s)$ and the other *from* $V_{ds}(s)$. Notice this also establishes the direction of the branch; that is, they are going from $V_{gs}(s)$ and $V_{ds}(s)$ and going to $I_d(s)$. These branches are shown in Fig. 8–13(b). We next determine the sign and transfer function for each branch. We see from Eq. (8–20) the branch from $V_{gs}(s)$ has a transfer function of $+g_f$ and that branch from $V_{ds}(s)$ is $+1/r_d$. Labeling these transfer functions we have Fig. 8–13(c).

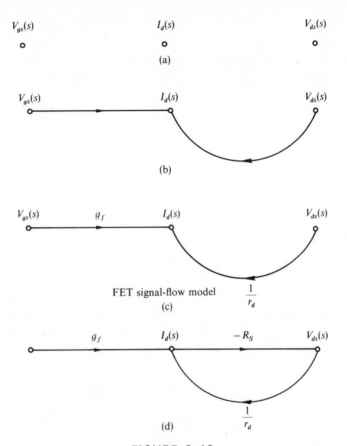

FIGURE 8–13

To complete the signal-flow diagram let us add R_s according to Fig. 8–11(d) and Eq. (8–21). From Eq. (8–21) we see that we have a branch from $I_d(s)$ and going to $V_{ds}(s)$. The transfer function is $-R_s$, where the -1 is phase shift of $I_d(s)$. This is shown in Fig. 8–13(d).

To firm up our signal-flow representation we will consider another example.

Example 8–4   Make a signal-flow diagram for the source follower shown in Fig. 8–14 (a source follower is like a cathode follower or an emitter follower).

Solution   We first make an ac model of the circuit as shown in Fig. 8–15. As in other examples we must realize that e_{in} and v_o of the ac model are *only* the ac portion of the

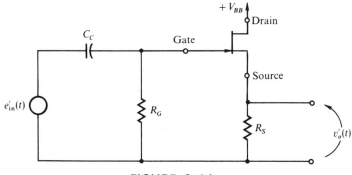

FIGURE 8–14

input e'_{in} and output v'_o of the circuit in Fig. 8–14. Our variables determined from the ac model are e_{in}, v_{gs}, i_d, v_{ds}, and v_o.

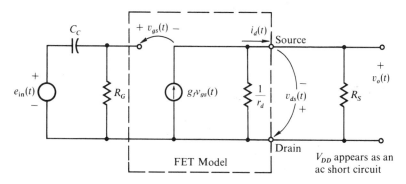

FIGURE 8–15

Since we have already analyzed an FET all that is necessary is to analyze the remaining circuitry relative to the FET variables v_{gs}, i_d, and v_{ds}, which is $-v_o$. We will first analyze the output circuit shown in Fig. 8–16.

We see that $v_{ds}(t) = -v_o(t)$, so

$$V_o(s) = -V_{ds}(s) \qquad (8\text{–}22)$$

Next determining R_s's function we write a nodal,

$$i_d(t) + \frac{v_{ds}(t)}{R_s} = 0,$$

or

$$V_{ds}(s) = -R_s I_d(s) \qquad (8\text{–}23)$$

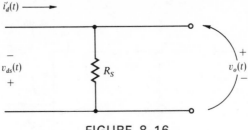

FIGURE 8–16

Equations (8–22) and (8–23) will be implemented shortly.

We next analyze the input circuit shown in Fig. 8–17. From the input circuit we see that the voltage across R_G is $v_{gs}(t) - v_{ds}(t)$, which can be found by writing a loop

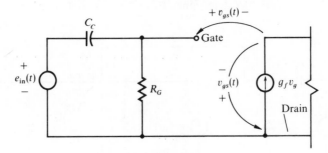

FIGURE 8–17

equation from drain to gate. Then a nodal equation written at the gate would be

$$C_C\frac{d}{dt}\{e_{in}(t) - [v_{gs}(t) - v_{ds}(t)]\} - \frac{v_{gs}(t) - v_{ds}(t)}{R_G} = 0$$

or

$$C_C s E_{in}(s) - \left(C_C s + \frac{1}{R_G}\right)V_{gs}(s) + \left(C_C s + \frac{1}{R_G}\right)V_{ds}(s)$$

We must now decide for what variable this equation is to be solved. We know this is the input circuit—hence the presence of $V_{ds}(s)$ in the equation must be feedback from the output. And since $E_{in}(s)$ is an independent variable, that is, it is the generator, we will change at will; then $V_{gs}(s)$ is the input variable for which we will solve. Thus

$$V_{gs}(s) = \frac{C_C s E_{in}(s) + \left(C_C s + \frac{1}{R_G}\right)V_{ds}(s)}{C_C s + \frac{1}{R_G}}$$

or

$$V_{gs}(s) = \frac{E_{in}(s)}{s + \dfrac{1}{R_G C_C}} + V_{ds}(s) \tag{8-24}$$

We are now ready to implement Eqs. (8–22), (8–23), and (8–24) into our FET signal-flow model of Fig. 8–13(c). Equation (8–22) states to put a branch from the node $V_{ds}(s)$ and go to a node labeled $V_o(s)$. The transfer function for this branch is to be -1. Equation (8–23) says a branch with $-R_S$ transfer function exists between nodes $I_d(s)$ and $V_{ds}(s)$. We know the direction is to be from $I_d(s)$ to $V_{ds}(s)$ since $IR = V$. Equation (8–24) states that node $V_{gs}(s)$ is to have two branches, one from node $E_{in}(s)$ with $1/(s + 1/R_G C_C)$ as its transfer function and the other from node $V_{ds}(s)$ with a transfer function of unity. The signal-flow diagram is shown in Fig. 8–18.

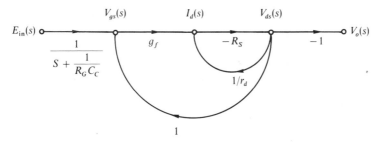

FIGURE 8–18

Example 8–5   Make a signal-flow diagram of the circuit shown in Fig. 8–19 having nodes $E_{in}(s)$, $V_1(s)$, and $V_2(s)$.

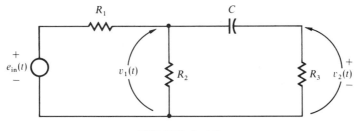

FIGURE 8–19

Solution   Writing the differential equations we have

$$\frac{e_{in}(t) - v_1(t)}{R_1} - \frac{v_1(t)}{R_2} + C\frac{d}{dt}[v_2(t) - v_1(t)] = 0$$

and

$$C\frac{d}{dt}[v_1(t) - v_2(t)] - \frac{v_2(t)}{R_3} = 0$$

Taking the Laplace transform

$$\frac{E_{in}(s)}{R_1} - \left(\frac{1}{R_1} + \frac{1}{R_2} + Cs\right)V_1(s) + CsV_2(s) = 0$$

$$(8\text{--}25)$$

$$CsV_1(s) - \left(\frac{1}{R_3} + Cs\right)V_2(s) = 0 \qquad (8\text{--}26)$$

We will put the signal-flow nodes in the order they appear on the circuit; hence we will want $E_{in}(s)$ first, then $V_1(s)$, and last will be the output $V_2(s)$. We will use the nodal equation we wrote for each node of the circuit to determine the branches and transfer functions of the signal-flow diagram, where the nodal voltages of the circuit correspond to the nodes of the signal-flow diagram. That is, to determine the branches and transfer functions for the signal-flow node $V_1(s)$ we will solve Eq. (8–25) for $V_1(s)$. Recall Eq. (8–25) was derived from the circuit node where v_1 appears. Hence from Eq. (8–25)

$$V_1(s) = \frac{E_{in}(s)}{R_1\left(Cs + \frac{1}{R_1} + \frac{1}{R_2}\right)} + \frac{CsV_2(s)}{Cs + \frac{1}{R_1} + \frac{1}{R_2}}$$

$$= \frac{E_{in}(s)}{R_1C\left(s + \frac{R_1 + R_2}{R_1R_2C}\right)} + \frac{sV_2(s)}{s + \frac{R_1 + R_2}{R_1R_2C}}$$

$$(8\text{--}27)$$

Solving Eq. (8–26) for $V_2(s)$ since Eq. (8–26) was written at the node where v_2 appears,

$$V_2(s) = \frac{sV_1(s)}{s + \frac{1}{R_3C}} \qquad (8\text{--}28)$$

We would next implement Eqs. (8–27) and (8–28) into a single signal-flow diagram representing the circuit. However, for clarity we will show the signal-flow diagrams for Eqs. (8–27) and (8–28) separately and then combine them into a single diagram. For Eq. (8–27) we have Fig. 8–20(a) and for Eq. (8–28) Fig. 8–20(b). Figure 8–20(c) is the total signal-flow diagram representing the circuit.

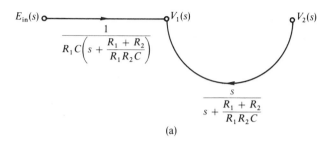

(a)

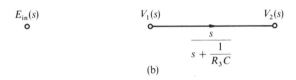

(b)

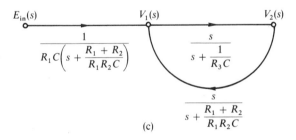

(c)

FIGURE 8–20

Example 8–6   Make a signal-flow diagram of the circuit in Ex. 8–5 (shown in Fig. 8–21), but now show nodes $E_{in}(s)$, $I_1(s)$, $V_1(s)$, $I_2(s)$, and $V_2(s)$, where $I_1(s)$ and $I_2(s)$ are loop currents.

Solution   We will arrange our signal-flow nodes in the order of $E_{in}(s)$, $I_1(s)$, $V_1(s)$, $I_2(s)$, and $V_2(s)$. We will determine the

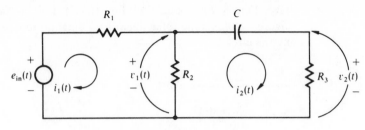

FIGURE 8–21

relationship between each node by writing a loop equation. When we wish the loop current $I_n(s)$ relationship to the other nodes we shall write a loop equation in the nth loop of the circuit and solve for $I_n(s)$. When wanting the $V_n(s)$ relationship with the loop currents we will write a loop equation, going through $V_n(s)$ and the components in parallel with $V_n(s)$, and then solve for $V_n(s)$. Hence, solving for $I_1(s)$ and $I_2(s)$ we have

$$e_{in}(t) - (R_1 + R_2)i_1(t) + R_2i_2(t) = 0$$

or

$$I_1(s) = \frac{R_2}{R_1 + R_2}I_2(s) + \frac{E_{in}(s)}{R_1 + R_2} \qquad (8\text{–}29)$$

and

$$R_2i_1(t) - (R_2 + R_3)i_2(t) - \frac{1}{C}\int i_2(t)\,dt = 0$$

which yields

$$I_2(s) = \frac{R_2}{(R_2 + R_3) + \dfrac{1}{Cs}} = \frac{R_2}{R_2 + R_3}\frac{sI_1(s)}{s + \dfrac{1}{(R_2 + R_3)C}} \qquad (8\text{–}30)$$

Solving for $V_1(s)$ and $V_2(s)$ we write the loop equations

$$v_1(t) - R_2i_1(t) + R_2i_2(t) = 0$$

or

$$V_1(s) = R_2I_1(s) - R_2I_2(s) \qquad (8\text{–}31)$$

and

$$v_2(t) = R_3i_2(t)$$

or

$$V_2(s) = R_3I_2(s) \qquad (8\text{–}32)$$

Implementing Eqs. (8–29), (8–30), (8–31), and (8–32) we have Fig. 8–22.

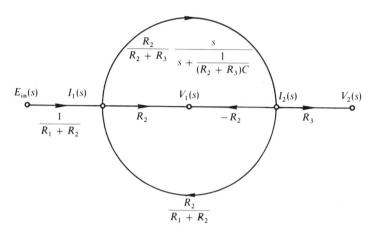

FIGURE 8–22

We see in Fig. 8–22 that the signal-flow diagram shows a closed loop between $I_1(s)$ and $I_2(s)$. This is true in the circuit also since i_1 affects i_2 and vice versa. We also see $V_1(s)$ is affected by both $I_1(s)$ and $I_2(s)$, where again this agrees with the physical circuit.

As our last example in this section we will again consider the circuit of Ex. 8–3; however, for this next example we will not use loop currents but rather branch currents. This should give us a fairly complete picture of the various ways open to us to represent the same circuit using signal-flow diagrams. To reiterate, it depends on what one wishes to show as to what variables he presents.

Example 8–7   Represent the circuit in Fig. 8–23 in a signal-flow diagram using nodes $E_{in}(s)$, $I_1(s)$, $V_1(s)$, $I_2(s)$, and $V_2(s)$, where i_1 and i_2 are branch currents as shown.

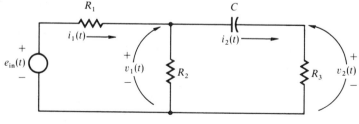

FIGURE 8–23

Solution   When wanting an equation for the signal-flow node $V_n(s)$, which corresponds to the circuit nodal voltage $v_n(t)$, we may write a nodal equation at the node of the circuit, take the Laplace, and then solve for $V_n(s)$. With this method we will put the branch currents in the nodal equations when possible. Thus

$$i_1(t) - i_2(t) - \frac{v_1(t)}{R_2} = 0$$

or

$$V_1(s) = R_2 I_1(s) - R_2 I_2(s) \qquad (8\text{–}33)$$

and

$$i_2(t) - \frac{v_2(t)}{R_3} = 0$$

or

$$V_2(s) = R_3 I_2(s) \qquad (8\text{–}34)$$

Notice this gives a relationship between the nodal voltages and the branch currents where the nodal voltages are the dependent variables. And to find the relationships between the nodal voltages $V_1(s)$ and $V_2(s)$ and the branch currents $I_1(s)$ and $I_2(s)$, where the branch currents are the dependent variable, we write a loop equation. Hence,

$$e_{in}(t) - R_1 i_1(t) - v_1(t) = 0$$

or

$$I_1(s) = \frac{E_{in}(s)}{R_1} - \frac{V_1(s)}{R_1} \qquad (8\text{–}35)$$

and

$$v_1(t) - \frac{1}{C} \int i_2(t)\, dt - v_2(t) = 0$$

or

$$I_2(s) = Cs V_1(s) - Cs V_2(s) \qquad (8\text{–}36)$$

Implementing Eqs. (8–33), (8–34), (8–35), and (8–36) we have Fig. 8–24.

Figure 8–24 tells us that in going from $E_{in}(s)$ to $I_1(s)$ we must pass $E_{in}(s)$ through $1/R_1$, whose product has the units of current. And at node $I_1(s)$ we see that $I_1(s)$ is the sum of the current $E_{in}(s)/R_1$ and $-V_1(s)/R_1$. We see also that $V_1(s)$ is the result of $I_1(s)$ passing through R_2 and feedback from $I_2(s)$ passing through $-R_2$; hence $V_1(s)$ is the result of $R_2 I_1(s)$ and $-R_2 I_2(s)$, and so on.

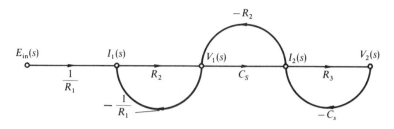

FIGURE 8–24

In the beginning of this chapter we spoke of the signal-flow diagram as being a method used for quick analysis; however, so far we have not witnessed evidence of that. The subject matter of our next section will be Mason's Rule, which will provide a technique for quick analysis once we have the signal-flow diagram.

8–5   Mason's Rule

Using Mason's rule we may analyze a signal-flow diagram by inspection. Mason's rule determines the over-all transfer function of a signal-flow diagram using the equation given in Eq. (8–37).

$$T(s) = \frac{\sum\limits_{n=1}^{m} F_n(s)\Delta_n(s)}{\Delta(s)} = \frac{F_1(s)\Delta_1(s) + F_2(s)\Delta_2(s) + \cdots + F_m(s)\Delta_m(s)}{1 - \Sigma L_i + \Sigma L_i L_j - \Sigma L_i L_j L_k + \cdots + \Sigma L_i \cdots L_y}$$

$$(8\text{–}37)$$

where ΣL_i is found by forming the sum of products of the transfer functions in each closed loop.

$\Sigma L_i L_j$ is the sum of products of transfer functions of all closed loops, found in L_i, taken two at a time. However, we omit the products of any two loops which share the same node (or nodes). $\Sigma L_i L_j L_k$ is the sum of products of transfer functions of all closed loops taken three at a time but omitting the products of loops which share common nodes.

For the terms $\Sigma L_i \ldots L_y$ we continue taking the product of closed loops omitting those products which share common nodes until we have used all combinations.

$F_n(s)$ is the product of transfer functions along the nth forward path, where a forward path is any sequence of branches that can be transversed from input to output while always traveling in the direction of the arrows.

$\Delta_n(s)$ is formed by omitting all terms in $\Delta(s)$ which share common nodes with the nth forward path. An example will better illustrate the use of Eq. (8–37).

Using Eq. (8–35) we will determine the over-all transfer function $T(s) = V_2(s)/E_{in}(s)$ of Fig. 8–24. There is one forward path starting at $E_{in}(s)$ and continuing through $I_1(s)$, $V_1(s)$, $I_2(s)$, and ending at $V_2(s)$. Since only one forward path is present, then $m = 1$ for $\sum_{n=1}^{m=1} F_n(s)\Delta_n(s)$ or $\sum_{n=1}^{m=1} F_n(s)\,\Delta_n(s) = F_1(s)\Delta_1(s)$. Transversing the forward path we find

$$F_1(s) = \frac{1}{R_1}(R_2)Cs(R_3) = \frac{R_2 R_3 Cs}{R_1} \qquad (8\text{–}38)$$

The product of closed loops is:

$$L_1 = R_2\left(-\frac{1}{R_1}\right) = -\frac{R_2}{R_1}$$

where the closed loop is going from node $I_1(s)$ to $V_1(s)$ and back to $I_1(s)$ *never* going in the opposite direction of the arrowheads. And

$$L_2 = Cs(-R_2) = -R_2 Cs$$

following loop from $V_1(s)$ to $I_2(s)$ and back to $V_1(s)$.

$$L_3 = R_3(-Cs) = -R_3 Cs$$

following loop from $I_2(s)$ to $V_2(s)$ and back to $I_2(s)$.

Then the sum of closed loop products L_1, L_2, etc. is:

$$\Sigma L_i = L_1 + L_2 + L_3 = -\frac{R_2}{R_1} - R_2 Cs - R_3 Cs$$

$$= -\left[\frac{R_2}{R_1} + (R_2 + R_3)Cs\right] \qquad (8\text{–}39)$$

and

$$\Sigma L_i L_j = (L_1 L_2 + L_1 L_3 + L_2 L_3) - (L_1 L_2 + L_2 L_3) = L_1 L_3$$

where the combinations $L_1 L_2$ and $L_2 L_3$ share common nodes, that is, L_1 and L_2 share node $V_1(s)$ and L_2 and L_3 share node $I_2(s)$. Thus

$$\Sigma L_i L_j = L_1 L_3 = \left(-\frac{R_2}{R_1}\right)(-R_3 Cs) = \frac{R_2 R_3 Cs}{R_1} \qquad (8\text{–}40)$$

Computing $\Sigma_1 L_i L_j L_k$ next we have

$$\Sigma L_i L_j L_k = L_1 L_2 L_2 - L_1 L_2 L_3 = 0$$

since there are common nodes among L_1, L_2, and L_3. Determining $\Delta_n(s)$ next we find

$$\Delta_1(s) = 1 \qquad (8\text{–}41)$$

since L_1, L_2, and L_3 all share common nodes with the forward path $F_1(s)$. Substituting Eqs. (8–38), (8–39), (8–40), and (8–41) into Eq. (8–37) we have

$$T(s) = \frac{V_2(s)}{E_{in}(s)} = \frac{\sum_{n=1}^{m} F_n(s)\Delta_n(s)}{\Delta(s)} = \frac{F_1(s)\Delta_1(s)}{1 - (L_1 + L_2 + L_3) + L_1 L_3}$$

$$= \frac{\left(\dfrac{R_2 R_3 Cs}{R_1}\right)1}{1 - \left\{-\left[\dfrac{R_2}{R_1} + (R_2 + R_3)Cs\right]\right\} + \dfrac{R_2 R_3 Cs}{R_1}}$$

$$= \frac{R_2 R_3 Cs}{R_1 + R_2 + R_1(R_2 + R_3)Cs + R_2 R_3 Cs}$$

or

$$\frac{V_2(s)}{E_{in}(s)} = \frac{R_2 R_3}{R_1(R_2 + R_3) + R_2 R_3} \frac{s}{\left\{s + \dfrac{R_1 + R_2}{[R_1(R_2 + R_3) + R_2 R_3]C}\right\}}$$

$$\text{(8-42)}$$

We can verify Eq. (8–42) from Eqs. (8–25) and (8–26) of Ex. 8–5. Setting those equations up in determinate form and solving for $V_o(s)/E_{in}(s)$ we have

$$\frac{E_{in}(s)}{R_1} = \left(\frac{1}{R_1} + \frac{1}{R_2} + Cs\right)V_1(s) - CsV_2(s)$$

$$0 = -CsV_1(s) + \left(\frac{1}{R_3} + Cs\right)V_2(s)$$

from which we derive

$$\Delta = \begin{vmatrix} \left(\dfrac{1}{R_1} + \dfrac{1}{R_2} + Cs\right) & -Cs \\[2mm] -Cs & \left(\dfrac{1}{R_3} + Cs\right) \end{vmatrix}$$

$$= \left(\frac{1}{R_1} + \frac{1}{R_2} + Cs\right)\left(\frac{1}{R_3} + Cs\right) - (Cs)^2$$

$$= \frac{1}{R_1 R_3} + \frac{1}{R_2 R_3} + \left(\frac{1}{R_1} + \frac{1}{R_2} + \frac{1}{R_3}\right)Cs$$

$$= \frac{1}{R_1 R_3} + \frac{1}{R_2 R_3} + \frac{(R_2 R_3 + R_1 R_3 + R_1 R_2)Cs}{R_1 R_2 R_3}$$

$$= \left(\frac{R_2 R_3 + R_1 R_3 + R_1 R_2}{R_1 R_2 R_3}\right)C\left[s + \frac{R_1 + R_2}{(R_2 R_3 + R_1 R_3 + R_1 R_2)C}\right]$$

and

$$\Delta V_2(s) = \begin{vmatrix} \dfrac{1}{R_2} + Cs & \dfrac{E_{in}(s)}{R_1} \\[2mm] -Cs & 0 \end{vmatrix} = \frac{CsE_{in}(s)}{R_1}$$

or

$$\frac{V_2(s)}{E_{in}(s)} = \frac{Cs}{\Delta R_1} = \frac{R_2 R_3 s}{(R_2 R_3 + R_1 R_3 + R_1 R_2)\left[s + \dfrac{R_1 + R_2}{(R_2 R_3 + R_1 R_3 + R_1 R_2)C}\right]}$$

which agrees with Eq. (8–42).

To gain experience with the use of Eq. (8–37) and to demonstrate that the choice of how a circuit, or system, is represented in a signal-flow diagram can be varied let us use Eq. (8–37) to find $V_2(s)/E_{in}(s)$ for the signal-flow diagrams of Figs. 8–20(c) and 8–22. Beginning with Fig. 8–20(c) we find:

$$F_1(s) = \left[\frac{1}{R_1 C\left(s + \dfrac{R_1 + R_2}{R_1 R_2 C}\right)}\right]\left[\frac{s}{s + \dfrac{1}{R_3 C}}\right]$$

where only one forward path exists.

$$L_1 = \left[\frac{s}{s + \dfrac{1}{R_3 C}}\right]\left[\frac{s}{s + \dfrac{R_1 + R_2}{R_1 R_2 C}}\right]$$

for the only closed loop that exists. And

$$\Delta(s) = 1 - L_1 = 1 - \left[\frac{s}{s + \dfrac{1}{R_3 C}}\right]\left[\frac{s}{s + \dfrac{R_1 + R_2}{R_1 R_2 C}}\right]$$

$$= \frac{\left(s + \dfrac{1}{R_3 C}\right)\left(s + \dfrac{R_1 + R_2}{R_1 R_2 C}\right) - s^2}{\left(s + \dfrac{1}{R_3 C}\right)\left(s + \dfrac{R_1 + R_2}{R_1 R_2 C}\right)}$$

$$= \frac{\dfrac{R_1 + R_2}{R_1 R_2 R_3 C^2} + \left(\dfrac{1}{R_3} + \dfrac{R_1 + R_2}{R_1 R_2}\right)\dfrac{s}{C}}{\left(s + \dfrac{1}{R_3 C}\right)\left(s + \dfrac{R_1 + R_2}{R_1 R_2 C}\right)}$$

Finding $\Delta_1(s)$ next $\Delta_1(s) = 1$. Then from Eq. (8–37)

$$T(s) = \frac{V_2(s)}{E_{in}(s)} = \frac{F_1(s)\Delta_1(s)}{\Delta(s)} = \frac{\dfrac{s}{R_1 C\left(s + \dfrac{R_1 + R_2}{R_1 R_2 C}\right)\left(s + \dfrac{1}{R_3 C}\right)}}{\dfrac{\dfrac{R_1 + R_2}{R_1 R_2 R_3 C^2} + \left(\dfrac{1}{R_3} + \dfrac{R_1 + R_2}{R_1 R_2}\right)\dfrac{s}{C}}{\left(s + \dfrac{R_1 + R_2}{R_1 R_2 C}\right)\left(s + \dfrac{1}{R_3 C}\right)}}$$

$$= \frac{s}{R_1 C\left[\dfrac{R_1 + R_2}{R_1 R_2 C^2} + \left(\dfrac{1}{R_3} + \dfrac{R_1 + R_2}{R_1 R_2}\right)\dfrac{s}{C}\right]}$$

$$= \frac{R_2 R_3 s}{(R_1 R_2 + R_3 R_1 + R_2 R_3)\left[s + \dfrac{R_1 + R_2}{(R_1 R_2 + R_3 R_1 + R_2 R_3)C}\right]}$$

which agrees with Eq. (8–42). And for Fig. 8–22 we have:

$$F_1(s) = \frac{1}{R_1 + R_2}\left[\frac{R_2}{R_2 + R_3}\frac{s}{s + \dfrac{1}{(R_2 + R_3)C}}\right]R_3$$

$$= \frac{R_2 R_3 s}{(R_1 + R_2)(R_2 + R_3)\left[s + \dfrac{1}{(R_2 + R_3)C}\right]}$$

$$L_1 = \left[\frac{R_2}{R_2 + R_3}\frac{s}{s + \dfrac{1}{(R_2 + R_3)C}}\right]\frac{R_2}{R_1 + R_2}$$

$$= \frac{R_2^2 s}{(R_1 + R_2)(R_2 + R_3)\left[s + \dfrac{1}{(R_2 + R_3)C}\right]}$$

$$\Delta(s) = 1 - L_1 = 1 - \frac{R_2^2 s}{(R_1 + R_2)(R_2 + R_3)\left[s + \dfrac{1}{(R_2 + R_3)C}\right]}$$

$$= \frac{(R_1 + R_2)(R_2 + R_3)\left[s + \dfrac{1}{(R_2 + R_3)C}\right] - R_2^2 s}{(R_1 + R_2)(R_2 + R_3)\left[s + \dfrac{1}{(R_2 + R_3)C}\right]}$$

$$= \frac{(R_1 R_2 + R_1 R_3 + R_2 R_3)s + \dfrac{R_1 + R_2}{C}}{(R_1 + R_2)(R_2 + R_3)\left[s + \dfrac{1}{(R_2 + R_3)C}\right]}$$

$$\Delta_1(s) = 1$$

$$\frac{V_2(s)}{E_{in}(s)} = \frac{F_1(s)\Delta_1(s)}{\Delta(s)} = \frac{R_2 R_3 s}{(R_1 R_2 + R_1 R_3 + R_2 R_3)s + \dfrac{R_1 + R_2}{C}}$$

$$= \frac{R_2 R_3 s}{(R_1 R_2 + R_1 R_3 + R_2 R_3)\left[s + \dfrac{R_1 + R_2}{(R_1 R_2 + R_1 R_3 + R_2 R_3)C}\right]}$$

which likewise agrees with Eq. (8–42). Notice, the node of Fig. 8–22 was useless since branches only lead into it.

We will now consider other examples of Mason's rule.

Example 8–8   Find $V_o(s)/E_{in}(s)$ from Fig. 8–18 using Eq. (8–37).

Solution

$$F_1(s) = \left(\frac{1}{s + \dfrac{1}{R_G C_c}}\right)g_f(-R_S)(-1) = \frac{g_f R_S}{s + \dfrac{1}{R_G C_c}}$$

$$L_1 = (-R_S)\left(\frac{1}{r_d}\right) = -\frac{R_S}{r_d}$$

$$L_2 = g_f(-R_S)(1) = -g_f R_S$$

L_1 and L_2 have the common nodes $I_d(s)$ and $V_{ds}(s)$, therefore L_1L_2 is omitted from $\Delta(s)$. So

$$\Delta(s) = 1 - (L_1 + L_2) = 1 + \frac{R_S}{r_d} + g_fR_S$$

$$= \frac{r_d + R_S(1 + r_dg_f)}{V_d}$$

$\Delta_1(s) = 1$. From Eq. (8–37)

$$\frac{V_o(s)}{E_{in}(s)} = \frac{\dfrac{g_fR_S}{s + \dfrac{1}{R_GC_C}}}{\dfrac{r_d + R_S(1 + r_dg_f)}{r_d}}$$

$$= \frac{g_fr_dR_S}{[r_d(1 + g_fR_S) + R_S]\left(s + \dfrac{1}{R_GC_C}\right)}$$

Usually r_d is so large compared to R_S that $r_d(1 + g_fR_S) \gg R_S$ so then

$$\frac{V_o(s)}{E_{in}(s)} \simeq \frac{g_fR_S}{(1 + g_fR_S)\left(s + \dfrac{1}{R_GC}\right)}$$

Realize that from the equation for $V_o(s)/E_{in}(s)$ we could make a Bode plot, or find that inverse Laplace once given e_{in} explicitly.

Example 8–9   Find $T(s)$ for the signal-flow diagram shown in Fig. 8–25.

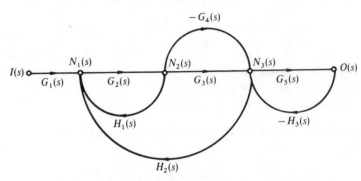

FIGURE 8–25

We have two forward paths, therefore we have $F_1(s)$ and $F_2(s)$; hence,

$$F_1(s) = G_1(s)G_2(s)G_3(s)G_5(s)$$

and

$$F_2(s) = G_1(s)G_2(s)[-G_4(s)]G_5(s)$$
$$= -G_1(s)G_2(s)G_4(s)G_5(s)$$

We have four closed loops, which are:

$L_1 = G_2(s)H_1(s)$: nodes $N_1(s)$, $N_2(s)$

$L_2 = G_2(s)G_3(s)H_3(s)$: nodes $N_1(s)$, $N_2(s)$, $N_3(s)$

$L_3 = G_2(s)[-G_4(s)]H_2(s) = -G_2(s)G_4(s)H_2(s)$:

nodes $N_1(s)$, $N_2(s)$, $N_3(s)$

$L_4 = G_5(s)[-H_3(s)] = -G_5(s)H_3(s)$: nodes $N_3(s), O(s)$

$$\Delta(s) = 1 - (L_1 + L_2 + L_3 + L_4) - L_1L_4$$
$$= 1 - G_2(s)H_1(s) - G_2(s)G_3(s)H_2(s)$$
$$+G_2(s)G_4(s)H_2(s) + G_5(s)H_3(s)$$

And $\Delta_1(s) = 1$ and $\Delta_2(s) = 1$ since all the closed loop nodes are on both forward paths. Therefore

$$\frac{O(s)}{I(s)} = \frac{F_1(s)\Delta_1(s) + F_2(s)\Delta_2(s)}{\Delta(s)}$$

$$= \frac{G_1(s)G_2(s)G_3(s)G_5(s) - G_1(s)G_2(s)G_4(s)G_5(s)}{1 - G_2(s)H_1(s) - G_2(s)G_3(s)H_2(s)} \\ {+ G_2(s)G_4(s)H_2(s) + G_5(s)H_3(s)}$$

This completes this chapter. It is hoped that enough material has been provided so that one can envision further applications and also if one has need for the material he will be knowledgeable enough to read the literature on the subject.

Problems

Chapter 1

1-1 For the explicit equations given write the functional notation.
(a) $t = 3y + 5$
(b) $x = bz^2 + 2z$
(c) $\beta = 3x + 2y + 10$
(d) $y = 2 \cos 10t$
(e) $z = 10 \sin (\omega_1 t + \Theta + 3x)$, where ω_1 and Θ are constants.
(f) $v = E(1 - e^{-t/RC})$
(g) $i = I(1 - e^{-t/k})e^{-x}$

1-2 Suppose that in problem 1-1 [parts (b) and (c)] z, x, and y are time-variant. Write an implicit expression for parts (b) and (c) to show that x and β are also functions of t due to z, x, and y.

1-3 We have a black box as shown in Fig. 1-3(a). We know that this black box is supposed to represent a network through which transmission occurs. (a) What variables would you choose to be the independent variables? (b) Write an implicit expression for part(a).

1-4 To which of the following equations can the principle of superposition be applied? Show how and why you arrived at your answer. HINT: Apply Eq. (1-4).
(a) $y = 3e^x + 10$
(b) $i = \dfrac{v}{R} + 5$, where R is constant.

(c) $i = C\dfrac{dv(t)}{dt} + K$, where C and K are constant.

(d) $x = Ct\dfrac{dv(t)}{dt} + K$

(e) $y = Cv(t)\dfrac{dv(t)}{dt}$

(f) $z = C\left[\dfrac{dv(t)}{dt}\right]^2$

(g) $h = C\dfrac{dv^2(t)}{dt}$

(h) $m = C\dfrac{d^2v(t)}{dt^2}$

(i) $v = \dfrac{1}{L}\displaystyle\int i(t)\,dt + K$, where K is constant.

(j) $y = \dfrac{t}{L}\displaystyle\int i(t)\,dt + \dfrac{di(t)}{dt}$

(k) $x = \dfrac{i(t)}{L}\displaystyle\int i(t)\,dt + K$

(l) $z = \dfrac{1}{L}\left[\displaystyle\int i(t)\,dt\right]^2 + K$

(m) $h = \dfrac{1}{L}\displaystyle\int i^2(t)\,dt + K$

(n) $m = \dfrac{1}{L}\displaystyle\int\int i(t)\,dt + K$

1-5   The graph given in Fig. 1–13 was plotted from the equation $y = x^2$, which is nonlinear. (a) For an excitation of $x'_1 = \sin \omega t + 2$ graphically determine y'_1, similar to the technique of Fig. 1–1(b). (b) Now draw a straight-line tangent to the intersection of the curve

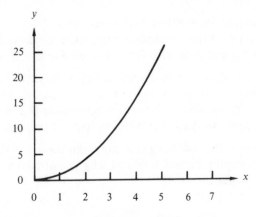

FIGURE 1–13

$y = x^2$ and the projection of $X_Q = 2$ on that curve. Once this line is completed make a projection of x_1 to the y-axis to determine y_1 using the tangent line. Discuss linearity and fidelity relative to parts (a) and (b).

1-6 For the linear equation $i = -(v/100) + 0.15$ plot a graph from $v = 0$ to $v = 15$. Now let $v'_1 = 2 \sin \omega t + 7$ and determine i'_1 mathematically and then verify your mathematical results graphically.

1-7 The graph given in Fig. 1–14 was plotted from the equation $p = 2i^2$. (a) Determine p'_1 graphically for $i'_1 = \sin \omega t + 3$. (b) Now

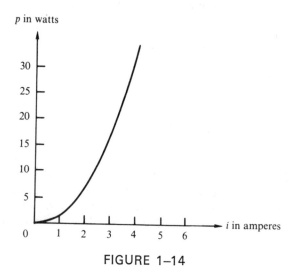

FIGURE 1–14

make a straight-line approximation of the curve $p = 2i^2$ by drawing a straight-line tangent to the curve at the $I_Q = 3$ and $P_Q = 2I_Q^2$ $= 2(3)^2 = 18$, which is written as the point (3, 18). Now graphically determine p'_1 for $i'_1 = \sin \omega t + 3$ using the tangent line for projection purposes. (c) By substituting $i'_1 = \sin \omega t + 3$ into the equation $p = 2i^2$ mathematically determine the error of your straight-line approximation and the dc term of p'_1 (verify dc term from graph).

1-8 Show that if the coefficients of Eqs. (1–22) are functions of their independent variables, then the principle of superposition cannot be applied. To do this let $y_{11} = y_{11}(v_1)$, $y_{12} = y_{12}(v_2)$, $y_{21} = y_{21}(v_1)$, and $y_{22} = y_{22}(v_2)$, or specifically let $y_{11} = m_1 v_1$, $y_{12} = m_A v_2$, $y_{21} = m_B v_1$, and $y_{22} = m_2 v_2$.

1-9 Given a black box find the equivalent T-network where, with 10 V sinusoidal applied to terminals 1-1' and terminals 2-2' open-circuited, you measured a current of 0.20 A for i_1 and a voltage of 5 V across terminals 2-2′. Then, applying the 10-V source to terminals 2-2′ with terminals 1-1′ open-circuited, you measured a current of 0.15 A for i_2 and 3.75 V for v_1.

1–10 Suppose we were given a black box and were asked to determine its equivalent T-network. If the black box contains the circuit shown in Fig. 1-15: (a) using circuit analysis and Eqs. (1–15)

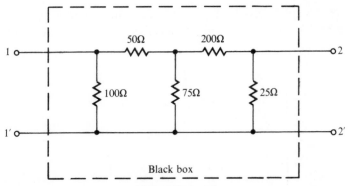

FIGURE 1–15

mathematically determine what numerical value will be measured when determining $z_{11}, z_{12}, z_{21},$ and z_{22}; (b) once $z_{11}, z_{12}, z_{21},$ and z_{22} are calculated find the T-network components $z_{11} - z_{12}$, $z_{22} - z_{12}$, and z_{12} of Fig. 1–5(d) and draw the equivalent T-network.

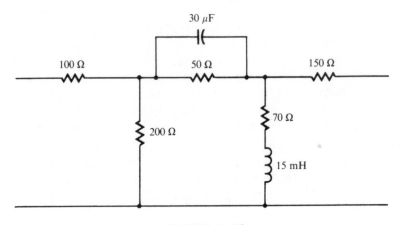

FIGURE 1–16

1–11 For the circuit shown in Fig. 1–16 determine its equivalent T- and π-network for a frequency of 100 Hz and then for a frequency of 10^3 Hz.

1–12 If you were modeling a black box in y-parameters which contained the circuit shown in Fig. 1–17, what would be the measured values in determining Y_{11}, Y_{22}, Y_{12}, or Y_{21}? Make your calculations at a frequency of 10^3 Hz.

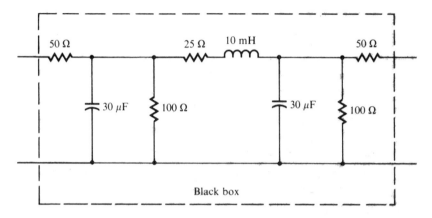

FIGURE 1–17

1–13 Determine the relationship between the z-parameters of Fig. 1–5(d) and the y-parameters of Fig. 1–11.

1–14 Suppose we wish to modify the black box of Fig. 1–3(a) to represent transmission. Under this condition we would reverse the direction of current i_2'. For a black box representing transmission derive a set of parameters where v_1' and i_1' are the independent variables.

Chapter 2

2–1 Suppose that a 100 ohm resistor, designated as R, has the resistance vs power characteristics as shown in Fig. 2–50. For this resistor plot a graph of i vs v up to 0.8 watts being dissipated. Over what range of your graph is the component linear? From Fig. 2–50 over what range of power is this component linear? Hint: Use $p = v^2/R = i^2R$ and Fig. 2–50 to determine i and v.

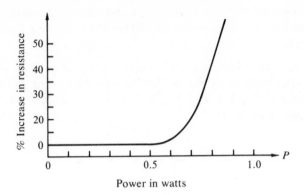

FIGURE 2–50

2–2   When capacitance can be approximated to be constant, Eq. (2–6)
       applies for determining the current i_c. What is the equation for
       i_c if $C = C(t)$? Will the waveform of i_c be distorted if $C = C(t)$
       and if so from which term(s)?

2–3   For a capacitor of $5\mu F$ determine the current if the voltage across
       it is measured to be $2e^{-0.2 \times 10^3 t}$.

2–4   Make a plot of i vs v for the equation $i = C(dv(t)/dt)$ if $v = \sin \omega t$,
       $C = 1$ farad, and $\omega = 1$Hz. Notice the relationship between i
       and v is not a linear one. Is it still possible to apply the principle of
       superposition? Hint: $q(t) = \int_0^t i(t)\, dt$.

2–5   Suppose we wish to determine the total voltage (both t-variant
       and constant) which developed across the capacitor C of Fig. 2–51
       from time t_1 to some general time t. This can be expressed by the
       definite integral

$$\frac{1}{C}\left[\int_{t_1}^{t} i_C(t)\, dt + q_C(0)\right]$$

       Equate the indefinite integral of Eq. (2–7) and the definite integral
       above and discuss the constant of integration of the indefinite
       integral relative to the constant $q_C(0)/C = v_C(0)$, where $v_C(0)$ is the
       voltage present across C just prior to $t = t_1$, or more simply stated:
       the initial conditions of the capacitor C. Hint: In compliance with
       section 1–2 rewrite Eq. (2–7) so that it indicates constants and
       variables are both present, that is,

$$v_C'(t) = \frac{1}{C}\int i_C(t)\, dt = \frac{1}{C}\left[\int_{t_1}^{t} i_C(t)\, dt + q_C(0)\right]$$

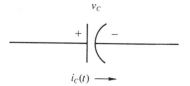

FIGURE 2–51

2–6 Show that for the voltage $v_C'(t) = v_C(t) + v_C(0)$ across C the constant voltage $v_C(0)$ does not contribute to the current i_C. If the voltage across the capacitor C could be expressed as $v_C'(t) = v(t) + v_C(0)e^{-t/RC}$ would the inital voltage $v_C(0)$ contribute to the current i_C? What conclusions can you arrive at concerning the current through a capacitor and dc voltages?

2–7 If the current through a capacitor C is $i_C = -Ie^{-t/RC}$ amp and we wish to determine if C is linear, we must find $[q_C(t)/v_C(t)] = [\int i_C(t)\,dt/v_C(t)]$ where we see we are interested in time variant terms only. Thus

$$\frac{\int i_C(t)\,dt}{v_C(t)} = \frac{\int i_C(t)\,dt}{\dfrac{1}{C}\int i_C(t)\,dt} = C$$

which is a constant, therefore, C is linear. However, suppose we performed

$$\int i_C(t)\,dt = -I\int e^{-t/RC}\,dt = IRC\,e^{-t/RC} + K$$

then

$$\frac{q_C(t)}{v_C(t)} = \frac{IRC\,e^{-t/RC} + K}{IR\,e^{-t/RC} + \dfrac{K}{C}}$$

which is not constant. But the equation $q_C(t)/v_C(t)$ states we wish time variant quantities only. Hence, remove K and K/C. Thus

$$\frac{q_C(t)}{v_C(t)} = \frac{IRC\,e^{-t/RC}}{IR\,e^{-t/RC}} = C$$

which is a constant and verifies the equation

$$\frac{\int i_C(t)\,dt}{\dfrac{1}{C}\int i_C(t)\,dt}$$

Using the above reasoning rationalize that C is a constant using the definite integral $\int_{t_0}^{t} i_C(t)\,dt$ where t_0 is some specific time t and the upper limit t is some general time t.

2-8 From problem 2-7 if one wished the static capacitance, or that capacitance resulting from voltages and accumulated charge, they would neglect the t-variant terms. Determine Q_C/V_C from problem 2-7.

2-9 The voltage across a capacitor C was measured and determined to be $5 \sin 10^3 t$ volts and the current determined to be $2.3 \times 10^{-3} \cos 10^3 t$ amps. Show that C is a constant and therefore a linear component.

2-10 For the conditions shown in Fig. 2-52 determine the current i_L. Which direction is i_L flowing? Show that i_L can never reverse its current flow direction.

$$v_L = 0.5\,e^{-10^7 t}\text{volts}$$

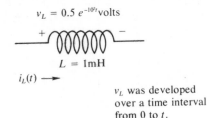

$$L = 1\text{mH}$$

$i_L(t) \longrightarrow$

v_L was developed
over a time interval
from 0 to t.

FIGURE 2-52

2-11 In the section on inductance we established that the voltage across an inductor could be expressed as $v_L(t) = N(d\phi(t)/dt)$. Also we derived that the current i_L could be expressed as $i_L(t) = (1/L)\int v_L(t)\,dt$. From these two equations demonstrate that the product $i \cdot L$ has the units of flux·turns.

2-12 Show that the constant of integration of the indefinite integral $\int v_L(t)\,dt$ is the initial condition $\phi(0)$ per turn. Be certain to work problem 2-11 first. Since the constant of integration is the initial flux $\phi(0) \cdot$ turns. What is K_1 if $i_L(t) = (1/L)v_L^{(-1)}(t) + K_1$, $v^{(-1)}(t)$ is the integral of $v_L(t)$, and K_1 the product of $1/L$ and the constant of integration?

2-13 Given the circuit of Fig. 2-11 determine $v_{L_2}(t)$ if $i_1 = 0.4 \sin 10^3 t$ amp and $M = 240$mH.

2-14 For the circuit of Fig. 2-11 determine v_{L_2} if $i'_1 = 0.4 \sin 10^3 t + 0.2$ amp, where the prime indicates the current differs from i_1 by a constant, and $M = 240$mH. Discuss your result as compared to the solution of problem 2–13.

2–15 Supposing the transformer core of problems 2–13 and 2–14 is toroidal as shown in Fig. 2–53. From problem 2–13 what magnitude is ϕ if $L_1 = 200$mH? From problem 2–14 what value is ϕ', where the prime defines ϕ as having a constant term present. Compare your results with Fig. 2–30 and discuss the comparison. From your results and discussion of the flux in the core explain why v_{L_2} is the same for both problems 2–13 and 2–14? Note: The units of L are:

$$L = \frac{N\phi(t)}{i(t)} = \frac{\text{weber} \cdot \text{turns}}{\text{ampere}} = \frac{\text{line} \cdot \text{turns}}{\text{ampere}} \times 10^8$$

ϕ has both units of lines and webers the former being the English system and the latter being the mKs system. 10^8 lines $= 1$ Weber.

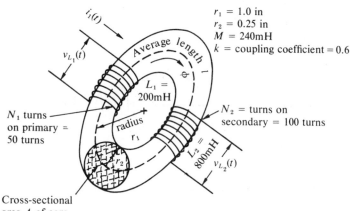

$r_1 = 1.0$ in
$r_2 = 0.25$ in
$M = 240$mH
$k =$ coupling coefficient $= 0.6$

$L_1 = 200$mH

N_1 turns on primary $= 50$ turns

$N_2 =$ turns on secondary $= 100$ turns

Cross-sectional area A of core
Note: Ignore winding directions of L_1 and L_2.

FIGURE 2–53

2–16 For the core of Fig. 2–53 what is the equation for the flux density B if $\phi = 160 \sin 10^3 t$ kilolines and for $\phi' = 160 \sin 10^3 t + 80$ kilolines, where the prime indicates a constant is present in ϕ. Relate your answers to linear requirements using Fig. 2–30 in your discussion.

2–17 Show that the induced voltage v_{L_2} of Fig. 2–53 can be determined by either $M(di(t)/dt)$, as was done in problems 2–13 and 2–14, or from ϕ using the relationship $N\{d[k\phi(t)]/dt\}$ where k is the coupling coefficient. Let i_1 equal $i_1' = 0.4 \sin 10^3 t + 0.2$ amp, where the prime indicates a dc term is present. Relate your results to Fig. 2–30b, especially how the loop $abcd$ and v_{L_2} relate.

2-18   For the core of Fig. 2-53 determine the permeability μ if in the English system, $L = (\mu A N^2 / l) \times 10^{-8}$ henries, where A is the cross sectional area and l is the average length of the path the flux travels. A is in units of sq. in and l in units of inches and μ in units of lines/amp · turn · inch, or lines/amp · turn per inch.

2-19   For the circuit of Fig. 2-12b determine v_{L_1} and v_{L_2} if the current i_1 is made up of both t-variant and a constant term, or specifically $i'_1 = 0.4 \sin 10^3 t + 0.2$ amp, and $i_2 = 0.3 \sin 10^3 t$ amp, where the transformer is that of Fig. 2-53. Now determine v_{L_1} and v_{L_2} using the concepts of Eq. (2-16), that is,

$$v_{L_1}(t) = N_1 \left[\frac{d\phi_1(t)}{dt} - k \frac{d\phi_2(t)}{dt} \right]$$

where $k = k_{12} = k_{21} = 0.6$.

2-20   Determine voltages v_{L_1} and v_{L_2} of Fig. 2-54 if $L_1 = 50$mH, $L_2 = 25$mH, $M = 3.54$mH and $i'_1 = 30 \cos 10^3 t + 10$mA, where the prime indicates a dc term is present. Also, what value is the coupling coefficient k?

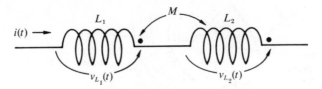

FIGURE 2-54

2-21   Suppose we have unintentional coupling which exists between two

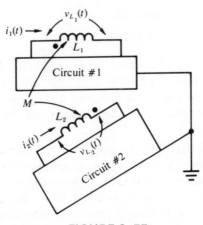

FIGURE 2-55

inductive components L_1 and L_2 as illustrated in Fig. 2–55. If $L_1 = 100$mH, $L_2 = 70$mH, $i_1(t) = 10 \sin 10^3 t$ mA, $i_2(t) = 5 \cos 10^3 t$ mA, and $k = 0.08$ determine v_{L_1} and v_{L_2}. Usually the mutually induced voltage of this type is an unwanted signal, or noise. What is the magnitude of the noise induced into circuit one and circuit two because of their inductive components?

2–22 Given that for Fig. 2–56 $i_1 = 7 \sin 10^4 t$ mA, $i_2 = 10 \cos 10^4 t$ mA, $i'_3 = 6 \sin 10^4 t + 5$ mA, $L_1 = 100$mH, $L_2 = 100$mH, $L_3 = 50$mH, $M_{12} = 10$mH, $M_{13} = 25$mH, and $M_{23} = 2$mH determine voltages v_{L_1}, v_{L_2}, and v_{L_3}.

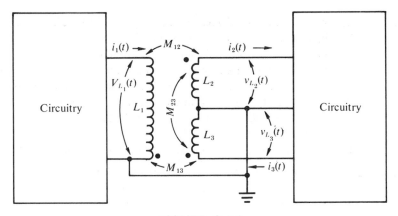

FIGURE 2–56

2–23 For the circuit of Fig. 2–54 determine the current i'_1, where prime indicates a dc term is to be present, if given that $v_{L_1} = 161 \sin 10^3 t$, $v_{L_2} = 85.5 \sin 10^3 t$, $L_1 = 50$mH, $L_2 = 25$mH, and $M = 3.54$mH. The polarity of v_{L_1} and v_{L_2} is such that the positive side of each voltage is at the dot of its corresponding inductor. Verify your answer with problem 2–20 and discuss the dc term.

2–24 For the circuit of Fig. 2–12b determine i'_1 and i'_2, where i_1 and i_2 are to have dc terms present, if $L_1 = 200$mH, $L_2 = 800$mH, $M = 240$mH, $v_{L_1} = 8 \cos 10^3 t$ volts, and $v_{L_2} = 144 \cos 10^3 t$ volts, where the positive side of v_{L_1} is at L_1's dot and v_{L_2}'s negative side is at L_2's dot. Also discuss the possibility of any dc terms. Compare your results with problem 2–19.

2–25 Determine the magnitudes and directions of currents i_1 and i_2 of Fig. 2–57 if $v_{L_1} = 6 \sin 6.28 \times 10^5 t$ volts, $v_{L_2} = 2 \cos 10^3 t$ volts, $L_1 = 10$mH, $L_2 = 50$mH and $M = 5$mH. No dc terms are present. Also discuss how frequency affects the magnitudes of these currents.

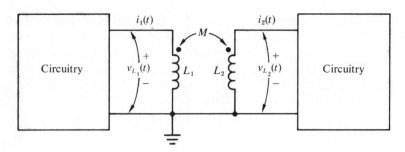

FIGURE 2–57

2-26 The circuit of Fig. 2–55 has voltages $v_{L_1} = -(\cos 10^3 t + 33.5 \times 10^{-3} \sin 10^3 t)$V and $v_{L_2} = 0.35 \sin 10^3 t + 67 \times 10^{-3} \cos 10^3 t$. Determine i_1 and i_2 if $L_1 = 100$mH, $L_2 = 70$mH, and $M = 6.7$mH. Also, the polarity of the algebraic designation v_{L_1} is such that the negative side is at the dot of L_1 and the positive side of v_{L_2} is at L_2's dot. Note that the self induced voltage polarities and the resultant voltage polarities of v_{L_1} and v_{L_2} do not agree. If the "noise" is the current resulting from the unwanted coupling, of what magnitude is this noise? Compare your results with problem 2–21.

2-27 For the inductors (L_1, L_2, and L_3) intercoupled, if

$$\Gamma_{M_{12}} = \frac{L_3 M_{12} - M_{13}M_{23}}{L_1 L_2 L_3 - L_1 M_{23}^2 - L_2 M_{13}^2 - L_3 M_{12}^2}$$

show that $\Gamma_{M_{12}}$ can also be represented as

$$\Gamma_{M_{12}} = \frac{k_{12} - k_{13}k_{23}}{\sqrt{L_1 L_2}[1 - (k_{23}^2 + k_{13}^2 + k_{12}^2)]}$$

Also discuss the physical meaning of $\Gamma_{M_{12}} < 0$ when $k_{13}k_{23} > k_{12}$. Recall $M_{12} = k_{12}\sqrt{L_1 L_2}$ etc.

2-28 Determine the currents i_1, i_2, and i_3 of Fig. 2–58 given that $L_1 =$

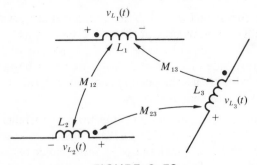

FIGURE 2–58

25mH, $L_2 = 50$mH, $L_3 = 6$mH, $M_{13} = 3$mH, $M_{12} = 0.1$ mH, $M_{23} = 16$mH, $v_{L_1} = 10 \sin 10^3 t$ volts, $v_{L_2} = 5 \cos 10^4 t$ volts, and $v_{L_3} = 8 \sin(2.5 \times 10^3 t + \Theta)$ volts, where Θ is the phrase shift relative to v_{L_1} and v_{L_2}.

2–29   For an iron-core transformer, say a transformer similar to that of Fig. 2–53 and schematically represented in Fig. 2–59, we have $k \simeq 1.0$. Determine v_{L_1}, v_{L_2}, and i_2 where the current i_1 shown has a value of $5 \sin 10^3 t$ mA. Also, for a voltage $v_{L_1} = 0.48 \sin(10^3 t + 90°)$ volts, what is the flux density B.

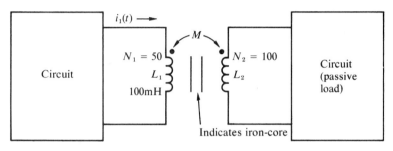

FIGURE 2–59

2–30   For the active device of Fig. 2–60 determine the ac equivalent circuit and the dc Q-point neglecting leakage current. What is the maximum swing of i_c and v_{ce} if we require $v_{ce} \geq 2$ volts?

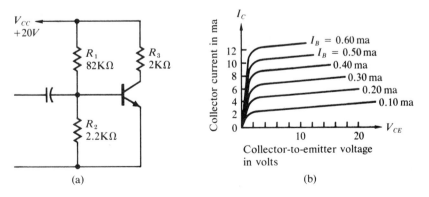

FIGURE 2–60

2–31   For the field-effect transistor (FET) of Fig. 2–61 derive the ac model, where we define:

g_f = transconductance ≡ A change in drain current i_d with respect to gate-to-source voltage v_{gs} while maintaining a constant drain-to-source voltage v_{ds}

$\dfrac{1}{r_d}$ = conductance of drain current ≡ $\dfrac{\partial i_d}{\partial v_d}\Big|_{v_{gs}=\text{constant}}$

Note: As for vacuum tubes $i_g = 0$.

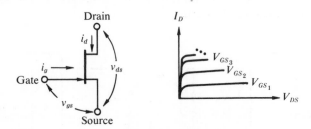

FIGURE 2–61

Chapter 3

3–1   Write the loop-current equations for the circuits shown in Fig. 3–16.

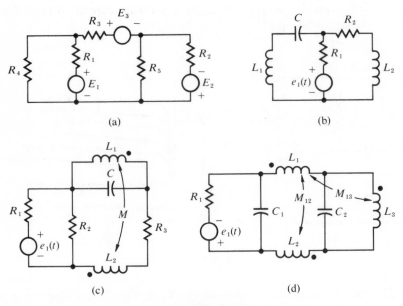

(a)

(b)

(c)

(d)

FIGURE 3–16

3–2 Write the nodal equations for the circuits of Fig. 3–17.

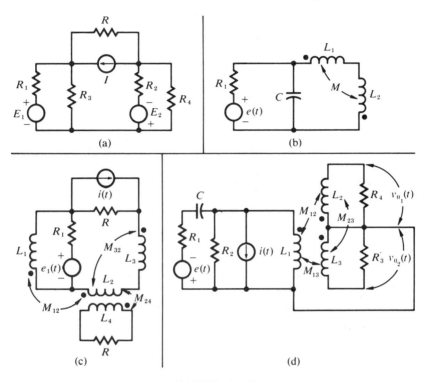

(a)

(b)

(c)

(d)

FIGURE 3–17

3–3 Write the nodal and mesh equations for those circuits of Fig. 3–18.

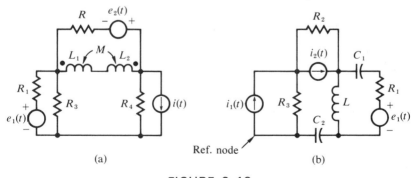

(a)

Ref. node

(b)

FIGURE 3–18

3–4 For the circuit shown in Fig. 3–19 write the mesh and nodal equations for its ac equivalent circuit.

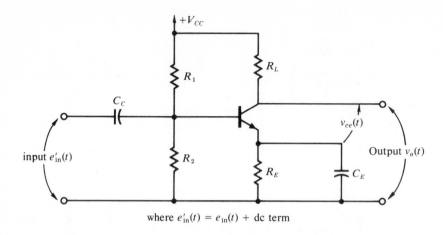

where $e'_{in}(t) = e_{in}(t) + $ dc term

FIGURE 3–19

3–5   Given the circuit shown in Fig. 3–20 write the mesh and nodal
       equations for its ac equivalent circuit. For the nodal equations
       put i_b and v_{ce} in terms of nodal voltages.

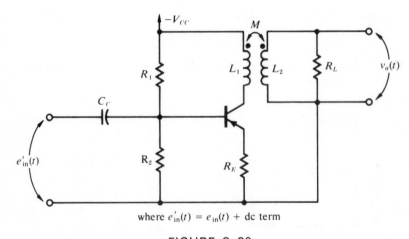

where $e'_{in}(t) = e_{in}(t) + $ dc term

FIGURE 3–20

3–6   Write nodal and mesh equations for the ac equivalent circuit of Fig.
       3–21, where i_e and v_{cb} are to be in terms of the nodal voltages and
       loop currents respectively.

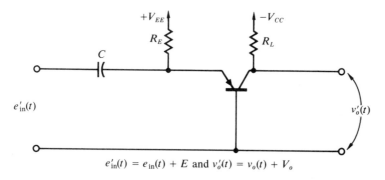

$$e'_{in}(t) = e_{in}(t) + E \text{ and } v'_o(t) = v_o(t) + V_o$$

FIGURE 3–21

3–7   Determine the mesh and nodal equations for the ac equivalent circuit of Fig. 3–22, where $r_d \gg R_s$.

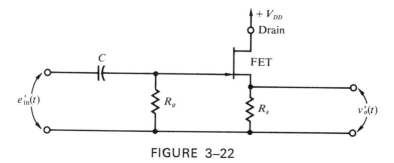

FIGURE 3–22

3–8   Write the nodal equations for the ac equivalent model of the FET bootstrap circuit shown in Fig. 3–23.

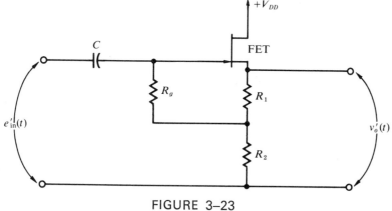

FIGURE 3–23

3-9   For the circuit of Fig. 3–24 determine the nodal equations.

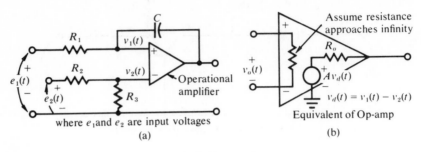

where e_1 and e_2 are input voltages

(a)

Assume resistance approaches infinity

$v_d(t) = v_1(t) - v_2(t)$

Equivalent of Op-amp

(b)

FIGURE 3–24

Chapter 4

4-1   Determine the Laplace transforms of the given functions.

(a) $10u(t)$

(b) $10u(t - 5 \times 10^{-3})$

(c) $5e^{-10t}u(t)$

(d) $t^2 e^{-3 \times 10^3 t}u(t)$

(e) $10e^{-15(t - 10^{-3})}u(t - 10^{-3})$

(f) $6\dfrac{d^2 e^{-3x}}{dx^2}u(x) + 13\displaystyle\int_0^x \int_0^x x\,dx + 2u(x - 5)$

(g) $3 \times 10^{-3}e^{-0.03 \times 10^3 t}\sin(0.296 \times 10^3 t + 1.47)u(t)$

(h) $[5 + 3e^{-0.6 \times 10^2 t}\sin 0.80 \times 10^2 t]u(t)$

(i) $[3(t - 2 \times 10^{-3})\sin 10^4(t - 2 \times 10^{-3})]u(t - 2 \times 10^{-3})$

(k) $2(t - 5 \times 10^{-3})u(t - 5 \times 10^{-3}) + 5e^{-10^2 t}u(t)$

(l) $(2 \times 10^{-6} - 2 \times 10^{-6}\cos 6.28 \times 10^3 t)u(t)$

(m) $v(t) = \dfrac{1}{C}\displaystyle\int i(t)u(t)\,dt$ and also:

(1) If $i = 10$ amp.

(2) If $i = 5 \times 10^{-3}e^{-10^3 t}$ amp.

(n) $v(t) = \dfrac{1}{C}\displaystyle\int_0^t i(t)u(t)\,dt$ and also:

(1) If $i = 15$ ma.

(2) If $i = 6 \times 10^{-3}\sin 10^2 t$.

(o) $\dfrac{df(t)}{dt} u(t)$ if:

    (1) $f = 5 \sin 10^3 t$ volts and $f(0^+) = 0$ volts

    (2) $f = E \sum\limits_{n=0}^{m} \{u(t - nT) - u[t - (t_d + nT)]\}$ volts

    and $f(0^+) = 2$ volts

    (p) $i = 10\delta(t) + 8e^{-10(t-5)}u(t - 5) + 15u(t)$

4–2   Determine $F(s)$ if $f(t) = \begin{cases} 2 & \text{for } 0 < t < a \\ 2e^{-6(t-a)} & \text{for } a < t < \infty. \end{cases}$

    Hint: $\displaystyle\int_0^\infty f(t)e^{-st}\,dt = \int_0^a g(t)e^{-st}\,dt + \int_a^\infty h(t)e^{-st}\,dt$

    for $f(t) = g(t) + h(t)$

4–3   Find $F(s)$ for the waveform shown in Fig. 4–27 using the Unit Step function. Compare this approach with that of problem 4–2 and discuss their similarities.

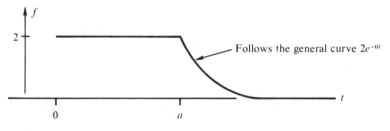

FIGURE 4–27

4–4   Determine the Laplace Transform of the equations below:

    (a) $10 \sum\limits_{n=0}^{m\to\infty} \{u(t - 3n \times 10^{-3}) - u[t - (1 + 3n) \times 10^{-3}]\}$ volts

    where $m \to \infty$ means: let m approach some large number.

    (b) $6 \sum\limits_{n=0}^{m\to\infty} \{\sin 1.25 \times 10^3(t - 5n \times 10^{-3})u(t - 5n \times 10^{-3})$

        $- \sin 1.25 \times 10^3[t - (5n + 2.5) \times 10^{-3}]$

        $\times u[t - (5n + 2.5) \times 10^{-3}]\}$ mA

    (c) $v(t) = 3 \sum\limits_{n=0}^{m\to\infty} \delta(t - 3n \times 10^{-3})$ volts

4–5   Write equations for the waveforms of Fig. 4–28 and find the Laplace transform of each equation. Also discuss the difference between a and b, b and c, and c and d. Compare your equations with Eq. (22) of Table 4–2.

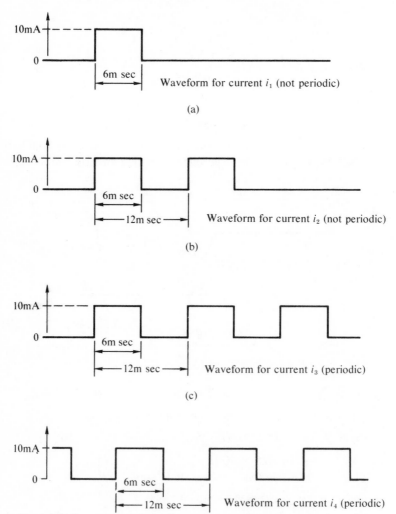

Waveform for current i_1 (not periodic)

(a)

Waveform for current i_2 (not periodic)

(b)

Waveform for current i_3 (periodic)

(c)

Waveform for current i_4 (periodic)

Note: i_4 is the same as i_3 but shifted to the right by 1.25m sec.
Use i_3 as a reference for i_4 and write the equation.

(d)

FIGURE 4–28

4-6 Write the required equation for the periodic waveforms of Fig. 4–29 $e(t)$ and then determine $E(s)$.

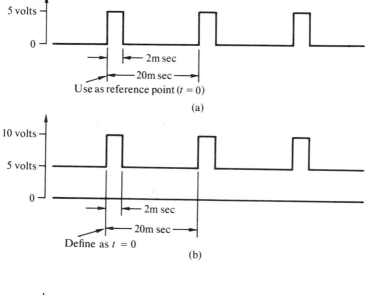

5 volts

0

2m sec

20m sec

Use as reference point ($t = 0$)

(a)

10 volts

5 volts

0

2m sec

20m sec

Define as $t = 0$

(b)

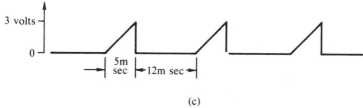

3 volts

0

5m sec

12m sec

(c)

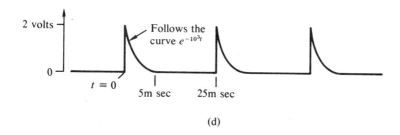

2 volts

Follows the curve $e^{-10^3 t}$

0

$t \equiv 0$

5m sec

25m sec

(d)

FIGURE 4–29

4-7   From the block diagram of Fig. 4–30 determine the Transfer Func-
       tion $T(s)$, where $T(s) \equiv V_o(s)/E_{in}(s)$, if $e_{in}(t)$ and $v_o(t)$ are as shown.

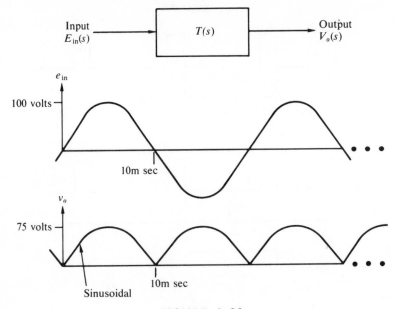

FIGURE 4–30

4-8   If $T(s) \equiv [V_o(s)/E_{in}(s)]$ then $V_o(s) = T(s)E_{in}(s)$. For the case where

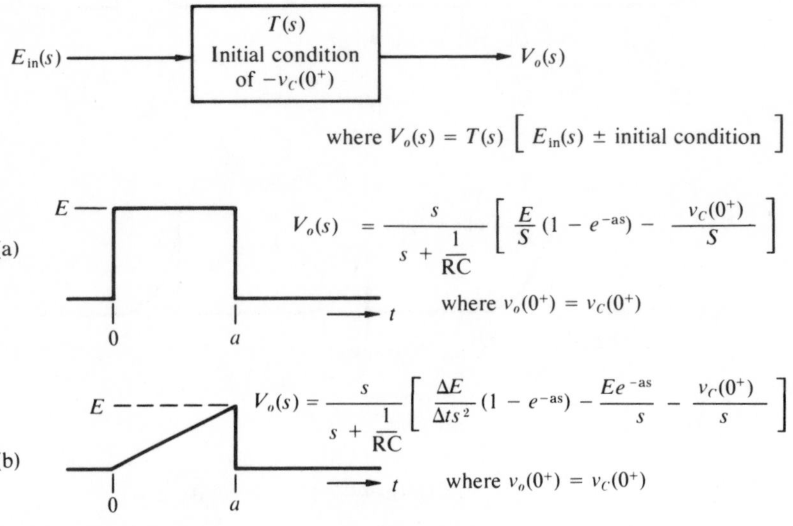

$E_{in}(s)$ ──────▶ $T(s)$
                    Initial condition
                    of $-v_C(0^+)$ ──────▶ $V_o(s)$

where $V_o(s) = T(s) \left[E_{in}(s) \pm \text{initial condition} \right]$

(a)

$$V_o(s) = \frac{s}{s + \dfrac{1}{RC}} \left[\frac{E}{S}(1 - e^{-as}) - \frac{v_C(0^+)}{S} \right]$$

where $v_o(0^+) = v_C(0^+)$

(b)

$$V_o(s) = \frac{s}{s + \dfrac{1}{RC}} \left[\frac{\Delta E}{\Delta t s^2}(1 - e^{-as}) - \frac{Ee^{-as}}{s} - \frac{v_C(0^+)}{s} \right]$$

where $v_o(0^+) = v_C(0^+)$

FIGURE 4–31

e_{in} is as shown in Fig. 4–31 and $T(s) = \{s/[s + (1/RC)]\}$ determine the initial and final values of $v_o(t)$. Also determine the slope of $v_o(t)$ at $t = 0^+$ for each case.

4–9   Determine the inverse Laplace Transform of those equations given below.

(a) $\dfrac{10}{s(s + 5)}$

(b) $\dfrac{10e^{-15s}}{s(s + 5)}$

(c) $\dfrac{50}{25s^2 + 5s + 100}$

(d) $\dfrac{50e^{-6s}}{25s^2 + 5s + 100}$

(e) $\dfrac{2s}{\dfrac{10}{s} + 5s + 6}$

(f) $\dfrac{2}{s} + \dfrac{10}{s}(1 - e^{-4s}) + 3$

(g) $I(s) = \dfrac{2}{s} + \dfrac{10}{s}(1 - e^{-7s}) \displaystyle\sum_{n=0}^{m} e^{-25ns} + 5$ amp

(h) $E_{in}(s) = \left[\dfrac{5}{s} + \dfrac{2 \times 10^3}{s^2}(1 - e^{-10^{-3}s}) - \dfrac{2}{s}e^{-10s^{-3}} \right]$

$\times \displaystyle\sum_{n=0}^{m} e^{-5 \times 10^{-3}ns}$ volts

4–10   Sketch the waveforms $i(t)$ and $e_{in}(t)$ of problems 4–8(g) and 4–8(h).

4–11   Determine the Inverse Laplace Transform of the functions using partial fractions

(a) $\dfrac{1}{s^2 + 12s + 20}$

(b) $\dfrac{100}{(s + 5)(s^2 + 12s + 20)}$

(c) $\dfrac{15}{(s + 4)^2(s + 2)}$

(d) $\dfrac{(s + 6)e^{-7s}}{s(s + 10)^3(s + 5)}$

(e) $\dfrac{10s}{\left(\dfrac{14}{s} + 6s + 10\right)(s + 6)}$

(f) $\dfrac{10s + 60se^{-5s}}{(s + 4)^2(s + 2)}$

4–12   Find $T(s)$, where $T(s) \equiv (V_o(s)/E_{in}(s))$, if $e_{in}(t)$ and $v_o(t)$ are as illustrated in Fig. 4–32.

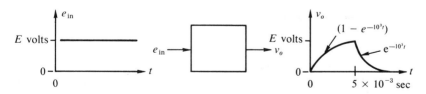

FIGURE 4–32

4–13   Using the Convolution Integral determine:

(a) $f(t)$ if $F(s) = \dfrac{1}{s(s + 10)}$

(b) $f(t)$ if $F(s) = \dfrac{10}{(s^2 + 100)s}$

(c) $i(t)$ if $I(s) = \dfrac{5}{(s + 3)^2}$

(d) $v(t)$ if $V(s) = \dfrac{1}{(s + 2)(s + 5)}$

4-14   Given that $I(s) = [E(s)/10(s + 15)]$ find $i(t)$ if:

(a) $E(s) = 6/s$ volts

(b) $e(t) = 10u(t)$ volts

(c) See Figure 4–33.

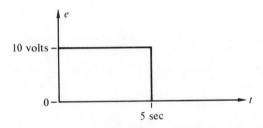

FIGURE 4–33

(d) See Figure 4–34.

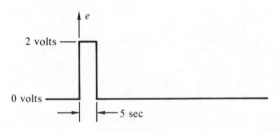

FIGURE 4–34

(e) See Figure 4–35.

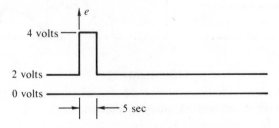

FIGURE 4–35

(f) Let e have the same waveform as part (d), except for this case e is periodic with a period at 17 sec.

4–15   Given that $T(s) = [E(s)/I(s)] = \{[10^2(s + 10^3)]/s\}$ determine:
(a) $I(s)$ if $E(s) = 10/s$ volts
(b) $i(t)$ if e is as shown in Fig. 4–36.

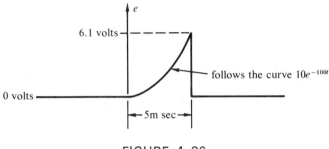

FIGURE 4–36

(c) $e(t)$ if $i(t)$ is as shown in Fig. 4–37.

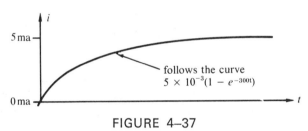

FIGURE 4–37

(d) What unit does $T(s)$ have?
(e) Recalling $s = \sigma + j\omega$ let $\sigma = 0$ and then subsitute $s = j\omega$ into $T(s)$, which is $Z(s)$. Rearrange the equation for $Z(j\omega)\big|_{s=j\omega}$ and then determine the equivalent circuit for $Z(j\omega)$.

Chapter 5

5–1   (a) For the circuit of Fig. 5–74 determine the voltage across L and the current flowing through it.
(b) Find the values of v_L and i_L 4 seconds after the switch has been closed.

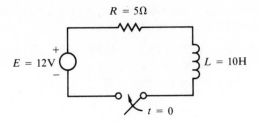

FIGURE 5–74

5–2   (a) Determine the output voltage v_0 of Fig. 5–75 as a function of
       time.
       (b) How long will it take for the capacitor to reach 3 volts?

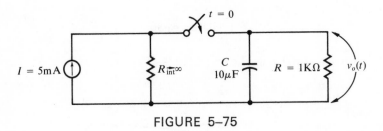

FIGURE 5–75

5–3   For the circuit of Fig. 5–76: (a) Determine i_L for the circuit shown.
       (b) What is the value of i_L after the switch has been closed for 0.03m
       sec and 10m sec. (c) Determine i_L at $t = 0$ using the equation of
       part (b) and verify your answer with the information of article 5–3.

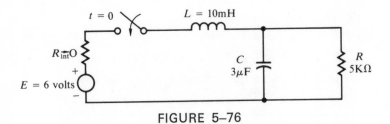

FIGURE 5–76

5–4   For the circuit of problem 5–3 determine the magnitude of the
       voltage across R, 5 seconds after the switch was closed.

5–5   Given the circuit of Fig. 5–77 determine the equation for the cur-
       rent i when the switch is in position 2, if the switch is in position 1
       for 2 seconds at which time the switch is then put in position 2.

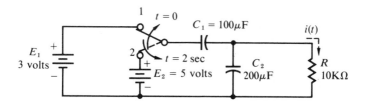

FIGURE 5-77

5-6 (a) Determine the equation for v_0 as a function of time for the circuit of Fig. 5-78. (b) Let $L_1 = 1\text{mH}$, $L_2 = 10\text{mH}$, $k = 0.5$, $R_1 = 600\ \Omega$ and $R_2 = 1\ \text{K}\Omega$. (c) Keep the same values as part (b) except let $R_1 \rightarrow 0$.

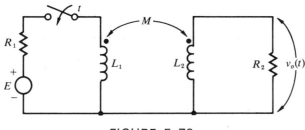

FIGURE 5-78

5-7 (a) For the circuit of problem 5-6 determine the equation describing the current through R_2. (b) Use the circuit parameters of part (b) and determine the magnitude of current flowing through R_2 at $t = 10\ \mu s$ if $E_1 = 7\text{V}$ dc.

5-8 Given the circuit of Fig. 5-79 determine the equation describing v_1.

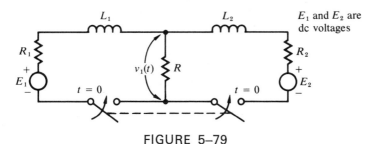

FIGURE 5-79

5-9 Determine the algebraic equation describing i_L of Fig. 5-80 and discuss what happens to its dc component I_1 as time progresses using your derived equation to verify your statement.

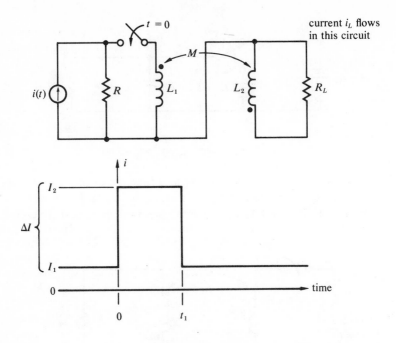

FIGURE 5–80

5–10 Work problem 5–9 for i periodic with period T_p.

5–11 Derive the equation describing v_0 as a function of time t for the circuit of Fig. 5–81.

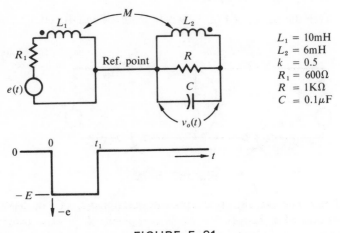

$L_1 = 10\text{mH}$
$L_2 = 6\text{mH}$
$k = 0.5$
$R_1 = 600\Omega$
$R = 1\text{K}\Omega$
$C = 0.1\mu\text{F}$

FIGURE 5–81

5–12 Rework problem 5–11 with the reference point connected to the junction of R_1 and L_1 as shown. Discuss the significance of relocating the reference wire.

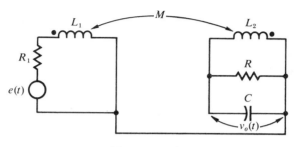

FIGURE 5–82

5–13 Derive the algebraic equation for v_2 of Fig. 5–83 and then quantitatively justify your solution by explaining the terms and how they relate physically to the circuit.

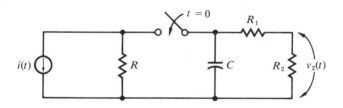

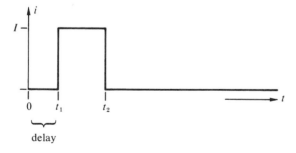

FIGURE 5–83

5–14 It is desired to have an RLC underdamped series circuit which reaches a maximum value of current of 5mA in 3ms and then settles to within 10% of its maximum value of current approximately 30ms later. The supply voltage is $E = 2\text{V}$ dc. Derive the required circuit parameter values for R, L, and C.

5–15   Design an underdamped system for the RLC circuit of Fig. 5–84 such that 20% overshoot. What is the maximum value of the output voltage $v_{0_{max}}$ and at what time does this value occur?

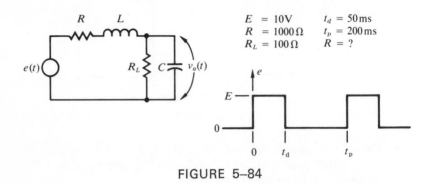

$$E = 10\text{V} \qquad t_d = 50\,\text{ms}$$
$$R = 1000\,\Omega \qquad t_p = 200\,\text{ms}$$
$$R_L = 100\,\Omega \qquad R = ?$$

FIGURE 5–84

5–16   Choose values for the circuit of Fig. 5–85 such that the rise-time of v_0 is $1\,\mu\text{s}$ and $v_{0_{max}}$ is 2 volts for $I = 3\text{mA}$.

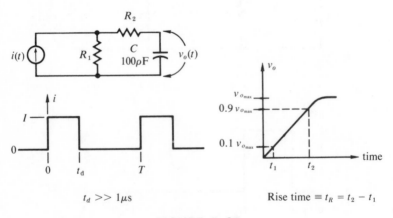

$t_d \gg 1\,\mu\text{s}$ Rise time $\equiv t_R = t_2 - t_1$

FIGURE 5–85

5–17   For the circuit of Fig. 5–86: (a) Determine the algebraic equation for the current i_L which flows through the resistor R_3. To simplify use definitions to represent large algebraic quantities. (b) What is the steady state equation for i_L? (c) What does the resultant equation of part (b) state about the dc component I_1?

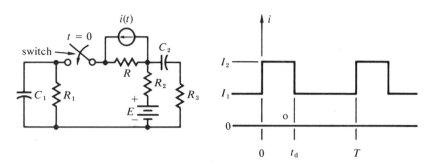

FIGURE 5–86

5–18 For the circuit of problem 5–17 determine the magnitude of i_L at $t = 120\text{ms}$ if: $C_1 = 1\mu\text{F}$, $C_2 = 0.5\mu\text{F}$, $R_1 = 1\text{K}\Omega$, $R = 10\text{K}\Omega$, $R_2 = 2\text{K}\Omega$, $R_3 = 5\text{K}\Omega$, $E = 6\text{V dc}$, $I_1 = 3\text{mA}$, $I_2 = 10\text{mA}$, $t_d = 10\text{ms}$, and $T = 50\text{ms}$.

5–19 Derive the algebraic equation describing v_1 of Fig. 5–87 as a function of the circuit parameters and time.

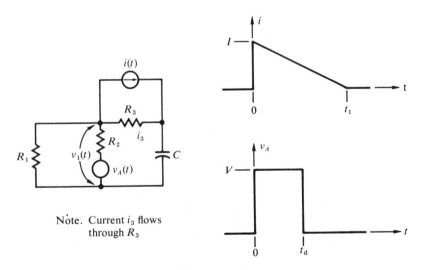

Note: Current i_3 flows through R_3

FIGURE 5–87

5–20 Derive an algebraic equation describing i_3 of problem 5–18 as a function of the circuit parameters and time. Why is it that you cannot convert the current generator to a voltage source?

5–21 For the source-follower given in Fig. 5–88 show the need for C and R_g in order that the dc component of e'_{in} is "filtered" out. (Gate

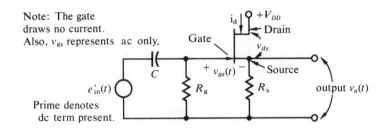

FIGURE 5–88

current is zero.) Also, from your derived equation derive some criteria for time-constant of that circuit in terms of t_d and T of Fig. 5–89.

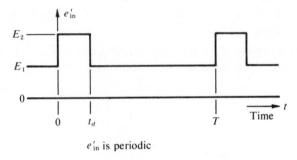

e'_{in} is periodic

FIGURE 5–89

5–22 For the source-follower of problem 5–21 determine the gain of the circuit, that is,

$$\text{gain} \equiv A_v = \frac{V_o(s)}{E_{in}(s)}$$

Then determine v_o given that e'_{in} is as shown in problem 5–21. Assume that the RC time-constant is properly adjusted such that no distortion occurs on the ac portion v_{gs}. To derive the active (ac) model for the FET use $i_1 = 0$ and $i_2 = i_2(v_1, v_2)$. Then define

$$\frac{i_2}{v_1} = g_{21} \equiv g_f = \text{forward transmittance}$$

$$\frac{i_2}{v_2} = g_{22} \equiv \frac{1}{r_d} = \text{reciprocal of drain resistance}$$

$$v_2 = v_{ds} \qquad i_2 = i_d$$

$$v_1 = v_{gs}$$

From the characteristic curves shown in Fig. 5–90 it can be seen that FET's are current sources.

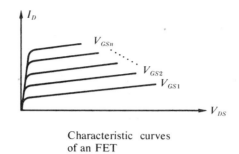

Characteristic curves
of an FET

FIGURE 5–90

5–23 For the FET linear amplifier shown in Fig. 5–91 determine v_o for
steady state only. Discuss design criteria for time-constants if fidelity
and an ac output only (no dc component) for v_1 is desired. Also
make C_s appear as an ac-short circuit. Note: Information needed
for modeling the FET is found in problem 5–22.

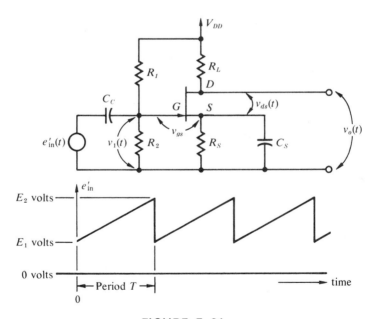

FIGURE 5–91

5–24 For the tube circuit given in Fig. 5–92 and the input voltage shown
select values for C_C and C_K based on the criteria that $e_{in} \cong v_{gk}$ (ac
term only) and that C_K is to provide an ac short-circuit. Assume

values for R_G, R_K, and R_L where determined from DC biasing considerations. Also the transformer and tube have been selected, thus we have values for the tube and transformer parameters. After writing the equations for properly selecting values for C_C and C_K, based on the derived equations, then write an algebraic equation for v_o assuming the design criteria for C_C and C_K are met.

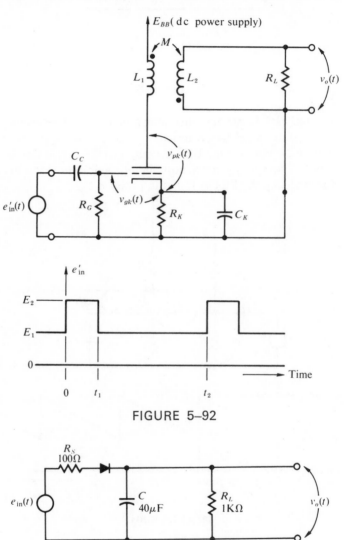

FIGURE 5–92

Let $e_{in} = 10 \sin 120\pi t\ u(t)$ volts

FIGURE 5–93

5-25 For the circuit of Fig. 5–93 sketch the output voltage v_o using equations derived describing v_o mathematically.

5-26 For the full-wave rectifier shown in Fig. 5–94 determine v_o, that is, both transient and steady state terms. Hint: Use a more complete set of Laplace transforms than those found in Table 4–2.

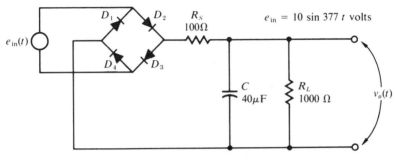

FIGURE 5-94

5-27 For the circuit shown in Fig. 5–95 suppose it is desired to apply a Unit Impulse Function. Given that e_{in} is to be 5 volts in amplitude and repetitive: (a) Approximately what should the duration and rate of e_{in} be. (b) Determine v_o for the e_{in}. (c) Repeat the problem solving for the current.

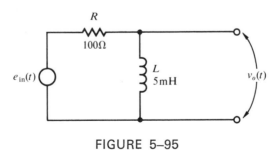

FIGURE 5-95

5-28 Given the transistorized circuit shown in Fig. 5–96 determine v_o and the duration of e_{in}, if e_{in} is to be a Unit Impulse with amplitude $E + E_1$ volts.

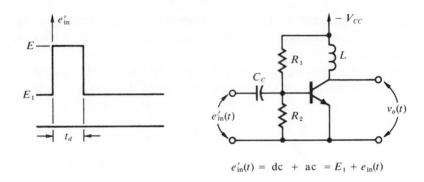

$$e'_{in}(t) = dc + ac = E_1 + e_{in}(t)$$

FIGURE 5-96

5-29 If the circuit parameters of problem 5-28 are:

$$L = 5mH \qquad h_{oe} = 100\mu\mho \qquad h_{fe} = 100$$
$$h_{ie} = 4K\Omega \qquad h_{re} = 3 \times 10^{-3} \qquad E = 5 \text{ volts}$$

graph v_o for a repetition rate of $T = 10\mu s$.

5-30 For the circuit of Fig. 5-97 determine v_o and graph this equation
for the e_{in} shown.

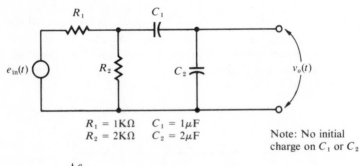

$$R_1 = 1K\Omega \qquad C_1 = 1\mu F$$
$$R_2 = 2K\Omega \qquad C_2 = 2\mu F$$

Note: No initial
charge on C_1 or C_2

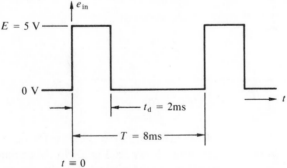

FIGURE 5-97

5-31 Solve problem 5-30 but now making: $t_d = 0.5$ ms and $T = 1$ ms. Discuss the transient portion of v_o in regards as to what is happening to C_2 to cause v_o to be transient.

5-32 For the circuit shown in Fig. 5-98 derive equations for v_1 and v_2 for the steady state portions *only*.

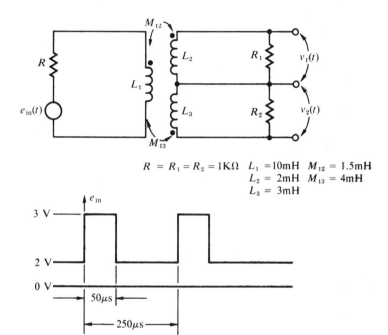

$$R = R_1 = R_2 = 1K\Omega \quad L_1 = 10mH \quad M_{12} = 1.5mH$$
$$L_2 = 2mH \quad M_{13} = 4mH$$
$$L_3 = 3mH$$

FIGURE 5-98

5-33 Given the circuit shown in Fig. 5-99 and realizing that the component at the output is a Zenier diode, having the characteristics shown, determine v_o and its graph.

Chapter 6

6-1 For the circuit of Fig. 6-19: (a) Determine the transfer function describing the voltage gain $G(s) \equiv [V_2(s)/E_1(s)]$. (b) What should be done to physically determine $G(s)$? (c) What would determine the values to be used for part (b)?

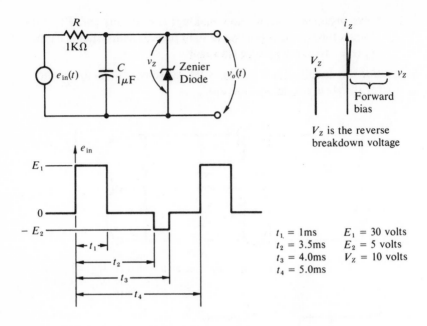

FIGURE 5–99

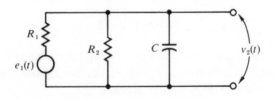

FIGURE 6–19

6-2   Determine the magnitude and duration of e_{in} of Fig. 6–20 if it is desired to display v_o on an oscilloscope where at least 50mV at v_o is needed.

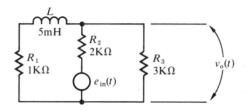

FIGURE 6–20

6–3 For the transformer circuit of Fig. 6–21 determine the necessary values for E and t_d in order to display $g(t)$, that is, $L^{-1}[G(s)]$, on an oscilloscope.

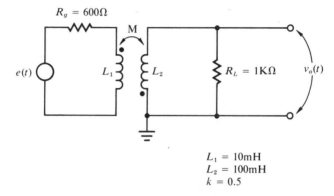

$L_1 = 10\text{mH}$
$L_2 = 100\text{mH}$
$k = 0.5$

FIGURE 6–21

6–4 Suppose you were shown an oscilloscope tracing of the output of a circuit for which you know the output was due to a unit impulse input and the output tracing could be mathematically described by $v_o = Ke^{-t/T}$ for a single pulse. Synthesize a circuit from this information. Also determine the value of the input voltage relative to K and t_d.

6–5 Supposing that for a unit impulse applied to a black box results in the waveform of Fig. 6–22. From this waveform synthesize a circuit.

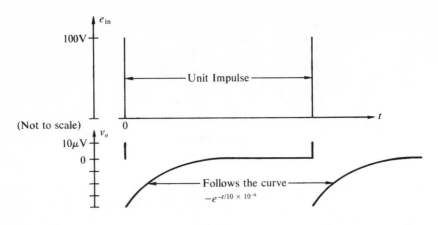

FIGURE 6–22

6–6   Using synthesis techniques determine the synthesized circuit of
       Fig. 6–23. (See problem 5–6.)

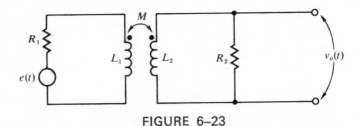

FIGURE 6–23

6–7   For the circuit of Fig. 6–24 find $Z_{11}(s)$, which is $E(s)/I_1(s)$ and then
       determine $Z(j\omega)$ by letting $s = j\omega$. Show this equation is valid by
       using elementary impedance concepts and determine $Z_{11}(j\omega)$, that
       is, determine the input impedance Z_{11}.

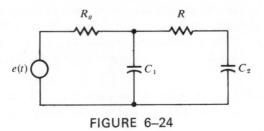

FIGURE 6–24

6–8   For the circuit of Fig. 6–25 determine the input impedance of the
       ac model using Laplace transforms, that is, $Z_{11}(s)$ where $E(s)/I(s)$
       $= Z_{11}(s)$.

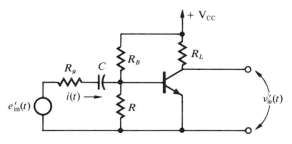

Note: Prime denotes dc term

FIGURE 6–25

6–9   For the circuit of Fig. 6–26: (a) Determine the ac input impedance $Z_{in}(s)$, which is defined as $Z_{in}(s) \equiv V_{be}(s)/I_b(s)$. (b) Sketch the response of the transfer function $T(t)$ and determine requirements for t_d of the unit impulse to be applied in displaying $T(t)$. (Assume $h_{re} \cong 0$.)

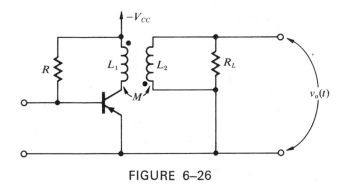

FIGURE 6–26

6–10   For the circuit of Fig. 6–24 determine the Z-parameters both in the s and ω-plane.

6–11   For the circuit of Fig. 6–25 determine: (a) The Z-parameters using two-port network analysis, where $v_1 = e_1$, $i_1 = i$, $v_2 = v_o$, and $i_2 = i_C$. Also let $h_{oe} = 0$ (that is $1/h_{oe} \rightarrow \infty$ or an open-circuit).

Chapter 7

7–1   For the circuit of Fig. 7–20 determine and sketch the frequency response using Bode plot for both magnitude and phase.

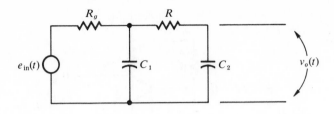

FIGURE 7–20

7–2   Suppose that an e_{in} shown in Fig. 7–21 is applied to the circuit of
       Fig. 7–20. Sketch the output waveform of the corresponding v_o
       for this e_{in} and note the fidelity of the output waveform. It can be
       seen that the output can only approach the input waveform, hence
       distortion is introduced. Compare this with the frequency response
       and draw some conclusions as to what frequencies affect the leading
       and/or lagging edge of a pulse.

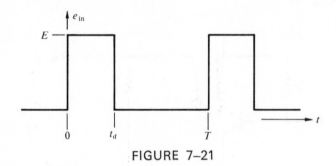

FIGURE 7–21

7–3   Repeat problem 7–2 for the circuit of Fig. 7–22.

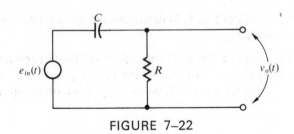

FIGURE 7–22

7–4   Return to problem 5–32 and determine the frequency response,
       both magnitude and phase, of $V_1(j\omega)/E_{in}(j\omega)$ for the circuit of Fig.
       5–98.

7-5   Given the circuit of Fig. 7–23 determine its frequency and phase
       response using Bode techniques.

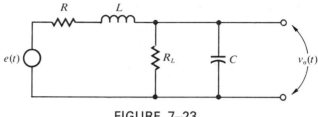

FIGURE 7–23

7-6   For the FET circuit of problem 5–21 (see problem 5–22) determine
       its frequency response.

7-7   For the circuit of problem 5–11 determine the phase and frequency
       response using Bode techniques.

7-8   Graph Bode plots of:

(a) $G(s) = \dfrac{s + 1}{s(s + 5)\left(1 + \dfrac{10}{s}\right)}$

(b) $G(s) = \dfrac{10s + 10}{10s^2 + 1,050s + 500}$

(c) $T(s) = \dfrac{128}{2s^3 + 40s^2 + 128s}$

7-9   For the conditions and circuit of problem 5–24 make a frequency
       response plot using Bode techniques.

Chapter 8

8-1   From the block diagrams of Fig. 8–26 determine $C(s)/R(s)$.

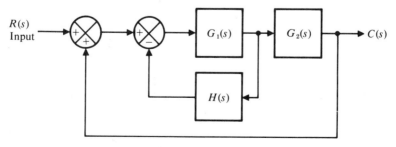

FIGURE 8–26

8–2   Determine $V_o(s)$ from Fig. 8–27 and make a Bode plot of the gain.

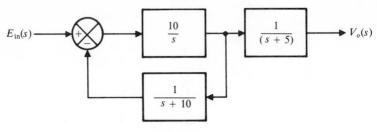

FIGURE 8–27

8–3   Convert Figs. 8–26 and 8–27 into signal-flow diagrams.

8–4   For the circuit of Fig. 8–28 determine the block diagram and the signal-flow diagram where the nodal signals are to be $E_{in}(s)$, $V_1(s)$, and $V_2(s)$.

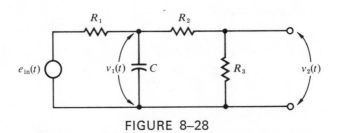

FIGURE 8–28

8–5   Develop both a block diagram and a signal-flow diagram for the ac model of a transistor (common-emitter). The signal nodes should be $I_b(s)$, $I_c(s)$, $V_{ce}(s)$ and $V_{be}(s)$.

8–6   For the circuit of Fig. 8–29 develop a signal-flow diagram for the ac model.

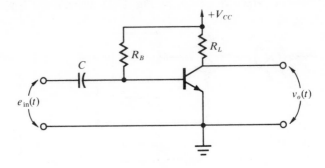

FIGURE 8–29

8–7   Develop a signal-flow diagram for the circuit of Fig. 8–30.

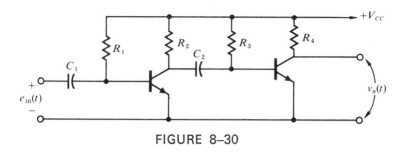

FIGURE 8–30

8–8   For the circuit of Fig. 8–31 develop a signal-flow diagram. (This
       in an FET bootstrap.)

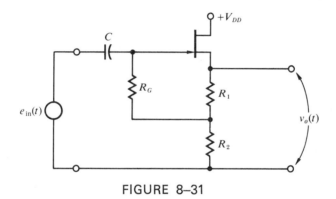

FIGURE 8–31

8–9   From the signal-flow diagram of problem 8–4 determine the voltage
       gain of the circuit.

8–10   From the signal-flow diagram of problem 8–6 determine the
       necessary equation to make a Bode plot of the gain and then do so.

8–11   Using the signal-flow diagram of problem 8–7 determine v_o if
       $e_{in} = Et_a\delta(t)$.

8–12   Given the signal-flow diagram of Fig. 8–32 determine the gain
       equation $V_o(s)/E_{in}(s)$.

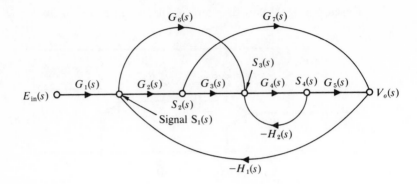

FIGURE 8–32

Index